THE ARDEN SHAKESPEARE

GENERAL EDITOR: UNA ELLIS-FERMOR

ADVISORY EDITOR: HAROLD F. BROOKS

KING JOHN

THE ARDEN EDITION OF THE
WORKS OF WILLIAM SHAKESPEARE

KING JOHN

Edited by

E. A. J. HONIGMANN

METHUEN AND CO. LTD, LONDON
36 Essex Street, Strand, W.C.2

The original editor of the Arden Shakespeare was W. J. Craig (1899–1906), succeeded by R. H. Case (1909–1944). Present editor, Una Ellis-Fermor; advisory editor, Harold F. Brooks. Ivor B. John's edition of *King John* was first published 1907. It was reprinted twice.

Fourth edition (E. A. J. Honigmann), revised and reset, 1954

CATALOGUE NO. 4737/U

PRINTED IN GREAT BRITAIN BY THE BROADWATER PRESS LTD
WELWYN GARDEN CITY, HERTFORDSHIRE, AND BOUND BY
JAMES BURN & CO. LTD, ESHER

CONTENTS

PREFACE

Ivor B. John's edition has been expanded in the footnotes and the collation: where his footnotes are retained they are acknowledged. The Introduction also departs from the older edition in a number of ways, new appendices are added, and the text reverts to the Folio in many readings.

I am indebted for help of various kinds to Mr J. C. Maxwell, Dr J. G. McManaway, Professor A. Nicoll, and Dr C. T. Onions; and to Mr J. R. Brown and Dr R. A. Foakes for much detailed criticism. Professor C. J. Sisson has kindly allowed me to collate *King John* from the proofs of his forthcoming edition of Shakespeare. Dr H. F. Brooks and the General Editor have spent more time in reading and re-reading my MS. than any reasonable editor could demand, and suggested many valuable improvements. Professor P. Alexander has advised and guided me over a period of years in the study of the King John plays: and not the least of my many debts to him is that he put me in touch with Mrs F. M. H. Bone, who placed all her notes on these plays at my disposal, and most generously allowed me to print some of her discoveries for the first time.

E. A. H.

The Shakespeare Institute
Stratford-on-Avon
   February, 1953.

ABBREVIATIONS

Abbott	E. A. Abbott, *Shakespearian Grammar* (ed. 1897).
Arber	E. Arber, *Transcript of the Registers of the Company of Stationers* (5 vols.) (1875–94).
B. & F.	F. Beaumont and J. Fletcher, *Comedies and Tragedies* (1647).
Carter	T. Carter, *Shakespeare and Holy Scripture* (1905).
Chapman	G. Chapman, *Plays and Poems* (2 vols., ed. T. Parrott) (1910–14).
Foxe	J. Foxe, *Actes and Monuments* (Vol. 1) (ed. 1583).
Furness	H. H. Furness, *King John* (Variorum ed.) (1919).
Heywood	T. Heywood, *Dramatic Works* (6 vols.) (1874).
Hol.	R. Holinshed, *Chronicles* (Vol. III) (1587).
Kyd	T. Kyd, *Works* (ed. F. S. Boas) (1901).
Lyly	J. Lyly, *Works* (3 vols., ed. R. W. Bond) (1902).
Nashe	T. Nashe, *Works* (5 vols., ed. R. B. McKerrow) (1904–10).
Noble	R. Noble, *Shakespeare's Biblical Knowledge* (1935).
On.	C. T. Onions, *Shakespeare Glossary* (ed. 1941).
Paris	M. Paris, *Historia Maior* (1571).
Schmidt	A. Schmidt, *Shakespeare-Lexicon* (2 vols.) (1874–5).
Sidney	P. Sidney, *Arcadia* (ed. A. Feuillerat) (1912).
Smith	G. C. Moore Smith, *King John* (Warwick ed.) (?1900).
S.R.	Stationers' Registers (see Arber, above).
Tilley	M. P. Tilley, *Dictionary of . . . Proverbs* (1950).
T.R.	*The Troublesome Raigne of Iohn King of England* (2 vols., ed. C. Praetorius) (1888).
Vaughan	H. H. Vaughan, *New Readings* (3 vols.) (ed. 1886).
Wilson	J. D. Wilson, *King John* (C.U.P. ed.) (1936).

The customary abbreviations are used for periodicals and well-known works: *D.N.B.* = *Dictionary of National Biography*; M.S.R. = Malone Society Reprint; *O.E.D.* = *Oxford English Dictionary*; *R.E.S.* = *Review of English Studies*, etc. The abbreviations of the titles of Shakespeare's plays and poems follow C. T. Onions, *Shakespeare Glossary*, p. x.

Unless otherwise stated, quotations from the Bible are from the Genevan version; quotations from Shakespeare (except those from *King John*) from *The Oxford Shakespeare* (ed. W. J. Craig) (1907).

References to the first leaf of the gathering and to the recto of the page in early printed books omit the usual "1" and the superior "r": thus in the note on I. i. 17 sig. D = sig. D_1^r; in the note on I. i. 110 sig. E^v = sig. E_1^v.

INTRODUCTION

I. The Sources

According to the large majority of critics, Shakespeare's *John* is based upon an anonymous play, *The Troublesome Raigne of Iohn King of England* (hereafter called the *T.R.*), which was published in two parts in 1591. Prof. J. Dover Wilson, having examined the claims of all other suggested sources in his valuable edition of *John*, has recently declared that Shakespeare "made use of no other source whatsoever".[1]

Evidence that Shakespeare consulted other authorities besides the *T.R.* is meagre, but Prof. Wilson's pronouncement may fall short of the truth. No one has had sufficient faith in Shakespeare's source-reading to bother to explore the possibilities: yet *John* may turn out to be a good example of his searching thoroughness, the very quality often denied him largely on the strength of this play. For it may be asserted with some confidence that he consulted at least two English and two Latin chronicles, apart from the *T.R.*—and probably more.

Prof. Wilson considered three points where "Shakespeare might appear to have made use of historical or quasi-historical material not found in the source-play" (p. xxxii). In his notes to IV. ii. 120, v. iii. 16, v. vi. 30, he explained away the coincidences that Queen Eleanor "the first of April died", that John is carried in a "litter", that John's poisoner's bowels "burst". Although direct access to the chronicles would account for this agreement between Shakespeare and three different sources available to him, Prof. Wilson disregarded this possible explanation to suit the framework of a larger theory. And we could scarcely blame him, for three such points by themselves carry little weight.

Before Prof. Wilson, Prof. Moore Smith had discussed the

---

1. *John* (1936), p. xxxiv (the C.U.P. Shakespeare).

sources of *John*, without finally hazarding a decision, and cited other instances where Shakespeare seemed to have used the chronicles.[1] One of these was the burial of John, to which Holinshed and both plays allude:[2]

(*a*) [John's men] marching foorth with his bodie . . . conueied it vnto Worcester, where he was pompouslie buried . . . not for that he had so *appointed* (as some write) but bicause it was thought to be a place of most suertie for the lords (Hol., 194, ii).

> Meane while to *Worster* let vs beare the King,
> And there *interre* his bodie, as beseemes (*T.R.*, ii. ix. 38–9)

> At Worcester must his body *be interr'd;*
> For so he *will'd* it (*John*, v. vii. 99–100)

John's appointment (will) to be buried at Worcester may mean that Shakespeare knew Holinshed, thought Smith. The editors have not noticed, however, that Holinshed reverts to John's funeral after a digression:

his buriall, whereof I saie thus much, that whether it was his *will* to *be interred*, as is aforesaid . . . (195, i)

Even though Shakespeare may have followed the *T.R.* for the other details, the word "will'd" (and "be interr'd"), coupled with the correspondences outlined below, persuades us that he did not neglect his favourite source-book.

· In illustration of Shakespeare's dependence upon Holinshed we must compare other similarities between the chronicle and the two plays. Unless otherwise stated, the same context is the subject of the three versions.

(*b*) K. Iohn commeth vpon his enimies *not looked for* (Hol., 164, ii, in the margin).

> How much *unlook'd for* is this expedition (*John*, ii. i. 79)

> I rather *lookt for* some submisse reply (*T.R.*, i. ii. 78)

In both plays King Philip, like Holinshed, comments on John's military speed: but only Shakespeare used "looked for" in the source's sense.

---

1. *John* (1900), p. xxviii ff.
2. For the sake of clarity we have added italics in our quotations from the sources.

(*c*) Stephan / Langton cho- / sen archbishop / of Canturbu- / rie (Hol., 171, i, in the margin).

> Stephen Langton, chosen archbishop
> Of Canterbury (*John*, III. i. 69–70)

Stephen Langhton, whom his Holines hath elected Archbishop of *Canterburie* (*T.R.*, I. v. 70–1)

Holinshed's gloss precedes Pandulph's appearance, but as the latter's first speech, so remarkably alike in the plays, contains the chronicle's words and perhaps its line-division in *John*, Shakespeare's deviation from the *T.R.* has significance.

(*d*) great *suit* was made to haue Arthur set at *libertie* (Hol., 165, i).

> our *suit*
> That you have bid us ask his *liberty* (*John*, IV. ii. 62–3)

> your *boone* . . .
> The *libertie* of Ladie *Constance* Sonne
>> (*T.R.*, I. xiii. 114–17)

(*e*) Other examples of Shakespeare's direct use of Holinshed will be found in many footnotes.

(*f*) Besides verbal similarities, the action of *John* frequently follows Holinshed more closely than the *T.R.* For instance, *John* (following Hol., 190, ii) reports that Melun crossed the Channel before Lewis to encourage the English nobles (IV. iii. 15–17). The *T.R.* omits this. Again, Melun tells the nobles in his dying speech that Lewis intends to reward their treachery to John with treachery (*John*, v. iv. 37–8). The *T.R.* portrays the French actually planning the coup (II. iii. 237–76); Holinshed, like *John*, reports Lewis's treachery in Melun's dying speech (193, ii), but the *T.R.* omits this detail of motivation in the corresponding passage (II. v. 1–47). Again, John's reactions to the death of Arthur appear to go back to Holinshed.[1]

Secondly, Shakespeare seems to have turned to John Foxe's *Actes and Monuments*.[2] Since *John*, more than any other of his plays, impinges on religious issues, we need not be surprised that Shakespeare glanced at the leading English Church historian, as the following quotations suggest.

1. See notes on IV. ii. 103, 208–14.
2. All our quotations are from the 1583 ed., vol. I.

(*a*) John's submission to the pope.

the king and his heirs should *take againe* these two dominions of the Pope to forme, (Foxe, 253, ii).

Then tooke the King the crowne from hys heade . . . saying in this wise. Here I resigne vp the crowne of the realme of England to the Popes hands Innocent the third (Foxe, 253, ii).

Foxe continues that John was later forced, as the pope's vassal, "to receiue it [the crown] *againe of him, at the handes of an other Cardinall*", and quotes "the letter obligatorie . . . concerning the *yelding vp* of the crowne" (Foxe, 253, ii).

he tooke the crowne from his owne head, and deliuered the same to Pandulph the legat, neither he, nor his heires at anie time thereafter to receiue the same, but at the popes hands (Hol., 177, i).

In the *T.R.* Pandulph orders John to surrender his crown (II. ii. 205), but the surrender is not represented. Later Pandulph is shown returning the crown to John (II. iv. 1 *sqq.*).

In *John*, v. i. 1–4 Shakespeare seems to follow Foxe in (i) giving John a speech as he hands over the crown; (ii) "yielded up"; (iii) "Take again / From this my hand".

(*b*) The death of John's poisoner.—Foxe contains a woodcut of this with the caption "The monke lyeth here burst of the poyson" (p. 256). Compare *John*, v. vi. 29–30: "A monk . . . / Whose bowels suddenly burst out".—The *T.R.* ascribes a similar death to John: "vnhappy Lord, / Whose bowells are deuided in themselues" (II. viii. 111–12). Prof. Wilson, discussing this coincidence, which he thought the only contact with Foxe, suggested that, as both men tasted the poison, "the same effect is naturally transferred".[1] (Query: Is it the same effect?)

(*c*) The Peter of Pomfret material.

Peter . . . an *idle* gadder about . . . a very *idle* vagabund . . . thys *phantasticall* Prophet went all the realme ouer . . . because he was then imprisoned for the matter, the *rumor* was the larger . . . old gossips tales went abroad, new tales were inuented, fables were added to fables, and lies grew vpon lyes . . . [various troubles being only due to Peter's] darke drousy *dreames* (Foxe, 252, ii, 253).

1. See Wilson's note on v. vi. 30.

> I find the people strangely *fantasied*;
> Possess'd with *rumours*, full of *idle dreams*
> (*John*, IV. ii. 144–5)

The *T.R.* parallels Shakespeare's later repetition ["Thou idle dreamer" (*John*, IV. ii. 153)] in an unhistorical meeting between John and Peter on Ascension Day ["*Peter*, vnsay thy foolish doting dreame" (*T.R.*, II. ii. 21)].

Moreover, the *T.R.* (I. xiii. 183–7) follows Holinshed (180, i, ii) in making Peter announce John's deposition to John himself. In *John* (IV. ii. 147–52) as in Foxe (pp. 252–3) Peter publishes this dangerous prophecy before facing John: and only Shakespeare and Foxe mention that the whole realm was disturbed by the consequent rumours.

(*d*) The anti-Roman recriminations in *John*.

charging the suffraganes and Bishops, to *meddle* no more (Foxe, 250, i); what great profite and *reuenewes*, hath proceeded hetherto to them out of the realme of England (Foxe, 250, ii)[1]; the *vsurped power* of the popes bulles (Foxe, 251, ii); the Popish Prelates . . . their crafty *iuggling* by their fained prophet (Foxe, 253, i).

his *usurp'd authority* (*John*, III. i. 86); this *meddling* priest (*ibid.*, l. 89); This *juggling* witchcraft with *revenue* cherish (*ibid.*, l. 95).

This is the standardized anti-papal abuse, but as it is missing in the *T.R.* and in Holinshed, and as Shakespeare has concentrated his echoes into a few lines, just as in (*c*) above, and as these echoes in (*d*) as in (*c*) all come from the same part of Foxe, we ought to take note.

Thirdly, Shakespeare seems to have looked at the *Historia Maior* (1571) of Matthew Paris. Two striking and a number of fugitive resemblances make this more or less certain.

(*a*) The loss of John's carriages in the Wash.

Mors Regis Iohannis.
. . . in fluuio qui Wellestrem dicitur, carretas omnes, bigas, & summarios, cum thesauris . . . *inopinato euentu* amisit. Aperta est enim in medijs fluctibus terra, & voragines abyssus, quae absorbuerunt vniversa cum hominibus & equis . . . Rex tamen cum exercitu suo *vix elapsus*, *nocte sequenti* apud Abbatiam, que Suenesheued dicitur, pernoctauit. Vbi, vt putabatur, de *rebus a fluctibus deuoratis* tantam

---

1. For Foxe's "reuenewes" Holinshed reads "gains" (171, i, 44).

mentis incurrit tristitiam, quod acutis correptus febribus, coepit
grauiter infirmari (pp. 384–5).

> When *in the morning* our troupes did gather head,
> Passing the washes with our carriages,
> The impartiall *tyde* deadly and inexorable,
> Came raging in with billowes threatning death,
> And *swallowed* vp the most of all our men,
> My selfe vpon a Galloway right free, well pacde,
> Out stript the *flouds* that followed waue by waue,
> I so *escapt* to tell this tragick tale (*T.R.*, II. vi. 46–53)

After a second report of the same disaster, the *T.R.* makes
Lewis exclaim

> Was euer heard such *vnexpected* newes ? (II. vii. 42)

When we compare *John*, v. vi. 39–44, v. vii. 61–64 several
points seem noteworthy: (i) Shakespeare's "Devoured by the
. . . flood" (v. vii. 64) = Matthew's "a fluctibus deuoratis";
the *T.R.* reads "The . . . tyde . . . swallowed", bringing in
"flouds" further down; (ii) Shakespeare and Matthew make
the disaster itself "unexpected"; in the *T.R.* the *news* of the disaster is "vnexpected"; (iii) Shakespeare's "*hardly* have escap'd" = Matthew's "*vix* elapsus"; the *T.R.* reads simply
"escapt", like Holinshed; (iv) Shakespeare explains twice that
the floods came at *night*, and Matthew seems to imply that; the
T.R. gives the time as "morning"; (v) Holinshed and Foxe
report this incident more briefly than Matthew, without any
of the verbal parallels which we have italicized.

(*b*) The reception of Lewis by the English nobles.

Barones Angliae in Regem eligunt Ludouicum Regem Galliae.
CIrca hos dies, cum denique Barones . . . tacti sunt dolore cordis
intrinsecus, & quid agerent, ignorabant, maledicentes Regis ver-
sutiam, tergiuersationes & infidelitatem, & dicentes, suspiria ge-
minando: Veh tibi Iohannes Regum vltime, Anglorum Principum
abominatio, Nobilitatis Anglicanae confusio. Heu Anglia iam vas-
tata & amplius vastanda: heu Anglia, Anglia, omnibus bonis
hactenus Princeps prouinciarum, facta es sub tributo . . . aduena-
rum imperio subiecta & subpeditata: . . . tu Iohannes . . . vt alios
tecum traheres in seruitutem, quasi cauda serpentina medietatem
stellarum a firmamento teipsum primo depressisti . . . Et sic
Barones lachrymantes & lamentantes, Regem & Papam male-
dixerunt (pp. 372–3).

This passage in Matthew was condensed by Holinshed,[1] who omitted a number of points common to Matthew and Shakespeare (*John*, v. ii. 8–39): (i) Following Matthew's "Barones lachrymantes & lamentantes" Shakespeare makes Salisbury *weep* (v. ii. 45–59), while Holinshed simply said "the Noble men . . . sore lamented the state of the realme" (186, ii); (ii) Matthew and Shakespeare apostrophize England ["Heu Anglia . . .", "O nation . . ." (v. ii. 33)], Holinshed cuts out this detail; (iii) the image of the nobles as stars (*John*, v. vii. 74), which has puzzled editors, may well derive from Matthew's allusion to *Revelation*, xii. 4 quoted above: and if so, it is curious that both Matthew and Shakespeare are led to the same image through the idea of servitude. Holinshed dropped the "cauda serpentina" and "stars".

(*c*) Other words and phrases where Shakespeare may be indebted to Matthew will be found in the footnotes.[2]

A fourth source of *John* may be the Latin MS. *Wakefield Chronicle*, from which alone, so far as we now know, Shakespeare could have learned that Queen Eleanor died on the first of April.[3] In the days when Shakespeare was not credited with any first-hand reading of chronicles for *John*, the "first of April" was practically always dismissed as a coincidence. Three reasons dissuade us against this attitude. Firstly, Shakespeare risks, three lines after the "first of April", another statement about dates, which is half-wrong—in the peculiar idiom adopted elsewhere in the play when he feels uncertain about his facts.[4] We suggest, therefore, that in the passage in question Shakespeare was writing from memory. Secondly, there are grounds for thinking that another Latin MS. chronicle was known to Shakespeare—that of Ralph Coggeshall—for the central scene in *John* (iv. i) seems to follow Ralph, who was the principal authority for the story, as Holinshed's margin records.[5] Thirdly, Shakespeare is now generally thought to have consulted MS. sources for *Richard II*—the twin-play to *John*—

1. Hol., 186, ii (cf. Appendix A, p. 159). The parallel scene in *T.R.* omits the lament of the nobles altogether (ii.iii).
2. See ii. i. 156, 236, 586, iii. i. 254, iv. ii. 4, iv. iii. 156, v. i. 44, v. ii. 33, notes.
3. See iv. ii. 120, and W. G. Boswell-Stone, *Shakspere's Holinshed* (1896), p. 61n.
4. See ii. ii. 14, iii. ii. 7, iv. ii. 123, v. vi. 23, notes.
5. See Hol., 165, i; and Appendix A (2).

B

which in itself is a sound blow against the old belief that he read as little as possible.

Prof. Wilson, ruling that Shakespeare's "direct access to the chronicles is an illusion", nevertheless cautions us that if he did read the chronicles "the case for his [Shakespeare's] dependence upon it [the *T.R.*] would be weakened".[1] We must pay heed to this warning. Indeed, the possibility that *John* preceded the *T.R.* cannot be ignored, for Prof. Peter Alexander, who revolutionized the interpretation of the early Shakespeare documents twenty and odd years ago, has insisted on many occasions that the *T.R.* follows *John*: and some recent writers have already accepted this view.[2]

Our difficulty in determining the precedence of the two plays arises, in part, from the number of the sources; but the sources also bring us nearer than any other approach to a decision. The authors of both the plays evidently read up their story carefully. *One of them also knew the other's work*—witness the "large body of verbal coincidence or similarity which is one of the most remarkable features of the problem we are studying".[3] Each, in fact, added many details not to be found in the other play.[4]

Having conceded the independent source-reading of both the authors we can still ask how accurately the sources were followed when both plays handle the same material. Does one take over the words of the source and the other paraphrase them?[5] Does one transplant an episode from its correct con-

---

1. *Op. cit.*, p. xxxii.

2. Notably A. S. Cairncross [*Problem of Hamlet* (1936), pp. 136–43]: cf. v. vii. 84, note. Cf. P. Alexander's *Shakespeare's Life and Art* (1939), p. 85; review in *M.L.R.*, vol. XLIV (1949), p. 263; *Shakespeare Primer* (1951), p. 63; also R. Noble's *Shakespeare's Biblical Knowledge* (1935), p. 113.

3. Wilson, *op. cit.*, p. xxvi.

4. John Elson's 'Studies in the King John Plays' [in *J. Q. Adams Memorial Studies* (1948), ed. J. G. McManaway] drew attention to some *T.R.* sources, among them Foxe's *Actes and Monuments*, which illustrate the *T.R.* author's independent source-reading (Elson did not consider the possibility of the *T.R.* following *John*). Further "source-reading" may be briefly indicated: Melun is a viscount in the *T.R.* (II. iii. 237), as in Hol. (193, ii), but a count in *John* (IV. iii. 15); Pembroke's name "William Marshal" occurs in the *T.R.* (I. i. 1), but not in *John*; Arthur is a youth in the *T.R.*, as in the chronicles, not a boy as in *John*; and so on.

5. See Hol. (*a*), (*c*), (*d*), Foxe (*b*), (*c*), Matthew Paris (*a*), above.

text, the other leave it there?[1] Or do both contain the words of the source, one not using them in the sense of the source?[2] While the second writer could conceivably revert to the source again and again, one is inclined to award the precedence to the accurate man. And, though the *T.R.* includes facts not given in *John*, Shakespeare is the accurate man in all the types of divergence that we have outlined. Upholders of the traditional theory about the relations of the two plays will have to ponder this.

Comparison with the chronicles provides us with no final answer. To penetrate to the heart of the problem we must consider dates. If the majority opinion which assigns *John* to the years 1595/6 be unassailable, little will be gained from a discussion that ignores chronology, since the *T.R* was printed in 1591. But that part of the "Shakespeare chronology" which supports this majority opinion has been under fire of late from a number of competent authorities. Newly discovered facts, moreover, suggest that, quite apart from the *T.R.*, *John* must probably be dated back to the winter of 1590/1. Our section on Date being, however, the proper place for the discussion of this and the other arguments which can alone unravel the difficult relations of the two plays, we must now momentarily drop the subject. Nevertheless it must be said here that we finally side with Prof. Alexander against the commoner view that the *T.R.* came before *John*: a decision which colours much of our comment in the ensuing pages.

If *John* precedes the *T.R.*, we must next account for the sources of those facts formerly said to be lifted straight out of the "source-play". With the four chronicle sources for which a claim was made above, only details omitted from the *T.R.* were grist to our mill: and only Holinshed and Matthew Paris passed muster with tolerable certainty. As soon as we brush aside the *T.R.*, however, there emerges a new picture. Holinshed, as we expect, turns out to be the primary source. Shakespeare studied his life of John in minute detail, also reading up Richard I and Henry III.[3]

1. See Hol. (*f*), Foxe (*b*), Matthew Paris (*a*), above.
2. See Hol. (*b*), Matthew Paris (*a*), above.
3. The first and last extracts from Holinshed in Appendix A (1) make this plain.

The case for Foxe as a source becomes watertight, which it was not before. For instance, Shakespeare's incorrect form of the name "Swineshead Abbey" follows Foxe's "Swinsted" (Foxe, p. 256; *John*, v. iii. 8 etc.), for Holinshed reads "Swineshead" (p. 194, ii) and Matthew Paris "Suenesheued" (p. 385). Pandulph's mission to John (*John*, III. i. 62–72), again, follows Foxe more closely than Holinshed:

[The pope] sent to ye king two Legates (the one called Pandulph, and the other Durant) to warne him *in the popes name* that he should cease his doinges to *holy church*, and amend the wrong he had done to the Archb. of Cant. . . . These two Legates comming into England, resorted to ye king to Northhampton, where he held his Parliament, & *saluting him*, sayd: *they came from the Pope of Rome*, to reforme ye peace of *holy church*. And first sayd they we monish you in the popes behalfe, that ye make full restitution of the goods & of the land that ye haue rauished *holy church* of: *and that ye receiue Stephen the Archbi. of Cant. into his dignity*. . . . (Foxe, 252, i).

the pope sent two legats into England, the one named Pandulph a lawier, and the other Durant a templer, who comming vnto king Iohn, exhorted him with manie terrible words to leaue his stubborne disobedience to the church, and to reforme his misdooings. The king for his part quietlie heard them . . . when they perceiued that they could not haue their purpose . . . the legats departed, leauing him accursed, and the land interdicted (Hol., 175, i).

Here, as in quotation (*a*) from Foxe above (p. xiv), Foxe and Shakespeare have direct speech as opposed to Holinshed's indirect. Shakespeare also follows Foxe in making John's hostility to Stephen Langton the main business of Pandulph's mission.

Beside Holinshed, Foxe, Matthew Paris, and perhaps the MS. *Wakefield Chronicle* and *Coggeshall Chronicle*, Shakespeare must also have been familiar with one of the Cœur-de-lion romances. We think that the medieval poem printed by Wynkyn de Worde as *Kynge Rycharde Cuer du Lyon* may be a "source", though Richard was so popular a national hero that obviously much literature about him may be lost.[1] Wynkyn's romance, at any rate, must serve as our authority for a number of points in *John* for the time being.

1. We use Wynkyn's ed. of 1528 throughout. A lost "boke intituled *kynge Rychard Cur De Lyon*" was entered in the S.R. in 1568–9 (Arber, 1, 389).

(*a*) The identification of Leopold, Archduke of Austria, with Widomar, Viscount of Limoges.—Richard I was killed while besieging Limoges,[1] shortly after building "Chateau Galiard" (Hol., 155, ii), the erection of the castle being otherwise unconnected with his death. In a complete hotch-potch of the facts, the romance (i) supplants Limoges by Austria, (ii) locates the scene at "castell gaylarde":

> And syth he came I vnderstonde
> The waye towarde englonde
> And thorugh treason was shotte alas
> At castell gaylarde there he was
> The duke of estryche in the castell
> with his hoost was dyght full well
> Rycharde thought there to abyde (sig. Q₅)

As in the romance Richard's two enemies in *John* are merged into one, with obvious dramatic advantages. Not through ignorance, but following an established tradition. Characteristically, Shakespeare has not silently *omitted* the name Limoges, but gives the one person both names, an equivocating method of compression used frequently in our play.[2]

(*b*) The characters of Richard's two principal enemies, Philip Augustus and Austria.—In *John* cowardice is the keynote of Austria, treachery that of King Philip, and the romance emphasizes these qualities above all others again and again. We have only room for two typical quotations:

> (i) Rycharde wende Phylyp had fought
> And he and his men dyde nought
> But made mery all that nyght
> And were traytours in that fyght
> For he loued no crownes to crake
> But to do treason and tresour take (sig. Mᵛ)

> (ii) The duke of estryche hyed faste
> Awaye with his meyne in haste
> And with hym the duke of burgoyne
> The folke of fraunce & the erle of coloyne

---

1. George H. Needler [*Richard Cœur de Lion in Literature* (1890), pp. 56–7] noted that the substitution of Austria for Limoges in Wynkyn's book was the source of their identification in the *T.R.* Cf. P. Simpson in *N. & Q.*, 12 Nov. 1898.

2. See p. xvii, n. 4.

> Kynge Rycharde let breke his baner
> And caste it into the ryuer
> And cryed on hym with voyce stepe
> Home shrewed cowarde and go slepe (sig. N₆ᵛ)

We gather from (ii) the reasons for Austria's unhistorical association with the French (*John*, II. i. 7); Faulconbridge's treatment of the cowardly duke (*John*, II. i. 135–40, III. i. 57, etc.) reproducing exactly the tone of his father.

(*c*) The invincibility of the Bastard.—

> That misbegotten divel, Faulconbridge,
> In spite of spite, alone upholds the day
>   (*John*, v. iv. 4–5)

It transpires that the superman "devil" appellation, recurring in *John*, II. i. 135, IV. iii. 95, IV. iii. 100 (Faulconbridge taking pride in the name) is part of the Cœur-de-lion heritage:

> The sarasynes as I you tell
> Sayd he was the deuyll of hell (sig. G₇ᵛ)

> Eueryche sate styll and plucked other
> And sayd this is the deuylles brother (sig. K₂)

> The sarasynes sayd than
> He was a deuyll and no man (sig. O₂ᵛ)

> The englysshe deuyll I come is
> And but we flee out of his waye
> An euyll deth shall we dye to daye (sig. P₇)

These are by no means the only instances where Richard is paid the compliment in the romance.

There remain many puzzles in *John* where Shakespeare falls in line with facts or traditions, his authority being disputable. The Cœur-de-lion romance gives help with the most important one.

(*a*) The Faulconbridge story.—Holinshed mentions Cœur-de-lion's bastard son:

Philip bastard sonne to king Richard, to whome his father had giuen the castell and honor of Coinacke, killed the vicount of Limoges, in reuenge of his fathers death (160, ii).

But whence the name Faulconbridge?—An anonymous play,

Looke About You (1600), probably written after *John*,[1] exhibits a Sir Richard Faulconbridge (not Sir *Robert* as in *John*) whose wife Prince Richard attempts to seduce. This play must be intimately connected with the Robin Hood plays by Munday and Chettle, written in 1598, and *The Funeral of Richard Coeur-de-lion*, a lost play which followed hard upon the latter,[2] being like them the property of the Admiral's company. If Chambers's date for *Looke About You*, viz. 1599, may be accepted, the play could be a kind of sequel to the two about Robin Hood, for the chief characters—Queen Eleanor, Prince Richard, Prince John, Robin Hood, Gloucester, and other nobles—are repeated in both stories. Richard's wooing of Lady Faulconbridge, moreover, not only resembles John's wooing of the fair Matilda: the *Looke About You* dramatist has made Lady Faulconbridge the (unhistorical) sister of Gloucester—Gloucester being the father of Matilda in the Robin Hood plays—so that the whole Faulconbridge set-up in *Looke About You* seems imitative and unauthentic.

In a second late publication, *The Famous History of George, Lord Fauconbridge Bastard Son to Richard Cordelion* (1616, 1635[3]), a prose pamphlet, Richard begets a son, George, on Austria's daughter, Claribel. The princess's infatuation with Richard goes back to pre-Shakespearean books, such as Warner's *Albions England* (1589), the germ of the idea existing already in the Wynkyn romance[4]: which suggests that the prose pamphlet *combines* two stories, (i) about Richard and the Austrian princess, (ii) about Richard and Lady Faulconbridge. Lord George's favourite garment, the lion-skin of his father, may be the fiction of Shakespeare,[5] like the pamphlet's other fugitive coincidences with *John*. The freedom the pamphleteer allowed himself with names suggests that facts were not his obsession.

But the names of the different versions are a stumbling-block

---

1. E. K. Chambers, *The Elizabethan Stage*, IV, 28.

2. Chambers, *op. cit.*, III, 446–7; W. W. Greg, *Henslowe's Diary*, II (1908), 190, 193.

3. We have only seen the 1635 ed., from which we quote. The copy was entered in 1614 by John Beale (Arber, III, 558), who was buying up the copies of the recently deceased stationer Barley.

4. *Albions England*, sig. P₃; Wynkyn's *Cuer de Lyon*, sig. C₃ᵛ, etc.

5. "Never wearing any other Garment, but that *Lyons skin*, by which his Kingly Father challenged his *Lyon-like* Title" (1635 title-page).

too. Cœur-de-lion's mistresses, christened "Margare" in Wynkyn's romance (sig. C₃ᵛ), "Ladie *Margaret*" (Faulconbridge)
in the *T.R.* (I. i. 222), "Marian" (Faulconbridge) in *Looke
About You* (sig. B₃ᵛ), may be throwbacks, in the extant treatments, to a lost original.

Looke About You and *The Famous History* must be earlier than
1600, 1614 respectively, but the Faulconbridge material in
them seems spurious, not going back beyond Shakespeare.
And that Shakespeare was in fact the inventor of it all the
Faulconbridge elements in his other plays may bear out. For
Shakespeare frequently resorted to the name, and this may
imply some personal relationship. Three "second period"
plays beside *John* use it significantly.[1] In his most topical
comedy, *Love's Labours' Lost*, two allusions to the house of Faulconbridge (II. i. 42, 203), have not yet been pounced upon by
the commentators. In the *Merchant of Venice* the "Baron Faulconbridge" described as the typical Englishman (I. ii. 70–81)
is a "proper" man, but unlanguaged, which reminds one of
the Bastard. In *Henry IV*, Part II, a Lord Faulconbridge was
excised from the Northumberland circle, to which Shakespeare's contemporary Faulconbridge family belonged[2]: and
it is tantalizing that in the same quarto text a Sir John Russell,
bearing the surname of one of Shakespeare's best friends, was
likewise dropped.[3]

Our conjectural solution is that Shakespeare (i) invented
the Faulconbridge story, possibly with some topical innuendo,
(ii) merged the invented bastard Faulconbridge with Holinshed's Philip. If Shakespeare had connections in the north in
the early 1590's, as Dr Hotson has shown to be likely,[4] and
as the theory that he was one of Strange's men confirms,[5] a
Faulconbridge (Belasyse)–Shakespeare contact grows less unlikely, and similarly the possibility that northern MS. chro-

1. The historical use of the name does not concern us here, as in *1 H 6*, IV. vii.
67, *3 H 6*, I. i. 239.
2. *2 H 4*, I. iii (Q1). The Faulconbridge title came to England with Belasius,
Lord Faulconbridge, in 1066. In Shakespeare's day the Belasyse family of Yorks.
(for which the title of Earl Fauconberg was revived in the 17th century) would be
the Faulconbridges. Their circle included the Northumberlands, Rutlands, Lord
Burghley, the archbishop of York (as their and their relatives' wills show).
3. *2 H 4*, II. ii; cf. L. Hotson's *I, William Shakespeare* (1937).
4. *Shakespeare's Sonnets Dated* (1949), p. 127 ff.   5. See pp. xlix–liii.

nicles were sources of *John*. Indeed, stray facts in *John* not available in published sources in 1590 may well go back to the family chronicle of a northern house. Perhaps Shakespeare's Philip Faulconbridge was based (iii) on the historical Philip de Falconbridge, Archdeacon of Huntingdon *anno* 1222,[1] introduced to Shakespeare by such a source: for the historical Philip was successor to William Cornehill, one of King John's right-hand men, and may therefore have been a receiver of Church goods seized by John like William Cornehill,[2] and like his namesake the Bastard in our play (iii. ii. 17–23, iv. ii. 141–2).

(*b*) "Cardinal" Pandulph.—Like John Bale in his *King Iohan* and other early writers about John's reign, Shakespeare elevates the papal legate Pandulph to a cardinalate. The historians tripped up first, confusing our Pandulph with Pandulf Masca (created a cardinal in the 1180's): it therefore seems likely that Shakespeare, falling in with an established tradition, knew at least one more "source". Foxe alone among the sources so far identified has one hint to the same effect, but probably too casual to have caused Shakespeare's change. He describes John's surrender of the crown to Pandulph, and John's acceptance of it again later "at the handes of an other Cardinall" (253, ii).

Over and above actual "source-books", plays on familiar subjects also follow the floating knowledge of the age, which may have a bearing on interpretation. Well-known historical facts do not have to be led up to or motivated as conscientiously as unknown ones, the audience being already conditioned to accept them.

That the reign of John was an open book to Shakespeare's first audience there can be no doubt. Ever since Bale's *King Iohan*, a morality written *c.* 1540, which pointed the parallel between the reigns of John and Henry VIII, religious controversialists had publicized John's life. The Protestants praised him as the first English king who tried to throw off the yoke of

---

1. See Browne Willis: *Survey of the Cathedrals of York, Durham, etc.* (1727 etc.), III, 105.
2. See Foxe's *Actes and Monuments* (ed. 1596), p. 227.

Rome, blackened the tale of his perfidious poisoning, and blamed earlier historians for blackening John[1]; the Catholics made much of John's surrender of the crown to the pope, claiming that Henry VIII was only a vassal as a consequence, and his Reformation civil as well as ecclesiastical rebellion. These issues were so dear to Shakespeare's contemporaries that non-specialist books often enter the fray at unexpected moments. Quasi-controversial works such as William Allen's *Admonition to the Nobility and People of England* (1588),[2] Sir Thomas Smith's *Common-Welth of England* (1589),[3] and innumerable others of equal fame, tacitly assume that the reader knows all about John: recurring digressions about him and his problems in, for instance, William Lambarde's *Perambulation of Kent* (1576),[4] might, however, seem less normal than they happen to have been, unless we see John through Elizabethan eyes.

The controversialist interest in John was reinforced, as Prof. Lily Campbell has recently shown, by the addition of the "Homilie against Disobedience and Wylfull Rebellion" to the Elizabethan *Book of Homilies* in 1571.[5] Here the enormity of John's nobles' crime, who aided the invader Lewis, was outlined and chastised at great length in the sixth part. Periodic reading of these homilies was compulsory in all churches.

During the "Armada period" (*c.* 1583–96), moreover, a new type of patriotic pamphleteering sprang into existence, wherein Englishmen were exhorted to defend their country, should the need arise, by means of plentiful citations of famous English exploits of the past. The sudden cult of the chronicle play in the 1590's was thus prepared for by a revival of interest in wars of long ago, and we deduce that the sermons and more ephemeral literature teaching history left an impression. Indeed, the unheralded historical allusion, so common in these pamphlets, makes this quite plain:

1. "Verelie, whosoeuer shall consider the course of the historie written of this prince, he shall find, that he hath beene little beholden to the writers of that time in which he liued: for scarselie can they afoord him a good word... The occasion whereof (as some thinke) was, for that he was no great freend to the clergie" (Hol., 196, i).

2. Sigs. A₅ᵛ, C₇.   3. Sig. Cᵛ.

4. See pp. 132–5, 217, 328, etc.

5. *Shakespeare's "Histories"* (1947), p. 143.

Let vs deale but with our selues, and with our owne feeling, knowledge and memorie. The accursing of King *Iohn*: the receyuing him
vassaill: the making his Realme subiect and feudatorie to the Pope:
the arming his Subiects against him: the poysoning of him at
length: the giuing the Land to the French Kinges sonne: the in-
uading thereof by the *Dolphin* of *Fraunce*: his so long possessing a
great part of it: the rebellion of the Barons to take the French mens
part: all the mischeefes that fell in all this whyle, were they not the
good workes of Popes and Papistes?[1]

It has been fashionable of late to condemn the motivation of
the last third of *John*.[2] Yet just the last third deals with the
events peculiarly fascinating for Elizabethans: the rebellion of
the nobles, John's surrender of the crown, the poisoning of
John. It is no accident that just these events are so often the
target of modern criticism. But perhaps Shakespeare expected
his first audience to look forward to them avidly, to accept
them unhesitatingly.

The story of John was familiar as a parallel to Elizabeth's.
Perhaps Shakespeare chose it on that account to mirror certain problems of the queen which he forced into the super-
structure of historical truth. For the Armada period itself is
another source of *John*. In 1874 this was strongly urged by
Richard Simpson, some of whose arguments we must recapitulate.[3] Eleanor, for instance, tells John that he holds the throne
through "strong possession", not through right (I. i. 40). While
the legitimacy of Elizabeth's title to the succession was in hot
debate, because the pope did not recognize it, John's "usurpation" is Shakespeare's fiction, for his "right" is not seriously
questioned in the chronicles. Again, Shakespeare seems to
think of Tudor rather than Plantagenet history when he mentions a will (II. i. 192–4) that bars Arthur's right to the throne.
Henry VIII left a will barring the right of Mary Queen of
Scots to the throne of England (the argument is that John =

---

1. A(nthony) M(unday)'s *Watch-Woord to Englande* (1584), sigs. L₄, L₄ᵛ.
   2. "the hero, without rhyme or reason, dies . . . murdered by an anonymous
monk, who . . . is not shown to have any motive whatever for his deed" (Edward
Rose, quoted approvingly by Wilson, p. xxi); "Shakespeare huddles together
and fails to motivate properly the events of the last third of his play" [Tillyard:
Shakespeare's History Plays (1944), p. 215].
   3. Cf. 'The Politics of Shakspere's Historical Plays' (in the *Transactions* of the
New Shakspere Society, 1874).

Elizabeth, Arthur = Mary). Another of Simpson's points was that Lewis's treachery to the English nobles (v. iv. 10 ff.) parallels that contemplated by Medina Sidonia, commander of the Spanish Armada, to the English Catholics who were ready to aid him against the Queen.[1] But, as the chronicles already provided the last two "parallels", we must not dwell unduly upon them, except to observe that elements in John's real story may have been emphasized in our play in order to underline the contemporary resemblances.

Simpson also followed up a suggestion of Warburton that John's order to Hubert to murder Arthur, and his violent recriminations when he thinks his rival dead (III. ii. 29–79, IV. ii. 208–48), have, on the one hand, no direct source in the chronicles, but on the other a curious likeness to Elizabeth's treatment of Secretary Davison. Elizabeth asked Davison to have Mary Queen of Scots murdered, so the rumour went, to save political unpleasantness. Entrusted at last with a warrant for the execution of Mary, Davison was made the queen's scapegoat when it was found that Mary's death afforded Elizabeth's enemies first-rate opportunities for propaganda. He was put on trial and fined a very large sum for his "fault"—modern historians agreeing that, in fact, he only carried out his duties. Though Shakespeare and Davison may well have known each other as fellow-members of the Essex-circle, and though Hubert's fate in *John* does resemble Davison's, many another cat's-paw has fared similarly and therefore it is now usual to belittle the "Davison parallel".

But the question of topicality is still not closed. Prof. L. Campbell has discovered that the right of Mary to the English crown was actually argued in at least two books in terms of Arthur's right to John's crown.[2] Whether Shakespeare knew

1. The significance of the Melun parallel only dawns on us as we recognize that even Roman Catholics believed that the Spaniards intended treachery [*v.* W. W., *Important Considerations* (1601), sig. E]. The treachery of foreign Roman Catholics had, curiously, been argued a little before Shakespeare through the very story of Melun: "Wil *Israell* trust to a reed? can Papists imagine that strangers will doe them good?... do they remember, or haue they forgotten, or haue they not reade county *Melunes* most memorable counsel to our English nobles?" [J. Prime, *Sermon* (1585), sig. B₅ᵛ]. Prime subjoined the whole of Melun's death-speech—as in *John*, v. iv—from M. Paris.

2. *Op. cit.*, p. 142. The two books were by John Leslie, Bishop of Ross. There were in fact more than two books: Leslie says that the Mary-Arthur parallel was

these books or not, the comparison may have reached him orally, and has importance. Again, the Davison-Hubert correspondences were even more pointed than has yet been shown. Shakespeare draws attention to the king's "hand and seal" (IV. ii. 215–17) which authorized the murder of Arthur: yet the chronicles do not mention them, nor does Shakespeare in any murder scene in his other plays drag in "hand and seal". The trial of Davison, however, revolved round the fact that Elizabeth *signed* the death-warrant, but that he then prematurely *sealed* it and sent it to Fotheringhay. John's very language, reproaching Hubert that he should have demanded "*express* words" (IV. ii. 234) when he "spake *darkly*" (IV. ii. 232), echoes the main issue of the Davison trial: "That she [the Queen] had *darkly* signified, but not *expressely* commanded" the sealing.[1]

Shakespeare's manipulation of the historical facts brings out the similarities of the reigns of John and Elizabeth excitingly, almost dangerously. An English sovereign, said to be a usurper (I. i. 40), and perhaps a bastard (II. i. 130), defies the pope (III. i. 73), becomes "supreme head" (III. i. 81), is excommunicated (III. i. 99), imprisons his rival (IV. i), who was barred from the crown by a will (II. i. 192); the pope promises his murderer canonization (III. i. 103), invites another king to invade England (III. i. 181), the English sovereign darkly urges the murder of the rival "pretender" (III. ii), then needs a scapegoat (IV. ii. 208), a foreign invasion is attempted (IV. ii. 110), the invaders intending to kill the Englishmen who help them (V. iv. 10), their navy is providentially wrecked off the English coast (V. v. 12), English unity being finally achieved through the failure of the invasion (V. vii. 115):—frequent "Armada idiom" hammering home the topicality of the play.[2] That Shakespeare found *some* of these facts in the chronicles does not detract from the overwhelming effect of the parallel, which is entirely due to the selection of incidents relevant to a particular purpose.

Not only does Shakespeare carefully guide his story towards the "disconnected" incidents of Act V, ineffective in the eyes

not his invention, but that of his "Aduersaries" [*Treatise Touching the Right* (1585), sig. D₇].

1. Camden's *Annales*, tr. Darcie (1625), p. 211.
2. See p. xlvi, n. 2.

of some modern critics, but possibly inevitable in those of his first audience: he also makes a sincere attempt to interpret the major facts as he found them as regards character. As in most of Shakespeare's plays, the hero seems to step straight out of the source (lesser characters are slightly altered to suit the more subtle dramatic plot). Certain repetitions in Holinshed must have suggested John's significant moodiness to Shakespeare, indeed "la psychose périodique" which Charles Petit-Dutaillis diagnosed in the historical king.[1] And beside many remarks about John's sudden fury, Holinshed also emphasized the king's power of self-restraint when intent on deception, the two polarities of his personality:

the king in a great rage sware, that . . . he would put out their eies, and slit their noses (172, i).

These words being signified vnto the king, set him in such an heat . . . (172, ii).

they were much deceiued, for the king hauing condescended to make such grant of liberties, farre contrarie to his mind, was right sorowfull in his heart . . . he whetted his teeth, he did bite now on one staffe, and now on an other . . . with such disordered behauiour and furious gestures (186, ii).

[Pandulph and Durant] exhorted him with manie terrible words to leaue his stubborne disobedience. . . . The king for his part quietlie heard them . . . (175, i).

Shakespeare adapts history by portraying in John's early career a suave man of the world, in the later acts expressing the king's consciousness of his helplessness through his moody outbursts: Act III being the transition. John's degeneration is reinforced by means of the symbol of military speed, with which he surprised the French,[2] only to be taken unawares by them himself in Act IV[3]; Holinshed, again, having signalized the extraordinary dualism of John's capacity for expedition and sluggishness:[4]

1. *Le Roi Jean et Shakespeare* (1944), chap. I.
2. II. i. 79, III. iii. 10–14.
3. IV. ii. 110–16.
4. Holinshed often mentions John's *haste*: "hasting towards Ireland" (174, i), "he brake foorth of Winchester, as it had beene an hideous tempest of weather" (193, ii), "the king hasted forward till he came to Wellestreme" (194, i), etc.

[King John] in all possible hast speedeth him foorth . . . he was vpon his enimies necks yer they could vnderstand any thing of his comming . . . (164, ii).

All this while king Iohn did lie at Rouen . . . and would saie often-times to such as stood about him; What else dooth my coosen the French K. now, than steale those things from me, which hereafter I shall indeuour my selfe to cause him to restore with interest? (166, ii).

Recreating the essential John, Shakespeare has, however, violated facts again and again, subordinating dates and like details to the truth of character, the credibility of climaxes. *John* has been called his most unhistorical play. Act iv, Sc. ii alone fakes the sequence of events more cleverly than perhaps any other part of the canon. John's new coronation (l. 1) and the rumoured death of Arthur (l. 85) took place in 1202; the landing of the French (l. 110) in 1216; the death of Eleanor (l. 120) in 1204; the death of Constance (l. 122) in 1201; the Peter of Pomfret episode (l. 131) belonging to the year 1213; the five moons (l. 182) to 1200: practically the whole span of John's reign being crammed into one scene and made to seem simultaneous, for the dramatic advantage of heaping up John's troubles and omens of misfortune.[1]

Compression must obviously be the historical dramatist's first thought, and there is a great deal of it in *John*. But to say that the story falls apart and dies in the author's hands because he attempted to concentrate too many unrelated events into five acts[2] is to ignore Acts i and ii, where Shakespeare has liberally invented and added without worrying about retailing facts. Act i, indeed, a prelude to the main theme, is entirely

1. P. A. Daniel's "time-scheme" for *John* (in the *Transactions* of the New Shakspere Society, 1877–9, pp. 257–64) shows how the whole reign has been made to seem a matter of a few months, the action requiring only seven separate days (with intervals). Day 1 is Act i, day 2 is Act ii—Act iii, Sc. ii, day 3 is Act iii, Sc. iii, day 4 is Act iv, day 5 is Act v, Sc. i, day 6 is Act v, Sc. ii–v, day 7 is Act v, Sc. vi–vii.—As in *Oth.*, *Troil.*, etc., Shakespeare probably intended a "double time-scheme", viz. John should seem to age, to lose physical vigour, in the two last acts—despite the "few months" duration, the purpose of which was simply to interlock causes and effects.

2. E. K. Chambers called *John* "incoherent patchwork" [*Shakespeare: A Survey* (1925), p. 105]; Brander Matthews said "the action is wandering and uncertain" [*Shakespeare as a Playwright* (1913), p. 97]. Equally typical condemnations are quoted on p. xxvii, n. 2, and p. lxvi.

original so far as we can tell. John judges the legality of a
"usurper", the Bastard, who took possession of his younger
and physically weaker relative's inheritance. A will is appealed
to (I. i. 109) and rejected (I. i. 116, 132), anticipating the main
story's will (II. i. 191–4), the Faulconbridge family quarrel
heralding that of the Plantagenets. Here Shakespeare has am-
plified history for the sake of thematic iteration. Similarly,
purely artistic reasons dictated the compression of source-book
facts in the later acts, for, loosely as the later episodes may seem
to cohere at first glance, a moment's reflection about the meaning of the play assures us that structural compactness might
have been Shakespeare's aim. The fourth section of our Introduction resumes this topic, and here it remains only to indicate
how the plot has been tightened. Arthur's plight, for instance,
becomes more clear when he accepts help from Limoges–
Austria, the two traditional enemies (compressed into one) of
his "great forerunner" (II. i. 2).—Angiers, where Eleanor was
almost taken by Arthur's men, and Arthur later captured, is
identified with Mirabeau,[1] the unhistorical location symboliz-
ing the whole of the disputed Angevin inheritance.—Cœur-
de-lion's bastard son Philip may be partially identified with
Faukes de Breauté, the soldier of fortune, also a bastard, to
whom John entrusted the leading of an army towards the end
of his life[2]; and Shakespeare's Bastard Faulconbridge must
almost certainly be a distillation from half a dozen sources,
inorganically related in so far as some are famous bastards, or
part of a topical story, or otherwise associable as "Faulconbridges"[3]—which makes clear the meticulous instincts behind
the play, ranging beyond history in pursuit of satisfactory tone
and balance.

   To sum up: Shakespeare sifted so many sources in order to
find incidents germane to his purpose. His drama was made to

---

1. See Hol., 164, ii.   2. Cf. *John*, v. ii. 77 and Hol., 189, ii.
   3. See pp. xxii, lii. W. G. Boswell-Stone [*Shakespere's Holinshed* (1896), p. 48,
etc.] cited various views about the origins of Faulconbridge—who may be
modelled on Faukes; on the "Stern Faulconbridge" of *3 H 6*, I. i. 239, another
famous bastard known to Shakespeare; and perhaps on Dunois (whose story
Shakespeare read while writing *I H 6*), who declared that his "noble corage"
assured him he was the bastard of Orleans, and that he scorned to be "the lawful
sonne of that coward cuckolde Cauny" despite the financial loss to him. Cf. also
G. Kopplow, *Shakespeares "King John" und seine Quelle* (1900), p. 14.

follow the *outlines* of a familiar story, but he nevertheless search-ed painstakingly for dramatic *details* to build up his idea of John—because contemporary ignorance allowed him freedom of detail. Fugitive facts are thrown at the audience to give the effect of authenticity, while at the same time larger truths are outraged. The ultimate purpose was a "truthful" interpreta-tion of behaviour in peculiar circumstances according to Eliza-bethan lights—consequently the truths of time and place and historical identity were sacrificed to the superior needs of the total impression.

2. THE TEXT

The Life and Death of King John was first published in the Folio of 1623, at the head of the Histories. The copy for the text was once thought to be a prompt-book,[1] but Prof. J. D. Wilson detected certain non-theatrical features,[2] and Sir Walter Greg, following up, finally proposed foul paper prove-nance,[3] a theory which at present holds the field.

Greg's attitude was determined by "inconsistency in the directions and speech prefixes—which McKerrow overlook-ed".[4] Stage directions that follow the action they are supposed to herald indicate a non-theatrical origin:

> The interruption of their churlish drums
> Cuts off more circumstance, they are at hand,
> *Drum beats.* (F1, ii. i. 76–7)

Because these late directions occur only in the first half of *John* (for others see i. i. 49, i. i. 220) Dr Alice Walker has suggested that Acts i–iii may have been printed from foul papers and Acts iv–v from prompt-copy.[5] Greg disagreed with Dr Walker, however, declaring that a composite MS. would be very un-usual.[6]

---

1. Cf. E. K. Chambers, *William Shakespeare* (1930), i, 143, *sqq.*
2. Cf. his C.U.P. *John*, pp. 92–4.
3. *The Editorial Problem in Shakespeare* (1951), pp. 142–3.
4. *Op. cit.*, p. 142; cf. R. McKerrow: 'A Suggestion Regarding Shakespeare's Manuscripts' [*R.E.S.* (1935), p. 463].
5. Greg, *op. cit.*, p. 143n.
6. Some editors thought that at iii. i. 81, v. vii. 60 "God" was altered to "heaven" in conformity with the Act of Abuses, 1606. But the F1 editor probably

C

Inconsistency in the speech headings which, according to McKerrow,[1] was foul paper rather than prompt-book practice, frequently confronts us in *John*. Queen Eleanor appears as *Elea.* (I. i. 5), *Ele.* (I. i. 31), *Eli.* (I. i. 40), *Queen* (II. i. 120), *Qu. Mo.* (II. i. 166), *Old Qu.* (II. i. 468); the French king is *King* until John appears, then becomes *France* (II. i. 37, 89); the Citizen of Angiers is *Cit.* from II. i. 201 to II. i. 281, and from II. i. 325 is *Hubert*, and so on.

Act II, more inconsistent in its speech headings than the rest of the play, also contains

some confusion in the use of the names in the text, which must be due to the author: the French king, whose name is Philip, sometimes appears as Lewis by confusion with the Dauphin. Modern editors have generally corrected this, and so doubtless would a playhouse scribe have done had he noticed it.[2]

If it is possible, as we think, to rationalize these confusions, the case for foul papers becomes even stronger.

(*a*) The first line of Act II provides the first probable "speech heading confusion". Although the Folio gives the speech to Lewis, line 7 can hardly be ascribed to anyone but the French king, as editors have realized.

(*b*) II. i. 149–51 brings further complications. The Folio reads:

> King *Lewis*, determine what we shall doe strait.
> *Lew.* Women & fooles, breake off your conference.
> King *Iohn*, this is the very summe of all:

Does Austria here appeal to the king *and* Lewis, or does Shakespeare confuse Lewis and Philip?[3] If the former, why does the king not answer?

(*c*) In II. i. 368, the speech heading *Fra.* has been generally rejected in favour of Hubert, the citizen, the speech being obviously his.

---

reformed profanity as well as the prompter (Greg, *op. cit.*, p. 155n.), as various non-theatrical F1 texts show (cf. *Oth.*, II. iii. 106, *1 H 4*, II. iv. 213, 523 etc.).

1. *Op. cit.*   2. Greg, *loc. cit.*

3. It is probably irrelevant to observe that Holinshed mistakenly names the king "Lewis" in one passage (Hol., 161, i).

Either through his absence where he should be present, or *vice versa*, France is the common factor in these three cruxes. Until John's entry (ii. i. 84) the speeches of France are consistently headed *King*: thereafter the form *France* replaces *King*. This *France* may well derive from Shakespeare himself. If, however, we assume that *King* was used throughout the act in the author's copy, and that an editor or compositor, attempting to clarify, reheaded the king's speeches *France* after John's entry, the three cruxes easily explain themselves. The coincidence of *King* and a proper name may have caused (*a*) and (*b*). France and Austria enter "at several doors" at the opening of Act ii: Lewis could say ii. i. 1, as the Folio directs, walking towards Austria and bringing him back to France. We suggest that a speech heading *King* was dropped before l. 2 because it seemed to be part of the text and was (i) hypermetrical, (ii) apparently nonsensical, i.e. Arthur is not a king. A similar confusion may be postulated for ii. i. 149–51, where the speech heading *King* was made part of the text (l. 149), and again dropped (l. 151). The MS. reading may be reconstructed thus:

> King. Lewis, determine what we shall doe strait.
> Lew. Women & fooles, breake off your conference.
> King. King Iohn, this is the very summe of all: (ii. i. 149–51)

If the stops had faded, the metre of l. 149 would be "improved" by the tenth syllable ("Lewis" was monosyllabic). In l. 151 dittography may have been diagnosed.[1]

This explanation is less far-fetched than appears at first sight. We refer to the last scene of the Folio *Henry V*, where two kings are on-stage as in *John*: sometimes the forms *France* and *England* are used, but plain *King* (for King Henry) occurs nine times without causing trouble. Again, compare the famous line

1. We have followed Capell's note on ii. i. 149–51: "The father, indeed, may very reasonably make his son the declarer of a thing praeconcerted . . . it shews the son's consequence, and weight with the father; and . . . rescues him from the state of a cypher in a scene of great length. . . [Capell is led to the same conclusion by the "free manner of opening" of l. 150] which has a juvenile air with it: The correction . . . [is] a slight one; for 'tis founded on the only supposal that the copy had "King" for French King, without scoring or stopping it, and that the printer was too faithful." Capell read as we do, but kept ll. 150–4 as one speech (Lewis's). But the *I* claiming *In right of Arthur* (l. 153) can only be Philip, and confusions (*a*) and (*c*) also weigh against Capell's reading of ii. i. 151.

Nath. Of persing a Hogshead (*LLL.*, Q1, iv. ii. 89)

which, as many editors agree, corruptly represents

Holof. Persing a Hogshead

Shakespeare, it seems, did not always use Italian script for speech headings, nor carefully distinguish speech headings and text.

Our contention that *King* was a speech heading throughout Act II gains strength from crux (*c*). *Hu*[*bert*] misread as *Fra.* looks improbable: *Hu* misread *Ki*[*n.*], or Hu. as Ki[n.] (Secretary hand)—normalized to *Fra.*—would be a simple error. Misreading of this kind, rather than a compositor's muddle-headedness, seems a safe guess where three different types of confusion can be linked by a common thread.[1]

Conjecture though it be, we depart from the *textus receptus* six times on the strength of our hypothesis. *K. Phi.* gives way to Folio *Lewis* at II. i. 1, 18, 150; new speech headings are allotted to *K. Phi.* at II. i. 2, 149, 151. Moreover, II. i. 368 *Fra.*, if we are right, no longer stands alone as a freak error. These corruptions, cutting deeper than has been suspected, point to a foul paper origin rather than prompt-copy—just like the parallel corruptions in other Shakespeare plays.

Like Prof. J. D. Wilson we detect two textual strata in *John.* Prof. Wilson defined these as (*a*) prompt-book, (*b*) Shakespeare's revision of the prompt-book[2]; we suggest that they are (*a*) foul papers, (*b*) printing-house interference in 1621. Hair-splitting such as this has even its practical rewards. Prof. Wilson, though the first to show that Hubert and the Citizen of Angiers were intended to be one person,[3] could not identify them in his text. The foul paper theory, on the other hand, allows us to scrap the Citizen as Shakespeare scrapped him during composition, and to reintroduce Hubert with all

1. Compare also *Ham.*, I. ii. 58 where Q2 reads "*Polo.* Hath", as against F1 (and Q1 and modern texts) "*Pol.* He hath". Prof. J. D. Wilson explains that Shakespeare wrote "Pol a hath" [*The Manuscript of Shakespeare's Hamlet* (1934), i, 110]. The speech heading *Kin.* (for *King*) is frequent in Shakespeare, and Elizabethan plays generally, occurring also in the Folio *John* (II. i. 79).

2. Cf. Wilson's note on the copy, pp. 91–4.

3. *Op. cit.*, pp. xlv–xlvii; cf. also Charles Petit-Dutaillis: *Le Roi Jean et Shakespeare* (1944), pp. 70-1. The speech heading *Cit.* (for *Citizen*) is replaced by *Hubert* and *Hub.* from II. i. 325.

his lines for the first time since the original prompt-book.[1]

Naturally the merging of the Citizen and Hubert startles one at first. The Citizen speaks impersonally throughout Act II; Hubert's test in IV. i is very personal indeed. But as *John* is full of impersonal "official" language cheek by jowl with other types, the important contrast of formality and passion being thus brought out (cf. p. lxvi), we must not take this too seriously. As Hubert still speaks impersonally in III. ii, where his presence cannot be disputed, Shakespeare may have decided to heighten the "impersonal" impression through identification with the Citizen, so that Hubert's thawing out in IV. i, his slow and reluctant recognition of a personal problem behind an official duty, would give edge to that central scene. Be this as it may, our conviction is strengthened by two other points. First, Shakespeare renamed many minor characters as he saw their places in their plays more clearly—a foul paper practice conspicuous in *Love's Labour's Lost* and *Much Ado*; while the favourite explanation of the Hubert-Citizen tangle (first advanced by Collier)—namely, that one actor doubled the two parts—has no comparable parallel in the canon.[2] Second, there is Hubert's "voluntary oath" (III. ii. 33). As the two other voluntary oaths (v. i. 29, v. ii. 10) show, a vassal's oath of allegiance is meant. John's thanks are not altogether too extravagant if *Hubert* swore on behalf of Angiers. The *Citizen* had repeatedly refused to pay allegiance on behalf of Angiers till one king should prove greatest: as John did prove greatest, and Angiers did submit to him (III. iii. 6), continuity of character seems to be urged by the action quite apart from the essential corroboration of the text.

A foul paper theory for the text also urges us to return to the Folio for our act and scene division. Greg, contending that

1. Though Wilson proves Hubert's mean birth (cf. IV. iii. 87, note) he describes him as "a burgher de Burgh". Shakespeare undoubtedly saw the name "Hubert de Burgh" in Holinshed, but, degrading the great justiciar of history, dropped the "de Burgh". Hubert becomes an *arriviste* like Faulconbridge, dependent on John, so that the murder of Arthur tempts him more searchingly.

2. See Greg, *The Editorial Problem in Shakespeare*, under "doubling of parts". In those plays where doubling is thought to have caused confusion of names only *isolated* instances of confusion are known (in the Folio *MND.*, v. i, Philostrate disappears altogether, which is a different matter): in *John* Hubert takes over the Citizen's part *systematically* from II. i. 325.

these divisions are "unlikely to have been made by the folio editor" because of the shortness of *Actus Secundus*, confirmed the impression of E. K. Chambers and Prof. Wilson that clearly "something has gone wrong".[1] Though erratic, these divisions conceal a five-act structure much like that of Shakespeare's other plays.[2] If Greg is right, and we are right about two textual strata, Shakespeare himself may be responsible for these curious divisions: that is, Shakespeare as interpreted by the Folio compositor.

We suggest that the compositor read certain numbers at the head of the scenes and interpreted these unmethodically, confusing acts and scenes. Thus "II" or "2" (for Act II?) he made *Scaena Secunda*; "2" (for Act II, Sc. ii?) he made *Actus Secundus*. Prof. J. D. Wilson has recently explained the ludicrously short *Actus Quintus* (Act v, Sc. v in modern texts) of *Henry VI*, Part i, on the same surmise, viz. that Scene v was "presumably labelled 'scena quinta' (or merely '5')".[3] Despite such progressive corruption earlier, the complete form *Actus Tertius, Scaena prima* in our play ought, we think, to be reconsidered with renewed faith.

Ever since Theobald, Act III, Sc. i replaces the Folio *Actus Secundus*, the Folio *Actus Tertius, Scaena prima* being dismissed as a mistake. Theobald's rearrangement must be attributed to his desire to spite Pope: his only argument of note, that Faulconbridge, being the poet's favourite character, very properly closes the act with his soliloquy on commodity, loses all its force once we recall the soliloquy in Act i. R. G. White, one of the few who preferred the Folio division to Theobald's, rejoined vigorously:

according to Theobald's disarrangement . . . when *Salisbury* delivers his message to *Constance* . . . the ceremony has already taken place; . . . the royal trains enter the tent . . . they have made some hasty preparation for the marriage, gone to Saint Mary's Chapel

---

1. *Loc. cit.*
2. Folio *Actus Primus, Scaena Prima* = Arden Act i, Sc. i; *Scaena Secunda* = ii. i; *Actus Secundus* = ii. ii (iii. i. 1–74 in *textus receptus*); *Actus Tertius, Scaena prima* = iii. i (iii. i. 75–347 in *textus receptus*); *Scaena Secunda* = iii. ii (iii. iii in the *textus receptus* begins at Arden iii. ii. 11); other divisions as in Arden, except that the Folio repeats *Actus Quartus* for Act v.
3. The C.U.P. *1 H 6* (1952), p. 104, following P. Alexander, *Shakespeare's Henry VI and Richard III*, p. 185.

in the town, had the ceremony performed, and come thence to the very place whither their "hasty messenger" (*sic*) was sent![1]

White clinched his argument by emphasizing that "consciousness that the ceremony awaited his return" must lie behind Salisbury's line

I may not go without you to the kings (II. ii. 62)

Theobald's division was perpetuated rather because the Folio is obviously wrong than because he is obviously right. The present-day sources of editorial misgivings are (i) the shortness of the Folio *Actus Secundus*; (ii) the absence of an exit after *Actus Secundus*; (iii) the typographical suspiciousness of *Actus Tertius, Scaena prima*, which lacks the usual rule beneath it; (iv) the apparent continuity of the action. These reasons have not all the same weight. We may disregard (i), if the compositor has misinterpreted "II" or "2", and also (iii), since the absence of a rule recurs in the next scene (III. ii) and need have no connection with the copy. Reasons (ii) and (iv) cause the real trouble.

(ii) The absence of a Folio exit coincides with Constance's declaration that she will not exit (II. ii. 73–4). Probably there was no exit in the copy, and the compositor (a careful worker) took a hint from the text and did not insert an exit. Dramatists sometimes ended scenes with no more than a line across the page, i.e. the printing-house must sometimes be responsible for end-of-scene exits.[2]

Besides Constance, Arthur and Salisbury appear in *Actus Secundus*; unlike her, they are not made to enter again in *Actus Tertius, Scaena prima*. Though their absence may be due to the fact that they have nothing to say in III. i, Arthur's absence in the *scene* would explain why Constance speaks throughout of herself, of *her* side,[3] and, a more difficult teaser, why John's side captures Arthur (III. ii. 1) and not Constance as well.

1. See Furness's *John*, pp. 174–8, where the commencement of Act III commands a lengthy footnote.

2. Bald "*Exeunt*", so common in old plays where only some of the characters go off and a "*Manet*" also seems necessary (as in *John*, II. i. 560, IV. ii. 102), may at times be a similar printing-house interpretation of a line.

3. Arthur's presence is not necessitated by "our oppression" (III. i. 32) or "my child" (III. i. 113).

(iv) Since a new act must begin somewhere between the first Folio *Scaena Secunda* (= the Arden II. i) and the second (= III. ii), and only two possible places recommend themselves, namely *Actus Secundus* (II. ii. 1) and *Actus Tertius, Scaena prima* (III. i. 1)—which would be more likely? Surely White interpreted Shakespeare's idea of continuity more soundly than Theobald's silent followers. The logic of time seems to support the Folio beginning for Act III.

The logic of the action suggests that Constance still sits on the stage at the opening of *Actus Tertius, Scaena prima*. But the more briefly she sits there, the less effective the device. May Shakespeare not have intended her to remain thus for the whole length of the ceremonies? Salisbury could take Arthur by the hand and walk off with him, or leave by himself; while the time-lapse would be conveyed by the formal procession opening *Actus Tertius*.

Four arguments persuade us that *Actus Tertius, Scaena prima* is a reliable notation. First, the madness of the Folio divisions seems to follow some (misunderstood) authority. Whereas *Scaena Secunda* (II. i) and *Actus Secundus* (II. ii) stand apart, perhaps because only one number could be deciphered, the complete form here inspires more confidence. Second, the support of the time-scheme. Third, if no break was intended at III. i. 1, the entry for Constance, who would be on-stage already, would be unnecessary. Whether Arthur and Salisbury be on or off, Constance is certainly on—if the stage direction goes back to Shakespeare, this would establish the break. If "*Constance*" was added to the stage direction by the act division "interpolator" we would expect this individual to have cleaned up the other loose ends—in brief, the state of the text as a whole confirms that the "interpolator" may be a superfluous fiction, that a sincere attempt to reproduce copy could have caused all these textual difficulties.[1] Fourth, the *T.R.*, though diverging in detail, introduces a division at this very juncture (I. v–vi)—strong collateral evidence for a break. In accordance

1. The *John* Act II–III transition can be parallelled, e.g. in the end of *Ham.*, Act III. In the (prompt-copy) Folio text Gertrude remains on-stage, there being an exit for Hamlet and Polonius's corpse, an entry for Claudius. In the (foul paper) Q2 the exit probably covers Gertrude as well—at any rate, she is made to re-enter for IV. i. 1. In (foul paper) *John* Constance is given an entrance for III. i. 1, though likewise on-stage.

with these arguments we revert, for our Act II, Sc. ii, Act III, Sc. i, to the divisions contained—or concealed—in the Folio. Similarly, our Act III, Sc. ii reverts to the Folio. Although modern editors start a new scene after III. ii. 10 (Arden text) the sense does not require it, and authority of weight, as we think, contradicts it.

This brings us to the problem of textual integrity. Prof. Wilson claimed *John* as "an indisputable example of textual revision".[1] E. K. Chambers had cautiously suggested the cutting of a scene,[2] and Prof. Wilson submitted that a scene with Hubert's "voluntary oath" has been dropped[3] between *Actus Secundus* and *Actus Tertius*. But this oath, less mysterious than he makes out, the 1591 audience would take for granted—the oath of allegiance of a new vassal (*v.* p. xxxvii). As the *T.R.* here follows the scene-sequence of *John* without trace of a "voluntary oath" scene, we cannot agree with Prof. Wilson.

Prof. Wilson's "most striking evidence of textual disturbance" comes from III. iii. 68, where Constance's "To England, if you will" replies to King Philip's "I prithee, lady, go away with me" (III. iii. 20). Aldis Wright long ago suggested that III. iii. 21–67 may be an interpolation.[4] Prof. Wilson took up the revision theory, rejecting Wright's alternative solution, that Constance relapses into apathy, because

it is unworkable on the stage, inasmuch as no audience after forty-six (*sic*) lines of dialogue would be able to associate Constance's reply with Philip's original question.[5]

But the resumption of momentarily dropped subjects forms part of Shakespeare's standard "frenzy technique" (compare especially *King Lear*). If Philip beckoned Constance to follow him, the audience would not forget his question: Constance may disdain to answer, until *he* temporarily forgets his question (ll. 61–7)—whereupon she turns upon him bitterly with "To England, if you will".[6]

1. *Op. cit.*, p. viii.   2. *William Shakespeare*, I, 365.   3. Cf. III. ii. 33.
4. Quoted Furness, *John*, p. 264.   5. *Op. cit.*, p. l.
6. Furthermore, the *T.R.* seems to echo this "interpolation" in 1591 already. Compare "all *counsel*, all *redress* . . . all *counsel*, true *redress*" (*John*, III. iii. 23–4), Death "Which *cannot hear* a lady's feeble voice, / Which *scorns* a modern invocation" (III. iii. 41–2)—and "counsell", "redresse" (*T.R.*, II. v. 51, 61), "Why dye I not? *Death scornes* so vilde a pray", (I sue to Life and Death) "But both are *deafe*, I can be heard of neither*" (*T.R.*, II. vi. 8, 11).

Although the evidence does not seem quite strong enough to warrant disintegration, signs of foul paper hurry, which may have been obliterated in the fair copy, litter the text. Words repeat themselves uneconomically, bad or weak lines crop up now and then. We are even led to wonder whether some of the grand lines in the *T.R.*, few though they be, represent Shakespeare's second thoughts as he copied out his play, and echo the *John* prompt-book: for instance, whether Shakespeare added two lines after II. i. 192 such as

> *K. Philip* But heres no proof that showes your son a King.
> *K. Iohn.* What wants, my sword shal more at large set down.
>   (*T.R.*, I. iii. 125–6)

Again, the part of the Earl of Essex (who appears only in Act I with one short speech) may have been expanded in the theatre to include Lord Bigot's, whose first entry comes at IV. iii. 11. Perhaps Shakespeare forgot the name of his third earl—he often forgot the names of his minor characters, an easy matter if one writes on odd scraps of paper—mistakenly called him Bigot, correcting the error when he prepared his fair copy. In the *T.R.*, at any rate, Essex continues to make a third with Salisbury and Pembroke, where in *John* Bigot takes over.[1]

Even if very minor alterations such as we suggest were introduced, the play as a whole cannot be further disintegrated. Its best poetry the *T.R.* author knew in 1591 already—including the soliloquies.[2]

Obviously the *T.R.*, if indeed derivative, helps us with many cruxes in *John*. Problems of scene-division, textual integrity, and character-parts it illumines to advantage. But how far may we trust its apparent substantiation of "doubtful readings" in *John*? Only two lines are the same in the two plays,[3] and, though the *T.R.* reproduces Shakespeare faithfully by

1. When *John* was thought prompt-copy, F. G. Fleay [*John* (1878), p. 24] suggested that Essex "was intended to be struck out altogether", since no other Essex appears in the canon and the contemporary earl fell out of favour in 1596. Cf. also Fleay's *Life and Work of Shakespeare* (1886), p. 197.

2. Wilson noted the connection between *John*, I. i. 182, 183, 206 and *T.R.*, I. i. 291 ("I haue no lands, honour is my desire"), I. i. 295 ("foote of land"), I. i. 261 ("this monnting minde"); again, between *John*, II. i. 561, 573, 598 and *T.R.*, I. iv. 112–13 ("To fill and tickle their ambieious eares, / With hope of gaine").

3. Cf. *John*, II. i. 528, v. iv. 42, notes.

and large, much telescoping and reshuffling vitiates its authority for questions of detail.[1] None the less, the *T.R.* compels us
on occasion to part ways with the *textus receptus*—especially
when it vindicates the Folio.[2]

As regards general textual procedure, the present edition
follows the Folio as closely as possible, collating all significant
changes. Thus variant word-forms are retained (e.g. vild,
winch), the modernized forms of the *textus receptus* (vile, wince)
not being collated; and some cases of hyphening are passed
over silently. No "normalization" of the metre is attempted,
except that verbs ending in "-ed" are contracted to "-d"
according to the requirements of scansion (the "-ed" form was
used indiscriminately for accented and unaccented syllables
in the Folio). False concords are not emended, as they were
common in the Elizabethan period. The punctuation of the
Folio has had to be modernized, our text being probably far
more heavily stopped than Shakespeare's MS. was (the Folio
punctuation must often be editorial). Literals, turned letters,
etc., are not collated unless some significance might attach to
them.

3. THE DATE

John was known to Francis Meres in 1598. Previous writers,
accepting the *T.R.* as its source, have therefore championed
every year between 1591 and 1598 as the date of composition.[3]
The death of Shakespeare's son Hamnet in 1596 once inclined
the sentimental to suspect autobiography in Constance's la-
ments for Arthur (in Act III, Sc. iii); and Prof. G. B. Harrison
has recently argued for this year because, in his opinion, topical preoccupation with war finds an echo in the play.[4] D. F.
Ash, discussing 'Anglo-French Relations in "King John"',[5]

1. The reader may dismiss as chop-logic our reliance upon the *T.R.* where it
agrees with *John* together with our inattention to it where it disagrees. We ignore
disagreement between the texts because the *T.R.* often disagrees intentionally:
derivative plays usually "embellished" their originals, even to the extent of
adding new characters.

2. Cf. I. i. 44, III. i. 185, IV. iii. 8, notes.

3. See the list of dates in Furness's *John*, pp. 443–4.

4. 'Shakespeare's Topical Significances' [*T.L.S.* (1930), p. 939].

5. *Études Anglaises*, III (1939), 349 ff.

suggested that the play parallels the political scene in 1595.
Earlier chronologers sometimes favoured 1593, because the
conversion of Henry IV to the Roman faith—"Paris vaut bien
une messe"—seemed to them to have inspired the tergiversa-
tion of Shakespeare's King Philip, and the Bastard's censure
of commodity.

Prof. J. D. Wilson ignored vague topicality and reinter-
preted a known *John–Spanish Tragedy* contact which moved
him to propose a new date. Steevens had noted the similarity
between *John*, II. i. 137–8, and the *Spanish Tragedy*:

> He hunted well that was a Lyons death,
> Not he that in a garment wore his skin:
> So Hares may pull dead Lyons by the beard.[1]

Wilson declared that here Kyd "is clearly alluding . . . to
Austria's wearing of Richard's lion's-skin",[2] dated the *Spanish
Tragedy* 1590 not 1589 (the usual *terminus ante quem*), and assigned a first draft of *John* to 1590. Since this dating is backed
by the definite allusion in *John* to *Soliman and Perseda* discovered
by Theobald, this play being generally dated 1590,[3] and by
an allusion to the defeat of the Spanish Armada,[4] Wilson's
date deserves at least as much consideration as any other.

Although the *Spanish Tragedy* "contact" admits of more than
one interpretation, our belief that *John* precedes the *T.R.*
(1591) naturally leads us, with Wilson, to prefer the year 1590.
Unlike Wilson we think that the whole Folio text belongs to
this year[5]: and this early date can be supported by other evidence hitherto unnoted.

(*a*) A contact between *John*[6] and stanza 12 of Samuel
Daniel's *Complaint of Rosamond* (1592). Though we have no sure

---

1. I. ii. 170–2.

2. C.U.P. *John*, pp. liii–liv.

3. See *John*, I. i. 244, II. i. 75, notes; E. K. Chambers, *The Elizabethan Stage*, IV, 46.

4. Armada allusions are more important than Wilson suggests: see pp. xxix, xlvi, n. 2.

5. Wilson assigns the Folio *John*, the revision of a postulated 1590 draft, to the year 1594 (C.U.P. *John*, pp. lv–lvii). We disagree with his disintegration of the play into two drafts since the *T.R.* author knew the whole of *John* in 1591 already: see p. xlii.

6. See *John*, II. ii. 52, note.

indication who borrowed from whom, the persisting "correspondences" in the works of Shakespeare and Daniel leave no room for doubt that contact there was, as in their sonnets, their treatments of the stories of the civil wars and of Cleopatra. Where dates are ascertainable, Daniel was the debtor. It seems reasonable to suppose that the *Rosamond* contacts with *Richard 3, Romeo*[1] and *John* likewise refer back to the greater poet's current stage successes, rather than that Shakespeare should recall one much less notable work on three separate occasions.

(*b*) A joke about the actor John Sincklo going the rounds in 1590. Sincklo's "thin-man" roles were detected in the plays of Shakespeare and others by Prof. A. Gaw,[2] and Prof. J. D. Wilson has argued that Robert Faulconbridge in *John* was one of these.[3] In *An Almond for a Parrat*, a pamphlet often credited to Thomas Nashe, which McKerrow convincingly dated early 1590,[4] we read, after a dedication to William Kempe (Shakespeare's later "fellow"), and constant allusions to the contemporary stage, the following:

Doest thou feare God in deede . . . ? What, by the smoothing of thy face, the simpering of thy mouth, or staring of thy eies? Why, if that be to feare God, Ile haue a spare fellowe shall make mee a whole quest of faces for three farthinges.[5]

Here only an actor could be meant, and amongst actors Sincklo was the notorious "spare fellowe". The joke, also reproduced in *John*, I. i. 143, turns on the commonplace jibe that actors were such poor rogues that they gladly played for *a penny*,[6] making of Sincklo's thinness a symbol of his more abject poverty.[7]

(*c*) Correspondences with other early books.—(i) Fortune's "golden hand" (*John*, II. i. 57) we find also in Peele's *Descensus Astraeae* (written for October, 1591), perhaps echoing *John* as

---

1. See A. Thaler, 'Shakspere, Daniel, and *Everyman*' [*Philological Quarterly*, xv (1936), 217 ff.].
2. 'John Sincklo as one of Shakespeare's Actors' [*Anglia*, XLIX (1926), 289 ff.].
3. *Op. cit.*, p. lii.   4. See McKerrow's Nashe, IV, 461.   5. Nashe, III, 349.
6. See quotations from *Theses Martinianae* (1589) and from *Martins Months Minde* (1589) in Chambers, *The Elizabethan Stage*, IV, 230.
7. Poverty attaches to Sincklo also in *Rom.*, v. i. 68–76, *Err.*, v. i. 238 *sqq.*

Peele's *Honour of the Garter* (1593) echoes *Titus Andronicus* (*c.* 1588).[1] (ii) Shakespeare may imitate the *Heroicall Devises* of C. Paradin (1591, S.R. August 1590) in III. iii. 164–8 (see note). (iii) *Arden of Feversham* (1592) seems to imitate *John*, II. i. 463, III. i. 126–7 (see notes). (iv) The two pre-Shakespearean giants of Elizabethan literature, Sidney's *Arcadia* and Spenser's *Faerie Queene* (Bks I–III) were published in 1590. *John* may echo both, in III. ii. 35, IV. i. 102, and in II. i. 63, v. vii. 36 (see notes).

(*d*) Correspondences with topical events.—(i) Armada idiom and allusions are more frequent in *John* than has been suspected.[2] (ii) The murder of a king by a fanatical Roman Catholic was topical after August 1589, when Henry III of France was killed by Jacques Clement. The League agitated for some time for canonization for Clement, to the indignation of French and English Protestants. Pandulph's promise of canonization for regicide (*John*, III. i. 102–5) perhaps took back Shakespeare's first audience to the Bull excommunicating Elizabeth (see our note), but the canonization of Clement was the burning question in 1589–90[3]; in his *Fig for the Spaniard*, 1591, one G. B. in fact lumped the murderers of John and Henry together, perhaps because the John plays were already popular:

> Such Hypocrites in Fryers habites lurke,
> That rapines, rapes, treasons, guyles, murders worke.
>
> Aske *France* heereof, such Hypocrites they rue,
> And *England* when king *Iohn* was poysoned[4]

(iii) Throughout 1590 the friends of Secretary Davison made many efforts to bring him back to the queen's favour, the most strenuous campaigner being the Earl of Essex.[5] John's repudi-

1. See C. Crawford, 'The Date and Authenticity of Titus Andronicus' [*Shakespeare Jahrbuch* (1900), p. 109].
2. See p. xxix, and notes to II. i. 23, 26, III. iii. 2, v. i. 65, v. ii. 151, 154, v. vii. 117.
3. See A. Colynet, *True History of the Ciuill Warres of France* (1591), p. 419; P. Le Roy, *Catholicon of Spayne* (1595), sigs. B, M₃.
4. Sig. A₄ᵛ.
5. See E. M. Tenison, *Elizabethan England*, vol. VIII (1947), p. 248 ff., and Davison in *D.N.B.* Lord Strange, to whose company of actors Shakespeare, in our opinion, belonged while writing *John* (cf. p. xlix), was a close friend of Essex.

ation of Hubert may be a reflection of Elizabeth's repudiation of Davison.[1] The other surprising topicalities in *John* make Shakespeare's "collaboration" with the Essex circle,[2] to which he certainly belonged a little later, quite plausible: but as Davison abandoned all hopes early in 1591, and agitation on his behalf then ceased, we must consider 1590(–91) as a possible date of composition for *John*.

Miss F. A. Yates has argued that the Traveller satire in *John* (I. i. 189–204) is bound up with the "school of night" controversy of the early 1590's, and imitates John Eliot's *Ortho-Epia Gallica* (1593).[3] A map in a painter's shop called forth, in one of Eliot's dialogues, the following eulogy:

Seest thou the Fennes of Nyle? Lo here the red Sea. Looke vpon the great Caire! ... Here are the Alpes, ouer which we go downe into Italie. There are the Appenines: and here are the Pyrenaean hilles, by which you may go directly into Spaine.

That the Bastard has in mind "modern language manuals" in his soliloquy, as Miss Yates contended, we find hard to believe. Indeed, the necessity of a connection between Eliot's and Shakespeare's Alps-Apennines-Pyrenean seems small. On the one hand alliteration would draw the words together, on the other both writers follow a type of geographical description familiarized by the classics.[4]

(*e*) A further topical reflection in *John* which, though now first suggested, may provide an upper and lower limit for dating quite independent of the otherwise all-important *T.R.*

In November 1590, a long-standing family-quarrel between

1. See p. xxix.
2. See pp. l–li. For backing up of Essex in *John* and other Shakespearean plays see E. M. Albright: 'Shakespeare's *Richard II* and the Essex Conspiracy' [*P.M.L.A.*, XLII (1927)].
3. *A Study of Love's Labour's Lost* (1936), p. 64.
4. Compare Ovid, *Metam.*: "Caucasus ardet, / Ossaque cum Pindo maiorque ambobus Olympus, / Aëriaeque Alpes et nubifer Appenninus" (ii. 224–6); and the translation of Claudian's *Rape of Proserpine* (1617) by Shakespeare's friend Leonard Digges: "The poore cold dweller on steepe *Appenine*, / And frozen passengers, that slowly climbe / The hoary *Alpes*, amazed stand, and doubt / Of some new broile 'twixt *Ioue* and *Gyant* rowt: / Those that (along thy streames) with naked limbe / Perpetuall trophie bearing *Tyber*, swimme, / And those that to thy current famous *Po* / Launch out their little barkes..." (sig. F₃).

James Burbage and the widow of his brother-in-law John Brayne (or Braynes) reached a temporary peak-point.[1] Having together built the Theatre (the first English play-house) in 1576, the in-laws fell out in 1578, and, after John Brayne's death in 1586, the widow Brayne, together with one Robert Miles, whom John Brayne had charged with being the cause of his death,[2] continued litigation. As this centred on the receipts for the Theatre's galleries, not only the Court of Chancery would cause publicity, since the suit was dealt with there on 4, 13, 28 November 1590: but events at the Theatre itself, where, on 16 November (beside other days unspecified[3]) the Burbages fought the widow and her friends with words and blows before the assembling audience, would familiarize *theatre-goers* in particular with it.

On the eventful 16 November the widow, with Robert Miles, Ralph Miles (the son of Robert), Nicholas Bishop (a friend of the Miles's), and others, took up stations at the gallery entrance, determined to collect her due share. On the 13th Chancery had awarded her an order that she might enjoy her moiety of the gallery receipts, and when James Burbage called her a "Murdring hor",[4] Miles produced it. Burbage was not at a loss: "hang her hor qd he she getteth nothing here",[5] declaring that he would commit twenty contempts of court rather than lose his possession.[6] Mrs Burbage and her eldest son Cuthbert also helped to rail. The hero of the day, however, was Richard, the second son (the principal "fellow" of Shakespeare from 1594 onwards), whom one witness found

wt A Broome staff in his hand of whom when this depot asked what sturre was there he answered in laughing phrase hew they come for A moytie But qd he (holding vppe the said ... broomes staff) I haue, I think deliuered ... him A moytie wt this & sent them packing[7]

N. Bishop, besides many others, made a deposition about this unhappy visit to the Theatre:

---

1. See C. W. Wallace, *The First London Theatre* (1913) (The University Studies of the University of Nebraska, vol. XIII).

2. "Braine ... at his deathe ... charged Miles wth his deathe, by certaine stripes geven him by Miles" (*op. cit.*, p. 86).

3. *Op. cit.*, pp. 97, 100, 105.   4. *Op. cit.*, p. 105.   5. *Op. cit.*, p. 100.

6. *Op. cit.*, p. 101.   7. *Loc. cit.*

And by cause this depot. spake then somewhat in the favor. of the por womman . . . Ry. Burbage scornfully & disdainfullye playing wt this depotes Nose sayd that yf he delt in the matter he wold beate him also and did chalendge the field of him at that tyme[1]

The upshot was that James Burbage was cited to answer for contempt of court. He denied the "odious termes" against Chancery and religion of which he was accused, pulling wool over the court's eyes with seeming humility. Furthermore, he had trouble with his actors. Two companies, Lord Strange's men and the Lord Admiral's men, had amalgamated to play at the Theatre.[2] When John Alleyn, who had pleaded with Burbage on behalf of Mrs Brayne, asked Burbage for money due to the Admiral's men, and he refused to pay, Alleyn "told him that belike he ment to deale wt them as he did wt the por wydowe"[3]: and some time thereafter the Admiral's, with several of Strange's men, left Burbage's management.[4]

Much has been written about Shakespeare's first company. If *John* precedes the *T.R.* the orthodox Shakespeare chronology necessarily falls, and with it most of our conjecture about the first company. Fresh speculation gets a good start, in recompense, through John Sincklo's part in our play. It is generally agreed that Sincklo was playing with the combined Admiral's and Strange's men in 1590, together with Edward Alleyn, the leading actor of the day, Richard Burbage, and others whose names are preserved in an old dramatic plot.[5] Possibly, then, *John* was written for Alleyn, Burbage, Sincklo, and the rest—written, if *John* precedes the *T.R.*, for the Theatre just as the Burbage-Brayne suit was approaching a new crisis.

Though not concerned with *John*, Prof. Wallace believed that the Brayne litigation, so annoying to the close business associates of Shakespeare, "can hardly have failed to leave a residuum of human experience plastic to the hand of the poet".[6] The possibility deserves exploration, for the resem-

1. *Op. cit.*, p. 115.   2. See Chambers, *The Elizabethan Stage*, ii, 120.
3. Wallace, *op. cit.*, p. 101.
4. In May 1591, according to Chambers (*loc. cit.*).
5. The plot of Part ii of *The Seven Deadly Sins*; cf. Chambers's *The Elizabethan Stage*, iii, 497.
6. *Op. cit.*, p. 157.

D

blances between the Burbage suit and some *fictitious additions* to the story of John are quite extraordinary.

(i) A widow appears with the man accused of the death of her husband to claim her possession.—In *John*, II. i. 2, 6, 13, Arthur is made the "off-spring" of Richard I, an intentional ambiguity reinforced later by the assertion that Arthur is Eleanor's "eldest son's son" (II. i. 177)—which creates the impression that Constance is aided by the man (Austria) who killed the father of her son, i.e. her husband. This impression Aldis Wright denounced as Shakespeare's "strange careless-ness". Once we realize, however, that Shakespeare may not have been revising an old play in great haste, but probably checked his story in half a dozen chronicles, reading up the accounts of other Plantagenets beside John, Wright's view, approved by so many editors, no longer satisfies. When we re-call, further, that Shakespeare has unhistorically resurrected Austria to champion Constance, the double violation of his-tory leads us, in the first place, to expect an overriding *purpose* rather than carelessness.

(ii) Richard Burbage browbeats the widow's secondary protector Nicholas Bishop, and later is himself largely respons-ible for the flight of her party.—In *John*, the Bastard bullies Austria as superciliously (II. i. 290; III. i. 57, etc.),[1] and later emerges as the strong man of the day (III. ii. 7). As well as Austria, the Bastard is Shakespeare's fiction.

(iii) The two parties quarrel outside the Theatre, disputing their rights to it.—In *John*, the blockade and abusive quarrel outside Angiers—which symbolizes the whole of the English inheritance—is Shakespeare's fiction.

(iv) James Burbage scornfully rejects the court order, but later knuckles under to Chancery.—In *John*, King Philip de-clares that he has a "commission" from "that supernal judge" (II. i. 110, 112) to call John to restitution. John derides this (but later submits to the pope: Act v, Sc. i).

(v) The Admiral's men fear similar treatment to the

1. In the *T.R.* the Bastard actually challenges Austria (I. v. 23), as R. Burbage did N. Bishop: the challenge being declined in both cases. Perhaps the *T.R.* here echoes an addition to the *John* prompt-book (cf. p. xlii above).

widow's and finally leave Burbage.—In *John*, the nobles are
dismayed by John's treatment of his rival (IV. ii. 47–66), fear
for themselves (IV. iii. 11–13), and likewise leave. Though
Shakespeare's *English* nobles react to Arthur's murder as
Holinshed's nobles of *Brittany*, historical truth has again been
abandoned, and Burbage and his men certainly provided a
situation similar to that of John and his men.

(vi) Since *John* describes a quarrel of in-laws in the first acts,
the Burbage–Brayne relations are again reproduced; the
widow being helped in both cases by a father and son (Robert
and Ralph Miles, France and Lewis) and *their* friend (N.
Bishop, Austria).

(vii) Minor coincidences may still be mentioned. Austria's
over-confident promise that he will maintain Constance's
quarrel (II. i. 19–31) corresponds to a report

> that the said Myles hath made great boast, that it is he, that will
> maynteyne and defend her herin, al be it she did procure his trouble
> before the coroners enquest, and did impute to him the deathe of
> her husband[1]

Again, it was said that Robert Miles declared that the Theatre
was his

> and that he would spend all that he had but he would pull the
> defendt out of the said Theatre by the eares[2]

Compare *John*, II. i. 263–6, and King Philip's other assevera-
tions of his unshakable purpose (II. i. 41–3, 343–9).

Although the correspondences are not consistent—Robert
Miles being reproduced, if we are right, both in King Philip
and in Austria, N. Bishop being likewise caricatured in Austria,
and so on—we know that such disguised lampooning was the
fashion on the Elizabethan stage.[3] We suggest that at certain
points, especially in Act II, Shakespeare saw the resemblances
in his story to a real-life drama with which he knew his audience to be familiar, and distorted history in details to enrich
his play with a topical back-cloth. He seems to celebrate the
victory of young Richard Burbage consciously; in other details

1. Wallace, *op. cit.*, p. 88.   2. *Op. cit.*, p. 119.
3. For proofs of this see C. J. Sisson's *Lost Plays of Shakespeare's Age* (1936),
pp. 57–71, 97–110, and *passim*.

he may sometimes be plastic to contemporary events unconsciously, because of the similarity of the action.

If the Bastard was created for swashbuckling Richard Burbage, the part of John, unless we are mistaken about the company, must have been meant for Edward Alleyn. Thus the age-
old question—why does the Bastard almost oust John from the
centre of interest in the play?—may partly reflect the growing
challenge of young[1] Burbage to the theatrical supremacy of
Alleyn. If this conjecture be correct—and it is no more than
conjecture—we are bound to recall that Alleyn left the
Theatre with the Admiral's men early in 1591. We cannot say
for certain what happened to Sincklo, but Richard Burbage,
with some of the principal actors of the 1590 amalgamation,
perhaps including Shakespeare, seems not to have gone with
Alleyn, probably staying on at the Theatre.

The suggested allusion to the Burbage–Brayne suit fits in
perfectly, of course, with the new theory about the *T.R.* Since
so much other evidence assigns *John* to the same year, we are
tempted to submit as the precise date of composition—which
the suit alone can indicate within that year—the winter/spring
of 1590/91. The squabbles in November 1590 would be the
terminus a quo for Act II at any rate—Act I might have been
completed before Shakespeare altered his plans—and the
secession of the Admiral's men the *terminus ante quem*.

Our impression that Shakespeare was writing for the amalgamated Strange's and Admiral's men gains further strength
from the 1594 quarto title-page according to which "the Earle
of Darbie, Earle of Pembrooke, and Earle of Sussex their
Seruants" had performed Shakespeare's *Titus Andronicus*. That
Sussex's were the last owners can scarcely be disputed, since
they played *Titus* as "ne" for Henslowe on 24 January 1594,
and on 6 February *Titus* was entered in the Stationers' Regis-
ter, while the theatres closed down for some months on account
of the plague.[2] Pembroke's must have been the previous
owners, since they were compelled to pawn their apparel in the

---

1. He was about 22 years old in 1590 (E. K. Chambers: *The Elizabethan Stage*,
II, 307): and the Bastard, though often played as an older man, must be of roughly
this age, in Act I at least, as "thou unreverend boy" (I. i. 227) and "thou most
untoward knave" (I. i. 243) indicate.

2. Chambers, *The Elizabethan Stage*, II, 95.

autumn of 1593, and apparently they sold other plays at this time.[1] Thus the *Titus* title-page seems to give the right sequence of ownership for Pembroke's and Sussex's. Unless we resort to far-fetched hypotheses,[2] we can hardly refuse to admit that Derby's (= Strange's)[3] must have owned *Titus* before Pembroke's, exactly as the title-page avers. We know, too, that the combined Strange's and Admiral's men were called simply Strange's in contemporary documents: and since Ben Jonson in the well-known quotation implied that *Titus* was written between 1584 and 1589,[4] we infer that the combined companies at the Theatre owned *Titus c.* 1590 *and employed Shakespeare*. Sincklo's part in *John*, the allusion to the Burbage lawsuit in *John*, and the *Titus* title-page testify independently and therefore the more persuasively concerning Shakespeare's first London company, if *John* may indeed be dated 1590.

But may it? The orthodox chronologers will hardly rush in at this stage to agree. Other plays seem so much less mature, eight or ten being practically always said to precede *John*: and yet, we are told, Shakespeare only began his writing career in 1590. Fortunately for us a distinguished body of critics, who believe that Shakespeare's first plays have been badly postdated, now counterpoises the authority of the formidable Malone and Chambers.[5] Our only possible attitude to the chronologers' *impasse* must therefore be to disregard dates. For, since the debated *John–T.R.* relationship must necessarily be a mainstay of either chronological theory, it would be illogical in any discussion of this relationship (which we now resume from p. xix) not to suspend preconceptions about dates until all the other evidence, judged *per se*, can be weighed against them.

We must now look a little more closely at the *T.R.* Thanks

1. See Chambers, *op. cit.*, II, 128.

2. That *Titus* is a revision of an older lost play *Titus and Vespasian*, etc. See E. K. Chambers, *William Shakespeare*, I, 316–21.

3. Title-pages usually gave the company's current name even though it had performed under another one. Lord Strange became the Earl of Derby in 1593.

4. See Chambers, *William Shakespeare*, I, 316.

5. See A. W. Pollard's review of Chambers' *William Shakespeare* (in *Library*, XI (1931), 380); T. W. Baldwin's *Shakspere's Five-Act Structure* (1947), chap. 33; L. Hotson's *Shakespeare's Sonnets Dated* (1949), pp. 32–6; P. Alexander's *Shakespeare Primer* (1951), p. 33.

to a notable work by Sir Walter Greg, we can fit this play into a general picture of theatrical dishonesty, which, precluding an unprofitable study in isolation, takes us a good step forward with most of its difficulties.[1]

For, on its title-page, the *T.R.* proclaims that it was "publikely acted by the Queenes Maiesties Players". Having been the principal company in the later eighties, the Queen's men had gone steadily downhill after the death, in 1588, of their chief comedian Richard Tarlton. In the nineties a number of their plays appeared in print in debased texts,[2] in a study of one of which Greg showed that the company itself was probably responsible for the perversion of the original sense. Greg suggested that, driven to the last extremes, the Queen's men sold their prompt-book to another company, then reconstructed a prompt-book for themselves from memory, with alterations to suit the taste of a lower class of audience, continuing to act the "sold" play—and finally sold the second prompt-book to a printer for a second fee.[3]

From the reconstruction of their own plays it would be a small step, for a hard-up company, to the "plagiarism" of the successes of other companies. Word for word reconstruction would, of course, save time where the company remembered the words of a play it had once possessed. Pirating another company's get-penny would make accuracy difficult, since the words would have to be learned first, or written down in the theatre. To surmount these obstacles, the Elizabethan pirate would probably anticipate the methods of Tate Wilkinson, who reconstructed Sheridan's *Duenna c.* 1777:

I locked myself in my room; set down first all the jokes I remembered, then I laid a book of the songs before me; and with magazines kept the regulation of the scenes; and by the help of a numerous collection of obsolete Spanish plays, I produced an excellent comic Opera.[4]

1. *Two Elizabethan Stage Abridgements: The Battle of Alcazar & Orlando Furioso* (The Malone Society Extra Volume, 1922), 1923.
2. About a dozen Queen's plays were sold in the 1590's (Chambers, *The Elizabethan Stage*, IV, 382–6), some certainly in "bad" texts, others in doubtful ones.
3. Greg, *op. cit.*, section VI.
4. Quoted by Prof. Alexander in illustration of the composition of *The Taming of a Shrew* [*Shakespeare's Henry VI and Richard III* (1929), p. 69].

That the *T.R.* is a hotch-potch of a numerous collection of old plays Prof. Rupert Taylor has already demonstrated in an article listing its correspondences with Marlowe.[1] Shakespeare, too, was put to good account, contacts with his early histories being particularly common; lesser dramatists were likewise pillaged.[2] Though it contains no extended borrowings such as *The Taming of a Shrew* (1594) took from *Tamburlaine* and *Faustus*, imitation runs riot in the *T.R.*, so that obvious suspicions gather head in the reader.

Rewriting the plays of other companies—a simple matter before the copyright laws—was not restricted to the John plays, whichever came first. G. B. Churchill has proved that there was contact one way or the other between Shakespeare's *Richard III* and the Queen's men's anonymous *True Tragedie of Richard the Third* (1594)[3]; and L. Kirschbaum has classed this *True Tragedie* as a "bad quarto".[4] *The Taming of a Shrew* —hereafter *A Shrew*—connects similarly with Shakespeare's *The Taming of the Shrew*—hereafter *The Shrew*. Though ascribed on the title-page to Pembroke's company, H. Dugdale Sykes has argued that the prose of *A Shrew* is the work of S. Rowley,[5] and critics of weight have approved.[6] Two other "Rowley plays", following Sykes's definition, *Orlando Furioso* (1594) and *The Famous Victories of Henry V* (1598), we know to have been Queen's men's plays. Sykes thought all the "Rowley plays" the property of the Admiral's men, since Rowley is first heard of as a member of that company in 1597–8. But as Rowley's earlier affiliations remain a mystery, and as several of the "Rowley plays" date from before 1594, it is more logical to associate him with the only company known to have possessed more than one of his plays. As this company (the Queen's) admittedly passed on plays to other companies and reconstructed them for itself, if Greg is right, it seems possible that

1. *P.M.L.A.*, vol. LI (1936), p. 633 ff.
2. H. Dugdale Sykes [*Sidelights on Shakespeare* (1919), p. 99 ff.] argued strongly on stylistic grounds for Peele's authorship of the *T.R.*; but more probably Peele was only imitated, like Shakespeare and Marlowe.
3. 'Richard the Third up to Shakespeare' [in *Palaestra*, x (1900)].
4. In 'A Census of Bad Quartos' [*R.E.S.*, XIV (1938), pp. 35–6].
5. *The Authorship of 'The Taming of A Shrew'*, etc. (Shakespeare Association Pamphlet), 1920.
6. Greg, *Alcazar and Orlando*, pp. 358–61; E. K. Chambers, *The Elizabethan Stage*, III, 472.

A Shrew was written in the first instance for the Queen's men and by them sold to Pembroke's. We suggest, in short, that three early Shakespeare plays—*John*, *The Shrew*, and *Richard III*—may have been rewritten for one company, the Queen's, in the early nineties.[1]

To proceed to the *T.R.* itself. We must glance at its printing-house history. Thomas Orwin, who printed the play, had a suspicious career: his press was seized during part of 1591, the very year the *T.R.* appeared, and had been suspended at least twice not long before.[2] Though the *T.R.* was printed "for Sampson Clarke", it seems to us that Orwin may have been responsible for it[3]: for the possible risks taken with an early "derivative play" turn our thoughts first to the man who lived dangerously. Though of course it would be wrong to exaggerate its bearing on our problem, Orwin's career should be kept in mind.

The shoddy text of the *T.R.* also concerns us. Exits and entrances are omitted, many speeches have no speech headings, speech headings are sometimes ambiguous, stage directions summarize the action or describe it as something already witnessed before.[4] Faults such as these, common in reported texts, can obviously be expected even in derivative plays such as we suppose *A Shrew* and the *T.R.* to be. For derivative plays had to be written in haste after the production of the source-play, if this latter was unprinted: and descriptive directions referring to the source-play would creep in quite naturally if imi-

1. In *Alcazar and Orlando* Greg quoted a private letter from J. D. Wilson suggesting that *A Shrew* was sold to Pembroke's by the Queen's men (pp. 361–2).

2. Orwin became a printer in 1587. In 1587–8 he was in trouble with the Court of Star Chamber; in 1589 the Master and both Wardens of the stationers waited at Lambeth a whole day "about an answere for the staie that came from his grace for Orwyn"; on 30 Aug. 1591 Whitgift wrote to the Stationers asking for the return of his press to Orwin [cf. Arber, 1, 527; 1, 555; v, li; also McKerrow, *Dictionary of Printers and Booksellers (1557–1640)* (1910); Strype's *Whitgift* (1718), p. 303].

3. Clarke's name survives on only three books: Lodge's *Alarum against Usurers* (1584); Greene's *Menaphon* (1589); and the *T.R.* (1591). Lodge's *Alarum* resumed the attack on Gosson for which an earlier book of his had run into trouble (cf. Lodge in *D.N.B.*); Greene's *Menaphon* contained the famous attack on the author of the *Ur-Hamlet*, probably Shakespeare. Thus Clarke's name appears on three potentially dangerous books, and he may have been used as a stooge publisher.

4. See our note on the text of the *T.R.*, Appendix C.

tation was the order. Typical foul paper omission of speech headings and stage directions in company with the above define the text more or less recognizably.

One last approach to the *John–T.R.* problem still remains open to us—a particularly fruitful one. The critics have long been aware that obscurities in Shakespeare's plays can sometimes be explained through his sources: where he has written hurriedly, he is said to have forgotten to transplant motives or other details which would otherwise have smoothed over his "inconsistencies". A large number of such "inconsistencies" has been claimed for *John*. It is possible, however, to turn the argument by pointing out inconsistencies in the *T.R.* which seem due to the precedence of *John*. In Appendix B we discuss the two plays from this angle and conclude, without prejudice we hope, that *John* is less inconsistent than has been thought, while the *T.R.* leaves the field with dishonour.

Let us now recapitulate the more important evidence concerning the *T.R.–John* relationship.

(*a*) *John* is in every way a good text (p. xxxiii ff.).—The *T.R.* features some recognized "bad quarto" characteristics, being (i) a tissue of stolen phrases; (ii) a text much more untidy than "foul paper plays" usually are, which, moreover, contains summarizing and descriptive directions (p. lv; Appendix C).

(*b*) The *T.R.* belonged to a company which, according to a distinguished critic, reconstructed for itself at least one other play just at the time when the *T.R.* came into existence. Three plays, two of which certainly belonged to this company, have curious contacts with three of Shakespeare's plays, and one of these (*A Shrew*) is now generally accepted as "derivative" (p. liii ff.).

(*c*) The writers of the two plays both consulted the chronicles (p. xviii). At one point the *T.R.* paraphrases M. Paris imperfectly, while *John* uses the words of the source in the right context: and whereas the *T.R.* shows no other sign of acquaintance with M. Paris, *John* follows him in at least one more passage (p. xv). Where both plays draw upon the same source material, Shakespeare is usually closer to the words of the source: which the intimate contact of the plays makes doubly interesting, since the second writer evidently thought first of the first play, referring only in the second place to the chronicles (p. xviii ff.).

(*d*) The *T.R.* contains structural inconsistencies which conflate (i) historical truth as retailed in the chronicles, and (ii) deviations therefrom such as appear also in *John* but there moulded into a consistent whole. Being comprehensible only as thoughtless echoing from a previous version, these inconsistencies alone plead strongly for the precedence of *John* (Appendix B).

(*e*) The "dates" of the plays must not enter the argument. We ask for disregard of the traditional "Shakespeare Chronology", since the relationship of the two John plays is part of the evidence (p. liii). New clues for the date of *John* suggest that the two plays were written within a few months of each other at most in 1590-1 (p. xliv ff.).

So far nothing has been said of the "internal evidence" for dating. Kinship of temper and style is generally taken to indicate proximity in composition. This is not necessarily right, but the parallels between *John* and *Richard II* are certainly startling. *Love's Labour's Lost* also has many verbal resemblances, as a glance at our footnotes will show, and likewise *Richard III*.[1] *Richard II* may well have been written within a very short time of *John*; *Richard III* at least a year earlier, and *Love's Labour's Lost* about a year later, in our opinion. *Romeo* and *Midsummer Night's Dream* belong more or less to the same period. To fit *John* into a more clear-cut "chronology" lies outside our present duties.

We believe that *John* was written in the winter/spring of 1590/91. Critics of exceptional authority prefer a date between 1593 and 1596. Students of the period will realize that more is at stake than meets the eye, and that the problem, obscure and elusive though it be, must be faced.

---

1. For the affinities of these plays cf. articles by König, Isaac, Sarrazin in the *Shakespeare Jahrbuch* for 1875, 1884, 1894, 1897–8.

4. THE PLAY

To praise the contrivance of a play which deviates very little from its "source-play" would be dangerous. The critics, consequently, have been content to admire the few virtues in *John* not plundered directly from the *T.R.*—the exuberance of the Bastard, the logic of Pandulph, the soliloquies, the verse generally. But if, as we suggest, the plot for *John* was not found ready-made by Shakespeare we must re-examine it with new respect.

An exception to those who saw *John* as a mere shadow was John Masefield. Disregarding sources altogether, he declared that the "great scheme of the play is the great achievement, not the buxom boor who flouts the Duke of Austria".[1] *John* "is an intellectual form in which a number of people with obsessions illustrate the idea of treachery".[2] Masefield's brief summary must be quoted:

John's mother, Elinor, has been treacherous to one of her sons. John has usurped his brother's right . . . [The Bastard's mother] confesses that she was seduced by . . . Coeur de Lion. The Bastard's half-brother, another domestic traitor, does not scruple to accuse his mother of adultery . . .

[In Act II the kings] turn from their pledged intention to effect a base alliance. . . . In the third act . . . the French King adds another falseness. He breaks away from the newly-made alliance at the bidding of the Pope's legate . . .

. . . Hubert fails to blind Prince Arthur. Even in the act of mercy he is treacherous. . . . John, thinking that the murder has been done, breaks faith with Hubert. . . . In the last act, the English nobles, who have been treacherous to John, betray their new master. . . . A monk treacherously poisons John. . .[3]

Persuasive as it is, Masefield's thesis that "treachery" is the

---

1. *William Shakespeare* (1911), p. 81.   2. *Op. cit.*, p. 76.

3. Pp. 78–80.—As all concepts contain their opposites, e.g. treachery supposes loyalty, Masefield's account ignores half the "treachery" theme. Shakespeare emphasizes the bond between Constance and Arthur, Eleanor and John, France and the Dauphin; a messenger professes loyal zeal instead of speaking in formulae (IV. ii. 180); various passages present treachery as the rider to loyalty (e.g. III. i. 253–62, v. ii. 9–44), and not *vice versa*; and so on. The Bastard's extravagant loyalty to the criminal John (cf. IV. iii. 142–4, notes) likewise counterpoises the generalized treachery—being partly a device to preserve the sanity and balance of *John*.

Leitmotiv of *John* does not wholly satisfy. Iteration of one topic in a "great scheme" does not necessarily make it central. An analysis of recurring features of style and imagery will show that Masefield's précis covers only a part of the play.

Remarkable in *John*, firstly, are the nicely-argued disquisitions on moral concepts, often illustrating the conflict of two value-systems in a finely-pointed dualism. Thus crime and punishment go together (II. i. 184–90), faith and need (III. i. 137–42), law and justice (III. i. 111–16), truth and perjury (III. i. 150–223), truth and deceit (V. iv. 26 ff.), honesty and commodity (II. i. 561–98). And no sooner are these concepts lined up than kindred material clamours for admission amongst them—madness and reason (III. iii. 43–60), perfection (II. i. 423–45), and ceremony (IV. ii. 1–39), that great Elizabethan bugbear. The middle star in this galaxy of elaborated concepts emerges, finally, as the age-old will-o'-the-wisp of right and wrong, or right and might.

A simple count of the frequency of words can often be a valuable first step in an examination of a play's themes, as F. C. Kolbe has shown.[1] Having noted the preoccupation with moral concepts, we are not surprised to find that the word "right" occurs more times in *John* (28 times) than in any other play of Shakespeare (*3 H 6* is next: 21 times).[2] Other words numerous enough to claim attention in *John* are "blood" (40 times, first place in Shakespeare),[3] "hand" (52, second to *Titus*), "eye" (47, third to *MND.* and *LLL.*). And, just as the chopped-off hand in *Titus*, and the symbolism of eyes in comedies of love, is not accidental to the main theme so, in *John* too, repeating words are firmly anchored in the action, they are not slip-shod writing. The dominant image-sequence of the play, with its clear interlocking, resolves all doubt on this head.

(*a*) We take IV. i to be the central scene,[4] and the spectacle

1. In *Shakespeare's Way* (1930). Kolbe did not discuss *John*.

2. All our figures are based on J. Bartlett's *Concordance* for Shakespeare.

3. Prof. W. Clemen pointed out the significance of blood in *John* [*Development of Shakespeare's Imagery* (1951), p. 86].

4. The action of the play is held together through Arthur, for whom France took up arms (Acts I–III), and whose "murder" caused the revolt of the nobles (Acts IV, V). Shakespeare exaggerates the French concern for Arthur, and the nobles had forgotten Arthur when they revolted in 1215, but Shakespeare's re-arrangement of history centres John's problems round Arthur. We suggest in

of Hubert threatening to blind Arthur to be the most exciting picture of the play. What Hubert saw in Arthur's eyes seems to have fascinated Shakespeare particularly, for the image of reflecting eyes gradually deepens in meanings. Fitly enough, in a play where impersonal rhetoric and passionate pleading continually supplant each other, the image first appears in a conventional setting: the lover sees himself mirrored in his lady's eyes (II. i. 496–503). Immediately after IV. i we find John searching the eyes of his lords (IV. ii. 2), while Hubert's eyes reflect the (supposed) blinding scene:

> The image of a wicked heinous fault
> Lives in his eye (IV. ii. 71–2)
>
> . . . foul imaginary eyes of blood
> Presented thee more hideous than thou art
> (IV. ii. 265–6) [1]

The sub-surface significances that gradually attach to repeating images convert eyes into symbols of right, and hands into might. When the "heavy hand" (IV. iii. 58) of might is later equated with "wall-ey'd wrath or staring rage" (IV. iii. 49), a terrible image of distortion and deformity applied to John, these repeating symbols, like the perpetual personifications of Death and Fortune, [2] almost achieve the stature of *dramatis personae*.

(*b*) Closely related to the imagery of blinding is a group denoting outrage to the body generally. The city (and state) conceived as body politic ranges fresh associative fields beside the more literal:

> . . . our cannon shall be bent
> Against the brows of this resisting town (II. i. 37–8)

Appendix A (2) that Shakespeare took the pains to look up R. Coggeshall's Latin MS. chronicle, the recognized authority for the death of Arthur, which, if we are right, implies Shakespeare's realization of the importance of IV. i.

1. Cf. also IV. iii. 150, V. iv. 60.

2. Death (II. i. 352, 453, 456, III. iii. 25 ff., IV. ii. 82, IV. iii. 35, V. ii. 177, V. vii. 15) reappears in disguise as War (III. i. 30, IV. iii. 149, V. ii. 74, 164) and Time (especially III. i. 250–1); Fortune (II. i. 391, II. ii. 52 ff., III. i. 44, III. iii. 119, V. ii. 58) as Occasion (IV. ii. 125). Prof. C. Spurgeon's *Shakespeare's Imagery* (1935) discussed personification as a special feature of *John* (pp. 246–53).

> We from the west will send destruction
> Into this city's bosom (II. i. 409–10)

John's first set speech to the men of Angiers is the most sustained expression (II. i. 206–34), but the cluster stands out throughout:

> Whose foot spurns back the ocean's roaring tides (II. i. 24)
>
> Austria and France shoot in each other's mouth (II. i. 414)
>
> . . . when I strike my foot
> Upon the bosom of the ground, rush forth (IV. i. 2–3)

Body-images are especially important in *John*, because of their variety and profusion. Apart from eye, hand, blood (cf. above) —mouth (14 times), breath (18), foot (12), bosom (10), brow (11), spleen (4), bowels (3), arm (27),[1] tooth and teeth (5) are all unexceeded in number in other plays of the canon, while some, such as tongue (23 times in *John*, third to *R 2* and *LLL.*), come not far behind. When we recall that *John* is only 2,600 lines long, definitely shorter than the plays that compare with it in the frequency of body-images, these statistics call for attention.[2]

(*c*) After body-outrage the next step is rape-imagery. The naturalness of the transition is best illustrated by the set speeches at the siege of Angiers. John's (II. i. 206–34) is shot through with threats of body-outrage, Philip's (II. i. 235 ff.) implies rape (l. 257), and the Bastard expounds with zestful innuendo (II. i. 381–7). All through *John* we meet this important connective theme:

> Outfaced infant state, and done a rape
> Upon the maiden virtue of the crown (II. i. 97–8)
>
> . . . on the marriage-bed
> Of smiling peace to march a bloody host (III. i. 171–2)
>
> And kiss the lips of unacquainted change (III. iii. 166)

Subsidiary here is the blot and stain imagery which, though usually toned down in petrified metaphors—

---

1. Bartlett's "arm" takes armour and arm (the limb) together.
2. Prof. Spurgeon (*loc. cit.*) thought body-images the outstanding device in *John*, apart from personification (cf. p. lxi, n. 2).

> To look into the blots and stains of right　(II. i. 114)
> The faiths of men ne'er stained with revolt　(IV. ii. 6)

—is highly charged when applied to Arthur (II. ii. 43–54), since a child's "stains" are imagined the equivalent of the rape-fornication qualities of the adults (II. ii. 54–65): physical deformity being equated with the spiritual deformity of adultery, the conceit is that Arthur's beauty (not his age) disqualifies him from the favours of strumpet Fortune. In II. i. 129–33 stain and fornication images are likewise bracketed.

(*d*) The bastardy-fornication theme proper is a cornerstone of *John*. Act I dwells upon it, and Act II at once resumes it (II. i. 122–33); the Bastard likes to remember his illegitimacy (I. i. 207, II. i. 276, 279), to soliloquize about "That smooth-fac'd gentleman, tickling commodity" (II. i. 573), to threaten to cuckold Austria (II. i. 290–3), and Shakespeare created him partly to fill the needs of this theme. Fortune, not unexpectedly, enters as a strumpet (II. i. 391–4, II. ii. 54–61, v. ii. 58–9). Perhaps the most brilliant jugglery comes in III. iii, where Constance invokes Death as a lover (ll. 25–36), rebukes him for being passionless and sleepy (ll. 39–41), then wonders how she "may be deliver'd" of her woes—her woes being a "child-substitute" (l. 55, note)—and finally brings forth a "babe of clouts" (l. 58). The sexual looseness of the elder Plantagenets had been emphasized to distinguish the correctness of the other party—France staid and cautious, Lewis a formal wooer (II. i. 496 ff.), Arthur a child. Constance believes in chastity (II. i. 124)—unlike Eleanor, who waives such considerations (II. i. 132), or Cœur-de-lion the seducer, or John or Faulconbridge. Constance's frenzy resembles Ophelia's insanity in its sexual prepossessions, but whereas Ophelia, whose mind has snapped, gives voice to something essential to her nature in her bawdy songs, Constance in III. iii is not true to herself, and her ravings show only how far from itself her mind has been bent.

(*e*) Bridging across to the final element in the sequence, a wealth of "over" and "under" images are clear pictures of suppression. The close affinity to group (*d*) emerges in verbal echoes,[1] and in the juxtaposition of similar over/under ideas:

1. Cf. I. i. 263–4 and II. i. 41–3.

> Sh' adulterates hourly with thine uncle John,
> And with her golden hand hath pluck'd on France
> To tread down fair respect of sovereignty, ...
> And leave those woes alone which I alone
> Am bound to underbear! (II. ii. 56–65)

Infrequent and nonce words help to give weight to the group: aloft (IV. ii. 139, note), brawl'd down (II. i. 383), overbear (III. iii. 9, IV. ii. 37), o'ermasterest (II. i. 109), overstain'd (III. i. 162), o'erswell (II. i. 337), supernal (II. i. 112), underbear (II. ii. 65), underprop (V. ii. 99), underwrought (II. i. 95), uphold (III. i. 83, 241, V. iv. 5).

(*f*) The last link in the interlocking group of major images, though not itself imagery, we take to be the device of perpetual analysis of moral concepts (cf. p. lx). Here we expect over/ under pictures, the simplest symbols of right and wrong:

> O then tread down my need, and faith mounts up:
> Keep my need up, and faith is trodden down! (III. i. 141–2)

Since all moral concepts are poor relations of right and wrong, we also expect to recognize the basic dichotomy despite its transmutations:

> ... when *law* can do no *right*
> Let it be lawful that *law* bar no *wrong*! (III. i. 111–12)

and the two primary concepts, disguised as truth and false-hood, honesty and commodity, faith and need, chastity and unchastity, and so on, thus continually re-enact for us the human drama of Arthur and John.

The key to the major "imagery of oppression" which we have outlined seems to be the theme of "right versus might". This theme also dictated many of the more striking deviations from history in *John*. Arthur, a young warrior in Holinshed, becomes a helpless child in the play; Constance a "widow, husbandless" (II. ii. 14, note); Limoges and Austria, the two enemies *par excellence* of Cœur-de-lion, are made one person, so that Arthur's plight—having to accept aid from Limoges–Austria—seems more abject; and, more significantly still, Shakespeare presents John as a usurper from the start (I. i. 40, note), whereas his right to the throne was declared as strong as Arthur's by the chroniclers.

Especially in the minor imagery the theme of "right versus might" can be shown to have occupied Shakespeare. For *John* follows the "wheel of Fortune" pattern for tragedy[1]—was probably billed as a tragedy in 1591—and various comparisons help to construe the rise and fall of the hero. Fortune's favours before III. ii, and her frowns thereafter, are expressed in different ways. Up to III. iii John's military speed repeatedly contrasts with French caution and slowness[2]; and Fortune helps John with good winds (II. i. 57); in IV. ii. 113 ff. Lewis's military speed surprises John. John recognizes that Fortune has turned against him (IV. ii. 125), now helping Lewis with favourable winds.[3] Various game and gambling allusions are thrown in to underline the participation of Fortune.[4] The antithesis of speed and slowness, again, continues in the parallel one of John's hotness and French coldness.[5] Impetuousness, indeed, may be said to be John's "tragic flaw", and the *burning* fever that kills him (v. vii. 30–48) the final irony of Fate. The story ends when the usurper's vitality has consumed itself, when even his legs fail him (v. iii. 16, v. vii. 10), and a child-figure, Arthur resurrected as Prince Henry, triumphs at last in undisputed "right".

A further stylistic device that requires some attention, being now unfamiliar, may be called "putting the case". In a sense, *John* develops into one continuous debate, broken up into separate issues. In Act I the Faulconbridges argue it out before the king; in Act II follow the twin-speeches of John and King Philip (II. i. 206–66), of the English and French heralds (II. i. 300–24), the twin rebukes of the kings (II. i. 334–49), the contrasting speeches of the Bastard advocating war (II. i. 373–96), and of Hubert advocating peace (ll. 423–55); in Act III King

1. Cf. R. Chapman, 'The Wheel of Fortune in Shakespeare's Historical Plays' [*R.E.S.*, I (1950), pp. 1–7], and I. i. I note.

2. Cf. also I. i. 178, II. i. 79, 233, 297, III. ii. 16, III. iii. 11, IV. ii. 170, 260–9, IV. iii. 74, v. vii. 50, etc.

3. Shakespeare manufactured a parallel by having the messenger of war delayed with the invading army (II. i. 57–9, IV. ii. 114–15).

4. Cf. II. i. 123, III. i. 144, IV. ii. 93–5, v. ii. 103–7, 118, 141, etc.

5. Cf. II. i. 53, 479, III. i. 31, 49, 243, 266, III. iii. 11, IV. iii. 74, v. iii. 3, etc.

Philip pleads for the sanctity of oaths (III. i. 150–78), and Pandulph's reply (ll. 189–223), the turning-point of John's career, whether *ratiocinatio* or not,[1] is universally acclaimed as wonderfully typical "school-logic", unique in Shakespeare; in III. ii John urges Hubert to kill Arthur, in IV. i Arthur persuades Hubert to let him live (the play's two best scenes); in V. ii. 9–39 Salisbury puts the case for rebellion; and other formal and contrasted speeches abound. Modern critics often condemn the consequent "motiveless zigzagging of the action", which meant that in "almost every act a new side-issue is treated with such breadth as to become the main issue".[2] They forget that the study of rhetoric trained educated Elizabethans in the refinements of debate, and that the "side-issues" in *John* may be viewed as thematic iteration, being always a continuation of the same high debate of right and wrong.

In Act II the soldiering distracts from the possible monotony of "putting the case". Elsewhere diversity of style provides a relief:

one feels at times that here Shakespeare is thinking consciously of the variety of characters and of the language which is appropriate to them[3]

And not only diversity as between individuals. The constant intrusion of formality—in the person of ambassadors, heralds, legates, messengers—extends to the presentation of character generally. Except for the Bastard's circle in Act I, everyone speaks impersonally on first appearance, and it is the doffing and donning of the "official" mask, the interplay of private passion and public duty, that throws a really distinctive light and shade through *John*.[4]

Arthur's conceits in IV. i, often dismissed as unnatural, are

1. Cf. III. i. 189, note.
2. Bulthaupt, quoted approvingly in G. C. Moore Smith's *King John* (1900), p. xxxi.
3. B. Ifor Evans, *The Language of Shakespeare's Plays* (1952), p. 44.
4. Cf. the problem of the Identity of Hubert and the Citizen of Angiers (p. xxxvii). Tillyard hinted at the more elaborate "interplay" that we suggest: "John is sometimes a conventionally dignified monarch and at others a mean and treacherous man, realistically portrayed" [*Shakespeare's History Plays* (1944), p. 223].

the pressure-point of the method.[1] For Hubert's short, simple answers help to heighten the impression of Arthur's artifice: and the man's uncompromising determination leaves open no door for the child except verbal wriggling. Perhaps, then, Shakespeare aimed at preciousness. Sudden necessity similarly drove Pandulph to verbal tricks in iii. i. 189–223, and anger and despair plunged Constance into involute declamation in ii. i and iii. i. By iii. iii the reasoning madness of Constance establishes verbal pyrotechnics as the language of emergency, so that Arthur in iv. i behaves *conventionally* (as does John in v. vii, quibbling on his deathbed). And, though some writers have felt that Arthur should be dumb with fright in iv. i, that his pleading is unnatural, the convention does not seem to us to jar with the purely psychological needs of the situation, but rather to harmonize with them. Arthur darts from conceit to conceit as from door to door, elaborating any point that might prize open Hubert's determination. He realizes that his pretty thoughts undermine Hubert's purpose, and the consequent wild dash to a new conceit, just as the one in hand fades out, reveals a more or less conscious *technique of pleading*. His conceits do not ring prettily because "innocent prate" (iv. i. 25) when turned "crafty" and "cunning" (iv. i. 53–4), like beauty selling itself, distorts and defaces itself. Hence, we think, the usual vague diagnosis of "unnaturalness" is only half-right. Arthur's conceits or contortions are unnatural, as all contortions must be: yet the situation calls for them. Physical disfigurement has to be avoided—even at the cost of spiritual stain. Not his terror, but the sight of a child forced into duplicity, produces the more subtle pathos of the scene.[2]

If *John* may not be dismissed as a hotch-potch of alarums

1. Walter Raleigh condemned them as typical of Shakespeare's immature writing [*Shakespeare* (1916), p. 222]; so Kreyssig (*apud* Furness, p. 291), and many more.

2. Mark Van Doren treated the stylistic extravagance in *John* somewhat differently: "The presence in 'King John' of a certain famous passage about painting the lily is not accidental but essential, for the theme of the play is excess . . ." Van Doren thought many orations of the play "bloated beyond all form", and that "the pole of hyperbole, the chill Thule of sigh-blasted excess is reached and passed by Constance. She is the last and most terrible of Shakespeare's wailing women" [*Shakespeare* (1939), pp. 106, 107, 109].

and excursions, can a good word be said for a "hero" of the play? The few who accept John as hero condemn his colour-lessness; some think the Bastard the hero, the majority, that there is none.[1]

Two considerations are usually allowed to stigmatize John as an unsatisfactory hero. Compared with the complementary *Richard II*, Shakespeare's "revision of the *T.R.*" is unambitious, therefore "its straightforward chronicling seems less mature than the psychological study of Richard".[2] In short, the failure of the hero is the fault of the "source-play", and of Shake-speare's neglect of possible improvements. Here the assump-tion, that an introspective hero imports better psychology or greater dramatic craftsmanship, must not pass unquestioned. Should not an exhibition of minds working on each other en-thrall as much as inner conflicts and soliloquies? This elemen-tary principle seems to have satisfied Shakespeare in some of his most mature plays, as in *John*. John explores and exploits his fellow-men. He tries to find everyone's price. The Bastard is bought with a knighthood (I. i. 162), France with five pro-vinces (II. i. 527 ff.), Hubert with promises (III. ii. 30–42), Arthur is promised lands (II. i. 551), the nobles are promised Arthur (IV. ii. 67), John tries to buy them off a second time (IV. ii. 168), buys off the pope with a nominal submission (V. i. 1), in order to buy off Lewis (V. i. 64). The outstanding speech of the play, analysing commodity, is not gratuitous, nor are the psychological implications of "this all-changing word" made a secret.

As John's few distinctive qualities, such as rebelliousness and patriotism, one by one prove to have been inessentials, his wielding of commodity assumes significance. One is tempted to regard the play as a study of a virtuoso politician. For, how-ever short-sighted his strategy, John's tactics are brilliant. No-where is this more patent than in III. ii. Having been tied down by his interfering mother, by the threats of France and the mere existence of Arthur, John throws off his chains for one brief moment with wonderful skill, but disastrous conse-quences. France has been repulsed. Meanwhile Eleanor lost

1. A. Bonjour gave samples of these various views in 'The Road to Swinstead Abbey' [*Journal of English Literary History*, XVIII (1951), 253–6].

2. M. R. Ridley, *Shakespeare's Plays A Commentary* (1937), p. 85.

face by nearly being captured (III. ii. 7): John seizes the opportunity to order her to remain in France (l. 11), rubbing in her failure ("strongly guarded", l. 12) to make sure she does not answer back. Then he fishes for Hubert's promise to murder Arthur. Scarcely has the scene ended, however, before Pandulph's strategic commentary (in III. iii) points out the fruitlessness of John's tactical master-stroke.

But in the last resort Shakespeare's John is Holinshed's John (cf. p. xxx), with ungovernable passion as well as cunning dissimulation in his heart. To some degree, therefore, the psychological interest in him springs from a simple dualism, a see-saw between seeming irreconcilables. For an audience he should be a puzzle and a surprise. In the study, of course, the theatrical trick loses power.

Like his distaste for introspection, John's collapse in Act v displeases the critics. A hero ought to be heroic, they contend (ignoring Richard II). But perhaps the very disappointment of the critics in the heartlessness of a man at death's door is a measure of unreasonable expectations, and a tribute to a contrived effect. Inaction is undramatic, and a heartless hero must indeed be a disappointment; but John's collapse in v. iii may be tensely dramatic within the context of the play as a whole, even if it seems mere inaction within the scene. The full-circle scheme of *John* demands that the hero who is Impetuousness must come to a dead stop (v. iii), while the transformation of his energy into raving madness (v. vii. 11), like the roaring of a car that will not go, finally brings home to us the tremendous power of the pent-up forces to which he was a slave.

Charges that John fails as hero are due to a confusion of terms. Admittedly, he cannot claim to be a national hero in Act v. But his personal qualities are one thing, and his structural position as the play's hero (or protagonist) another. That John occupies the middle of his play need not be laboured, but two series of parallels can help to show how structural tightening consolidates his position.

Firstly, the fortunes of Lewis are made to resemble John's. Lewis, dominated by his father (as John by Eleanor at the outset), gambles for a kingdom, goes to ruin once his parent's influence is discarded (as John after III. ii), deciding on a cowardly murder of the English lords (as John decides on Arthur's, the turning-point in both cases); he is let down by clashing loyalties in Melun (as John by Hubert), defies the pope, and finally, his supplies lost at sea (as John's devoured by the Wash), knuckles under (like John) to—Pandulph and Fortune. Such parallelism Shakespeare used often, most successfully perhaps in the stories of Gloucester and Lear in *King Lear*.

Secondly, John's tragedy is interpreted as a family drama. Three sons of Henry II, beside John, fill in the background. Richard I, crusader and adulterer, symbolizes the conflicting passions of the Plantagenets; Salisbury, his half-brother, almost personifies Nobility ["noble . . . nobility . . . noble" (v. ii. 40–3)], and it may be no coincidence that he alone in *John* expresses a desire to crusade (v. ii. 33–8); Geoffrey seems to have been a nonentity, hag-ridden like his father; Faulconbridge takes over from Richard I ["perfect Richard" (i. i. 90)[1]]; and Arthur resembles Salisbury ["noble boy" (ii. i. 18)]. John fights against "nobility", crusades against Rome, and dies a nonentity, and all the while other *dramatis personae* overshadow him, in one sense. His abuse of the pope cannot rival the railing of Eleanor and Constance; he boasts neither the vigour of Faulconbridge, nor the generalship of Cœur-de-lion, nor the virtues of Salisbury. But, though he appears colourless by comparison, being the centre where all the strong colours of the family meet and neutralize each other, Shakespeare created the family as the complement to John, and not the other way about. That is, John seems to be the product of his family, but really the family was devised as a projection of John.[2]

Structurally John seems to be the centre of his play; if he is not the hero, he is certainly the villain. Nevertheless, the Bastard's ascendancy at the end may still perplex readers. As soon as we view him as one of a type, however, his place in the play becomes more clear. Like Mercutio, Falstaff, Touchstone and Jaques, and Autolycus, the Bastard is a cynic, Shakespeare's

1. Cf. ii. i. 294, iii. ii. 1, v. i. 57, notes.
2. Most of the Plantagenets (e.g. Arthur, Geoffrey, Salisbury, Faulconbridge) are given characters which are entirely Shakespeare's fiction, the rest (Eleanor, Constance, Richard I) having subsidiary traits emphasized, new traits added, for the purposes of the play. Only John remains more or less as in Holinshed.

customary addition to the stories that he followed closely. True to type, he stands outside the inner framework of his play, mainly as a commentator. Whether or not he is the chorus,[1] as many have thought, his irrepressible candour, which dovetails with the functions of a chorus, makes him immensely likeable. But, however likeable, the chorus cannot be the hero. It might help, furthermore, to compare the Honesty or Simplicity of the moralities, for the Bastard's expository tirades and various other touches indicate his descent.[2] Indeed, to make his subordinate position crystal clear, Shakespeare has him snubbed again and again—by Eleanor (I. i. 64), by Lady Faulconbridge (I. i. 227, 243), by Austria (II. i. 147), by John (III. i. 60), by Salisbury (IV. iii. 94), by Lewis (V. ii. 160).

Countering the theory that *John* has no hero, Dr A. Bonjour, in a stimulating article, has recently argued that

we have to deal here with a deliberately contrasted evolution. John's career represents a falling curve, the Bastard's career a rising curve; and both curves, perfectly contrasted, are linked into a single pattern. The structure of the play is thus remarkably balanced . . . in very simple terms: decline of a hero—rise of a hero.[3]

This is ingenious, but we feel that Dr Bonjour concedes too much. We cannot accept the Bastard as a hero even in Act v. Nowhere in the play does his interference "make history". Impressed by John's delegation of authority to him (v. i. 77), some take this as a sign of the Bastard's greatness: whereas, we think, it was meant to be only a sign of John's dejection that he hands over to a servant, a bastard, and a boon companion. Modern democratic ideas distort our response to John's action. The immediate result—defeat in battle, and then the loss of John's army in the Wash, an act of criminal stupidity accredit-

---

1. His chorus duties at times impinge upon his psychological integrity. In II. i. 561–98 he has to denounce that sly devil, commodity, with whom he as a person really sympathizes: the sudden *volte-face* ("And why rail I on this commodity?") makes Shakespeare's machinery creak. In IV. iii. 139–59 Shakespeare walks a tight-rope, bringing Faulconbridge to the verge of recognizing John's usurpation during a chorus (cf. ll. 142, 143, 154, notes); in II. i. 585 the chorus Faulconbridge calls France's support of Arthur "honourable".

2. I. i. 182 ff., II. i. 561 ff., IV. iii. 140 ff., v. vii. 110 ff. are the "choruses"; cf. also II. i. 135, 573, IV. iii. 145, notes.

3. *E. L. H.*, XVIII (1951), 270.

ed to the Bastard by Shakespeare and dwelt upon twice to belittle him[1]—surely proves that this "hero" fails in the higher
spheres, despite his triumphs as a bully. Those who find in the
Bastard the regal qualities of "the character of the genuine
king"[2] seem to us to have overstated their case.

The Bastard's "rising curve" cannot, of course, be denied.
But we are doubtful whether it is integral rather than accidental to the structure. If John does not carry the play entirely
by himself, the challenge comes not so much from another
character as from the spirit of England. Yet England is not on
that account the "hero" of the play, nor its structural centre.
Various quibbles guide us to the old commonplace of the
identity of king and country[3] : in a way John and England are
one and the same theme. As in many of Shakespeare's political
plays, the tragedy of the hero leads to the regeneration of his
country. A further reason for the Bastard's ascendancy towards
the end may therefore lie in the fact that "His function is to
embody England, to incorporate the English soul".[4] The
Bastard is carried upwards by the theme of England, of which
he forms so essential a part.

Uncertainty about the hero may be indicative of a larger
problem of approach. We no longer feel as did the Elizabethans about some of the subsidiary themes. Horror of rebellion was universal when Shakespeare wrote[5] : we must not forget this when reading the long-winded apology for rebellion in
v. ii. Protestantism was still in the balance: a new and greater
Armada was expected from abroad, while Martin Marprelate

1. v. vi. 37 ff., v. vii. 59 ff.

2. Tillyard, *Shakespeare's History Plays* (1944), p. 227.—In *John*, even more
immediately than in the two historical tetralogies, "Shakespeare's problem is
how to legitimize the illegitimate" [J. F. Danby, *Shakespeare's Doctrine of Nature*
(1949), p. 75]. Illegitimate kingship plunges John into crime, while the Bastard
rises from country boor to national spokesman by dint of his illegitimate birth.
Dr Bonjour's theory of a "deliberately contrasted evolution" works in more ways
than one. Yet the Bastard fails to develop in personality, he is not "a man whose
every syllable makes him better understood", as Van Doren recognized (*Shakespeare*, p. 115), and his consequent failure as general and statesman may not be
passed over lightly.

3. Cf. ii. i. 91, 202, iv. iii. 142–3, notes.

4. J. M. Murry, *Shakespeare* (1936), p. 156.

5. Tillyard, *op. cit.*, p. 221 ff.; L. B. Campbell, *Shakespeare's "Histories"* (1947),
p. 155 ff.

made the foundations of the Church tremble at home.[1] The play has topical qualities that may too easily elude us today (cf. p. xxix). But it is worth the effort to come to grips with it: not alone because it seems an admirable piece of craftsmanship to a late apologist, but also because it was the first of Shakespeare's plays which contemporaries thought good enough for plagiarism.

5. The Stage History

John was probably the first of Shakespeare's plays to be pirated. New editions of the *T.R.*, first printed anonymously in 1591, pay tribute to the popularity of the parent-play, for in 1611 the *T.R.* title-page read "by W. Sh.", and in 1622 "by W. SHAKESPEARE". In other words, the *T.R.* was being sold under the pretence that it was *John*, a play in demand.[2] Francis Meres remembered *John*, though he forgot other early plays of Shakespeare, when he made his list in 1598. Munday, whether part-author of the *T.R.* or not (p. 175), alluded to *John* in his *Death of Robert, Earle of Huntington* (1601), as to a play familiar to all.[3] Deloney in 1602, writing *The Lamentable Death of King Iohn*, recalled tags from Shakespeare's play,[4] as did Richard Niccols in his account of John's life in *A Winter Nights Vision* (1610).[5] As the text of *John* was not available in print till 1623,

1. Many critics debate Shakespeare's religion at great length on the evidence of *John*. Roman Catholic writers have felt that Shakespeare was pro-Rome, since he toned down the anti-Roman violence of the *T.R.*, and "eliminated all anti-Catholic elements"(!) [G. M. Greenewald, *Shakespeare's Attitude Towards the Catholic Church in "King John"* (1938), p. 179; cf. J. H. de Groot, *The Shakespeares and "The Old Faith"* (1947), pp. 180–224]. But the Protestant (Armada) bravado in *John* contradicts such special pleading, and if Shakespeare was not "toning down" the *T.R.* we can scarcely doubt that he was a Protestant in 1590.
2. The S.R. entry for the Folio (8 Nov. 1623) did not include *John* or *The Shrew*: apparently the stationers, in whose eyes the possession of a "bad quarto" gave "copy-right" covering the good text [cf. W. W. Greg, 'The Spanish Tragedy—A Leading Case?' (in *Library*, VI (1926), 47)] allowed "derivative plays" to cover their source-plays as well, taking the two as one work.
3. The *John* story is alluded to in dumb show (Austria, Constance and Arthur appear on sig. D₃ᵛ); Hubert is addressed as "*Hubert*, thou fatall keeper of poore babes" (sig. F₄)—Shakespeare faked Arthur's age, but the *T.R.* left him a young warrior as in the chronicles (cf. p. xviii).
4. Cf. v. vii. 2, note.
5. Cf. stanza 52 (Niccols), and III. i. 102–5 (Shakespeare).

we infer that the initial success of 1591 was followed by several revivals.

After Shakespeare's death no record of performance remains until the revival at Covent Garden on 26 February 1737. The playbill for the Drury Lane production of 1745 said "Not acted 50 years", but probably this only meant "not acted for a long time".

In the 1720's Colley Cibber (the later poet laureate) rewrote *John*, calling it *Papal Tyranny*; but general ridicule kept the adaptation off the boards until the imminent Jacobite rebellion in 1745.[1] Cibber's play met the opportunity generously: Act I and the parts of Eleanor and Constance were cut completely, to give the "French invasion" more space, and very few lines were left as Shakespeare wrote them. Unfortunately for Cibber, however, Drury Lane managed to put on *John* itself five days after his first night at Covent Garden—with Garrick as John, Delane as Bastard, Macklin as Pandulph, Mrs Cibber as Constance, and Miss Macklin as Arthur.

Another famous adaptation also owed its success to contemporary politics. Valpy, headmaster of Reading School, "refined" Shakespeare's dialogue for his boys, also cut out Act I, so that, with the help of anti-French insertions, his version reached the Covent Garden stage in 1803, and

made so strong an impression on the feelings of an English audience, on the renewal of the War, that the Play was acted in almost every Town in Great Britain and Ireland.[2]

The most famous of all productions of *John* came in 1823–4 at Covent Garden. J. R. Planché (the later Somerset herald) was responsible for the exact imitation of antiquity—"The whole of the Dresses and Decorations being executed from indisputable Authorities, such as Monumental Effigies, Seals, Illumined MSS., &c.", according to the playbill. This was London's first "antiquarian production". The actors were dismayed by Planché's historicity, but the public enjoyed the spectacle. One enthusiastic critic wrote:

1. The story found its way into Pope's *Dunciad* (ed. 1742): "King John in silence modestly expires" (i, 252).
2. John Nichols, *Literary Anecdotes*, vol. ix (1815), p. 758.

Charles Kemble never more distinguished himself than by his powerful personation of the bastard *Falconbridge*. His first and second dresses were particularly graceful and picturesque. We never saw this distinguished actor to greater advantage.[1] .

Planché's researches were preserved in an illustrated booklet published in 1823, and historical accuracy became the producers' mania. Kean's *John* (1852) brought theatrical pedantry to its high-point. Only in the present century did simplicity and Elizabethan styles return to favour.

Never a firm favourite, except when the political situation gave it edge again, *John* has usually been produced at regular intervals. Most of the stars of the theatre have appeared in it. But, short as it is, it has practically always been cut. Few producers have dared to retain the scolding of Eleanor and Constance, and the longer speeches have suffered. Often the principal actor played Faulconbridge, not John, which must also have distorted the play. The custom of casting girls to play Arthur seems quite as dangerous.

Harold Child added an excellent section, 'The Stage-History of *King John*', to Prof. J. D. Wilson's C.U.P. *King John* (1936). This supplements Prof. G. C. D. Odell's *Shakespeare from Betterton to Irving* (2 vols., 1920). Productions after 1936 include one by the Old Vic Theatre in Leeds in 1941 (Ernest Milton as John, Lewis Casson as Bastard, Sybil Thorndike as Constance, Renee Ascherson as Blanche, Sonia Dresdel as Lady Faulconbridge); one by the Birmingham Rep. Theatre in 1945 (David Read as John, Paul Scofield as Bastard); one at Stratford in 1948 (Robert Helpmann as John, Anthony Quayle as Bastard); and one on television in 1952 (Donald Wolfit as John).

1. Quoted by G. C. D. Odell, *Shakespeare from Betterton to Irving*, II, 172.

THE LIFE AND DEATH OF
KING JOHN

DRAMATIS PERSONÆ*

KING JOHN.

PRINCE HENRY, *son to the king.*

ARTHUR, *Duke of Brittany, nephew to the king.*

THE EARL OF SALISBURY.

THE EARL OF PEMBROKE.

THE EARL OF ESSEX.

THE LORD BIGOT.

ROBERT FAULCONBRIDGE, *son to Sir Robert Faulconbridge.*

PHILIP *the Bastard, his half-brother.*

HUBERT, *a citizen of Angers.*

JAMES GURNEY, *servant to Lady Faulconbridge.*

PETER *of Pomfret, a prophet.*

PHILIP, *king of France.*

LEWIS, *the Dauphin.*

LIMOGES, *Duke of Austria.*

MELUN, *a French lord.*

CHATILLON, *ambassador from France to King John.*

CARDINAL PANDULPH, *the Pope's legate.*

QUEEN ELEANOR, *mother to King John.*

CONSTANCE, *mother to Arthur.*

BLANCHE *of Spain, niece to King John.*

LADY FAULCONBRIDGE, *widow to Sir Robert Faulconbridge.*

> *Lords, Sheriff, Heralds, Officers, Soldiers,*
> *Messengers, and other Attendants.*

SCENE: *Partly in England, and partly in France.*

* The list of *dramatis personæ* does not appear in the Folios. It was first given by Rowe.

THE LIFE AND DEATH OF
KING JOHN

ACT I

SCENE I.—[*The Court of England.*]

Enter KING JOHN, QUEEN ELEANOR, PEMBROKE, ESSEX,
SALISBURY, *and Attendants, with them* CHATILLON *of France.*

K. John. Now, say, Chatillon, what would France with us?
Chat. Thus, after greeting, speaks the King of France
    In my behaviour to the majesty,
    The borrow'd majesty, of England here.
Elea. A strange beginning: "borrow'd majesty"!   5
K. John. Silence, good mother; hear the embassy.
Chat. Philip of France, in right and true behalf

ACT I

Scene 1

Act I *Scene* I.] Actus Primus, Scaena Prima. F1.   The . . . England.] Pope;
om. F1.   S.D.] This ed.; Enter King Iohn, Queene Elinor, Pembroke, Essex,
and Salisbury, with the Chattylion of France. F1; King *John*, discovered upon a
Throne, . . . Bell.   S.D. and Attendants] Om. F1; and Others Capell.   S.D.
with them] This ed.; with Rowe, edd.   1. *Chatillon*] Johnson (throughout);
Chatillion F1 (throughout).

The . . . *of*] *John*, *R 2*, and *R 3* have
the "life and death" formula in F1
(also *Caes.* in the F1 Catalogue). As *R 2*
and *R 3* omit it in their quartos, which
promise *The Tragedy of* —, we assume
that *John* acquired it in F1, and was
first known as a tragedy. Meres in 1598
called it that, and *T.R.* was also described thus (Pt II, sig. A₂).
   S.D. with them *Chatillon*] F1 "the
Chattylion" might be a confusion with
a title ("the Chatelain"): but an omit-

ted suspension-mark (for "m") seems
more likely.
   1. *Now . . . us?*] Cf. Kyd's *Spanish
Tragedy*: "Now say L. Generall, how
fares our Campe?" (I. ii. 1).
   Chatillon] Trisyllabic: cf. *H5*, III. v. 43.
   3. *In my behaviour*] In my person:
"the king of *France* speaks in the *character* which I here assume" (Johnson).
Cf. v. ii. 129.
   4. *borrow'd*] stolen, counterfeit.
   6. *embassy*] ambassador's message.

Of thy deceased brother Geoffrey's son,
Arthur Plantagenet, lays most lawful claim
To this fair island and the territories: 10
To Ireland, Poictiers, Anjou, Touraine, Maine,
Desiring thee to lay aside the sword
Which sways usurpingly these several titles,
And put the same into young Arthur's hand,
Thy nephew and right royal sovereign.   15
K. John. What follows if we disallow of this?
Chat. The proud control of fierce and bloody war,
       To enforce these rights so forcibly withheld.
K. John. Here have we war for war and blood for blood,
       Controlment for controlment: so answer France.   20
Chat. Then take my king's defiance from my mouth,
       The farthest limit of my embassy.
K. John. Bear mine to him, and so depart in peace.
       Be thou as lightning in the eyes of France,

---

9. *most*] F1; om. Pope.   18. *To*] F1; *T'* Pope.   20. *for controlment*] F1; *for control* Vaughan conj.   22. *farthest*] F1; *furthest* Steevens.

10. *territories:*] i.e. dependencies. This "rather odd use of the word" puzzled Wilson (C.U.P. *John*, p. xxv), but, as I. John had noted, the *T.R.* in a later passage reads like Shakespeare: "King to *England, Cornwall* and *Wales*, & to their Territories" (II. iii. 222–3).

12. *Desiring*] Asking; commanding.

12–13. *sword . . . sways*] The usual cliché was "the sceptre which sways" i.e. rules, and Shakespeare's twist emphasizes that John *rules by the sword*. Cf. I. i. 40, note.

13. *titles*] possessions.

14. *young Arthur*] Arthur is called *young Arthur* a dozen or so times (following Hol., 164, ii), to emphasize his helplessness.

15. *Thy . . . sovereign.*] Cf. Appendix A, p. 166.

16. *disallow of*] disapprove of, reject.

17. *proud control*] overbearing mastery, or compulsion. Cf. G. Whetstone's *Censure of a Loyall Subject* (1587): "subiect to the proud controlement

of euery raskal *Spaniard*" (sig. D).

fierce and bloody] *fierce* meant "proud, haughty" as well as "wild, excessive", and thus ties *proud* to *bloody* (*bloody* could = "passionate"). Cf. v. ii. 158, III. iii. 17–19, note.

19–20. *Here . . . controlment*] Steevens compared *The First Part of Ieronimo* (1605): "*And.* Thou shalt pay trybute, Portugalle, with blood. / *Bal.* Trybute for trybute, then: and foes for foes. / *And.* I bid you sudden warres" (Kyd, p. 309).

19. *blood for blood*] Cf. II. i. 329, note.

20. *for controlment*] Wilson "restores the metre" with Vaughan, since his reading "gives better sense, i.e. 'a check to your compulsion,' ".

22. *farthest limit of*] most extreme course granted me in.

23. *and . . . peace*] Noble cited the Nunc Dimittis in the *Book of Common Prayer:* "Lord, now lettest thou thy servant depart in peace." Also *Luke*, ii. 29.

For, ere thou canst report, I will be there: 25
The thunder of my cannon shall be heard.
So, hence! Be thou the trumpet of our wrath
And sullen presage of your own decay.
An honourable conduct let him have:
Pembroke, look to't. Farewell, Chatillon.   30
             [*Exeunt Chatillon and Pembroke.*

Elea. What now, my son! have I not ever said
How that ambitious Constance would not cease
Till she had kindled France, and all the world,
Upon the right and party of her son?
This might have been prevented and made whole   35
With very easy arguments of love,
Which now the manage of two kingdoms must
With fearful-bloody issue arbitrate.

K. John. Our strong possession and our right for us.

Elea. Your strong possession much more than your right,   40
Or else it must go wrong with you and me:
So much my conscience whispers in your ear,
Which none but heaven, and you, and I, shall hear.

---

25. *report*,] F1; *report* Capell.   *there:*] F1; *there,* Rowe.   28. *sullen*] F1;
sudden Collier MS.   30. S.D.] Exit Chat. and Pem. F1.   38. *fearful-bloody*]
Craig (*ap.* I. John); no hyphen F1.   40.] F1; [aside to K. John] Dyce ii.

25. *report*] announce; thunder. Ll.
24–6 mean: "Be as swift as lightning in
your return to France; [And yet,] before you will be able to *announce* your
message, I will be there, and instead of
you the *thunder* of my cannon shall be
heard." The secondary meaning of
report was new in 1590.
    26. *cannon*] A typical anachronism.
Gunpowder was invented about a century later (Z. Grey).
    27. *trumpet*] "our tongues are *Trum-
pets* . . . to giue warning of any euill
approching, Esay 58.1" [T. White,
Sermon (1589), sig. F₄ᵛ]. Delius suggested an allusion to the trumpet of
doom, presaging the last judgment.
    28. *sullen* . . . *decay*] "*The sullen pre-
sage* . . . means, *the dismal passing bell,
that announces your own approaching dissolution*" (Steevens); *sullen* = gloomy,
dismal (Malone compared *2 H 4*, I. i.

102); *decay* = downfall, perdition.
    29. *conduct*] escort, or safe-conduct.
    32. *ambitious Constance*] Cf. II. i. 123,
note.
    34. *Upon . . . party*] Cf. *R 3*, III. ii. 47
(Furness), *Mac.*, III. vi. 30 (Wilson).
    35. *made whole*] "set right" (Smith).
    36. *arguments of love*] evidence of
your love; "friendly discussions"
(Smith).
    37. *manage*] government, administra-
tion.
    39–41. *Our . . . me*] W. Rushton
[*Shakespeare's Legal Maxims* (1859), p.
12] thought Shakespeare had in mind
the maxim "In aequali jure melior est
conditio possidentis" (= Where the
right is equal, the claim of the party in
possession shall prevail). Shakespeare
emphasizes the (unhistorical) illegality
of John's kingship: see Introduction,
p. lxiv.

F

Enter a Sheriff.

Essex. My liege, here is the strangest controversy,
    Come from the country to be judg'd by you,   45
    That e'er I heard: shall I produce the men?
K. John. Let them approach.
    Our abbeys and our priories shall pay
    This expeditious charge.

Enter ROBERT FAULCONBRIDGE, *and* PHILIP
his bastard brother.

                     What men are you?
Bast. Your faithful subject I, a gentleman,   50
    Born in Northamptonshire, and eldest son,
    As I suppose, to Robert Faulconbridge,
    A soldier, by the honour-giving hand

44. S.D.] F1; om. Rowe; Enter *Essex*. Johnson; Enter the Sheriff of *Northampton-shire*, and whispers *Essex*. Capell; after l. 38 Kemble.   46.] F1; Exit Sheriff. Capell.   47.] F1; Exit Sheriff; and Re-enters, with *Philip*, the Bastard . . . and Robert . . . Capell.   49. *expeditious*] F1; *expeditions* F2, edd.   49. S.D.] Malone; Enter Robert Faulconbridge, and Philip. F1 (after l. 49); Enter . . . the Bastard. Rowe; after *charge* l. 49 Johnson.   50.] F1; *Scene* II. Pope.   50 . . . 132. Bast.] Rowe; Phil. (Philip) F1.   50. *subject I*,] Capell; *subiect, I* F1. 53. *honour-giving hand*] *Honor-giuing-hand* F1.

44. S.D.] Various edd. put the S.D. earlier, to allow a longer whisper before Essex speaks. But the *T.R.* S.D. "Enter the Shriue, & whispers the Earle of *Sals* in the eare" (I. i. 66) is followed immediately by a speech by Salisbury. The pirate witnessed a very brief whisper. Surely the Sheriff only reminds Essex of business already discussed, and a word is enough.

45. *Come . . . country*] John was the last king to whom a controversy might come from the country for judgment— Magna Carta vested this authority in the Court of Common Pleas (Verplanck). Cf. *T.R.*, I. i. 80.

49. *expeditious*] speedy, sudden; cf. *Tp.*, v. i. 315. For John's speed cf. Introduction, p. lxv. The case for "expedition's", that the adjective was unknown in the 1590's, is unfounded: cf. W. R.'s *English Ape* (1588): "The

expeditious practise of vice" (sig. A₂).
What] Of what name, who.

50. *I*] From here to the end of Act I the pronoun *I* is used fifty-eight times, fifty-one times by Faulconbridge: indicating his self-reliance, and his narrow limits.

51. *Northamptonshire*] Holinshed often mentions John's stays in Northampton, but *Come from the country* (l. 45) suggests that we may be in London, and the county may not have been guess-work: see Introduction, p. xxv.

53. *honour-giving hand*] Hyphens were used to compress into a single concept. Our reading might suggest a hand giving honour on a single occasion, the F1 spelling implies one that gave honour always, as part of its nature. Cf. II. i. 582, III. iii. 133, IV. ii. 8, IV. iii. 24, v. i. 11, 67.

Of Cœur-de-lion knighted in the field.
K. John. What art thou?   55
Rob. The son and heir to that same Faulconbridge.
K. John. Is that the elder, and art thou the heir?
You came not of one mother then, it seems.
Bast. Most certain of one mother, mighty king;
That is well known; and, as I think, one father: 60
But for the certain knowledge of that truth
I put you o'er to heaven and to my mother:
Of that I doubt, as all men's children may.
Elea. Out on thee, rude man! thou dost shame thy mother
And wound her honour with this diffidence.   65
Bast. I, madam? no, I have no reason for it;
That is my brother's plea and none of mine;
The which if he can prove, a pops me out
At least from fair five hundred pound a year:
Heaven guard my mother's honour, and my land!   70
K. John. A good blunt fellow. Why, being younger born,
Doth he lay claim to thine inheritance?
Bast. I know not why—except to get the land—
But once he slander'd me with bastardy:

---

54. *Coeur-de-lion*] Cordelion F1 (throughout).   64. *rude man*] F1; *rudeman* Walker conj.   68. *a*] F1; *he* Pope; *'a* Capell.   69. *pound*] F1; *pounds* ed. 1735.   73. *why* —... *land*—] This ed.; *why*, ... *land:* F1.   74. *But once*] F1; *But, once,* Theobald.

54. *knighted . . . field*] Knighthoods were not hereditary in Shakespeare's time. They were conferred (*a*) before or after battle as a rule, and (*b*) "out of warre they [knights] are made for . . . some good hope of vertues that doo appeare in them" [W. Segar: *Booke of Honor and Armes* (1590), sig. Q₂]. Old Sir Robert Faulconbridge was knighted the first way, Philip the second (i. i. 162), and Robert, though son and heir of a knight, remained a squire (i. i. 177).

57. *that*] he.
61. *that truth*] the true facts.
62. *put you o'er*] refer you.
64. *rude man*] = rude-man. Cf. *rudesby* (*Shr.*, iii. ii. 10, *Tw.N.*, iv. i. 55). Some think that "man" in compounds had an enclitic force—as in "goodman" (youngman, rudeman). "Rude"

= uncivilized; ignorant, unskilled.
65. *diffidence*] mistrust.
68. *a*] Unstressed form of "he". In ll. 68–9, Shakespeare portrays Faulconbridge's familiarity by means of colloquialisms — *a*, the undignified *pops*, the singular *pound*.
71. *Why*] This must be the exclamation (= "What's this!"), which Faulconbridge pretends to understand the other way.
74. *once*] "in short" or "sometime in the past" (edd.). We suggest "on a single occasion" (viz. Robert did not dare to repeat the slander). Faulconbridge simulates ignorance (*I know not why*) to insinuate that no other claim has been substituted, also to be able to twist into l. 74, answering "why" = "for what end", and = "on what grounds".

But whe'r I be as true begot or no,   75
That still I lay upon my mother's head;
But that I am as well begot, my liege—
Fair fall the bones that took the pains for me!—
Compare our faces and be judge yourself.
If old Sir Robert did beget us both   80
And were our father, and this son like him,
O old Sir Robert, father, on my knee
I give heaven thanks I was not like to thee!

K. John. Why, what a madcap hath heaven lent us here!

Elea. He hath a trick of Cœur-de-lion's face;   85
The accent of his tongue affecteth him.
Do you not read some tokens of my son
In the large composition of this man?

K. John. Mine eye hath well examined his parts
And finds them perfect Richard. Sirrah, speak,   90
What doth move you to claim your brother's land?

Bast. Because he hath a half-face, like my father!
With half that face would he have all my land:
A half-fac'd groat five hundred pound a year!

Rob. My gracious liege, when that my father liv'd,   95
Your brother did employ my father much—

---

75. *But*] F1 ; *Now* Wright conj.   84. *lent*] F1 ; *sent* Heath [*Revisal* (1765), p. 222].
93. *half that face*] F1 ; *that half-face* Theobald.

---

75. *But*] Not repetitive, as Wright
thought, if in l. 74 it is adverbial and
in l. 75 conjunctive.

whe'r] whether. The monosyllable
was a common variant.

76. *lay . . . head*] let my mother answer for.

78. *Fair fall*] Fair hap befall, may
good befall. For similar *double entendre*
cf. *LLL.,* ii. i. 123–5, *Ven.,* l. 472. Possibly Faulconbridge falls heavily on
his knee as he speaks, leading up to
l. 82.

80. *old*] In *Looke About You* (1600),
"olde *Faukenbridge*" (as he calls himself in his first line) is the butt of a
cuckold sub-plot. See Introduction,
p. xxiii.

84. *madcap*] mad-brained fellow.

lent] bestowed upon. Already ar-

chaic, but familiar in wills: "the worldly goods that heaven has lent me".

85. *trick*] characteristic expression,
trait.

86. *affecteth*] resembles.

92. *half-face*] profile.

93. *With . . . face*] Probably playing
on the familiar exclamation "With
that face!" (=You're not the man,
not likely), as in *LLL.,* i. ii. 147 (see
R. David's note); also punning on *face*
as "impudence". Read: "He wants
my land—but he's not likely to get
it!"

94. *half-fac'd groat*] groat with an
effigy in profile. "Half-faced" also
meant "imperfect", as in *1 H 4,* i. iii.
208, and *2 H 4,* iii. ii. 286 (another
part of J. Sincklo, the probable first
actor of Robert Faulconbridge).

Bast. Well sir, by this you cannot get my land:
　　　　Your tale must be how he employ'd my mother.
Rob. —And once dispatch'd him in an embassy
　　　　To Germany, there with the emperor   100
　　　　To treat of high affairs touching that time.
　　　　Th' advantage of his absence took the king
　　　　And in the mean time sojourn'd at my father's,
　　　　Where how he did prevail I shame to speak;
　　　　But truth is truth: large lengths of seas and shores   105
　　　　Between my father and my mother lay,
　　　　As I have heard my father speak himself,
　　　　When this same lusty gentleman was got.
　　　　Upon his death-bed he by will bequeath'd
　　　　His lands to me, and took it on his death   110
　　　　That this my mother's son was none of his;
　　　　And if he were, he came into the world
　　　　Full fourteen weeks before the course of time.
　　　　Then, good my liege, let me have what is mine,
　　　　My father's land, as was my father's will.   115
K. John. Sirrah, your brother is legitimate;
　　　　Your father's wife did after wedlock bear him,
　　　　And if she did play false, the fault was hers;

---

110. *death*] F1; *oath* Anon. conj. *ap.* Cambridge.

98. *tale*] For the pun cf. *Gent.*, ii. iii. 56, *Oth.*, iii. i. 6–11, *O.E.D.*, tail, 5c.

employ'd] Could be used like Latin "implicare" (*O.E.D.*, employ, 5).

99. *dispatch'd*] sent; got rid of.

embassy] Shakespeare's disregard of time has been criticized. Richard I became king in 1189, so that Faulconbridge could be only nine or ten in Act I. But Richard could have sent embassies as Duke of Aquitaine, and be referred to by his latest title. *Looke About You* dates the seduction in the reign of Henry II (see Introduction, p. xxiii).

105. *truth is truth*] certain facts are beyond argument. A common phrase. Cf. *Meas.*, v. i. 45, *LLL.*, iv. i. 48 (Tilley, p. 686).

lengths of seas] No child born of a married woman could be bastardized in Shakespeare's day—unless the husband was "beyond the four seas during the whole period of the wife's pregnancy" [C. K. Davis: *Law in Shakespeare* (1884), p. 144]. But as Robert admits his father's return before the birth of Philip (l. 113), John rightly ignores the point.

108. *lusty*] merry.

110. *took*] took the oath, swore. *Wiv.*, ii. ii. 13, *1 H 4*, ii. iv. 9 have been compared.

took . . . death] swore most solemnly. To swear thus on one's deathbed signified extraordinary conviction [cf. S. Rowlands, *Crew of Kind Gossips* (1613): "But if I were this instant houre to die, / Ile take it on my death, that she doth lie" (sig. E^v)].

112. *And if*] (= An if) = If. One might read *And, if*—.

Which fault lies on the hazards of all husbands
That marry wives. Tell me, how if my brother,   120
Who, as you say, took pains to get this son,
Had of your father claim'd this son for his?
In sooth, good friend, your father might have kept
This calf, bred from his cow, from all the world;
In sooth he might; then, if he were my brother's,   125
My brother might not claim him; nor your father,
Being none of his, refuse him: this concludes;
My mother's son did get your father's heir;
Your father's heir must have your father's land.

Rob. Shall then my father's will be of no force   130
  To dispossess that child which is not his?
Bast. Of no more force to dispossess me, sir,
  Than was his will to get me, as I think.
Elea. Whether hadst thou rather be a Faulconbridge,
  And like thy brother, to enjoy thy land,   135
  Or the reputed son of Cœur-de-lion,
  Lord of thy presence and no land beside?

---

134. *Whether*] F1; *Say* Pope; *Whe'r* Staunton conj.   *rather be*] F1; *rather,—be*
Capell.

119. *lies . . . hazards*] "belongs to the
chances" (Wilson).
124. *calf . . . cow*] "he which maried
the woman, shall bee saide to bee the
father of the childe, and not hee which
did beget the same . . . for whose the
cow is, as it is commonly said, his is the
calfe also" [H. Swinburne, *Briefe
Treatise of Testaments* (1590), sig. Y6].
127. *concludes*] "This is a *decisive argument*" (Johnson). Wright quoted *LLL.*:
"The text most infallibly concludes
it" (IV. ii. 171).
130-3. *Shall . . . think.*] Shakespeare
reproduces the law for John's reign,
not Elizabeth's: "From the time of the
Norman conquest, lands in England
ceased to be devisable. . . This remained in force until the statute of wills, in
32 Henry VIII" (Verplanck).
135. *like . . . land*] rated the *like* of
your brother, so as to enjoy possession
of your land. It was thought that a

child could resemble a possible adulterer physically, yet the husband be
the true father: "Wherein diuerse (I
confesse) of no small aucthoritie haue
contended mightilie . . . [But] forme
or similitude maie happen to the infant
by the mothers . . . firme imagination
at the time of the conception" (Swinburne: *op. cit.*, sig. Y7); cf. *T.R.*, I. i.
200-2. Eleanor therefore tests Faulconbridge's spiritual likenesses: Is he
mean-spirited like a Faulconbridge,
or a gambler like a Plantagenet?
to] When two infinitives follow
whether, a *to* before the second was
common (Abbott, sect. 350).
137. *Lord . . . presence*] "Lord of thine
own person" (Heath); "master of that
dignity, . . . that may sufficiently distinguish thee from the vulgar without
the help of fortune" (Johnson). Cf. II.
i. 367, 377, notes.
no land] Every title had its equiva-

Bast. Madam, and if my brother had my shape,
 And I had his, Sir Robert's his like him;
 And if my legs were two such riding-rods,   140
 My arms such eel-skins stuff'd, my face so thin
 That in mine ear I durst not stick a rose
 Lest men should say "Look, where three-farthings goes!"
 And, to his shape, were heir to all this land,
 Would I might never stir from off this place,   145
 I would give it every foot to have this face:
 It would not be Sir Knob in any case.
Elea. I like thee well: wilt thou forsake thy fortune,

---

138. Bast.] F1 (throughout); Phil. Theobald (throughout). 139. *Robert's his*]
As F1; Robert *his* Theobald; Robert's, *his*, Hanmer. 144. *his . . . this*] F1; *this
. . . his* J. M. Mason [*Comments* (1797), p. 35]. 146. *I would*] F1; *I'd* Pope.
face] F1; *hand* Fleay. 147. *It*] F1; *I* F2, edd. *Sir Knob*] This ed.; *Sir Nob* F1
(*sir nobbe*), edd.

lent in income: in 1590 a knight had to
have £120 p.a. (Segar, *op. cit.*, sig.
Q₂ᵛ).

 139. *Robert's his*] A reduplicated
genitive, *his* being an obsolescent de-
notation of possession as in "J. Smith
his book".

 140. *riding-rods*] switches used by
riders.

 142. *ear*] Lovers once wore flowers
behind the ear (Steevens, citing Bur-
ton's *Anatomy of Melancholy*).

 rose] On 6d., 3d., 1½d., ¾d. coins a
rose was placed behind the queen's
ear, to avoid confusion with 4d., 2d.,
1d., ½d. (Theobald).

 143. *three-farthings*] Cf. Introduction,
p. xlv.

 144. *to his*] in addition to his.

 all this land] Often thought = "all
this land that is in question" (I. John).
But Faulconbridge dichotomizes
Richard I and Sir Robert, their lands,
their shapes: his point here is that he
rejects Sir Robert's shape even if it
brings *Richard's* land (all this land =
England).

 145. *from off*] Shakespeare alters the
common "Would I might never stir
from this place!" His new preposition
means "stir from off this place (to
another)", and "stir, (after I have

moved) from off this place" (this alternative Shakespeare adds to help his
puns: cf. *stir*, l. 147, notes).

 146. *I would*] For extra-metr. *I
would* cf. II. i. 292; for the contracted
form cf. II. i. 385, etc.

 147. *It*] In l. 146 *it* stands for *shape*
and *land* (l. 144), in l. 147 primarily for
shape. Cf. l. 147, notes.

 Sir Knob] "a pet name for 'Robert' "
(Smith, comparing the surname
Nobbs). *Nob* probably also meant *head*
(Capell); cf. T. Harman, *Caueat . . . for
Commen Cursetors* (ed. 1567): "Nab. a
head. Nabchet. a hat or cap" (slang
index, sig. G₃ᵛ). *Knob* and *nob* were
alternative spellings, whence a further
meaning: cf. next note.

 in any case] "by any means", or "in
any state". But this is also the climax of
a series of indecent puns. For *shape*
(l. 144) cf. *O.E.D.*, shape, 16, *Tim.*, II.
ii. 113–21; for *stir* (l. 145) cf. I. i. 172,
below, *Per.*, IV. ii. 159; for *foot* (l. 146)
cf. I. i. 182, below, *H 5*, III. iv. 54–64,
LLL., V. ii. 671–3; for *case* (l. 147) cf. E.
Partridge, *Shakespeare's Bawdy* (1947),
p. 84, *Wiv.*, IV. i. 60–82; for *eel-skin*
with *case* and *shape* cf. *2 H 4*, III. ii. 354–
62. *Sir Knob* (l. 147) also belongs to this
context, and probably *riding-rods* (l.
140) too (cf. *O.E.D.*, ride, 3).

Bequeath thy land to him and follow me?
I am a soldier and now bound to France.   150
Bast. Brother, take you my land, I'll take my chance.
Your face hath got five hundred pound a year,
Yet sell your face for five pence and 'tis dear.
Madam, I'll follow you unto the death.
Elea. Nay, I would have you go before me thither.   155
Bast. Our country manners give our betters way.
K. John. What is thy name?
Bast. Philip, my liege, so is my name begun;
Philip, good old Sir Robert's wive's eldest son.
K. John. From henceforth bear his name whose form thou
bearest: 160
Kneel thou down Philip, but rise more great,
Arise Sir Richard, and Plantagenet.
Bast. Brother by th' mother's side, give me your hand:
My father gave me honour, yours gave land.
Now blessed be the hour, by night or day,   165
When I was got, Sir Robert was away!
Elea. The very spirit of Plantagenet!
I am thy grandam, Richard; call me so.

152. *pound*] F1; *pounds* Steevens.   159. *wive's*] F1 (*wiues*); *Wife's* Rowe.
eldest] F1; *eld'st* Dyce ii.   160.] One line Pope; two lines F1 (ending *name/ . . .
bearest:/*).   *bearest*] F1; *bear'st* Pope.   161. *rise*] F1; *rise up* Pope; *arise*
Variorum 1773.   162.] F1; [knighting him. Capell.   168. *grandam, Richard;*]
As Capell; *grandame* Richard, F1; *grandam;* Richard, Pope.

149. *Bequeath*] Formally assign, hand over.
152. *face*] Cf. l. 93.
153. *Yet . . . dear.*] "Because a groat (cf. l. 94) was worth 4*d.*" (Wilson).
154–6. *Madam . . . way.*] "Madam, I'll serve (= *follow*) you to the best of my ability (= *unto the death*)." Eleanor in a quibble prefers him to precede her, i.e. "on the road to death" (Deighton). Was the point that Faulconbridge says he'll follow, without stirring (viz. he'll serve—without kneeling)? As squires went *before* their masters, Eleanor means that he is not yet properly her squire. Cf. Tilley, p. 524; and III. ii. 26, IV. ii. 169, V. vi. 1–5, notes, for Faulconbridge's independent slowness.

156. *manners*] Cf. IV. iii. 28–33.
162. *Richard*] Cf. I. i. 168, 178, 185, IV. iii. 41, V. iii. 12.
163. *Brother . . . hand*] i.e. "In so far as we have one mother we are equals (but not otherwise)". Cf. III. i. 118, note.
165. *hour*] H. Kökeritz has shown that *hour* and *whore* were homophones [*R.E.S.*, XIX (1943), p. 358]. Cf. *Err.*, IV. ii. 53–62, *2 H 6*, II. i. 179. If the pun is thought too violent, cf. *Ham.*, V. ii. 64.
168. *grandam*] F1 *grandame* does not show whether the second syllable is long or short, but "Grandams" in *T.R.* (I. i. 293) supports the favourite reading.

Bast. Madam, by chance but not by truth; what though?
　　Something about, a little from the right,   170
　　　　In at the window, or else o'er the hatch:
　　Who dares not stir by day must walk by night,
　　　　And have is have, however men do catch.
　　Near or far off, well won is still well shot,
　　　　And I am I, howe'er I was begot.   175
K. John. Go, Faulconbridge: now hast thou thy desire;
　　A landless knight makes thee a landed squire.
　　Come, madam, and come, Richard, we must speed
　　For France, for France, for it is more than need.
Bast. Brother, adieu: good fortune come to thee!   180
　　For thou wast got i' th' way of honesty.

　　　　　　　　　　　　　　　[Exeunt all but Bastard.

170. *about,*] F4; *about* F1.

169. *truth*] = honesty = honourable
conduct.
　　though] then. Cf. *AYL.*, III. iii. 53,
H 5, II. i. 9.
　　170-5. *Something . . . begot*] "The proverbial sayings which follow are characteristic of the Bastard's rusticity of
breeding" (Wright, comparing *Cor.*,
I. i. 211). But the first purpose is indelicate innuendo. Note the climax:
absence of verbs in ll. 169-71, then the
highly charged *stir, walk, have, catch,
shot.*
　　170. *Something about*] A little indirectly, or irregularly.
　　from the right] "Suggesting the 'bar
sinister'" (Wilson).
　　171. *In . . . hatch*] Proverbial expressions meaning to be born out of wedlock [Steevens, comparing Middleton's *Famelie of Love* (1608): "Woe
worth the time that euer I gaue sucke
to a Child that came in at the window" (sigs. F₄, I₂); *Northward Hoe*
(Dekker & Webster): "kindred that
comes in o'er the hatch" (I. i.);
etc.].
　　o'er the hatch] over the lower part of
a door that opened in two parts.
　　172. *Who . . . night*] Shakespeare
combines three themes: (*a*) "walking"
in love-poetry, as in Venus's line

"Rome thou abroad for I intend to
range" [R. Wilson, *Coblers Prophesie*
(1594), sig. Eᵛ]; (*b*) the play on *stir*
(cf. I. i. 147, note); (*c*) walking by
night, which was thought suspicious—
night-walker was slang for *thief.*—The
verb *to walk* = to be in motion (cf. IV.
ii. 128).—Furness took this line to refer to Faulconbridge, not to Richard.
　　173. *have*] Idiomatic, as in *1 H 4*,
III. iii. 144; "to have is to have" recurs
in *AYL.*, V. i. 45.
　　catch] take hold of suddenly.
　　174. *Near . . . shot*] In *The Institucion
of a Gentleman* (1568) occurs a proverb
"He shoteth like a gentleman faire &
fur of", and "welshot" = the formula
of appreciation of good marksmanship
(sig. D₈). Perhaps Faulconbridge
ironically gives social approbation to
his father's "shooting" (Partridge,
Shakespeare's Bawdy, p. 187, noted that
shooting often has a sexual subaudition in Shakespeare, as in *LLL.*, IV. i.
121-43).
　　177. *knight . . . squire*] Cf. I. i. 54,
137, notes. The Bastard, not John
("John Lackland"), is the knight.
　　180-1. *good . . . honesty*] "Alluding to
the proverb, that 'bastards are born
lucky'" (Collier).
　　181-2. *honesty . . . honour*] Shake-

A foot of honour better than I was,
But many a many foot of land the worse.
Well, now can I make any Joan a lady.   184
"Good den, Sir Richard!"—"God-a-mercy, fellow!"—
And if his name be George, I'll call him Peter;
For new-made honour doth forget men's names:
'Tis too respective and too sociable
For your conversion. Now your traveller,
He and his toothpick at my worship's mess,   190

182.] F1; *Scene* III. Pope; II. Capell.   *A*] Rowe; Bast. *A* F1.   187. *new-made*]
Pope; no hyphen F1.   189. *conversion*.] Capell; *conuersion*, F1; *conversing*.
Pope.

speare preserves the distinction between the middle-class and the aristocratic virtues.

182.] Wilson thought that the F1
speech heading "was added at the time
of the second revision" (cf. Introduction, p. xxxvi). But a new heading was
not uncommonly added with a new
form of speech (aside, soliloquy, quotation).

foot] footing, status, degree; for the
pun cf. I. i. 147, note.

182-3. *foot . . . foot*] The juxtaposition of feet was a common trope, de-
riving from the Bible. Cf. II. i. 144,
note, and *Ado*, II. iii. 67.

183. *many a many*] "A many" was
often used where we use "many a";
many a many is unique here in Shakespeare, typical of Faulconbridge's
loose language.

foot of land] A set phrase long before
Shakespeare, used in *Cuer du Lyon*
(1528): "He shall not haue a fote of
londe / Neuer more but of my honde"
(sig. G₄).

184. *Joan*] "A generic name for a
female rustic" (*O.E.D.*). But often
Joan = whore, which may be Shakespeare's thought, as in *LLL.*, III. i. 215.
In B. Googe's translation of Palin-
genius's *Zodiake of Life* (1576) "Joan"
stands for "scortum" (sig. E₄ᵛ); cf.
B. & F.'s *Sea Voyage* (ed. 1647): "when
I am drunk, / *Joane* is a Lady to me,
and I shall / Lay about me like a
Lord" etc. (sig. 5Cᵛ).

185. *Good den*] Common abbreviation of "God give ye good even".

God-a-mercy] God reward you; "response to a respectful salutation or a
wish, usu. expressed by an inferior"
(On.).

187-9. *For . . . conversion*] "an ellipse
. . . *remembering* (not forgetting) men's
names implies too much regard"
(Ridley).

188. *respective*] respectful.

189. *conversion*] Could mean "converse (= conversation)" (Halliwell).
We must choose whether to put a stop
after l. 188, or after *conversion* (=
change). But Shakespeare, punctuat-
ing lightly, probably intended both
meanings.

traveller] Travellers carried round
the news. Johnson compared *All's W.*:
"A good traveller is something at the
latter end of a dinner" (II. v. 31).

190. *toothpick*] The affectation of
travellers long before Shakespeare.
Steevens quoted one of Gascoigne's
poems ridiculing it.

my . . . mess] "at that part of the table
where I, as a *knight*, shall be placed . . .
'Your *worship*' was the regular address
to a knight or esquire" (Malone). "A
mess was properly a party of four . . . at
great dinners the parties were always
arranged in fours" (Wright).—It is
just possible that F1 *tooth-picke at*
should be *tooth-pick eat*, though the
absence of a verb is typical of Faulconbridge's impulsive thought.

And when my knightly stomach is suffic'd,
Why then I suck my teeth and catechize
My picked man of countries: "My dear sir,"—
Thus, leaning on mine elbow, I begin,
"I shall beseech you,"—that is Question now;   195
And then comes Answer like an Absey book:
"O sir," says Answer, "at your best command;
At your employment; at your service, sir:"
"No, sir," says Question, "I, sweet sir, at yours:"
And so, ere Answer knows what Question would,   200
Saving in dialogue of compliment,
And talking of the Alps and Apennines,
The Pyrenean and the river Po, —
It draws toward supper in conclusion so.
But this is worshipful society,   205
And fits the mounting spirit like myself;
For he is but a bastard to the time
That doth not smack of observation;

---

193. *picked*] F1; *piked* Pope; *picqued* Theobald.   *man*] F1; *man,* Heath (*Revisal*, p. 223).   196. *Absey book*] F1; *A B C-book* Pope.   201. *Saving*] F1; *Serving* Warburton conj.   203. *Pyrenean*] *Perennean* F1.   208-9. *smack . . . smoke*] Pope; *smoake . . . smacke* F1; *smack . . . smack* Theobald.

193. *picked*] = (*a*) dandified (cf. *LLL.*, v. i. 14); (*b*) who has picked his teeth; (*c*) select (because a traveller).

195-200. *Question . . . Answer*] In 16th-century children's manuals, e.g. catechisms, ABC books, instruction was often given in dialogues between Question and Answer. Faulconbridge is a mere child in travelling.

196. *Absey book*] a primer, introductory book.

200. *ere . . . would*] So Sir J. Davies, on meeting a traveller: "so neyther of vs vnderstanding eyther / We part as wise as when we came together" [*Epigrammes* (c. 1595), sig. C].

201. *dialogue of compliment*] Shakespeare ridicules excessive formality. The epigram writers soon followed him. Cf. *AYL.*, II. v. 26: "that they call compliment is like the encounter of two dog-apes" (Wright), *Ham.*, v. ii. 81-190 (Wilson), *LLL.*, I. i. 167.

202-3. *Alps . . . Pyrenean*] See Introduction, p. xlvii.

205. *worshipful society*] In the *De Officiis* Cicero, discussing ambition (Faulconbridge's theme here), says that it leads to "contentio, ut difficillimum sit servare 'sanctam societatem'" (Bk I, cap. 8). Faulconbridge's *worshipful* is sarcastic (cf. I. i. 190, note); but Shakespeare may have recalled a popular classic.

206. *mounting spirit*] The cliché was "mounting mind": cf. *LLL.*, IV. i. 4. *T.R.* reverted to this (I. i. 261).

207. *but . . . time*] no true child of the age (Belden).

208. *observation*] "obsequiousness" is a secondary sense, as in *Ham.*, III. i. 163 "observed of all observers" (Wright).

208-9. *smack . . . smoke*] The F1 transposition shows that these forms were not distinct; cf. II. i. 139. In Greene's *Notable Discouery* (1591)

And so am I, whether I smoke or no.

And not alone in habit and device,   210
Exterior form, outward accoutrement,
But from the inward motion to deliver
Sweet, sweet, sweet poison for the age's tooth:
Which, though I will not practise to deceive,
Yet, to avoid deceit, I mean to learn;   215
For it shall strew the footsteps of my rising. ✓
But who comes in such haste in riding-robes?
What woman-post is this? hath she no husband
That will take pains to blow a horn before her?

Enter LADY FAULCONBRIDGE *and* JAMES GURNEY.

212. *to*] F1; *too* Hanmer.   220. S.D.] Capell; after l. 221 F1; after *mother* l. 220
Staunton.

smack and *smoke* were used indifferent-
ly, *passim*, signifying "to see through,
be suspicious about". This slang sense
is present in l. 209, after *observation*.
Another possibility for l. 209 is
"whether I smoke (tobacco) or not".
Puritans condemned tobacco as immoral ("bastard to the time"), and
Faulconbridge glories in irrelevance;
but this would be an early use of intransitive "to smoke".

210–16. *And . . . rising.*] Shakespeare
laughs at moralists who called extravagant apparel and hypocrisy the twin
vices of travellers. Cf. W. R., *The English Ape, the Italian Imitation, the Foote-
steppes of Fraunce* (1588): "the cunning
conuey of his imitation in inwarde disposition, and externall habite . . . to
follow the footsteps of other Nations"
(sig. A^v); "Ambition like vnto stronge
poyson" (sig. B^v).

210–11. *habit . . . accoutrement*] "He
refers . . . to the knightly 'accoutrement' he will wear, of which the
'device' with its bar sinister will be a
prominent feature" (Wilson).

212. *motion*] inclination, impulse.

213. *sweet poison*] A favourite phrase
for flattery. Cf. H. Swinburne, *op. cit.*:
"flatteries . . . with whose sweete poison

and pleasant sting manie men are so
charmed" (sig. 2D₄^v); Marlowe,
Ovid's Elegies: "Let thy tongue flatter
while thy mind harm works :/ Under
sweet honey deadly poison lurks"
(i. viii).

tooth] appetite.

216. *For . . . rising*] "as I rise flattery
will be strewn before me like flowers
before one making a progress" (I.
John). Or he may refer to the rushes
strewing the presence-chamber of a
king, and the stage (C. Porter).

217–20. *But . . . mother.*] The usual
formula to describe an entering person
in pre-Shakespearean drama. Cf.
Udall's *Roister Doister*: "But who commeth forth yond . . . ?", "But what two
men are yonde . . . ?" (M.S.R., ll. 255,
1342).

219. *take . . . horn*] In cuckold stories
the husband who "blows the horn"
proclaims his own misfortune: cf.
Chapman, *All Fools*, v. ii. 180, Middleton, *Famelie of Love* (1608), sig. H₄^v.
With *take pains* cf. i. i. 78, 121. Read:
"Has she no husband who will proclaim her a loose woman (i.e. must she
do so herself by gadding about)?" The
post (never a woman) was always *in
haste*, therefore *blew the post-horn*.

O me! 'tis my mother.—How now, good lady?   220
What brings you here to court so hastily?
Lady F. Where is that slave, thy brother? where is he,
That holds in chase mine honour up and down?
Bast. My brother Robert? old Sir Robert's son?
Colbrand the giant, that same mighty man?   225
Is it Sir Robert's son that you seek so?
Lady F. Sir Robert's son! Ay, thou unreverend boy—
Sir Robert's son?—why scorn'st thou at Sir Robert?
He is Sir Robert's son, and so art thou.
Bast. James Gurney, wilt thou give us leave awhile?   230
Gur. Good leave, good Philip.
Bast.   Philip?—sparrow!—James,
There's toys abroad: anon I'll tell thee more.

                              [*Exit Gurney.*

Madam, I was not old Sir Robert's son:

---

220. *'tis*] F1; *it is* Pope, edd.   222.] F1; *Scene* IV. Pope.   231. *Philip?—sparrow!—*] Upton; Philip, *sparrow*, F1.   232. S.D. Gurney.] Iames. F1.

220. *'tis*] Edd. have conspired to ignore the facetiousness of Faulconbridge's mincing *'tis*.

223. *holds in chase*] pursues; cf. *Cor.*, I. vi. 19 (Furness).

225. *Colbrand*] In the old romances of Guy of Warwick, Colbrand is Guy's last and doughtiest opponent. Shakespeare might have looked on Guy as his own ancestor, through the Ardens and Beauchamps: cf. I. i. 232, note.

231. *Good ... Philip*] "Good leave" = (*a*) "I give you willing *permission*" [as in R. W.'s *Three Ladies of London* (1584), sig. C3]; (*b*) "What a courteous *dismissal!*" (veiled). The formula "Good ..., good ..." was used with equals and inferiors, as in "Good words, good brother!" Furness thought Gurney a friend (he is usually thought a servant). His familiarity and Lady Faulconbridge's impulsiveness sketch in the two major qualities Faulconbridge derived from his background.

Philip? — sparrow! —] "Mere Philip", exclaims Faulconbridge "is a name good enough for a sparrow!" He is now *Sir Richard*. Philip was a favourite name for (tame) sparrows. Skelton's elegy for *Philip Sparowe*, Gascoigne's *Praise of Philip Sparrow* (written for a hen-sparrow), are well-known.

232. *There's toys abroad*] Trifling gifts (i.e. knighthoods) are being handed out. Some take *toys* = "rumours, whims", which would suit A. Harbage's thesis that *Guy Earl of Warwick* (1661) ("by B. J.") contains an early satire of Shakespeare. [See *Shakespeare Association Bulletin*, xvi (1941), pp. 42–9.] Guy's servant, the clown Philip Sparrow, may skit Shakespeare in a number of ways, even declares "I was born ... at *Stratford* upon *Aven* in *Warwickshire*" (sig. E2v). It is curious that Shakespeare drags in the Guy story (l. 225), then recalls P. Sparrow (l. 231), whom B. J. first associated with Guy, adding "There's *rumours* abroad".

Sir Robert might have ate his part in me
Upon Good Friday and ne'er broke his fast: 235
Sir Robert could do—well, marry, to confess—
Could . . . get me? Sir Robert could not do it.
We know his handiwork: therefore, good mother,
To whom am I beholding for these limbs?
Sir Robert never holp to make this leg.   240

Lady F. Hast thou conspired with thy brother too,
That for thine own gain shouldst defend mine honour?
~~What means this scorn, thou most untoward knave?~~

Bast. Knight, knight, good mother, Basilisco-like:

236. *do . . . confess*—] As Alexander (*do: well—marry, to confess*—); *doe well, marrie to confesse* F1; *do well; Marry, to confess*, Capell, edd.   237. *Could . . . me?*] This ed.; *Could get me* F1; *Could he get me?* Pope, edd.

234-5. *Sir . . . fast*] Steevens compared Heywood's *Proverbs* (1564): "he may his parte on good fridaie eate, And fast never the wurs, for ought he shall geate."

236-7. *Sir . . . it.*] Here *do* = "copulate", as in *Tim.*, IV. i. 8, *All's W.*, II. iii. 245 (see Schmidt, do, 5). Read: "Sir R. could do—well, at any rate he could marry; to confess the truth he could (*interrupting himself*)—beget me? He could not do it!" Edd. generally take *marrie* as exclamation; Wilson paraphrased *marrie to confesse* as "though I says it, as shouldn't". Our textual surgery is not drastic, since Faulconbridge habitually interrupts himself (cf. I. i. 191, II. i. 571), and breaks were not always indicated in the old texts.

237. *Could*] Occurring three times in two lines, this word might here be a compositor's repetition. "But" would read smoothly in its place.

238. *handiwork*] Cf. I. i. 267, note. Faulconbridge's irreverence = Elizabethan slang for begetting children ("fair work", "good workmanship", cf. *Wint.*, III. iii. 75). In the Bible the earth is often called the work of God's hands.

239. *beholding*] beholden, indebted.

240. *Sir . . . leg.*] A *leg* was an obei-

sance. But after *handiwork*, *limbs*, Faulconbridge also means "Sir R. never helped to beget this leg." Cf. H. Swinburne, *op. cit.*, who writes of "fathers" who were not "any way priuie to the begetting either of a leg or an arm, no not somuch as of the litlefinger" of their wives' children (sig. Z); J. Gough, *Strange Discovery* (1640): "to father a child, of which I did not beget so much as the least finger or the least toe" (sig. D₄ᵛ). Perhaps Shakespeare told the actor to make a mock-obeisance, slapping his leg (*this leg*), to imply that Sir R.'s son would bow humbly, for the words contradict the sense: "Sir R. never helped to make me, *high-spirited as I am*." In *T.R.* Faulconbridge asks the question "on knees" (I. i. 338); cf. *John*, I. i. 82.

holp] helped. The older form.

243. *untoward*] unmannerly.

244. *Basilisco-like.*] Theobald spotted the point in *Soliman and Perseda*, a play of this time: "*Pist*[*on*]. I, the aforesaid *Basilisco*— / *Bas*[*ilisco*]. I, the aforesaid *Basilisco*—Knight, good-fellow, Knight, Knight— / *Pist.* Knaue, goodfellow, Knaue, Knaue—" (Kyd, p. 173). Here the bragging knight Basilisco knuckles under to the servant Piston—Faulconbridge laughs at himself in the allusion. Cf. II. i. 75, note.

What! I am dubb'd! I have it on my shoulder.   245
But, mother, I am not Sir Robert's son:
I have disclaim'd Sir Robert and my land;
Legitimation, name and all is gone.
Then, good my mother, let me know my father;
Some proper man, I hope: who was it, mother?   250
Lady F. Hast thou denied thyself a Faulconbridge?
Bast. As faithfully as I deny the devil.
Lady F. King Richard Cœur-de-lion was thy father:
By long and vehement suit I was seduc'd
To make room for him in my husband's bed.   255
Heaven, lay not my transgression to my charge
That art the issue of my dear offence,
Which was so strongly urg'd past my defence!
Bast. Now, by this light, were I to get again,
Madam, I would not wish a better father.   260
Some sins do bear their privilege on earth,

---

247. *Robert . . . land;*] Theobald; Robert . . . land, F1; *Robert; . . . land,* Fleay.
256. *Heaven,*] As Knight (*Heaven!*); *Heauen* F1.   *to my*] F1; *to thy* Staunton conj.
257. *That*] F1; *Thou* F4.

---

245. *dubb'd*] Used half a dozen times in Shakespeare, often facetiously, because old-fashioned: "that terme dubbing was the old terme in this poynt, and not creating" (Segar, *op. cit.*, sig. Q₃).

I have it] Facetious twist of an idiom which meant "I have been (mortally) struck", as in *Rom.*, III. i. 113, *A Larum for London* (1602): "See Captaine, now I haue it on my brest, / The Honourable cognisance of death" (sig. F₄ᵛ).

247. *disclaim'd*] " 'Disclaim' can hardly mean both *disavow* and *renounce;* here it seems to apply to Sir Robert alone" (Furness). But loose grammar was natural to Faulconbridge: cf. I. i. 190, note.

252. *As . . . devil*] Furness detected an echo from the Catechism: "renounce the devil and all his works". The repeated *deny* Delius took as = "disavow" (l. 251) and "abjure" (l. 252); Schmidt took both = "disavow".

256-7. *Heaven, . . . offence*] For

Heaven's sake, lay not (thou) my transgression to my charge that art the issue of it. The reply of Faulconbridge immediately deprecates any intention of upbraiding his mother (Knight). Shakespeare often uses "O heaven!", "Heavens!"; in *Per.*, I. i. 109 occurs "Heaven! that I had thy head!"—we need not boggle at the exclamation. —Carter compared *Acts*, vii. 60: "Lorde, lay not this sinne to their charge" (cf. also *Deuteronomy*, xxi. 8, 2 Timothy, iv. 16). So *A Larum for London* (1602): "The bloud that I haue spilt . . . / Heauen lay not to my charge" (sig. G). But Knight must be right.

258. *urg'd . . . defence*] importuned, beyond my power to forbid it; forced through my defences.

259. *by . . . light*] A common oath. But *by night or day* (I. i. 165) is resumed as well, suggesting "If I had to be got again by this day-light".

261. *Some . . . earth*] Alluding to the

And so doth yours: your fault was not your folly.
Needs must you lay your heart at his dispose,
Subjected tribute to commanding love,
Against whose fury and unmatched force   265
The aweless lion could not wage the fight,
Nor keep his princely heart from Richard's hand.
He that perforce robs lions of their hearts
May easily win a woman's. Ay, my mother,
With all my heart I thank thee for my father!   270
Who lives and dares but say thou didst not well
When I was got, I'll send his soul to hell.
Come, lady, I will show thee to my kin;
    And they shall say, when Richard me begot,
If thou hadst said him nay, it had been sin;   275
Who says it was, he lies: I say 'twas not!   [*Exeunt.*

Roman Catholic doctrine of venial sin? In a similar context A. C. wrote: "But he that could command thee, made thee sin: / Yet that is no priuiledge, no sheeld to thee" [*Beawtie Dishonoured* (1593), sig. E^v].

262. *fault . . . folly*] The *fault* and *folly* of a lapse such as Lady Faulconbridge's were conventionally juxtaposed: cf. *The Cobler of Caunterburie* (1590), sig. C_3, *Brittons Bowre of Delights* (1591), sig. E_3, R. W.'s *Tancred and Gismund* (1591), sig. E_3.

263. *dispose*] disposal.

264. *Subjected*] *The Book of Common Prayer,* following various biblical verses, enunciated "Let wiues be subiect to their owne husbands" (in "Of Matrimonie"); and Shakespeare quibbles etymologically.

266. *lion*] Various accounts of Richard's nickname were current. The favourite one describes him en-

countering a lion unarmed, thrusting his hand into the lion's mouth, and plucking out his heart and lungs.

267. *hand*] Cf. 1.i.53, 238.

270. *heart*] After the joke about the exchange of hearts, Faulconbridge may now intend a quibble: "*I,* my dear mother, *I* thank thee *on behalf of* my father with the tender of all *my* heart (since he owed you a heart)".

271–6. *lives . . . lies*] Cf. III.i.264, note.

276. *not*] The F1 reading has been called lame. But *not* was the unstressed form of *naught*, these words being interchangeable. Shakespeare wrote *not* for the rhyme's sake, but *naught* (="wickedness", or specifically "a sexual lapse") seems typical of Faulconbridge, and the actor would linger on the word. Cf. *Meas.*: "this house, if it be not a bawd's house . . . is a naughty house" (II.i.77–9).

ACT II

SCENE I.—[*France. Before Angiers.*]

Enter, on one side, the Archduke of Austria, and Forces; on the other,
PHILIP, *King of France, and Forces,* LEWIS, CONSTANCE, ARTHUR,
and Attendants.

Lew. Before Angiers well met, brave Austria.
K. Phi. Arthur, that great forerunner of thy blood,
    Richard, that robb'd the lion of his heart
    And fought the holy wars in Palestine,
    By this brave duke came early to his grave: 5
    And for amends to his posterity
    At our importance hither is he come,
    To spread his colours, boy, in thy behalf,
    And to rebuke the usurpation
    Of thy unnatural uncle, English John: 10
    Embrace him, love him, give him welcome hither.
Arth. God shall forgive you Cœur-de-lion's death
    The rather that you give his offspring life,

ACT II
Scene 1

Act II *Scene* I.] Rowe iii; Scaena Secunda. F1; *Act* I *Scene* III. Donovan.   S.D.]
As Capell; Enter before Angiers, Philip King of France, Lewis, Daulphin,
Austria, Constance, Arthur. F1.   1. Lew.] Lewis. F1; K. Phi. Theobald conj.
2. K. Phi.] This ed.; speech contd. F1.

Angiers] Angers. Holinshed repeatedly mentions Angiers (160, ii;
170, i; etc.), but Acts II and III really
expand on the siege of Mirabeau
(Hol., 164, ii).
    2. K. Phi.] Cf. Introduction, p. xxxiv.
    forerunner] Cf. ll. 6, 13, 177, notes,
Introduction, p. l. In Marlowe's
Faustus (ed. 1616) the pope talks of
"Pope *Alexander* our Progenitour"
(sig. D3).

    5. *By . . . grave*] For the identification
of Limoges and Austria cf. Introduction, p. xxi.
    7. *importance*] entreaty, importun-
ity.
    8. *colours*] military ensigns.
    13. *offspring*] Arthur means not him-
self, but the whole of Richard's family
collectively, as is shown by *their* in l. 14
(Delius). Or does *their* refer to Richard
and Arthur? Shakespeare follows the

Shadowing their right under your wings of war:
I give you welcome with a powerless hand,   15
But with a heart full of unstained love:
Welcome before the gates of Angiers, duke.
Lew. Ah, noble boy, who would not do thee right?
Aust. Upon thy cheek lay I this zealous kiss,
As seal to this indenture of my love: 20
That to my home I will no more return,
Till Angiers and the right thou hast in France,
Together with that pale, that white-fac'd shore,
Whose foot spurns back the ocean's roaring tides
And coops from other lands her islanders,   25
Even till that England, hedg'd in with the main,
That water-walled bulwark, still secure
And confident from foreign purposes,
Even till that utmost corner of the west
Salute thee for her king; till then, fair boy,   30

18. Lew.] Lewis. F1; K. Phi. Theobald conj.   *Ah*,] This ed.; *A* F1.

language of official documents "in which kings are held to be *descended* from their predecessors. So even Henry VII. repeatedly speaks of 'our royal progenitor, King Edward the Fourth'" (Moberly).

14. *Shadowing . . . war*] *Shadowing* = sheltering. Shakespeare uses a favourite image of the Psalmist ["hide me under the shadow of thy wings" (*Psalms*, xvii. 8) which fuses with *wings of war* (= flanks of an army)].

16. *unstained*] Cf. Introduction, p. lxii; IV. ii. 6. He means "no longer stained with hatred as before".

18. *Ah*,] The exclamation "Ah!", often printed "A" in old texts, is appropriate since Arthur is addressed. So *T.R.*: "Ah boy, thy yeares I see are farre too greene" (I. iv. 196).

do thee right] treat thee right, take thy part.

19. *zealous*] Zeal usually = religious fervour in *John*.

20. *seal*] Wilson suspected a quibble on *zealous*, comparing II. i. 477-9.

indenture] a (sealed) agreement. After *cheek* and *kiss* there is a quibble

in *indenture* (< Latin *dentem*, a tooth).

23. *pale*] "*England* is supposed to be called *Albion* from the *white rocks* facing *France*" (Johnson); *pale* is in apposition to both *white-fac'd* and *shore*, being a quibble on the sense "an enclosed place" (resumed by *water-walled*, l. 27, etc.).

23–9. *that . . . west*] Patriotic descriptions of invincible England became popular in the Armada period: cf. *R 2*, II. i. 40–63, Greene's *Bacon and Bungay* (1594), sig. C^v, Peele's *Alcazar* (1594), sigs. C4^v, D. *John* makes dramatic capital out of the convention (the French nearly conquer England in Act v).

25. *coops*] encloses for protection.

26. *hedg'd*] Halliwell compared Greene's *Spanish Masquerado* (1589): "reposing our selues in that our owne strength, for that wee were hedged in with the sea" (sig. B4); so A. Andreson, *Sermon* (1581): God has "set *a Hedge of defence* rounde aboute" England (sig. C2^v). Armada common-place.

29. *utmost . . . west*] Cf. v. vii. 116, note.

Will I not think of home, but follow arms.
Const. O, take his mother's thanks, a widow's thanks,
    Till your strong hand shall help to give him strength
    To make a more requital to your love!
Aust. The peace of heaven is theirs that lift their swords   35
    In such a just and charitable war.
K. Phi. Well then, to work; our cannon shall be bent
    Against the brows of this resisting town.
    Call for our chiefest men of discipline,
    To cull the plots of best advantages: 40
    We'll lay before this town our royal bones,
    Wade to the market-place in Frenchmen's blood,
    But we will make it subject to this boy.
Const. Stay for an answer to your embassy,
    Lest unadvis'd you stain your swords with blood: 45
    My Lord Chatillon may from England bring
    That right in peace which here we urge in war,
    And then we shall repent each drop of blood
    That hot rash haste so indirectly shed.

Enter CHATILLON.

K. Phi. A wonder, lady! lo, upon thy wish,   50
    Our messenger Chatillon is arriv'd!
    What England says, say briefly, gentle lord;
    We coldly pause for thee; Chatillon, speak.

37, 50. K. Phi.] King. F1.   37. *then, to work;*] Theobald; *then to worke* F1.
49. *indirectly*] F1; *indiscreetly* Collier MS.

34. *more*] greater.

37. *bent*] aimed, directed. "The terms of archery were applied to other weapons than the bow" (Wright). Semantic contamination may have been caused by the phrase "to be bent to" = "to be intent on" (cf. II. i. 422).

39. *discipline*] From "instruction, learning" this word acquired the technical meaning "military training, or experience".

40. *cull . . . advantages*] choose the places (plots of ground) with most advantages (for the cannon).

42. *Wade . . . blood*] A common image. Cf. *The First Part of Ieronimo* (1605): "Ide wade up to the knees in bloud, / Ide make a bridge of Spanish carkases, / To single thee out of the gasping armye" (Kyd, p. 310).

43. *But*] Unless.

49. *indirectly*] Hot haste is usually direct; *indirect* here means "round about, out of course", and refers to the motives (*indirectly* or wrongly assessing John) which dictate haste.

53. *coldly*] dispassionately. After *hot* (l. 49), Shakespeare already points to the hypocrisy of France, beneath whose hot zeal cold calculation presides.

Chat. Then turn your forces from this paltry siege
　　　　And stir them up against a mightier task.　　　　　　　55
　　　　England, impatient of your just demands,
　　　　Hath put himself in arms: the adverse winds,
　　　　Whose leisure I have stay'd, have given him time
　　　　To land his legions all as soon as I;
　　　　His marches are expedient to this town,　　　　　　　60
　　　　His forces strong, his soldiers confident.
　　　　With him along is come the mother-queen,
　　　　An Ate, stirring him to blood and strife;
　　　　With her her niece, the Lady Blanche of Spain;
　　　　With them a bastard of the king's deceas'd,　　　　　　65
　　　　And all th'unsettled humours of the land;
　　　　Rash, inconsiderate, fiery voluntaries,
　　　　With ladies' faces and fierce dragons' spleens,
　　　　Have sold their fortunes at their native homes,

---

63. *Ate*] Rowe; *Ace* F1.　　65. *king's*] As F1; *King* F2.　　65–6. *deceas'd, . . . land;*]
Pope; *deceast, . . . Land*, F1; *deceas'd: . . . land,*—Capell.

55. *stir . . . against*] animate them in
preparation for.

56. *just demands*] In the "sawcie
speech of proud Pandulph the popes
lewd legat, to king Iohn", a similar
context, we read: "I would aduise you
. . . to obeie the popes iust demands"
(Hol., 177, i).

60. *expedient*] expeditious, hasting.

63. *Ate*]. Rowe's emendation supposes the common *t* : *c* misreading.
Ate was familiar in Elizabethan
drama, as is shown by "More Ates,
more Ates! stir them on! stir them on!"
(*LLL.*, v. ii. 692–3). Perhaps the derivative *Atin* in *Faerie Queene* influenced
Shakespeare: "For all in *blood* and
spoile is his delight. / His am I Atin, his
in wrong and right, / . . . And *stirre* him
up to *strife* and cruell fight" (Bk II, c. iv,
st. 42).

64. *niece*] grand-daughter, a common meaning at this time, though the
modern one was also in use (cf. II. i.
424). In his will Shakespeare referred
to his grand-daughter as "my Neece
Elizabeth Hall".

65. *of the king's*] Double genitive.

Cf. *T.R.*: "Next them a Bastard of the
Kings deceast" (I. ii. 69).

66–75. *And . . . Christendom*] Upton
and Malone thought this an allusion
to the Cadiz expedition of 1596; Wilson noted that "the suggestion might
equally well have come from the
French campaigning of 1591 under
Essex and Sir Roger Williams". But
topicality is not necessary.

66. *unsettled humours*] "restless, dis-
satisfied men" (Wilson). The *land* is
envisaged as a body (cf. IV. ii. 243–8,
v. i. 5–16), the humours being the four
chief fluids which were thought to determine its qualities; *unsettled humours*
may = fluids of choler.

67. *inconsiderate*] not considering
themselves, reckless.

voluntaries] volunteers.

68. *spleens*] The spleen was the seat
of passions and emotions in the old
physiology. Here, as often, it simply
means "fiery temper". Cf. *R 3*, v. iii.
351.

69. *native homes*] A set phrase [as in
W. Rankins's *English Ape* (1588), sig.
A₂ᵛ; G. Gerbier D'Ouvilly's *False*

Bearing their birthrights proudly on their backs,   70
To make a hazard of new fortunes here:
In brief, a braver choice of dauntless spirits
Than now the English bottoms have waft o'er
Did never float upon the swelling tide,   74
To do offence and scathe in Christendom.   [*Drum beats.*
The interruption of their churlish drums
Cuts off more circumstance: they are at hand,
To parley or to fight; therefore prepare.

K. Phi. How much unlook'd for is this expedition!

Aust. By how much unexpected, by so much   80
We must awake endeavour for defence,
For courage mounteth with occasion:
Let them be welcome then; we are prepar'd.

Enter KING JOHN, ELEANOR, BLANCHE, *the* BASTARD, *Lords,*
and Forces.

K. John. Peace be to France, if France in peace permit
Our just and lineal entrance to our own;   85
If not, bleed France, and peace ascend to heaven,
Whiles we, God's wrathful agent, do correct
Their proud contempt that beats His peace to heaven.

75. S.D.] After l. 77 F1.   77–8. *hand, . . . fight;*] Capell; *hand, . . . fight,* F1;
hand. . . . fight, Pope.   79. K. Phi.] Kin. F1.   81. *awake*] F1; *awake,* Rowe.
84.] F1; *Scene* II. Pope.   84. S.D.] Enter K. of England, Bastard, Queene,
Blanch, Pembroke, and others. F1.   88. *beats*] F1; *beat* Hanmer.

Favourite Disgrac't (1657), sig D₂ᵛ],
meaning "native land(s)".

70. *Bearing . . . backs*] Johnson compared *H 8*, I. i. 83–4; Tilley (p. 392)
called this the proverb "He wears a
whole Lordship on his back."

73. *bottoms*] ships.

waft] Past tenses and participles of
verbs ending in "t" often retained the
present form unaltered; cf. *heat* (IV. i.
61), and Abbott, sect. 342.

75. *scathe in Christendom*] In *Soliman
and Perseda* (cf. I. i. 244, note) these
words also go together: "Till it haue
prickt the hart of Christendome, /
Which now that paltrie Iland keeps
from scath" (I. v. 16–17); "What mil-

lions of men, opprest with ruine and
scath, / The Turkish armies did oer-
throw in Christendome" (III. v. 5–6).

76. *churlish*] inferior, miserable; cf.
III. i. 229, *Ven.*, l. 107.

77. *circumstance*] detailed discourse.

77–8. *hand, . . . fight;*] On the stage
the flow of phrase can ignore the need
of a semi-colon.

79. *unlook'd for*] See Introduction,
p. xii.

82. *occasion*] emergency (Wilson).
Tilley (p. 122) called this the proverb
"Great Courage is in greatest dangers
tried."

85. *lineal*] due by right of descent;
cf. v. vii. 102.

K. Phi. Peace be to England, if that war return
  From France to England, there to live in peace. 90
  England we love; and for that England's sake
  With burden of our armour here we sweat.
  This toil of ours should be a work of thine;
  But thou from loving England art so far,
  That thou hast underwrought his lawful king, 95
  Cut off the sequence of posterity,
  Outfaced infant state, and done a rape
  Upon the maiden virtue of the crown.
  Look here upon thy brother Geoffrey's face;
  These eyes, these brows, were moulded out of his: 100
  This little abstract doth contain that large
  Which died in Geoffrey: and the hand of time
  Shall draw this brief into as huge a volume.
  That Geoffrey was thy elder brother born,
  And this his son; England was Geoffrey's right, 105
  And this is Geoffrey's; in the name of God
  How comes it then that thou art call'd a king,

95. *his*] F1; *its* Rowe. 105. *right,*] F1; *right,* [he points to Angiers Wilson.
106. *this*] F1; *his* J. M. Mason [*Comments* (1785), p. 154]. *Geoffrey's;*] As Rowe;
Geffreyes F1; *Geffrey's* [points to *Arthur*] Sisson. *God*] Pope; *God:* F1.

89–90. *Peace . . . peace.*] "Perhaps
Philip points at the English army (war)
as he speaks" (Moberly). This is the
type of inconsistency Jonson ridiculed
with Shakespeare's "Caesar did never
wrong, but with just cause."
 91. *England's*] Arthur's. Philip in-
sists Arthur is rightful king by linking
the two Englands of l. 91 with *that*, as
if they were one.
 93. *toil . . . work*] Philip has to *toil*
because contending with John and Angiers; John, if loyal to Arthur, would
only have had to *work* against Angiers.
 95. *underwrought*] "underworked,
undermined" (Steevens).
 his] its. The old possessive.
 97. *Outfaced*] Intimidated, defied; as
in v. i. 49.
 state] rank, majesty.
 101. *abstract*] "epitome (of something greater), compendium (of many
qualities" (On.). So *Ant.*, i. iv. 9.

103. *draw*] write out, compose.
 brief] "short note, or description"
(Malone).
 106. *And . . . Geoffrey's;*] This right is
Geoffrey's (C. Porter); " 'this' means
the city of Angiers . . . King Philip
points to it as he speaks" (Wilson). If
this resumes l. 105 *this*, Philip's two
points may be "And this is (Arthur,
who is) Geoffrey's (heir)."
 God] Knight supported the F1
colon, since "Philip makes a solemn
asseveration that this (Arthur) is Geffrey's son and successor . . . in the name
of God; asserting the principle of legitimacy, by divine ordinance". We
think *in the name of God* goes with l. 106
and l. 107, the colon being *connective*.
Perhaps Shakespeare thought of the
usual opening of wills, as in "In the
name of god Amen I William Shack-
speare . . ."
 107. *How . . . king*] Cf. *Faustus*:

When living blood doth in these temples beat,
Which owe the crown that thou o'ermasterest?

K. John. From whom hast thou this great commission, France,
To draw my answer from thy articles?   111

K. Phi. From that supernal judge that stirs good thoughts
In any beast of strong authority
To look into the blots and stains of right.

That judge hath made me guardian to this boy: 115
Under whose warrant I impeach thy wrong
And by whose help I mean to chastise it.

K. John. Alack, thou dost usurp authority.

K. Phi. Excuse it is to beat usurping down.

Elea. Who is it thou dost call usurper, France?   120

Const. Let me make answer: thy usurping son.

Elea. Out, insolent! thy bastard shall be king,
That thou mayst be a queen, and check the world!

Const. My bed was ever to thy son as true
As thine was to thy husband; and this boy   125

---

109. *owe*] F1; *own* Pope.   110. *France*] F1; om. Rowe.   111. *from*] F1; *to* Pope.   113. *beast*] F1; *breast* F2, edd.   113-14. *authority . . . right.*] Pope; *authoritie, . . . right*, F1; *authority; . . . right*, Fleay.   119. *Excuse it is*] F1; *Excuse it, 'tis* Rowe iii; *Excuse; it is* Malone.   120, 122, 132, 159. Elea.] Queen. F1.

"How comes it then that thou art out of hell?" (i. iii).

109. *owe*] own.

o'ermasterest] make yourself master of (*O.E.D.*, overmaster).

111. *draw*] extract, demand.

articles] Each of the distinct charges of an accusation (*O.E.D.*).

112. *supernal*] celestial.

113. *beast*] A conceit is required to exaggerate John's inhumanity, and *beast* is as effective as in *Caes.*: "O judgment! thou art fled to brutish beasts, / And men have lost their reason" (III. ii. 110-11).

114. *blots*] blemishes.

115. *guardian*] "Constance . . . doubting the suertie of hir sonne, committed him to the trust of the French king, who receiuing him into his tuition, promised to defend him . . ." (Hol., 158, i, ii).

119. *is*] Malone's punctuation,

favourite for a century, assumes an absolute use of the verb *excuse* which P. Simpson found un-English (*N. & Q.*, 3 Mar. 1900). Simpson defended F1 as meaning "It is sufficient excuse for my usurpation of authority that I am fighting against usurpation."

123. *queen . . . check*] Staunton saw an allusion to chess.—Shakespeare follows Holinshed closely: "Elianor . . . was sore against hir nephue Arthur, rather mooued thereto by enuie conceiued against his mother . . . she saw if he were king, how his mother Constance would looke to beare most rule within the realme" (158, i).

124-5. *My . . . husband*] "Constance alludes to Elinor's infidelity to her husband Lewis the Seventh, when they were in the Holy Land; on account of which he was divorced from her. She afterwards (1151) married our King Henry II" (Malone).

Liker in feature to his father Geoffrey
Than thou and John in manners; being as like
As rain to water, or devil to his dam.
My boy a bastard! By my soul, I think
His father never was so true begot: 130
It cannot be and if thou wert his mother.

Elea. There's a good mother, boy, that blots thy father.

Const. There's a good grandam, boy, that would blot thee.

Aust. Peace!

Bast.   Hear the crier!

Aust.   What the devil art thou?

Bast. One that will play the devil, sir, with you,   135
And a may catch your hide and you alone:
You are the hare of whom the proverb goes,
Whose valour plucks dead lions by the beard.
I'll smoke your skin-coat, and I catch you right;
Sirrah, look to't; i' faith I will, i' faith.   140

---

127. *John in manners;*] Roderick; Iohn, *in manners* F1.   133.] One line Pope; two lines F1 (ending *boy/ . . . thee./*).   *grandam*] F1 (*grandame*).   140. *i' faith I*] As F1; *i'faith, I* Theobald.

132. *blots*] calumniates.

134. *Peace!*] Austria's ineffective exclamation is characteristic: cf. II. i. 293, III. i. 38, also his pious thought about "the peace of heaven" (II. i. 35).

crier] "Alluding to the usual proclamation for *silence*, made by criers in courts of justice" (Malone).

135. *devil*] Cf. Introduction, p. xxii. "To play the devil", a phrase first recorded in the 16th century in *O.E.D.*, is one of the references to the older drama which Shakespeare has concentrated round Faulconbridge (Introduction, p. lxxi).

136. *hide*] The lion-skin seems to have been Shakespeare's embellishment of the Cœur-de-lion story (Introduction, p. xxiii). *MND.* also calls for this property (v. i. 129), and belongs to the same years.

137. *the proverb*] "The proverb alluded to is, 'Mortuo leoni et lepores insultant.'" (in the *Adagia* of Erasmus) (Malone). Steevens (cf. Introduction,

p. xliv) noted the close resemblance to *The Spanish Tragedy*. Nashe, in 1592, needing a quotation for a similar situation, remembered Kyd, not Shakespeare: "Out vppon thee for an arrant dog-killer, strike a man when he is dead? *So Hares may pull dead Lions by the beards. Memorandum:* I borrowed this sentence out of a Play" (Nashe, I, 271).

138. *plucks . . . beard*] From Alciatus: "sic cassi luce leonis / Conuellunt barbam vel timidi lepores" (*Emblemata, v.* "Cum laruis non luctandum."). To *beard* a man was an outrage compelling a challenge.

139. *smoke*] Cf. I. i. 208–9, note. The two meanings are (a) I'll give you a thrashing (Wright); (b) I'll smoke (disinfect) your lion-skin (Delius). Wilson also proposed "a glance at the smoke caused by branding the skins of sheep or cattle".

skin-coat] skin. A common word in "thrashing" contexts.

140. *i'faith . . . i'faith!*] So in W.

Blanche. O, well did he become that lion's robe
  That did disrobe the lion of that robe!
Bast. It lies as sightly on the back of him
  As great Alcides' shoes upon an ass:
  But, ass, I'll take that burthen from your back,   145
  Or lay on that shall make your shoulders crack.
Aust. What cracker is this same that deafs our ears
  With this abundance of superfluous breath?
K. Phi. Lewis, determine what we shall do straight.
Lew. Women and fools, break off your conference.   150
K. Phi. King John, this is the very sum of all:
  England and Ireland, Anjou, Touraine, Maine,

---

144. *shoes*] F1 (*shooes*); *shews* Theobald.   149. *K. Phi. Lewis, determine*] As
Capell; *King* Lewis, *determine* F1; *King* Philip, *determine* Theobald; *King,—Lewis,
determine* Malone conj.   150. Lew.] F1; *K.* Philip. Theobald.   151. K. Phi.]
This ed.; speech contd. F1.   152. *Anjou*] Theobald; Angiers F1.

Haughton's *English-men for my Money*
(1616): "Ile haue my will ynfayth,
y'fayth I will" (sig. I^v).

141-3. *O . . . him*] After the emphasis
on *robbing* lions (I. i. 268, II. i. 3) we suspect an intended *rob/robe* quibble. If
we may postulate a lost line, the *lion/
lies on* echo may have had more point.
Faulconbridge might have begun:
"I'll robe him, and make better lie
on's back: It lies as sightly . . ." [I'll
robe him, i.e. rob, i.e. disrobe; and
make (*a*) something better lie on his
back, i.e. a beating; (*b*) better lions
back away; (*c*) a better man than he
lie on his back.]

144. *shoes*] *shows* and *shoes* were
homophones (Fleay), and both meanings are present. The two words could
be spelt the same (Maxwell: *N. & Q.*,
18 Feb. 1950). Steevens showed that
comparison with the *shoes* of Hercules
was proverbial (Tilley, p. 600, quoted
many examples, one from Gosson,
1579: "toyles too draw the Lyons skin
vpon Aesops Asse. Hercules shoes on a
childes feete"). And *shows* makes sense
too: "As great A. appears upon an
ass". Segar mentions that one order of
knighthood had a rule that knights
"should not bee seen mounted vppon
any Mule, or other vnseemelie Hack-

ney" (*op. cit.*, sig. S₃^v). Theobald's
"*Alcides*' shews", thirdly, refers us to
(*a*) the lion-skin of Hercules; (*b*) the
fable of the ass in the lion-skin.

146. *lay on*] "lay on (load)" = thrash
soundly. The first sense is "lay on (a
load of) blows", but a technical *burthen*
(l. 145) is also implied. When a knight
was dishonoured "the burthen shall
rest vpon him" (Segar, *op. cit.*, sig. B₃),
i.e. he has to challenge. Faulconbridge
insinuates that Austria will carry any
burthen rather than challenge. The
T.R. makes Faulconbridge challenge
Austria and Austria basely evade the
issue (I. v. 15-56).

147. *cracker*] braggart.

149-51. K. Phi. . . . K. Phi.] See
Introduction, p. xxxiv.

151-5. *King . . . France.*] In 1202
King Philip "commanded king Iohn
with no small arrogancie . . . to restore
vnto his nephue . . . all those lands now
in his possession on that side the sea,
which king Iohn earnestlie denied to
doo" (Hol., 164, i).

152. *Anjou*] Cf. II. i. 487. Wilson, intent on belittling Shakespeare's historical knowledge, claimed that "Shakespeare imagines Anjou and Angiers
to be the same", which is unfair. Probably a printing-house error.

In right of Arthur do I claim of thee.
Wilt thou resign them and lay down thy arms?

K. John. My life as soon: I do defy thee, France.   155
Arthur of Britain, yield thee to my hand;
And out of my dear love I'll give thee more
Than e'er the coward hand of France can win:
Submit thee, boy.

Elea.   Come to thy grandam, child.

Const. Do, child, go to it grandam, child;   160
Give grandam kingdom, and it grandam will
Give it a plum, a cherry, and a fig:
There's a good grandam.

Arth.   Good my mother, peace!
I would that I were low laid in my grave:
I am not worth this coil that's made for me.   165

Elea. His mother shames him so, poor boy, he weeps.

Const. Now shame upon you, whe'r she does or no!
His grandam's wrongs, and not his mother's shames,
Draws those heaven-moving pearls from his poor eyes,
Which heaven shall take in nature of a fee;   170
Ay, with these crystal beads heaven shall be brib'd

---

156. *Britain*] F1 (Britaine throughout); Bretagne Hanmer (throughout).
160. *Do, child,*] F1; *Do, go, child, go;* Capell.   160–1. *it . . . it*] F1 (*yt . . . it*);
it' . . . it' Johnson.   166. Elea.] Qu. Mo. F1.   167. *whe'r*] F1 (*where*);
whether Johnson.   169. *Draws*] F1; *Draw* Capell.

156–9. *Arthur . . . boy.*] So M. Paris described John's words to Arthur (when Arthur was captured): "coepit eum [Arturum] Rex blandis alloqui verbis, & multos honores promittere, exhortans vt a Rege Francorum recederet, & sibi vt Domino & auunculo fideliter adhaereret" (p. 278).

156. *Britain*] Brittany.

160–2. *it . . . it*] Here *it* = (a) the early possessive (later "its"), as in *Lr.*, i. iv. 239; (b) baby language (hence contemptuous, of older persons, as in *LLL.*, v. ii. 338).

162. *Give . . . fig:*] In Heywood's *If You Know Not Me* (1605), a boy is cajoled "Come tell me what letters thou carryedst her, / Ile giue thee figgs and suger plummes" (sig. D₃ᵛ). Per-

haps Shakespeare does not mean fresh fruit either.—*Give . . . a fig* also alludes to the cant "to give the fig", as in *2 H 6*, II. iii. 68, *H 5*, III. vi. 62, etc.

164. *low laid*] Quibbling on "lay low" = kill.

165. *coil*] uproar, commotion.

167. *whe'r*] Cf. I. i. 75, note.

171. *crystal*] Though "crystal tears" was a poetic cliché in 1590, the adjective is appropriate since in the Elizabethan world-picture heaven was "crystalline" (therefore the more likely to be so bribed?).

beads] "There is here an implied reference to *prayers* as one of the meanings of the word *beads*" (J. Hunter). This meaning implied the rosary (*O.E.D.*, bead, 1b); cf. III. i. 35, note.

To do him justice and revenge on you.

Elea. Thou monstrous slanderer of heaven and earth!

Const. Thou monstrous injurer of heaven and earth!
 Call not me slanderer; thou and thine usurp   175
 The dominations, royalties and rights
 Of this oppressed boy: this is thy eldest son's son,
 Infortunate in nothing but in thee:
 Thy sins are visited in this poor child;
 The canon of the law is laid on him,   180
 Being but the second generation
 Removed from thy sin-conceiving womb.

K. John. Bedlam, have done.

Const.   I have but this to say,
 That he is not only plagued for her sin,
 But God hath made her sin and her the plague   185
 On this removed issue, plagued for her
 And with her plague; her sin his injury,

---

177. *boy: this is*] As F1; *boy:* Ritson; *boy, this* Vaughan.   *eldest*] F1; *eld'st*
Capell.   183. *Bedlam*] F1; *Beldam* Ritson.   184. *he is*] F1; *he's* Johnson.
185, 187. *sin*] F1; *son* Spence (*N. & Q.*, 27 Jan. 1894).   186. *her*] F1 (*her,*);
her; Capell.   187. *her plague; her sin*] Roby (*ap.* Cambridge); *her plague her
sinne:* F1; *her.—Plague her sin;* Johnson; *her plague, her sin;* Malone.

Craig (*ap.* I. John) suggested an allusion to Indians being bribed with
beads.
    176. *dominations*] dominions.
    177. *eldest . . . son*] Not "the son of
your eldest son", but "your eldest
grand-son". The form, as in *R 2*, II. i.
105, is biblical (cf. *Deuteronomy*, vi. 2:
"thou, and thy sonne, and thy sonnes
sonne"). Edd. have said that here
Shakespeare makes Arthur the son of
Richard I, and compared II. i. 2, 6, 13.
Shakespeare may have intended this
genealogy (cf. Introduction, p. 1),
though Richard was not Eleanor's
eldest son.
    179. *visited*] punished (biblical).
    180. *The . . . law*] canon = law or
decree of the Church; *law* = the system of divine commands contained in
Holy Scripture (On.). Constance
alludes to *Exodus*, xx. 5, a canon much
quoted in the Bible. Shakespeare here

remembers Holinshed's Life of Henry
III: "neither shall the child (as the
scripture teacheth vs) beare the iniquitie of his father . . ." (p. 197).
    182. *sin - conceiving*] Shakespeare
turns the Psalmist's "in sin hath my
mother conceived me" (li. 5) (Noble)
to imply that anything conceived by
Eleanor must be sinful.
    183. *Bedlam*] Lunatic.
    184. *plagued . . . sin*] That plagues
punish sin was the watch-word of
preachers in plague-infested London.
The idea, biblical ultimately, helped
to give *plague* the new meaning of
"punishment", as here.
    185-90. *But . . . her!*] Following the
sin of ll. 182, 184, *sin* in ll. 185, 187, 188
= moral sin and the person of John
(sin-conceived) [Johnson]. The sense
of these intentionally obscure lines is
that Arthur is punished for Eleanor's
sins and by her person.

Her injury the beadle to her sin,
All punish'd in the person of this child,
And all for her; a plague upon her!   190
Elea. Thou unadvised scold, I can produce
A will that bars the title of thy son.
Const. Ay, who doubts that? a will! a wicked will;
A woman's will; a cank'red grandam's will!
K. Phi. Peace, lady! pause, or be more temperate: 195
It ill beseems this presence to cry aim
To these ill-tuned repetitions.

Some trumpet summon hither to the walls
These men of Angiers: let us hear them speak
Whose title they admit, Arthur's or John's.   200

Trumpet sounds. Enter HUBERT *upon the walls.*

Hub. Who is it that hath warn'd us to the walls?
K. Phi. 'Tis France, for England.
K. John.   England, for itself.

---

197. *ill-tuned*] F1; no hyphen F2, edd.   201.] F1; *Scene* III. Pope.   201. S.D.]
This ed.; Trumpet sounds./Enter a Citizen vpon the walles. F1; Trumpets . . .
ed. 1760; Trumpets . . . citizens . . . Variorum 1773.   Hub.] This ed.;
Cit. F1 (throughout to l. 281); *1* Cit. Variorum 1773, edd.

188. *injury*] taunts, reviling.

beadle] whipper. The beadle, or parish officer, had to whip petty offenders. Read: "Eleanor's injurious tongue like a beadle whips John (into a fury against Arthur)".

191. *scold*] railer, quarreller.

192. *A will*] Richard I, before dying, "ordeined his testament . . . Vnto his brother Iohn he assigned the crowne of England . . ." (Hol., pp. 155–6). Shakespeare belittles the will (ll. 193–4) to make John seem a usurper (cf. I. i. 40, note).

bars] A bar was an objection that could arrest entirely an action at law (On.).

194. *A woman's will*] Women in 1590 were not allowed to make wills for their lands, tenements, etc., if married, as the husband's influence was feared [H. Swinburne, *Briefe Treatise of Testaments* (1590), sig. H₃]. A "woman's

will" was proverbially an influenced will: Constance (reversing the process to emphasize Eleanor's domination) suggests that Richard's will was influenced by a woman. Cf. Chapman's *All Fools*, III. i. 230–5.

196. *cry aim*] to encourage archers when shooting, hence "to applaud, encourage".

197. *repetitions*] recitals.

198. *trumpet*] trumpeter.

201. Hubert] See Introduction, p. xxxvi.

warn'd] summoned.

202. *'Tis . . . itself.*] "It is the king of France for the king of England" says Philip. John's three words imply that the real England needs no spokesman, that he therefore is the true king. This quibble on the identity of king and country (as in II. i. 91, 365, IV. iii. 142 *sqq.*) drives home the moral of the history.

You men of Angiers, and my loving subjects—
K. Phi. You loving men of Angiers, Arthur's subjects,
    Our trumpet call'd you to this gentle parle—   205
K. John. For our advantage; therefore hear us first.
    These flags of France, that are advanced here
    Before the eye and prospect of your town,
    Have hither march'd to your endamagement.
    The cannons have their bowels full of wrath,   210
    And ready mounted are they to spit forth
    Their iron indignation 'gainst your walls:
    All preparation for a bloody siege
    And merciless proceeding by these French
    Comforts your city's eyes, your winking gates;   215
    And but for our approach those sleeping stones,
    That as a waist doth girdle you about,
    By the compulsion of their ordinance
    By this time from their fixed beds of lime
    Had been dishabited, and wide havoc made   220
    For bloody power to rush upon your peace.
    But on the sight of us your lawful king,

---

215. *Comforts*] *Comfort* F1 ; *Confront* Rowe; *Come 'fore* Collier MS.   *your*] F3;
yours F1.   217. *doth*] F1 ; *do* Rowe.

---

205. *parle*] parley, conference.

207–34. *These . . . walls.*] For the imagery cf. Introduction, p. lxii. Shakespeare reverses the "siege" convention of love-poetry, in which the lady is a fortress to be stormed, threatening the city as a woman.

207. *flags*] An anachronism. Flags were not known till the 15th century (cf. *O.E.D.*).

    advanced] raised. So *Tp.*, 1. ii. 405, *R 3*, 1. ii. 40.

210–12. *The . . . walls:*] So Greene's *Alphonsus, King of Aragon* (1599): "the roaring cannon shot / Spit forth the venome of their fiered panch" (sig. G₄).

210. *bowels*] The bowels were thought the seat of pity and compassion.

215. *Comforts*] F1 was rejected since irony was said to be out of place. As

John's speech is full of innuendo, of over- and under-statement, the *winking* of this very line being playful, as though the gates are no stronger than eyelids, we return to F1. With Capell we transfer the "s" of *yours* to *Comfort(s)*.

    winking] closing; thus both eyes could wink at once.

217. *waist*] girdle, or garment for the waist.

    doth] Singular, attracted by *waist*.

220. *dishabited*] dislodged; stripped. Shakespeare's coinage.

    wide havoc] a wide breach with stones tumbling in confusion.

221. *bloody*] blood-smeared; fierce, passionate (cf. 1. i. 17). Chastity (= Right), i.e. cold stones sleeping in their beds, attacked by passionate *power* mirrors the scheme of the play— the zestful vitality of Wrong fighting the sickly coldness of Right.

Who painfully with much expedient march
Have brought a countercheck before your gates,
To save unscratch'd your city's threat'ned cheeks,   225
Behold, the French amaz'd vouchsafe a parle;
And now, instead of bullets wrapp'd in fire,
To make a shaking fever in your walls,
They shoot but calm words folded up in smoke,
To make a faithless error in your ears: 230
Which trust accordingly, kind citizens,
And let us in, your king, whose labour'd spirits
Forwearied in this action of swift speed
Craves harbourage within your city walls.

K. Phi. When I have said, make answer to us both.   235
Lo, in this right hand, whose protection
Is most divinely vow'd upon the right
Of him it holds, stands young Plantagenet,
Son to the elder brother of this man,
And king o'er him and all that he enjoys: 240
For this down-trodden equity we tread
In warlike march these greens before your town,
Being no further enemy to you
Than the constraint of hospitable zeal
In the relief of this oppressed child   245

---

232. *in, your king,*] Ed. 1735; *in. Your King,* F1; *in, your king;* Capell.   234.
Craves] F1; *Crave* Pope.   243. *further*] F1; *farther* Collier.

---

223. *expedient*] speedy.

227. *bullets*] cannon-balls.

wrapp'd in fire] So *The Spanish Tragedy*: "violence . . . / Wrapt in a ball of fire" (Kyd, p. 60); T. Andrewe, *Unmasking of a Feminine Machiauell* (1604): "bullets in fire wrapt round, / Circled in smoke" (sig. D4); B. & F.'s *Maid in the Mill* (ed. 1647): "a bullet / Wrapt in a cloud of fire" (p. 2).

228. *To . . . walls,*] For the reverse image cf. *this wall of flesh* (III. ii. 30).

229. *smoke*] The idiom may be illustrated from *The Contre-Guyse* (1589): "A pitifull case, that they should take the shadow for the substance, smoke for fire, the visage and lies, for truth . . ." (sig. Ev). Malone compared *Lucr.*,

1027: "This helpless smoke of words doth me no right."

233. *Forwearied*] Tired out.

235. *said*] finished speaking, spoken my mind.

236. *in . . . hand*] "Compare Richard III, IV. i. 2: 'Led in the hand of her kind aunt of Gloucester.' And Genesis xxi. 18" (Wright). Or Shakespeare may follow M. Paris: "Constantia . . . tradidit ei [Regi Francorum] Arturum memoratum, quem Rex continuo misit Parisios . . . & accepit in manu sua ciuitates omnes & castella, quae Arturi erant" (p. 263).

241-2. *tread . . . march*] The common expression was "to tread a march".

Religiously provokes. Be pleased then
To pay that duty which you truly owe
To him that owes it, namely this young prince:
And then our arms, like to a muzzled bear,
Save in aspect, hath all offence seal'd up;   250
Our cannons' malice vainly shall be spent
Against th' invulnerable clouds of heaven;
And with a blessed and unvex'd retire,
With unhack'd swords and helmets all unbruis'd,
We will bear home that lusty blood again   255
Which here we came to spout against your town,
And leave your children, wives and you in peace.
But if you fondly pass our proffer'd offer,
'Tis not the roundure of your old-fac'd walls
Can hide you from our messengers of war,   260
Though all these English and their discipline
Were harbour'd in their rude circumference.
Then tell us, shall your city call us lord,
In that behalf which we have challeng'd it?
Or shall we give the signal to our rage   265

---

248. *owes*] F1; *owns* Pope.   250. *hath*] F1; *have* Hanmer.   259. *roundure*]
Capell; *rounder* F1.

248. *owes*] owns.
251. *malice*] power to harm.
253. *unvex'd*] unmolested.
254. *helmets...unbruis'd*] So Spenser:
"And helmes unbruzed wexen daylie
browne" [*Shepheardes Calender* (October)]; Chapman: "my helmet yet unbruis'd" (*All Fools*, v. i. 15); T. Andrewe: "broken Pikes, bruz'd Helmets, batterd shields" (*op. cit.*, sig. E).
258. *proffer'd*] Proffer could mean "attempt" (*O.E.D.*, proffer, 3), but here only the empty jingle of the old alliterative drama may be intended, as in *Tom Tyler*: "I never did proffer you such an offer" (ed. 1661, sig. C₂), to score off this inflated speech.
259. *roundure*] So Sonnet xxi.—The experts on fortification advised against sharp angles in walls, because hard to defend. Angiers, with circular walls, would not be easily stormed. [See Paul

Ive, *Practise of Fortification* (1589), p. 7.]
old-fac'd] Not only the walls, but the faces (outer layers of stone) were old. Walls were often built with vertical scarp, so as to lean inwards, and tended to *shoot* (crumble): *old-fac'd walls* were therefore well-built.
260. *messengers of war*] i.e. cannon-balls. Shakespeare may have had in mind the biblical cliché "messengers of death"—as in "The wrath of a King (is as) messengers of death" (*Proverbs*, xvi. 14).
261. *discipline*] See II. i. 39, note.
263. *call us lord*] Arthur, it is implied, has done homage to Philip. Cf. II. i. 115, note, and Hol., 160, ii.
264. *In ... which*] On behalf of him for whom.
265. *signal ... rage*] Philip is so inhuman that he controls even his rage (uncontrolledness); cf. II. i. 53, note.

And stalk in blood to our possession?

Hub. In brief, we are the king of England's subjects:
For him, and in his right, we hold this town.

K. John. Acknowledge then the king, and let me in.

Hub. That can we not; but he that proves the king,   270
To him will we prove loyal: till that time
Have we ramm'd up our gates against the world.

K. John. Doth not the crown of England prove the king?
And if not that, I bring you witnesses,
Twice fifteen thousand hearts of England's breed—   275

Bast. Bastards and else.

K. John. To verify our title with their lives.

K. Phi. As many and as well-born bloods as those—

Bast. Some bastards too.

K. Phi. Stand in his face to contradict his claim.   280

Hub. Till you compound whose right is worthiest,
We for the worthiest hold the right from both.

K. John. Then God forgive the sin of all those souls
That to their everlasting residence,
Before the dew of evening fall, shall fleet,   285
In dreadful trial of our kingdom's king!

K. Phi. Amen, amen! Mount, chevaliers! to arms!

Bast. Saint George, that swindg'd the dragon, and e'er since

276, 279.] F1; Aside. Pope.   282.] F1; [Exeunt Citizens. Donovan.   288–9.
Saint . . . door,] Pope; two lines F1 (ending *Dragon,/ . . . dore/*).

266. *stalk*] Less specific than to-day, *stalk* could mean simply walk: but the modern sense is present here, suggesting Philip's haughtiness.

270. *he*] Classed as a noun absolute by Abbott, who compared *H 5*, IV. iii. 35, *R 3*, III. ii. 58, adding "These three examples might, however, come under the head of construction changed [through change of thought]" (p. 304).

273. *crown of England*] Cf. I. i. 40. C. K. Davis compared a statute of Henry VII: "If there be a king regnant in possession of the crown, though he be but *rex de facto* and not *de jure*, yet he is *seignior le roy*; and if another hath right, if he be out of possession, he is not within the meaning of the statute"

[*Law in Shakespeare* (1884), p. 150].

276. *Bastards and else*] "bastards and otherwise" (Smith); "Bastards and such-like" (Schmidt, On.). Surely the words mean both.

278. *bloods*] men of mettle, spirit; men of good stock or family.

281. *compound*] agree, settle.

285. *fleet*] (flit) pass away, vanish; cf. the cliché "his fleeting soul".

287. *Amen, amen!*] Philip is impatient to have been preceded in a pious thought.

288–9. *Saint . . . door*] Tilley (p. 581) quoted the proverb: "Like Saint George, who is ever on horseback yet never rides."

288. *swindg'd*] thrashed.

Sits on's horse-back at mine hostess' door,   289
Teach us some fence! [*To Aust.*] Sirrah, were I at home,
At your den, sirrah, with your lioness,
I would set an ox-head to your lion's hide,
And make a monster of you.
Aust.   Peace! no more.
Bast. O, tremble: for you hear the lion roar!
K. John. Up higher to the plain; where we'll set forth   295
In best appointment all our regiments.
Bast. Speed then, to take advantage of the field.
K. Phi. It shall be so; and at the other hill
Command the rest to stand. God and our right!
                [*Exeunt, severally, the English and French Kings, etc.*

Here, after excursions, enter the Herald of France,
with Trumpeters, to the gates.

F. Her. You men of Angiers, open wide your gates,   300
And let young Arthur, Duke of Britain, in,

---

289. *on's*] F1; *on his* Pope.   290. S.D.] Rowe iii; om. F1.   292. *I would*] F1;
I'd Pope.   299. S.D.] Dyce; Exeunt F1.   300.] F1; *Scene* IV. Pope; II.
Capell; *Act* II *Scene* I. Fleay.   300. S.D.] Heere after excursions, Enter the
Herald of France with Trumpets to the gates. F1.   301. *Britain*] As F1;
Bretagne Rowe iii.

---

289. *on's*] "The abbreviation is almost certainly due to the extra long line . . . which the compositor could only just crowd into the available space" (Wilson). Since *on's* staggers the rhythm in the manner of galloping, possibility of corruption should not outweigh an acceptable reading.

hostess'] Why not *host's* (apart from metre)? Perhaps to imply a viler domestication. In John's reign there were no inn-signs; in Elizabeth's St George was popular on them (Halliwell).

290. *fence*] swordsmanship (cf. *Ado*, v. i. 75); defence (cf. *3 H 6*, IV. i. 44).

291. *lioness*] A double insult. Apart from the horn-joke, Faulconbridge calls Austria's duchess a *lioness* [slang for *whore*: cf. Sir J. Davies, *Epigrammes* (c. 1595), "In Faustem" (16); Sir J.

Harington, *Letters and Epigrams*, ed. McClure, p. 175; Jonson, *Alchemist* (IV. iii. 49)].

294. *lion*] The reincarnation of Cœur-de-lion in Faulconbridge is brought out in *the lion* (cf. Introduction p. lxx).

296. *regiments*] In the modern sense, "a definite unit of an army", which *O.E.D.* first records in the 16th century.

297. *advantage*] Cf. II. i. 40, note.

299. *God . . . right!*] An English royal motto in Shakespeare's time, given to France, perhaps, to underline his claim that he fights for England.

300. S.D. Trumpeters] See II. i. 198, note.

301. *Duke of Britain*] Cf. II. i. 551 (John promises to make Arthur Duke of Brittany), II. i. 156 (he addresses him

Who by the hand of France this day hath made
Much work for tears in many an English mother,
Whose sons lie scatter'd on the bleeding ground:
Many a widow's husband grovelling lies,　　　305
Coldly embracing the discolour'd earth;
And victory, with little loss, doth play
Upon the dancing banners of the French,
Who are at hand, triumphantly display'd,
To enter conquerors, and to proclaim　　　310
Arthur of Britain England's king, and yours.

Enter English Herald, with Trumpeter.

E. Her.　Rejoice, you men of Angiers, ring your bells;
　　　King John, your king and England's, doth approach,
　　　Commander of this hot malicious day.
　　　Their armours, that march'd hence so silver-bright,　315
　　　Hither return all gilt with Frenchmen's blood;
　　　There stuck no plume in any English crest
　　　That is removed by a staff of France;
　　　Our colours do return in those same hands
　　　That did display them when we first march'd forth;　320
　　　And, like a jolly troop of huntsmen, come

309. *Who . . . display'd*] F1; *Triumphantly display'd; who are at hand*, Keightley.
312. S.D. Trumpeter.] F1 (Trumpet.); trumpets. Hanmer.

as "Arthur of Britain"). Arthur inherited Brittany from Constance, and
was already its duke at this time (Hol.).
Shakespeare seems to think that (*a*)
Arthur was "of Britain" (II. i. 156,
311), because born there; (*b*) Arthur
had been wrongly made duke by his
adopted lord, France; (*c*) John, not
recognizing France's creation, promises the dukedom himself (II. i. 551).
Or perhaps Shakespeare followed
Holinshed (161, ii) at II. i. 551 and
failed to notice that John did not *create*
Arthur Duke of Brittany, but merely
received homage for Brittany.

305. *grovelling*] prone, lying on his
belly.

306. *embracing*] "they that were
brought vp in skarlet, embrace

the dongue" (*Lamentations*, iv. 5).

309. *display'd*] Furness suggested the
(pre-Shakespearean) military sense
("deployed, spread out in an extended
line"). Others refer *triumphantly display'd* to banners.

312. *Rejoice . . . Angiers*] This and the
last speech resemble that opening
Tamburlaine, Pt I, IV. i: "Awake, ye
men of Memphis!"

315–16. *silver-bright . . . gilt*] Gold was
thought of as red, as well as yellow.
Johnson compared *Mac.* ["His silver
skin lac'd with his golden blood" (II.
iii. 119); "I'll gild the faces of the
grooms withal; / For it must seem their
guilt" (II. ii. 57–8)].

318. *staff*] spear (literally "shaft of a
spear", implying *accidental* removal).

Our lusty English, all with purpled hands,
Dyed in the dying slaughter of their foes:
Open your gates and give the victors way.

Hub. Heralds, from off our towers we might behold,   325
From first to last, the onset and retire
Of both your armies; whose equality
By our best eyes cannot be censured:
Blood hath bought blood and blows have answer'd
      blows;
Strength match'd with strength, and power confronted
      power: 330
Both are alike, and both alike we like.
One must prove greatest: while they weigh so even
We hold our town for neither, yet for both.

Re-enter, on one side, KING JOHN, ELEANOR, BLANCHE, *the*
BASTARD, *Lords and Forces; on the other,* KING PHILIP, LEWIS,
AUSTRIA, *and Forces.*

K. John. France, hast thou yet more blood to cast away?
Say, shall the current of our right roam on?   335

323. *Dyed*] F1; *Stain'd* Pope.   325. Hub.] Hubert. F1; Citi. Rowe.   334.]
F1; *Scene* V. Pope.   334. S.D.] Dyce; Enter the two Kings with their powers,
at seuerall doores. F1.   335. *roam*] F1; *runne* F2, edd.

322. *lusty*] vigorous; the sense
"merry" is also present (cf. I. i. 108)
after *jolly.*

323. *Dyed*] It was "one of the savage
practices of the chase, for all to stain
their hands in the blood of the deer"
(Johnson). *Caes.*, III. i. 205 was compared, but modern edd., for want of
other allusions to the practice, thought
it figmentary. But cf. *The Brazen Age*:
"al our bore-speares stain'd / And gory
hands lau'd in his reeking bloud"
(Heywood, III, 194); W. Cavendish,
The Varietie (1649): "those were the
dayes . . . such brave jeasts, at the
death of a Stag, and Buck, to throw
blood up and downe, upon folkes
faces" (sig. C_{12}^v) (this might explain
jolly, l. 321).

325. Hub.] F1 here first introduces
Hubert (cf. Introduction, p. xxxvi).

Wilson thought that Shakespeare
decided at this stage to merge Hubert
and the citizen, which would indicate
how far he thought ahead.

328. *censured*] "estimated" (usual
gloss). But, as Malone noted, their *in-
equality* cannot be estimated. Perhaps
an early use of the modern sense: their
equality allows of no adverse opinion,
no flaw can be found in it.

329. *Blood . . . blood*] Cf. I. i. 19. Tilley (p. 55) referred to the "Blood will
have blood" proverb, which goes back
to *Genesis*, ix. 6.

335. *roam*] Ridley, comparing *Ham.*,
I. iii. 109, wondered whether "instead
of putting both readings down to error
we should not be wiser to accept the
word in both places, even at the cost of
an addition to O.E.D." Malone compared "the *wandering* brooks" (*Tp.*, IV.

Whose passage, vex'd with thy impediment,
Shall leave his native channel and o'erswell,
With course disturb'd, even thy confining shores,
Unless thou let his silver water keep
A peaceful progress to the ocean.   340

K. Phi. England, thou hast not sav'd one drop of blood,
In this hot trial, more than we of France;
Rather, lost more. And by this hand I swear,
That sways the earth this climate overlooks,
Before we will lay down our just-borne arms,   345
We'll put thee down 'gainst whom these arms we bear,
Or add a royal number to the dead,
Gracing the scroll that tells of this war's loss
With slaughter coupled to the name of kings.

Bast. Ha, majesty! how high thy glory towers   350
When the rich blood of kings is set on fire!
O, now doth death line his dead chaps with steel;
The swords of soldiers are his teeth, his fangs;
And now he feasts, mousing the flesh of men,

---

345. *down*] F1; *by* Pope.   354. *mousing*] F1; *mouthing* Pope.

i. 128). Dyce pleaded for *run* on
account of the "repetition" in v. iv. 56.
Tilley (p. 637) quoted the proverb
"The Stream (current, tide) stopped
swells the higher."

337. *o'erswell*] The image of overflowing water to express *rebellion* was
conventional. The *confining shores* may
be the boundaries inside France between John's lands and Philip's. Holinshed told Shakespeare that John did
homage for his French lands: Shakespeare may have in mind a vassal's
rebellion.

339. *silver water*] An army marching
in armour must have sparkled at a distance like a river: cf. *R 2*, III. ii. 106–11
("silver rivers . . . hard bright steel").

343. *this hand*] Arthur's hand, held
up by Philip (Furness); his own hand
(Wilson, taking *climate* = France).

344. *climate*] portion of the sky. I.
John quoted Cotgrave: "*Climat:* a
clime, or *climate;* a division in the skie,
or portion of the world".

346. *put . . . down*] subdue, overthrow.

347. *a royal number*] "a royal item in
the list [of dead]" (Smith).

348. *scroll*] In *H 5* a herald brings a
note which contains "the number of the
slaughter'd French" (IV. viii. 79), and
Shakespeare thinks of the same after-
battle procedure here.

349. *With . . . kings.*] With a royal
name in the list of the dead.

350. *glory*] vaunting, boastful spirit.
towers] soars. A hawking term (cf.
v. ii. 149).

351–3. *set . . . fangs;*] *chaps* = jaws;
fangs = teeth, tusks. The image is ultimately biblical: "the children of men,
that are set on fyre: whose teeth (are)
speares and arrowes, and their tongue
a sharpe sworde" (*Psalms*, lvii. 4; cf.
Proverbs, xxx. 14; *Revelation*, i. 16, ii. 16,
xix. 15, etc.)

354. *feasts*] Tilley (p. 704) quoted
the proverb "War is death's feast."
This follows the biblical common-

In undetermin'd differences of kings.   355
Why stand these royal fronts amazed thus?
Cry "havoc!" kings; back to the stained field,
You equal potents, fiery kindled spirits!
Then let confusion of one part confirm
The other's peace; till then, blows, blood, and death! 360
K. John. Whose party do the townsmen yet admit?
K. Phi. Speak, citizens, for England; who's your king?
Hub. The king of England, when we know the king.
K. Phi. Know him in us, that here hold up his right.
K. John. In us, that are our own great deputy,   365
And bear possession of our person here,
Lord of our presence, Angiers, and of you.
Hub. A greater power than we denies all this;
And till it be undoubted, we do lock

---

358. *potents*] F1; *potent* Collier ii.   *fiery kindled*] F1; *fire-ykindled* Collier ii (MS).
363, 416, 423, 480. Hub.] F1; Citi. Rowe.   368. Hub.] This ed.; Fra. F1;
Citi. Rowe.   *we*] F1; *ye* Warburton conj.

place: "death devoureth them"
(*Psalms*, xlix. 14, etc.).

mousing] tearing, as a cat tears a
mouse, as in *MND.*, v. i. 276.

355. *In . . . kings.*] "making no difference between the flesh of kings and
that of common men" (Wilson). We
would read "In the unsettled disputes
of kings", or "In the unresolved in-
equalities of kings" (connecting with
II. i. 327–8, 358; III. i. 164).

356. *fronts*] foreheads, (hence) faces.

357. *havoc*] The cry *havoc!* was the
signal for indiscriminate slaughter.
Edd. compare *Caes.*: "with a monarch's voice / Cry 'Havoc!' and let slip
the dogs of war" (III. i. 272–3). Furness
thought that "to 'cry havoc' was the
prerogative of the Monarch".

358. *potents*] potentates. An early
use of the substantive—unique in
Shakespeare. Possibly we should read
potent.

359. *confusion*] defeat.

part] party. The legal jargon "on the
one part . . . on the other part" brought
a dual meaning to this word (= one of
two parties) as here and in v. vi. 2.

361. *yet*] "as yet, in the present state
of affairs" (Wright).

364. *hold . . . right*] "uphold his rightful claim"; or "hold up his right hand"
(cf. II. i. 236–8).

365. *our . . . deputy*] Cf. II. i. 202, note.
John suggests: The king of England
does not need a deputy.

366. *And . . . here*] Wilson takes this
line, and *Lord of our presence* in the next,
to imply feudal supremacy. Arthur
does not bear possession of his person,
is not lord of his presence (for this
phrase cf. I. i. 137, II. i. 377).

368. Hub.] Cf. Introduction, p.
xxxiv.

power] "Tollet thought that *a greater
power* might mean the Lord of Hosts
. . . but, surely, the *greater power* is their
fears" (Deighton). As kings have just
been called deputies (l. 365; cf. III. i.
62), an Elizabethan would have
thought like Tollet, though *fears* have
a claim too.

369. *undoubted*] As *doubt* = (a) uncertainty; (b) fear, *undoubted* in a "fear"
and "certainty" context = put beyond doubt (with both meanings).

Our former scruple in our strong-barr'd gates: 370
Kings of our fear, until our fears, resolv'd,
Be by some certain king purg'd and depos'd.
Bast. By heaven, these scroyles of Angiers flout you, kings,
And stand securely on their battlements,
As in a theatre, whence they gape and point   375
At your industrious scenes and acts of death.
Your royal presences be rul'd by me:
Do like the mutines of Jerusalem,
Be friends awhile and both conjointly bend
Your sharpest deeds of malice on this town.   380
By east and west let France and England mount
Their battering cannon charged to the mouths,
Till their soul-fearing clamours have brawl'd down

---

371. *Kings*] F1; *King'd* Tyrwhitt, edd.   *fear*] F1; *fears* Theobald.   377.
Your] F1; *You* Rowe.   381. *mount*] mount. F1.

371-2. *Kings of . . . by*] Tyrwhitt's
reading is ingenious but unnecessary.
Cf. Abbott: "*by* is used of external
agencies, *of* is used of internal motives,
thus: 'Comest thou hither by chance,
or *of* devotion?' (*2 H 6*, II. i. 88), 'The
king *of* his own royal disposition.'
(*R 3*, I. iii. 63)" (p. 111). Read: "We
must be our own kings on account of
our fear, until all our fears (and thus
our kingship, which follows from our
fears) be deposed." Staunton thought
that *strong-barr'd gates* are the *Kings*.
Malone compared *Lucr.*, l. 659, *Lr.*,
IV. iii. 15–17.

373. *scroyles*] scabby scoundrels.

375. *gape*] In pre-Shakespearean
drama the audience was often ridiculed for *gaping*, and Shakespeare
adapts the joke. Cf. R. W.'s *Three
Ladies of London* (1584): "But yonder is
a fellow that gapes to bite me or els to
eate that which I sing. / Why thou art
a foole canst not thou keepe thy mouth
strait together?" (sig. D₃ᵛ).

376. *industrious*] your laborious *in-
dustry* of war (Steevens, comparing
Mac., v. iv. 17); "clever, ingenious"
(On.). Comparison of the business of
actors and the idleness of spectators

was common in the old drama.

scenes and acts] acting, performance.
This untechnical quibble was common, as in the old *King Leir* (1605):
"When will this Scene of sadnesse haue
an end, / And pleasant acts insue, to
moue delight?" (sig. E₂).

377. *presences*] "persons" (On.); cf.
I. i. 137, II. i. 367, also the idiom "in the
presence" (viz. royal presence).

378. *mutines of Jerusalem*] mutineers
of Jerusalem. In the civil war of Jerusalem the factions united to fight the
Romans. The story was well known
c. 1590: Strange's company had an old
play *Jerusalem* in 1592 (Greg, *Henslowe's Diary*, I, 13, 14); in 1584 and
1591 a play on this subject was acted at
Coventry, sixteen miles from Stratford
(Harris, *N. & Q.*, 8 Aug. 1931).

382. *Their . . . mouths*] *battering cannon*
= the great cannon. These, "filde
with peeces of yron, or of some other
Mettall, or with stones or chaynes, for
these thinges worke a marueilous
effect", could be used to clear breaches
or walls [W. Garrard, *Arte of Warre*
(1591), p. 288]. Here *charged* = filled;
mouths is technical.

383. *soul-fearing*] soul-frightening.

The flinty ribs of this contemptuous city:
I'd play incessantly upon these jades,　　　　385
Even till unfenced desolation
Leave them as naked as the vulgar air.
That done, dissever your united strengths,
And part your mingled colours once again;
Turn face to face and bloody point to point;　　　390
Then, in a moment, fortune shall cull forth
Out of one side her happy minion,
To whom in favour she shall give the day,
And kiss him with a glorious victory.
How like you this wild counsel, mighty states?　　　395
Smacks it not something of the policy?

K. John.　Now, by the sky that hangs above our heads,
I like it well. France, shall we knit our powers
And lay this Angiers even with the ground;
Then after fight who shall be king of it?　　　400

Bast.　And if thou hast the mettle of a king,
Being wrong'd as we are by this peevish town,
Turn thou the mouth of thy artillery,
As we will ours, against these saucy walls;
And when that we have dash'd them to the ground,　405
Why then defy each other, and pell-mell
Make work upon ourselves, for heaven or hell.

Shakespeare's coinage makes sense, but the emendation "soul-searing" is tempting.

brawl'd down] beaten down with clamour.

385. *play . . . upon*] fire at, play the guns upon (technical); play with, mock (resuming l. 373); cf. *Per.*, I. i. 84.

jades] a word of contempt for women, (hence) sorry creatures.

387. *vulgar*] common.

392. *minion*] darling.

395. *states*] persons of rank.

396. *the policy*] Machiavellian statesmanship, low cunning. Abbott (sect. 92) shows that *the* could "denote notoriety", as in "I am alone the villain of the earth" (*Ant.*, IV. vi. 30). Faulconbridge delights naively in *policy* because it does not come naturally to him.

401. *mettle*] = substance, material (cf. *Lr.*, I. i. 71); spirit, courage (cf. *Oth.*, IV. ii. 207); material from which arms are made, (hence) sword. F1 spells "metal" *mettle* in V. ii. 16, below.

406. *pell-mell*] in disorderly manner, hand to hand, with broken ranks. Furness compared *R 3*, V. iii. 313–14.

407. *Make . . . hell*] Make work for heaven or hell amongst ourselves, being killed; set upon each other on behalf of heaven or hell (as we wish to invoke them). The French side in *John* claim the sanction of heaven throughout, and John's side that of hell. Furness noted that Shakespeare uses *make work* as in II. i. 303, and *Cor.*: "what work he makes / Amongst your cloven army" (I. iv. 20–1).

K. Phi. Let it be so. Say, where will you assault?

K. John. We from the west will send destruction
    Into this city's bosom.   410

Aust. I from the north.

K. Phi.   Our thunder from the south
    Shall rain their drift of bullets on this town.

Bast. [*Aside.*] O prudent discipline! From north to south
    Austria and France shoot in each other's mouth:
    I'll stir them to it.—Come, away, away!   415

Hub. Hear us, great kings: vouchsafe awhile to stay,
    And I shall show you peace and fair-fac'd league;
    Win you this city without stroke or wound;
    Rescue those breathing lives to die in beds,
    That here come sacrifices for the field: 420
    Persever not, but hear me, mighty kings!

K. John. Speak on, with favour; we are bent to hear.

Hub. That daughter there of Spain, the Lady Blanche,
    Is near to England: look upon the years
    Of Lewis the Dolphin and that lovely maid: 425
    If lusty love should go in quest of beauty,
    Where should he find it fairer than in Blanche?
    If zealous love should go in search of virtue,
    Where should he find it purer than in Blanche?
    If love ambitious sought a match of birth,   430
    Whose veins bound richer blood than Lady Blanche?
    Such as she is, in beauty, virtue, birth,
    Is the young Dolphin every way complete:
    If not complete of, say he is not she;

411. *thunder*] F1; *thunders* Capell conj.   413. S.D.] Capell; om. F1.   422. *on,
with favour ;*] Theobald; *on with fauour,* F1; *on ; with Favour* Rowe.   424. *near*] F1;
niece Collier MS.   434. *complete of*] F1; *completed* Sisson.   *of,*] F1; *oh!* Hanmer; *so,* B. G. Kinnear [*Cruces Sh.* (1883), p. 192]; *I* Kittredge; *all* Wilson conj.

411. *thunder*] cannon.

412. *drift*] shower. A "rain" of cannon-balls was a familiar conceit.

414. *mouth*] The mouths of the men
and of the cannon.

422. *bent*] inclined, willing.

424. *near*] near, dear (relation) to
John. A common idiom. Blanche was
John's *niece*, but emendation is unjusti-
fied.

425. *Dolphin*] Dauphin.

426. *lusty*] full of healthy vigour *or*
sexual desire.

428. *zealous*] pious.

431. *bound*] enclose (cf. l. 442, below).

433. *complete*] perfect.

434. *of*] "*thereof*, or *therein*" (Rolfe).
Fleay compared *Fair Em*: "But father,
are you assured of the wordes he spake,

And she again wants nothing, to name want,   435
If want it be not that she is not he:
He is the half part of a blessed man,
Left to be finished by such as she;
And she a fair divided excellence,
Whose fulness of perfection lies in him.   440
O, two such silver currents, when they join,
Do glorify the banks that bound them in;
And two such shores, to two such streams made one,
Two such controlling bounds shall you be, kings,
To these two princes, if you marry them.   445
This union shall do more than battery can
To our fast-closed gates; for at this match,
With swifter spleen than powder can enforce,
The mouth of passage shall we fling wide ope,
And give you entrance: but without this match   450
The sea enraged is not half so deaf,
Lions more confident, mountains and rocks

---

438. *as she*] F1; *a She* Thirlby conj. (*ap.* Theobald).   447. *fast-closed*] Theobald;
no hyphen F1.   448. *spleen*] F1; *speed* Pope.

---

were concerning *Manuile?*" (M.S.R.,
sig. E₂ᵛ); Marston's *Antonio and Mellida*
(1602): "Ile . . . suruey . . . my seruants; & he that hath the best parts of,
Ile pricke him downe for my husband"
(sig. I₄ᵛ). F1 is idiomatic, though *oh*
was often printed *of* [S. Rowley's
When You See Me (1605), sig. I₄; Glapthorne's *Ladies Priviledge* (1640), sig.
E₂; etc.].

434-40. *If . . . him.*] C. Wordsworth
thought these lines so unworthy of
Shakespeare that they could not be
his.—As often, Shakespeare uses the
nice balance of formal poetry to point
to human formalities.

435. *wants*] lacks (after *not complete*,
l. 434); desires (after *go in quest, go in
search* etc., ll. 426-30).

436. *If . . . that*] Unless it be a want
that.

438. *finished*] Cf. *fast-closed* (l. 447),
enraged (l. 451). These falsely stressed
participles with the colourless verbs
and auxiliaries of the speech, and the

balance of pictures (ll. 451-5), all reinforce the formal effect.

440. *perfection*] In the doctrine of
courtly love, human perfection was
impossible without love.

441. *currents*] Similar order-disorder
pictures occur in ii. i. 335, v. i. 12,
v. iv. 53, v. vii. 38. The "marriage =
two joining streams" image was in
great vogue (boosted by Spenser).

447. *match*] Johnson noticed the
pun.

448. *spleen*] Cf. v. vii. 50.

449. *mouth*] gates; in ii. i. 215 likened
to eye-lids. Appropriate for *double*
gates. Cf. *R 2*: "Doubly portcullis'd
with my teeth and lips" (i. iii. 167).

451-4. *The . . . peremptory*] Note the
antithesis: *half so, more, more, half so,* as
in iii. iii. 11-12.

451. *sea . . . deaf*] Cf. *R 2,* i. i. 19.
Proverbial.

452-3. *mountains . . . motion*] The
"moving mountains" image is popular
in the Bible (cf. note to iii. iii. 39).

More free from motion, no, not death himself
In mortal fury half so peremptory,
As we to keep this city.

Bast.   Here's a stay   455
That shakes the rotten carcass of old death
Out of his rags! Here's a large mouth indeed,
That spits forth death and mountains, rocks and seas,
Talks as familiarly of roaring lions
As maids of thirteen do of puppy-dogs!   460
What cannoneer begot this lusty blood?
He speaks plain cannon, fire, and smoke, and bounce;
He gives the bastinado with his tongue;
Our ears are cudgell'd; not a word of his
But buffets better than a fist of France.   465

455.] F1; [The *Kings*, &c., talk apart. Collier iii.   *stay*] F1; '*Stay!*' Kittredge.
462. *cannon, fire,*] Capell; *Cannon fire*, F1.

454. *peremptory*] determined.

455. *stay*] Much discussed. After l. 416 (*stay* = pause) it means "interruption"; but it = "check" too. "The B. refers to the sudden check in a manage, which shakes the rider (Death) from his seat [on his horse]" (Wilson).

456–7. *That . . . rags!*] Cf. *Cor.*: "Hence, rotten thing! or I shall shake thy bones / Out of thy garments" (iii. i. 178–9).

457–61. *Here's . . . blood?*] "I haue tearmes (if I be vext) laid in steepe in *Aquafortis*, & Gunpowder, that shall rattle through the Skyes, and make an Earthquake in a Pesants eares" wrote Nashe in 1592 (I, 195). Martin Marprelate and Nashe introduced "gunpowder terms" in 1588–9. Steevens noted the parallel in *Thomas Stukeley* (1605): "Why heers a gallant, heers a king indeed, / He speaks all Mars tut let me follow such a / Lad as this: This is pure fire. / . . . He brings a breath that sets our sailes on fire, / Why now I see we shall haue cuffs indeed" (sig. K₂ᵛ).

460. *puppy-dogs*] The last word in foolishness for Shakespeare; as in *H 5*: "no more directions in the true discip-

lines of the wars, look you, of the Roman disciplines, than is a puppy-dog" (iii. ii. 78–81).

461. *What . . . blood?*] Cf. i. i. 108; *blood* quibbles on the sense "man of fire, mettle".

462. *He . . . bounce;*] He plainly speaks the language of cannon, fire, etc. To "speak fire and smoke" may have been an idiom; cf. Mrs Centlivre's *Basset-Table*: "the Sea Captain . . . can entertain one with nothing but Fire and Smoke" [*Works* (1761), I, 205]. "Bounce" was Elizabethan for modern "bang".

speaks . . . cannon] Cf. *Ado*: "She speaks poniards" (ii. i. 257); *H 5*: "I speak to thee plain soldier" (v. ii. 155) (Smith).

463. *bastinado*] cudgel (hence) cudgelling. Cf. *Arden of Feversham* (1592): "Zounds I hate them as I hate a toade, / That cary a muscado in their tongue. / And scarce a hurting weapon in their hand" (sig. F₂). Here *muscado* is a nonce-word (*O.E.D.*), which suggests unintelligent imitation.

465. *But . . . France*] The *buffeting* of *fists* was a cliché, common in the Bible, etc. In the old romances duels of strength were sometimes tried in buf-

Zounds! I was never so bethump'd with words
Since I first call'd my brother's father dad.

Elea. Son, list to this conjunction, make this match;
Give with our niece a dowry large enough:
For by this knot thou shalt so surely tie   470
Thy now unsur'd assurance to the crown,
That yon green boy shall have no sun to ripe
The bloom that promiseth a mighty fruit.
I see a yielding in the looks of France;   474
Mark, how they whisper: urge them while their souls
Are capable of this ambition,
Lest zeal, now melted by the windy breath
Of soft petitions, pity and remorse,
Cool and congeal again to what it was.

Hub. Why answer not the double majesties   480
This friendly treaty of our threat'ned town?

468. Elea.] Old Qu. F1.   468–79.] F1; Aside. Capell.

fets; Richard I killed Austria's son in
one of these. Buffets were aimed at the
head ("our *ears* are cudgell'd"), each
party having to stand still in turn.

466. *Zounds!*] = "(God's) wounds!"
Apparently thought profane and ex-
cised in many prompt-books after the
Act of Abuses, 1606.

467. *dad*] Perhaps playing on the
dialectal (northern) verb "to dad"
(= to beat, thump), which was pre-
Shakespearean; cf. Introduction, p.
xxv, where the existence of northern
Faulconbridges, prototypes of those in
John, is suggested.

468. *list*] listen.

470–3. *For . . . fruit.*] John had high
hopes of this marriage, says Holinshed,
and "supposed that by his affinitie,
and resignation of his right to those
places, the peace now made would
haue continued for euer" (161, ii).

470–1. *surely . . . assurance*] Cf. II. i.
534–5 ("assur'd . . . assur'd"); *assurance* = certainty, security; legal settle-
ment of property; betrothal.

472. *green*] youthful, inexperienced
(cf. III. iii. 145).

473. *The . . . fruit.*] Cf. *Soliman and*

Perseda for this common thought:
"*Sol.* The Prince of Cipris to is likewise
slaine. / *Erast.* Faire blossome, likely to
haue proued good fruite" (Kyd, p.
206). That kingship = fruition had
been established by Marlowe's great
line "The sweet fruition of an earthly
crown" (*Tamburlaine*, Pt I, II. vii).

477–9. *Lest . . . was.*] Lest Philip's
zeal to help Arthur, melted by Hubert's petitions for pity for Angiers,
cool and harden against you as before.
Johnson thought the image unjust,
because *zeal* is usually seen as a flame.
Steevens took zeal = metal in a state
of fusion, and Wilson = wax ["accompanied, too, with the inevitable
quibble (zeal-seal), cf. note 2. 1. 19–
20"]. But Shakespeare has already emphasized the *coldness* (cf. II. i. 53, note)
and fake *zeal* (II. i. 19, 244, 428, etc.) of
the French side, and the "icy zeal" envisaged may be a significant paradox.
Cf. III. i. 31, note.

478. *pity and remorse*] A stock phrase;
remorse usually = "pity" at this time
(cf. IV. iii. 50).

481. *treaty*] negotiation, proposal.

K. Phi. Speak England first, that hath been forward first
    To speak unto this city: what say you?

K. John. If that the Dolphin there, thy princely son,
    Can in this book of beauty read "I love",   485
    Her dowry shall weigh equal with a queen:
    For Anjou, and fair Touraine, Maine, Poictiers,
    And all that we upon this side the sea—
    Except this city now by us besieg'd—
    Find liable to our crown and dignity,   490
    Shall gild her bridal bed, and make her rich
    In titles, honours and promotions,
    As she in beauty, education, blood,
    Holds hand with any princess of the world.

K. Phi. What say'st thou, boy? look in the lady's face.   495

Lew. I do, my lord; and in her eye I find
    A wonder, or a wondrous miracle,
    The shadow of myself form'd in her eye;
    Which, being but the shadow of your son,
    Becomes a sun and makes your son a shadow: 500
    I do protest I never lov'd myself

---

482. *first, that*] sir st, *that* F1.   486. *queen*] F1; *queen's* Keightley.   487. *Anjou*] Theobald; Angiers F1.   494. *hand*] F1; *hands* F2.

482. *forward*] Glancing at John's forwardness in II. i. 202–6?

485. *Can . . . love*",] "The book is Lily's Grammar '*amo*, I love'; the beauty is Blanch" [T. W. Baldwin: *William Shakspere's Small Latine* (1944), I, 569]. Lily used *amo* as paradigm. The *book* may be Blanche's face or eyes: cf. *Mac.*, I. v. 63, *2 H 4*, I. i. 60, *LLL.*, I. i. 72–87, IV. iii. 302–4.

486. *queen*] i.e. queen's.

487. *Anjou*] Cf. II. i. 152, note.

489. *Except . . . besieg'd*] Shakespeare follows Holinshed: "Iohn . . . resigned his title to . . . all those townes which the French king had by warre taken from him, the citie of Angiers onelie excepted" (161, i).

490. *liable*] subject.

493. *education*] Cf. II. i. 426–32; *education* (= breeding, upbringing) corresponds to *virtue*. But in the progressive aristocratic circle to which Shakespeare probably belonged learning (= *education*) was now thought necessary in a lady.

494. *Holds . . . with*] Is equal to.

496. *in her eye*] For this popular conceit cf. *Ven.*, l. 119, and IV. i. 64, note.

498. *shadow*] reflected image. In l. 499 a pun on the modern sense, in l. 500 only the modern sense.

500. *sun*] The hackneyed mistress-sun image emphasizes the formality of the wooing.

501. *lov'd myself*] In "courtly love", the lover loves himself, i.e. his good qualities, in his lady, beholding himself (cf. l. 502) abstractly in her. So Chapman said of Beauty that it is doomed unless it loves: "Enamourd (like good selfe-loue) with her owne,/ Seene in another, then tis heauen alone" [*Ouids Banquet of Sence* (1595), st. 51].

Till now infixed I beheld myself
Drawn in the flattering table of her eye.

                           [Whispers with Blanche.

Bast. [*Aside.*] Drawn in the flattering table of her eye!
   Hang'd in the frowning wrinkle of her brow!   505
And quarter'd in her heart! he doth espy
   Himself love's traitor: this is pity now,
That, hang'd and drawn and quarter'd, there should be
In such a love so vile a lout as he!

Blanche [*to Lew.*] My uncle's will in this respect is mine: 510
If he see aught in you that makes him like,
That any thing he sees, which moves his liking,
I can with ease translate it to my will;
Or if you will, to speak more properly,
I will enforce it eas'ly to my love.   515
Further I will not flatter you, my lord,
That all I see in you is worthy love,
Than this: that nothing do I see in you,
Though churlish thoughts themselves should be your
    judge,

504. S.D.] Dyce; om. F1.   510. S.D.] Capell; om. F1.   510. *mine:*] Capell;
mine, F1; *mine.* F3.   512. *any thing*] F1; *anything* Knight.   516. *Further*] F1;
Farther Collier.

503. *table*] board, surface, on which a picture is painted.

S.D. *Whispers*] As an aside follows, we need not assume that *only* Lewis and Blanche whisper, merely that their being placed together is essential.

504. *Drawn*] Quibbling on the sense "disembowelled", as in *Meas.*, II. i. 221, *Ado.* III. ii. 22. Traitors to the realm were hanged, drawn and quartered.

506. *quarter'd*] Quibbling on the sense "lodged in, having quarters in", the cliché that the lover's heart is locked up in his mistress's bosom.

509. *love*] passion of love; loved person.

so . . . he!] Lewis's cold-blooded formality rouses Faulconbridge (cf. also Appendix B, p. 167). Furness noted that the poetic style ridiculed (ll. 496–503) resembles Shakespeare's own sonnets (especially no. 24).

510. *in . . . respect*] Edd. adopting the F1 stop presumably read: "My uncle's will governs mine completely in this matter." But *respect* = particular (*O.E.D.*, 8b), and the possibility of the opposite sense can be left open with a colon ("My uncle's will governs mine (only) in this particular: Supposing he sees aught etc."): so that l. 513 surprises more.

512. *any*] adjectival: "That thing, whatsoever it may be". Blanche is vague to cover the remotest possibilities.

513. *translate . . . will*] transform it so as to suit my *wishes* too (though it may really jar with them); *or* carry it across (from his *liking*) to my *good-will*.

514. *properly*] accurately (as in *AYL.*, I. i. 8); beseemingly.

517. *all*] Cf. *any*, l. 512.

519. *churlish*] niggardly, miserly.

That I can find should merit any hate.   520

K. John. What say these young ones? What say you, my
    niece?

Blanche. That she is bound in honour still to do
    What you in wisdom still vouchsafe to say.

K. John. Speak then, prince Dolphin: can you love this
    lady?

Lew. Nay, ask me if I can refrain from love;   525
    For I do love her most unfeignedly.

K. John. Then do I give Volquessen, Touraine, Maine,
    Poictiers, and Anjou, these five provinces,
    With her to thee; and this addition more,
    Full thirty thousand marks of English coin.   530
    Philip of France, if thou be pleas'd withal,
    Command thy son and daughter to join hands.

K. Phi. It likes us well; young princes, close your hands.

Aust. And your lips too; for I am well assur'd
    That I did so when I was first assur'd.   535

K. Phi. Now, citizens of Angiers, ope your gates,
    Let in that amity which you have made;
    For at Saint Mary's chapel presently
    The rites of marriage shall be solemniz'd.
    Is not the Lady Constance in this troop?   540

---

521. *young ones*] Rowe; hyphened F1.   523. *still*] F1; *will* Pope; *shall* Capell
conj.   535. *assur'd*] F1; *affied* Walker.

522–3. *still*] always.

527. *Volquessen*] "now called *the Vexin*; in Latin, *Pagus Velocassinus*" (Steevens); i.e. Rouen and district.

528. *Poictiers . . . provinces,*] One of the two lines in *John* identical in *T.R.* (cf. v. iv. 42, note). Malone compared "Then I demaund *Volquesson, Torain, Main,* / *Poiters* and *Aniou,* these fiue Prouinces" (*T.R.*, I. iv. 158–9).

529. *addition*] Could mean *title,* and there is a quibble after ll. 527–8.

530. *Full . . . marks*] So Holinshed: "thirtie thousand markes in siluer, as in respect of dowrie assigned to his said neece" (161, i). The mark = 13s. 4d. The five provinces are Shakespeare's invention—John gave far less —to underline John's impulsiveness.

533–4. *close . . . too;*] Rolfe compared *Tw.N.*: "A contract of eternal bond of love, / Confirm'd by mutual joinder of your hands, / Attested by the holy close of lips" (v. i. 160–2). Some thought only the joining of hands legally necessary in troth-plighting, others included a kiss. Middleton (*Mad World,* 1608) says "What ist a match, if't be clap hands & lips" (sig. G₃ᵛ). It seems that Austria only kissed because he thought it legally necessary!

535. *assur'd*] betrothed.

538. *Saint Mary's*] Halliwell identified this with "the church of Ronceray". But it must have been a safe guess that any Roman Catholic city would have a St Mary's chapel.

I know she is not, for this match made up
Her presence would have interrupted much:
Where is she and her son? tell me, who knows.

Lew. She is sad and passionate at your highness' tent.

K. Phi. And, by my faith, this league that we have made   545
Will give her sadness very little cure.
Brother of England, how may we content
This widow lady? In her right we came;
Which we, God knows, have turn'd another way,
To our own vantage.

K. John.   We will heal up all;   550
For we'll create young Arthur Duke of Britain
And Earl of Richmond; and this rich fair town
We make him lord of. Call the Lady Constance;
Some speedy messenger bid her repair
To our solemnity: I trust we shall,   555
If not fill up the measure of her will,
Yet in some measure satisfy her so
That we shall stop her exclamation.
Go we, as well as haste will suffer us,
To this unlook'd for, unprepared pomp.   560
                        [*Exeunt all but the Bastard.*

Bast. Mad world! mad kings! mad composition!

543. *son?...knows.*] Steevens; *sonne,...knowes?* F1.   544. *She is*] F1; *She's* Pope.
560. S.D.] Rowe; Exeunt. F1.   561.] F1; *Scene* VI. Pope.

544. *passionate*] full of violent feelings, very sorrowful. I. John compared *Arden of Feversham*: "How now, Alice? what, sad and *passionate?*" (sig. E₄); cf. notes to II. i. 463, III. i. 126.

551. *Duke*] Cf. II. i. 301, note. Holinshed says that Arthur did homage to John for Brittany and Richmond (p. 161, ii); Shakespeare added Angiers (cf. II. i. 489, note). This is interesting, since some early sources called Geoffrey "Count of Angiers" (Arthur's title to Brittany came from Constance). Shakespeare may here think of Angiers as Arthur's patrimony.

556–7. *measure ... measure*] A variation of the "Measure for measure" proverb (Tilley, p. 452), for which cf.

3 H 6, II. vi. 55, *Meas.*, title and v. i. 412.

558. *stop*] stop up (or, put a stop to) her loud complaints; cf. III. iii. 32.

560. *pomp*] ceremony, pageant.

S.D.] "F. 'Exeunt' The absence of 'manet Bastard' suggests that the Bastard's speech may have been an afterthought. T.R. contains nothing corresponding to it" (Wilson).—For *T.R.* echoes of the soliloquy cf. Introduction, p. xlii.

561. *Mad world!*] A common exclamation (cf. Middleton's *A Mad World, My Masters*). The state of the world was used by other dramatists to introduce an analysis of the situation, e.g. by Greene in *Iames the Fourth*:"*And.* Go, and the rot consume thee? Oh

John, to stop Arthur's title in the whole,
Hath willingly departed with a part:
And France, whose armour conscience buckled on,
Whom zeal and charity brought to the field   565
As God's own soldier, rounded in the ear
With that same purpose-changer, that sly divel,
That broker, that still breaks the pate of faith,
That daily break-vow, he that wins of all,
Of kings, of beggars, old men, young men, maids,   570
Who, having no external thing to lose
But the word "maid", cheats the poor maid of that,
That smooth-fac'd gentleman, tickling commodity,
Commodity, the bias of the world,
The world, who of itself is peised well,   575

what a trim world is this? My maister lius by cousoning the king, *I* by fllattering him: *Slipper* my fellow by stealing . . ." (ed. 1598, sig. G₃).

562. *stop . . . whole*] *stop* = bar, preclude (legal). Shakespeare may quibble on "stop a hole" (cf. *Ham.*, v. i. 236, *1 H 4*, IV. i. 71), following l. 558 (= stop her *mouth*): viz. "to stop the hole (Arthur's *title* or claim) through which he might lose his lands".

563. *departed with*] given up.

566. *God's . . . soldier*] I. John compared Siward's last words about his dead son: "Why then, God's soldier be he!" (*Mac.*, v. vii. 76).

rounded] whispered.

567. *With*] By.

divel] Variant of "devil": cf. IV. iii. 95, 100, V. iv. 4.

568. *broker*] "*pimp* or *procuress*" [Malone, comparing the same quibble in *Ham.*, "Do not believe his vows, for they are brokers" (I. iii. 127)].

569. *wins of*] wins something from.

571. *Who, having*] "the relative 'who' appears to refer to 'maids', especially when taken with the following parenthesis, but actually is connected with 'cheats' and so points back to 'Commodity'" [D. A. Traversi, *Approach to Shakespeare* (1938), p. 28]. Malone took *Who having* as the "absolute case,

in the sense of '*they* having'", comparing *Wint.*, v. iii. 149–51. Abbott (sect. 399) classified as "Ellipsis of Nominative", presumably reading "Who, (they) having—".

573. *smooth-fac'd*] bland, deceitful. *tickling*] Also = flattering.

commodity] self-interest, gain. The harangue follows the moralities' denunciations of lucre, like that in Lyly's *Midas* (*c.* 1589), Act I, Sc. i.

574. *bias . . . world*] The bias was the lead weight on one side of bowls which caused the swerving motion. Chapman imitated this passage, also with an *astronomical image*: "Now is it true, earth moves, and heaven stands still;/ . . . The too huge bias of the world hath sway'd / Her back-part upwards, and with that she braves / This hemisphere" (*Bussy D'Ambois*, v. i. 161–5). Like Chapman, Shakespeare refers to the heliocentric system (*world* = earth); an early allusion, but Prof. Hotson has proved Shakespeare's connections with the main English champion of Copernicus [cf. *I, William Shakespeare* (1937), chap. 6].

575–6. *peised . . . even*] Cf. F. Sabie's *Adams Complaint* (1596): "For thee he fram'd earths euen-peysed globe,/ Hanging it in the aire to humaine woonder:" (sig. Bᵛ).

Made to run even upon even ground,
Till this advantage, this vile drawing bias,
This sway of motion, this commodity,
Makes it take head from all indifference,
From all direction, purpose, course, intent:　　　　580
And this same bias, this commodity,
This bawd, this broker, this all-changing word,
Clapp'd on the outward eye of fickle France,
Hath drawn him from his own determin'd aid,
From a resolv'd and honourable war,　　　　585
To a most base and vile-concluded peace.
And why rail I on this commodity?
But for because he hath not woo'd me yet:
Not that I have the power to clutch my hand,
When his fair angels would salute my palm;　　　　590
But for my hand, as unattempted yet,
Like a poor beggar, raileth on the rich.
Well, whiles I am a beggar, I will rail
And say there is no sin but to be rich;

577. *vile drawing*] F1; hyphened Pope.　　　582. *all-changing word*] Pope; *all-changing-word* F1.　　　584. *own determin'd*] F1; hyphened Capell.　　　*aid*] F1; *end* Maxwell conj. (*N. & Q.*, 18 Feb. 1950).

578. *sway*] management, control (On.). Probably also = "that which sways" (cf. l. 574, note).

579. *take head*] rush away.

indifferency] impartiality. Tillyard [*Shakespeare's History Plays* (1944), p. 219] compared the Degree speech in *Troil.*: "The heavens themselves, the planets, and this centre / Observe degree, priority, and place, / Insisture, course, proportion, season, form" (I. iii. 85–7). This (cf. l. 574, note) is an *astronomical* parallel.

583. *Clapp'd . . . eye*] "suddenly presented to the eye" (Smith, comparing III. i. 161); "France is now the bowl, 'drawn' aside by the bias, and 'eye' is used in the double sense of (i) eyeball . . . (ii) the hole in the bowl in which the lead for the bias was inserted (Staunton). 'Clapped in' = stuck in; 'outward eye' = the worldly or physical eye, as distinct from the

'inward eye' of conscience" (Wilson).

586. *base and vile*] base and vile was a common cliché. This comment on the *composition* (l. 561) is Shakespeare's, but echoes M. Paris's condemnation of Magna Carta, which he (more than once) called "compositio vilis et turpis" (p. 357, etc.).

588. *for because*] = because.

589. *clutch*] close (refusing the gift). The *clenched fist* balances the *palm*, symbol of peace.

590–2. *angels . . . salute . . . raileth*] "Our gold is either old or new . . . we have yet remaining, the *riall*, the George noble, the Henry *riall*, the salut, the angell" [Holinshed, quoted by W. Rushton, *Shakespeare Illustrated* (1867), I, 15].—Shakespeare may quibble on angel–salute–rail (riall) (Furness).

591. *unattempted*] unassailed, untempted.

I

And being rich, my virtue then shall be   595
To say there is no vice but beggary.
Since kings break faith upon commodity,
Gain, be my lord, for I will worship thee!   [*Exit.*

SCENE II.—[*The French King's Pavilion.*]

Enter CONSTANCE, ARTHUR, *and* SALISBURY.

Const. Gone to be married! gone to swear a peace!
    False blood to false blood join'd! gone to be friends!
    Shall Lewis have Blanche, and Blanche those provinces?
    It is not so; thou hast misspoke, misheard;
    Be well advis'd, tell o'er thy tale again.   5
    It cannot be; thou dost but say 'tis so.
    I trust I may not trust thee, for thy word
    Is but the vain breath of a common man;
    Believe me, I do not believe thee, man:
    I have a king's oath to the contrary.   10
    Thou shalt be punish'd for thus frighting me,
    For I am sick and capable of fears,
    Oppress'd with wrongs and therefore full of fears,
    A widow, husbandless, subject to fears,

Scene II

Act II *Scene* II.] White; Actus Secundus F1; *Scene* VII. Pope; *Act* III *Scene* I.
Theobald, edd.   The . . . Pavilion.] Theobald; om. F1.   7. *I trust*] F1;
I think Pope.

596. *vice*] Possibly glancing at the *vice*-like *clutch* of the *hand* that is *beggary* (ll. 589–92), which a gesture could convey.

597. *upon*] on account of.

Scene II

Scene II] Cf. Introduction, p. xxxvii.
Pavilion] For tents on the stage cf. Chambers, *Elizabethan Stage*, III, 53, 106.

2. *blood . . . blood*] Resuming I. i. 19, II. i. 329.

12. *For . . . sick*] "This point of phy-sical disturbance is rarely omitted by Shakspeare in the development of insanity" [J. C. Bucknill, *Mad Folk of Shakespeare* (1867), p. 276].

12–15. *fears*] Furness noted similar antistrophe in *Mer. V.*, v. i. 193–7.

14. *husbandless*] Constance was Geoffrey's widow, but married at this time to her third husband. Shakespeare suppressed the later husbands (cf. Introduction, p. lxiv), which may explain his afterthought that a widow is not necessarily husbandless.

subject to] Cf. I. i. 264, note.

A woman, naturally born to fears;   15
And though thou now confess thou didst but jest
With my vex'd spirits I cannot take a truce,
But they will quake and tremble all this day.
What dost thou mean by shaking of thy head?
Why dost thou look so sadly on my son?   20
What means that hand upon that breast of thine?
Why holds thine eye that lamentable rheum,
Like a proud river peering o'er his bounds?
Be these sad signs confirmers of thy words?
Then speak again; not all thy former tale,   25
But this one word, whether thy tale be true.

Sal. As true as I believe you think them false
That give you cause to prove my saying true.

Const. O, if thou teach me to believe this sorrow,
Teach thou this sorrow how to make me die,   30
And let belief and life encounter so
As doth the fury of two desperate men
Which in the very meeting fall, and die.
Lewis marry Blanche! O boy, then where art thou?
France friend with England, what becomes of me?   35
Fellow, be gone: I cannot brook thy sight.
This news hath made thee a most ugly man.

---

15. *born*] F1 (*borne*).   16–17. *jest . . . spirits*] This ed.; *iest . . . spirits*, F1; *jest, . . .*
Spirits Rowe, edd.   17. *spirits*] F1; *sprites* Fleay.   24. *signs*] F1; *sighs* Warburton.

---

15. *born*] Punning on "borne" (=
carried).
16. *jest*] For Shakespeare's puns on
jest-just (joust), cf. *Err.*, II. ii. 8, *R 2*,
I. iii. 95, *Troil.*, I. ii. 221; *take a truce* (=
make peace) of l. 17 supports the
quibble, which plays on two ways of
not being in earnest.
17. *spirits*] The F1 comma is not
disjunctive, but connective: yet to
take *With my vex'd spirits* with either
the preceding or the following
clause spoils the jest, for it goes with
both.
22. *Why . . . rheum,*] Why does thy
eye contain those sorrowful tears?
23. *Like . . . bounds?*] The "disorder
image" (cf. II. i. 337, note) emphasizes

Arthur's unnatural situation. With
rivers, seas, etc., *proud* = swollen, in
flood.
26. *one word*] To say in one word =
to make a simple statement. The *one*
word Constance wants is "The tale is
(not) true."
27. *you*] "Notice Salisbury's use of
the deferential 'you,' while Constance
uniformly addresses him with 'thou'"
(Furness).
32. *fury*] The traditional Furor of
emblematists. Cf. W. Lightfoote's
Complaint of England (1587): "the picture of *Furie*, who is painted with a
sword in his hand, and . . . desperately
rusheth vpon a iauelin, slayeng himselfe" (sig. H₃).

Sal. What other harm have I, good lady, done,
　　But spoke the harm that is by others done?
Const. Which harm within itself so heinous is   40
　　As it makes harmful all that speak of it.
Arth. I do beseech you, madam, be content.
Const. If thou, that bid'st me be content, wert grim,
　　Ugly, and sland'rous to thy mother's womb,
　　Full of unpleasing blots and sightless stains,   45
　　Lame, foolish, crooked, swart, prodigious,
　　Patch'd with foul moles and eye-offending marks,
　　I would not care, I then would be content,
　　For then I should not love thee: no, nor thou
　　Become thy great birth, nor deserve a crown.   50
　　But thou art fair, and at thy birth, dear boy,
　　Nature and fortune join'd to make thee great:
　　Of nature's gifts thou mayst with lilies boast

42. *be content*] be calm, quiet (cf. *R 2*, v. ii. 82).

43–8. *If . . . content*] Cf. *Ven.*, ll. 133–8.

44. *sland'rous*] "that is a disgrace or reproach" (On., comparing *Lucr.*, l. 1001).

45. *blots*] stains.
sightless] unsightly.

46. *swart*] swarthy, dark.
prodigious] "*portentous*, so deformed as to be taken for a *foretoken of evil*" (Johnson).

47. *Patch'd*] Cf. iv. ii. 32–4. Shakespeare seems to have looked on patches as signs of deficiency, not of carefulness.
eye-offending] For the imagery of this important speech cf. Introduction, pp. lxi–lxiii.

50. *deserve*] A fair body (reflecting a fair mind) was thought a recommendation for high office. Tilley (p. 198) quoted the proverb "A fair Face must have good conditions."

51–2. *But . . . great:*] See Introduction, p. xliv. S. Daniel's *Complaint of Rosamond* (1592) is close to Shakespeare: "The blood I staind was good and of the best, / My birth had honor,

and my beautie fame: / Nature and Fortune ioyn'd to make me blest,/ Had I had grace t'haue knowne to vse the same:" (sig. H₄ᵛ). Repeated, beside l. 52, is the collocation of beauty-birth, Nature-Fortune; the lament that these advantages have been lost; the adultery context.

52. *Nature and fortune*] The gifts of Nature and Fortune were often compared in the pre-Shakespearean love-novel. Shakespeare's best summary is in *AYL.*: "Fortune reigns in gifts of the world, not in the lineaments of Nature" (i. ii. 45–6).

53–4. *lilies . . . rose*] The imagery of female beauty is applied to Arthur partly because his *stains* (ll. 43–7, above) = fortune's *adultery* (ll. 56–61) (cf. Introduction, p. lxiii); the feminine beauty of Adonis is similarly described (*Ven.*, 8–12). Miss Porter thought that the rose of England and lily of France were implied, blended in the boy born of both races and heir in both lands. Furness disagreed, since the lily-rose comparison was common, also "one other objection . . . the rose was not adopted as the national emblem until after the Wars of the Roses."

And with the half-blown rose. But fortune, O,
She is corrupted, chang'd and won from thee;   55
Sh' adulterates hourly with thine uncle John,
And with her golden hand hath pluck'd on France
To tread down fair respect of sovereignty,
And made his majesty the bawd to theirs.
France is a bawd to fortune and King John,   60
That strumpet fortune, that usurping John!
Tell me, thou fellow, is not France forsworn?
Envenom him with words, or get thee gone,
And leave those woes alone which I alone
Am bound to underbear!

Sal.   Pardon me, madam,   65
I may not go without you to the kings.

Const. Thou mayst, thou shalt; I will not go with thee:
I will instruct my sorrows to be proud,
For grief is proud an't makes his owner stoop.
To me and to the state of my great grief   70

---

68. *sorrows*] F1; *Sorrow* Rowe ii.   69. *an't*] Anon. *ap.* Cambridge; *and* F1.
his] F1; *its* Variorum 1821.

54. *half-blown*] half-blossomed.

56. *adulterates*] The idea may derive from the whore of Babylon in *Revelation*: "With whom the kings of the earth haue committed fornication" (xvii. 2).

57. *golden hand*] The *golden hand* of *Fortune* recurs in Peele's *Descensus Astraeae* (Oct. 1591) (ed. Bullen, I, 362). Cf. Introduction, p. xlv; I. i. 267, note.

58. *tread down*] The treading down of enemies and opposition is a biblical image, common also in Shakespeare.

63. *Envenom*] Poison, destroy (Schmidt); vituperate (Wilson).— Perhaps Shakespeare had in mind the Psalmist's notion that lies are as venomous as the poison of a serpent, and intended "Tell your *lies* to (Envenom) him, or at any rate leave me."

65. *underbear*] endure; imitated in Chapman's *Alphonsus*, IV. i. 183.

68–74. *I . . . it.*] Shakespeare depicts Constance bowed down by the pride

which Grief is said to possess, and "actuated by this very pride . . . exacting the same kind of obeisance from others" (Malone). Cf. T. White's *Sermon* (1589): "for the *Affliction of an houre wil make the prowdest stoope and sit vpon the grounde, and forget all former felicitie.* Sirac. 11. 27" (sig. E4ᵛ). Or should we read *prov'd . . . prov'd* (ll. 68–9), resuming ll. 28–30? The ideas of *teaching* (*instructing*) Constance's *sorrow(s)* [and of *proving* sorrow(s)] repeat, and *prov'd* was often spelt *proud*. The sense would be: "I will instruct my sorrows to be *tested*; for grief is *experienced* (suffered, i.e. proved to exist) if it makes its owner stoop (to this course of proving it)."

69. *an't*] Often spelt "and". Cf. *Ham.*, IV. vi. 8 (Q₂); *Knacke to Know an Honest Man* (1596): "And shal please your honors" (sig. B₂).

70. *state*] high rank, majesty; seat of state, throne.

Let kings assemble; for my grief's so great
That no supporter but the huge firm earth
Can hold it up: here I and sorrows sit;
Here is my throne, bid kings come bow to it.

[*Throws herself on the ground. Exit Salisbury.*

72. *earth*] F1; *earth* [throwing herself upon it. Capell.   73. *sorrows*] F1; *sorrow*
Pope.   74. S.D.] This ed.; om. F1; [Sits down on the Floor. Theobald.

71–3. *for . . . up:*] *sorrows* (l. 68), *grief* (ll. 69, 70, 71), *sorrow* (l. 73), all resume the *woes* of l. 64, which *adulterate* with Constance as Fortune with John. The dualism is now extended: behind the picture in ll. 71–3 we must see the emblem of Fortune standing on the rolling earth.

74. S.D.] Cf. Introduction, p. xxxix. In *MND.* at the end of Act III, F1 prints "They sleepe all the Act" (i.e. all the *act-interval*): so Constance (and Arthur?) remain on-stage during this interval.

ACT III

SCENE I.—[*The French King's Pavilion.*]

CONSTANCE *and* ARTHUR, *seated. Enter* KING JOHN, KING
PHILIP, LEWIS, BLANCHE, ELEANOR, *the* BASTARD, AUSTRIA,
SALISBURY, *and Attendants.*

K. Phi. 'Tis true, fair daughter; and this blessed day
    Ever in France shall be kept festival:
    To solemnize this day the glorious sun
    Stays in his course and plays the alchemist,
    Turning with splendour of his precious eye   5
    The meagre cloddy earth to glittering gold:
    The yearly course that brings this day about
    Shall never see it but a holy day.
Const. A wicked day, and not a holy day!   [*Rising.*

ACT III
Scene 1
Act III *Scene* I.] F1 (Actus Tertius, Scaena prima.); scene contd. Theobald,
edd.; *Act* III *Scene* II. Hanmer.   The . . . Pavilion.] As Theobald; om. F1.
S.D.] This ed.; Enter King Iohn, France, Dolphin, Blanch, Elianor, Philip,
Austria, Constance. F1; King *John*, King *Philip*, discovered on a Throne, . . . Bell.
8, 9. *holy day*] F1; *holiday* ed. 1753.   9. S.D.] Theobald; om. F1.

Act III *Scene* 1] For the division cf.
Introduction, p. xxxvii.
    1. *'Tis true*] Resuming II. ii. 26?
    1–2. *this . . . festival:*] Cf. R. W.'s
Three Lordes and Three Ladies of London
(1590): "By my consent one day shal
serue vs all,/ Which shall be kept for
euer festiuall" (sig. H₂).
    3–4. *To . . . course*] Carter compared
Joshua, x. 12–4: "Sunne, staye thou
in Gibeon," etc.
    3. *the glorious sun*] A favourite cliché
of Shakespeare and contemporaries
(cf. *LLL.*, I. i. 84; *Tw.N.*, IV. iii. 1;
2 H 6, III. i. 353); *glorious* was a richer
word than now.

    4. *plays the alchemist*] So Sonnet 33
(Malone).
    5–6. *Turning . . . gold:*] An old min-
eralogical theory, as in Peele's *Descensus Astraeae* (1591): "in Tellus' veins
the parching sun / Doth gold and glit-
tering minerals create" (ed. Bullen,
1, 367).
    5. *precious eye*] The sun as eye was a
common-place image.
    6. *meagre*] barren.
    8. *holy day*] "Holy day" and "holi-
day" were not yet distinct.
    9, etc. *day*] With this repetition of
day cf. *Zephaniah*, i. 15, 16 and Constance's style throughout.

59

What hath this day deserv'd? what hath it done,   10
That it in golden letters should be set
Among the high tides in the calendar?
Nay, rather turn this day out of the week,
This day of shame, oppression, perjury.
Or, if it must stand still, let wives with child   15
Pray that their burthens may not fall this day,
Lest that their hopes prodigiously be cross'd:
But on this day let seamen fear no wrack;
No bargains break that are not this day made;
This day, all things begun come to ill end,   20
Yea, faith itself to hollow falsehood change!
K. Phi. By heaven, lady, you shall have no cause
To curse the fair proceedings of this day:
Have I not pawn'd to you my majesty?
Const. You have beguil'd me with a counterfeit   25
Resembling majesty, which, being touch'd and tried,

18. *But on this day*] Dyce; *But (on this day)* F1.   26. *being*] F1; om. Pope.

12. *high tides*] festival days (usual gloss). Malone suggested that they are the high tides of the sea, "marked in every almanack", withdrawing the note when criticized that in this sense they are wicked, not holy. Deighton thought the Golden Number might be referred to. (N.B. The Golden Number is explained in one old calendar as written "with letters of gold, right at that day whereon the Moone changed"; Furness thought that *golden letters* (l. 11) meant "red letters", comparing *LLL.*, v. ii. 44: cf. our note to II. i. 316.) The "tides of the sea" sense recurs in l. 18, and must be present. Read: "How has this day deserved to be set with golden letters with the (holy) festivals *and likewise with the* (wicked) *tides* (even these latter being too good company for it)? Nay—".

13–14. *Nay*, . . . *perjury*] Following *Job.*, iii. 3, v. 6 (Upton).

15–17. *Or*, . . . *cross'd:*] Following *Matthew*, xxiv. 19 (Deighton).

15. *wives*] women, the older sense.

17. *prodigiously*] "(?) by monstrous births" (On.); "by the production

of a prodigy, a monster" (Steevens).

18. *But*] Except. The transition from *wives with child* to *seamen* may be due to the Litany, where they were prayed for together.

19. *No* . . . *break*] "In the ancient almanacks . . . days supposed to be favourable or unfavourable to bargains, are distinguished" (Steevens); *bargains* = agreements.

20. *This* . . . *end*] Alluding to the proverb "An ill Beginning has an ill ending" (Tilley, p. 41).

23. *fair*] favourable, fortunate; equitable, honest.

25. *counterfeit*] "a false coin. A *counterfeit* formerly signified also a portrait.—A representation of the king being usually impressed on his coin, the word seems to be here used equivocally" (Malone).

26. *touch'd and tried*] "tested by being rubbed on a touchstone . . . the trained eye could tell the fineness of gold rubbed on it by the character of the streak left" (I. John). Shakespeare at times used *touch'd* alone in this sense; possibly *and tried* was added by the

Proves valueless: you are forsworn, forsworn!
You came in arms to spill mine enemies' blood,
But now in arms you strengthen it with yours.
The grappling vigour and rough frown of war   30
Is cold in amity, and painted peace,
And our oppression hath made up this league.
Arm, arm, you heavens, against these perjur'd kings!
A widow cries; be husband to me, heavens!
Let not the hours of this ungodly day   35
Wear out the day's in peace; but, ere sunset,
Set armed discord 'twixt these perjur'd kings!
Hear me, O, hear me!

Aust.   Lady Constance, peace!
Const. War! war! no peace! peace is to me a war.
O Limoges! O Austria! thou dost shame   40
That bloody spoil: thou slave, thou wretch, thou
      coward!

---

31. *cold*] F1; *cool'd* Hanmer.   *in amity*] F1; *inamity* Crowdown (*N. & Q.*, 16 Dec.
1871).   *amity,*] F1; *amity* Pope.   36. *day's*] F1 (*daies*); *day* Theobald, edd.

compositor unconsciously completing
a familiar phrase.

28–9. *in arms . . . in arms*] "*You came
in war to destroy my enemies*, but *now you
strengthen them* in embraces" (Johnson).
Perhaps the quartering of the arms of
England and France in the marriage
of Blanche and Lewis is also meant.
Cf. II. i. 345–6.

28. *spill*] shed; destroy, kill (as in
Ham., IV. v. 20, *Lr.*, III. ii. 8).

31. *cold*] The metaphor has been
called inconsistent, but is so no more
than II. i. 479 (see note).

painted peace] "feigned, unreal
peace"; or perhaps "patched up
peace"; in apposition to *amity* and to
oppression.

32. *our*] The only (and very slight)
evidence that Arthur is present in this
scene (cf. Introduction, p. xxxix).

33. *perjur'd kings*] Cf. Appendix B,
p. 169.

34. *A . . . heavens!*] Many biblical
passages where *heaven* is the *husband* of
widows were compared by Carter, e.g.:
"Thou . . . shalt not remember the re-

proch of thy widowhood. . . . Hee that
made thee is thine husband" (*Isaiah*,
liv. 4–5).

35–6. *Let . . . peace;*] In R.C. Latin
religious verse "hora" was often used
with a quibbling sense (= hour;
prayer), and here *hours* may mean
prayers (cf. *O.E.D.*, hour, 5), viz.
"Let not my prayers on this ungodly
day see the hours of the day come to a
peaceful conclusion." The Roman
Catholic views of John's enemies are
clear (cf. III. i. 62 ff.; II. i. 171, note),
and F1 makes sense.

36–7. *ere . . . kings!*] Adapted from
Ephesians, iv. 26? ("let not the sunne
go downe vpon your wrath").

39. *peace . . . war.*] So in B. and F.'s
Laws of Candy (ed. 1647): "I found no
difference 'twixt War and Peace / For
War was peace to me, and Peace was
war" (sig. 3G2v).

40. *Limoges . . . Austria*] Cf. Introduction, p. xxi.

41. *spoil*] Cœur-de-lion's lion's-skin.
Following Ovid's *spolium leonis* (*Metam.*,
ix. 113).

Thou little valiant, great in villainy!
Thou ever strong upon the stronger side!
Thou fortune's champion, that dost never fight
But when her humorous ladyship is by　　　　　45
To teach thee safety! thou art perjur'd too,
And sooth'st up greatness. What a fool art thou,
A ramping fool, to brag, and stamp, and swear
Upon my party! Thou cold-blooded slave,
Hast thou not spoke like thunder on my side,　　50
Been sworn my soldier, bidding me depend
Upon thy stars, thy fortune and thy strength,
And dost thou now fall over to my foes?
Thou wear a lion's hide! doff it for shame,
And hang a calve's-skin on those recreant limbs.　55
Aust. O, that a man should speak those words to me!
Bast. And hang a calve's-skin on those recreant limbs.
Aust. Thou dar'st not say so, villain, for thy life.
Bast. And hang a calve's-skin on those recreant limbs.
K. John. We like not this; thou dost forget thyself.　60

Enter PANDULPH.

K. Phi. Here comes the holy legate of the pope.
Pand. Hail, you anointed deputies of heaven!

49. *cold-blooded*] F4; no hyphen F1. *calve's-skin* throughout); *calf's-skin* Capell, edd. 61. S.D.] F1; . . . attended. Capell.

55. *calve's-skin*] F1 (*Calues skin* or *Calues-skin* throughout); *calf's-skin* Capell, edd. 61.] F1; *Scene* II. Pope; III. Hanmer.

43. *strong upon*] "determined, resolute (to side with the stronger)"; or "strong, *because* on the stronger side".

45. *humorous*] capricious.

47. *sooth'st up*] flatterest; *up* is emphatic.

48. *ramping*] "'Ramping' is suggested by the lion's skin which Austria wears, and is a proper epithet of the lion, in the sense tearing, pawing. So in 3 Henry VI, v. 2. 13" (Wright). Furness interpreted "rushing wildly about".

53. *fall over*] revolt.

55. *calve's-skin*] "When fools were kept for diversion in great families, they were distinguished by a calf's-

skin coat . . . that they might be known for fools" (Hawkins, *ap.* Furness). Ritson thought Austria's cowardice not his foolishness is jeered at, for *calf* = meek fellow was pre-Shakespearean. Both meanings were probably intended.

56. *O . . . me!*] Dyce compared Sidney's *Arcadia* (1590): "O God (cried out *Pyrocles*) that thou wert a man that usest these wordes unto me" (p. 486).

62. *anointed deputies*] Reminding the kings of their place in the religious scheme of the world.

62–72. *Hail, . . . thee.*] A speech very similar in *John* and *T.R.* Pandulph's reference to Langton comes from

To thee, King John, my holy errand is.
I Pandulph, of fair Milan cardinal,
And from Pope Innocent the legate here, 65
Do in his name religiously demand
Why thou against the church, our holy mother,
So wilfully dost spurn; and force perforce
Keep Stephen Langton, chosen archbishop
Of Canterbury, from that holy see: 70
This, in our foresaid holy father's name,
Pope Innocent, I do demand of thee.

K. John. What earthy name to interrogatories
Can taste the free breath of a sacred king?
Thou canst not, cardinal, devise a name 75
So slight, unworthy and ridiculous,
To charge me to an answer, as the pope.
Tell him this tale; and from the mouth of England
Add thus much more, that no Italian priest
Shall tithe or toll in our dominions; 80
But as we, under God, are supreme head,
So under Him that great supremacy,

---

73. *earthy*] F1; *earthly* Pope.　74. *taste*] F1; *tax* Rowe iii; *task* Theobald.
81. *God*] Collier MS.; *heauen* F1.

Foxe, but the words of the reference from (a different context in) Holinshed. (Cf. Introduction, pp. xiii, xx.)

63–71. *holy*] Cf. *noble*, v. ii. 40–3, *honourable* in *Caes.*, III. ii. 88, *sqq.* The "holy father Pope, holy mother Church" jargon was detested by Protestants.

64. *cardinal*] The Cardinal Pandulf with whom the legate Pandulph in *John* was confused by Shakespeare and some earlier writers (Introduction, p. xxv) was not cardinal of Milan.

65. *Innocent*] Innocent III, the great upholder of papal authority.

68. *force perforce*] by compulsion; so *2 H 6*, I. i. 259.

69. *Stephen Langton*] Cf. Appendix A, p. 155.

73–4. *What . . . king?*] Cf. II. i. 110–12.

73. *earthy*] John compares the dis-

parity between kings and others through the elements air (= *breath*) and earth; "earthly" and "earthy" were not sharply distinct as now.

name to interrogatories] title or claim to demand answers as from interrogatories. An accused person or witness had to answer interrogatories (questions formally put) as upon oath; cf. *All's W.*, IV. iii. 198, *sqq.*, *Mer.V.*, v. i. 298.

74. *taste*] put to the proof, try, test (*O.E.D.* taste, 2), as (quibblingly) in *Troil.*: "Praise us as we are tasted, allow us as we prove" (III. ii. 97), *Tw.N.*, III. i. 89, III. iv. 270, etc.; *task* is no improvement.

breath] "speech" (Malone); or perhaps "life".

81. *God*] Cf. Introduction, p. xxxiii n. In *T.R.* John says "I raigne next vnder God, supreame head" (I. v. 80).

Where we do reign, we will alone uphold
Without th' assistance of a mortal hand:
So tell the pope, all reverence set apart   85
To him and his usurp'd authority.

K. Phi. Brother of England, you blaspheme in this.

K. John. Though you and all the kings of Christendom
Are led so grossly by this meddling priest,
Dreading the curse that money may buy out;   90
And by the merit of vild gold, dross, dust,
Purchase corrupted pardon of a man,
Who in that sale sells pardon from himself;
Though you and all the rest so grossly led
This juggling witchcraft with revenue cherish,   95
Yet I alone, alone do me oppose
Against the pope, and count his friends my foes.

Pand. Then, by the lawful power that I have,
Thou shalt stand curs'd and excommunicate:
And blessed shall he be that doth revolt   100
From his allegiance to an heretic;
And meritorious shall that hand be call'd,

---

91. *by*] F1; *buy* Warburton (press-corrected).

86. *usurp'd authority*] Cf. II. i. 118.—
In Protestant England the "usurped
power" of the pope became a watch-
word. In Bale's *King Iohan* "Usurped
Power" is a character; Foxe often used
the phrase (cf. Introduction, p. xv);
"usurped authority" was almost
equally common.

87. *Brother of England*] Common
form of address between kings in the
old drama.

89. *grossly*] "stupidly"; or perhaps
"materially, opposed to spiritually"
as in *Mer. V.*, v. i. 65, *Tw.N.*, v. i.
247.

91. *merit*] Alluding to the doctrine of
merit. Whereas the Protestants expected "through thonelie merittes of
Jesus Christe . . . to be made partaker
of lyfe everlastinge" (Shakespeare's
will), Roman Catholics held that forgiveness of sins is impossible unless
man himself "satisfy", "which they

for money sake haue inuented,
in steede of the bloodsheeding of
Iesus Christ" (Protestant pamphlet,
1588).

gold, dross] The thought that "gold
is dross" was common.

93. *from himself*] "i.e. not from God.
Some take it as 'sells away his own
pardon.' " (Wilson).

95. *juggling witchcraft . . . revenue*] Cf.
Introduction, p. xv; *juggling* = trick-
ing.

100–1. *And . . . heretic*] Tilley (p. 200)
quoted the proverb "No Faith with
heretics." Protestants hated this Roman Catholic doctrine.

102. *meritorious*] In the trials of the
intending assassins of the Queen in the
1580's the "merit" (cf. l. 91, note) of
the murder became notorious. Shakespeare's cousin Edward Arden was
executed for such attempted regicide
in 1583.

Canonized and worshipp'd as a saint,
That takes away by any secret course
Thy hateful life.

Const.   O, lawful let it be   105
That I have room with Rome to curse awhile!
Good father cardinal, cry thou amen
To my keen curses; for without my wrong
There is no tongue hath power to curse him right.

Pand. There's law and warrant, lady, for my curse.   110

Const. And for mine too: when law can do no right
Let it be lawful that law bar no wrong!
Law cannot give my child his kingdom here,
For he that holds his kingdom holds the law;
Therefore, since law itself is perfect wrong,   115
How can the law forbid my tongue to curse?

Pand. Philip of France, on peril of a curse,
Let go the hand of that arch-heretic;
And raise the power of France upon his head,
Unless he do submit himself to Rome.   120

Elea. Look'st thou pale, France? do not let go thy hand.

---

106. *room*] F1; *leave* Pope.   111. *too* : . . . *right*] *too*, . . . *right*. F1.

---

103. *Canonized*] For the accent cf.
III. iii. 52, *Ham.*, I. iv. 47. Canonization
was promised to the murderers of
Elizabeth, not of John (Furness). In
1590 an audience would think first of
Jaques Clement, the murderer of
Henry III, whose proposed canonization was causing great indignation:
cf. Introduction, p. xlvi.

106. *room with Rome*] Cf. *Caes.*, I. ii.
155. Two pronunciations of "Rome"
were current, a variant ru:m (=
room) as well as ro:m. The obvious
pun was pre-Shakespearean, as in W.
Lightfoote's *Complaint of England*
(1587): "But roome now, els shall we
bring all *Rome* on our back" (sig. G₂).

107-8. *Good* . . . *curses*;] Noble suggested a reference to the Commination
Service (which was compulsory four
times a year). The minister recited the
curses and the people had to answer
"Amen" (cf. *Deuteronomy*, xxvii. 14–

26). N.B. Constance reverses the role
of the priest.

111-16. *when* . . . *curse?*] Noble compared *Romans*, iii. 19, iv. 15, vii. 6–7.

112. *bar*] Cf. II. i. 192, note.

113. *here*] Cf. IV. ii. 89, note.

115-16. *law . . . law*] M. Joseph
detected equivocation: "Constance
argues as if the law of England, mis-
held by John and by him made perfect
wrong, is identical with the law of
God forbidding individuals to curse"
[*Shakespeare's Use of the Arts of Language*
(1949), p. 231].

118. *hand*] The holding of hands was
a sign of courtesy and affection between equals. Its significance here has
been prepared for: cf. I. i. 163, note,
II. i. 494, 532, 533. Cf. also *Proverbs*:
"(Thogh) hand (ioyne) in hand, the
wicked shal not be vnpunished" (xi.
21).

119. *head*] = head; army (Wilson).

Const. Look to that, devil, lest that France repent,
　　And by disjoining hands, hell lose a soul.

Aust. King Philip, listen to the cardinal.

Bast. And hang a calve's-skin on his recreant limbs.　　125

Aust. Well, ruffian, I must pocket up these wrongs,
　　Because—

Bast.　　　　　Your breeches best may carry them.

K. John. Philip, what say'st thou to the cardinal?

Const. What should he say, but as the cardinal?

Lew. Bethink you, father; for the difference　　130
　　Is purchase of a heavy curse from Rome,
　　Or the light loss of England for a friend:
　　Forgo the easier.

Blanche.　　　　　That's the curse of Rome.

Const. O Lewis, stand fast! the devil tempts thee here
　　In likeness of a new untrimmed bride.　　135

Blanche. The Lady Constance speaks not from her faith,
　　But from her need.

Const.　　　　　O, if thou grant my need,
　　Which only lives but by the death of faith,
　　That need must needs infer this principle,

---

122. *that*] F1; *it* Maxwell (*N. & Q.*, 18 Feb. 1950).　　135. *untrimmed*] F1; *and trimmed* Theobald; *uptrimmèd* Dyce.

122. *that*] "The normal expression before a clause beginning 'that' or 'lest' is 'look to it,' " (Maxwell, postulating "it", spelt "yt").

125. *calve's-skin*] The jibe may be resumed in contempt of Austria's support of the pope. After the Bull of Excommunication the pope was nicknamed the "bull" of Rome, and his supporters his "calves"—an idiom still popular in 1590.

126-7. *Well . . . them.*] Did Austria wear breeches with extra-large pockets? Steevens compared *King Leir* (1605): "Well, I haue a payre of slops for the nonce, / Will hold all your mocks" (sig. G2). Cf. also *Arden of Feversham* (1592): "But rather then I pocket vp this wrong. / *Francklin.* What will you doo sir? / *Mos.* Reuenge it on the proudest of you both:" (sig. B2).

"Pocket up" had only recently acquired the sense "put up with".

135. *untrimmed*] "unbedded" (Ridley). This slang sense of *trim* was once common (cf. *Tit.*, v. i. 92-9). The allusion to the temptation of St Anthony (St Dunstan) supports it (noted by Z. Grey. The devil tempted Anthony as a naked woman). Some take *untrimmed* = "with hair hanging loose in the fashion of a bride". Malone compared *Rom.*: "Go waken Juliet, go and trim her up" (IV. iv. 25).

136-7. *speaks . . . need.*] "says not what she thinks but what suits her purpose" (Wilson).

137-42. *O . . . down!*] "Here 'need' = her distress, and 'faith' = the promise of France. The image of the last two lines reminds us of *Rich. II*, 4. 1. 181-99" (Wilson).

That faith would live again by death of need. 140
O then tread down my need, and faith mounts up:
Keep my need up, and faith is trodden down!
K. John. The king is mov'd, and answers not to this.
Const. O, be remov'd from him, and answer well!
Aust. Do so, King Philip; hang no more in doubt. 145
Bast. Hang nothing but a calve's-skin, most sweet lout.
K. Phi. I am perplex'd, and know not what to say.
Pand. What canst thou say but will perplex thee more,
If thou stand excommunicate and curs'd?
K. Phi. Good reverend father, make my person yours, 150
And tell me how you would bestow yourself.
This royal hand and mine are newly knit,
And the conjunction of our inward souls—
Married in league, coupled and link'd together
With all religious strength of sacred vows; 155
The latest breath that gave the sound of words—
Was deep-sworn faith, peace, amity, true love
Between our kingdoms and our royal selves.
And even before this truce, but new before,
No longer than we well could wash our hands 160
To clap this royal bargain up of peace,
Heaven knows, they were besmear'd and overstain'd
With slaughter's pencil, where revenge did paint
The fearful difference of incensed kings:

153–6. *souls*— . . . *vows;* . . . *words*—] This ed; *soules* . . . *vowes,* . . . *words* F1; *soules* . . . *vowes:* . . . *words* F2.

141. *tread down*] Cf. II. ii. 58.
144. *O . . . well*] Perhaps a chess-allusion (cf. II. i. 123), i.e. to the danger when kings are near one another; *remove* = our "move", *answer* = make a counter-move.
150. *make . . . yours*] put yourself in my place (Wilson).
153–5. *And . . . vows;*] "It seems doubtful whether the construction here is, 'the conjunction of our souls *is* married in league,' the words 'coupled . . . vows' being an amplification of 'married in league'; or, 'the conjunction of our souls *being* married in league' is 'coupled,' etc. In either case

there is tautology" (Deighton). We prefer a parenthesis (ll. 154–6), with l. 156 an amplification of *vows* (l. 155).
154. *coupled*] = both *Married* and *link'd*: cf. III. iii. 17–19, note.
159. *even before*] just before.
new before] recently, lately before.
161. *clap . . . up*] "clap hands and a bargain" (*H 5*, V. ii. 134) was proverbial since a hand-shake sealed a bargain; *clap up* = settle hastily (On. compared *Shr.*, II. i. 319).
163. *pencil*] a (thick) paint-brush.
164. *difference*] disagreement; cf. II. i. 355.

And shall these hands, so lately purg'd of blood,   165
So newly join'd in love, so strong in both,
Unyoke this seizure and this kind regreet?
Play fast and loose with faith? so jest with heaven,
Make such unconstant children of ourselves,
As now again to snatch our palm from palm,   170
Unswear faith sworn, and on the marriage-bed
Of smiling peace to march a bloody host,
And make a riot on the gentle brow
Of true sincerity? O, holy sir,
My reverend father, let it not be so!   175
Out of your grace, devise, ordain, impose
Some gentle order, and then we shall be blest
To do your pleasure and continue friends.

Pand. All form is formless, order orderless,
Save what is opposite to England's love.   180
Therefore to arms! be champion of our church,
Or let the church, our mother, breathe her curse,
A mother's curse, on her revolting son.
France, thou mayst hold a serpent by the tongue,

166. *strong in both*] Both "love so strong in both parties" and "hands (i.e. kings) so strong in blood (i.e. enmity) and love" have been proposed.

167. *seizure*] clasp, grasp.

regreet] "A(return of a) salutation or greeting" (*O.E.D.*).

168. *Play . . . loose*] i.e. cheat; *fast and loose* was a cheating game in which a leather belt was folded up, the victim having to thrust a skewer through the middle. The belt was "fast" or "loose" at the wish of the holder, who had only to move the ends to change the middle (Furness). Cf. *Ant.*, IV. x. 41, *LLL.*, I. ii. 164.

169. *children*] i.e. children of the Church.

170. *palm*] i.e. the symbol of peace.

173. *brow*] forehead. The brow reflected character to the Elizabethans (cf. v. ii. 176), so that *gentle brow* = gentleness. Read: "do an outrage to

the person of our gentle bride (i.e. *true sincerity*)".

174. *true sincerity*] Theologians had made "the true sincerity of Christianity" a cliché.

176-7. *devise . . . order*] Pseudo-legal jargon, as in royal proclamations, where it was a set formula, after the statement of a grievance, that "some present (or good, or fair) order be ordained (or devised, or imposed etc.)", with the usual multiplication of terms; *order* = suitable measures.

179. *form . . . order*] Synonyms (cf. IV. ii. 22). Pandulph does not take *order* in Philip's sense, but = ordered government, a sacrosanct Tudor conception (for which see *Troil.*, I. iii. 75–137).

181. *champion*] Cf.III.i. 193, note.

184. *a . . . tongue,*] So *Ado*, v. i. 90. Tilley (p. 739) took the common origin of ll. 184–6 to be the proverb "He holds a Wolf by the ears."

A cased lion by the mortal paw,　　　　　185
A fasting tiger safer by the tooth,
Than keep in peace that hand which thou dost hold.
K. Phi.　I may disjoin my hand, but not my faith.
Pand.　So mak'st thou faith an enemy to faith,
And like a civil war set'st oath to oath,　　　　　190
Thy tongue against thy tongue. O, let thy vow
First made to heaven, first be to heaven perform'd,
That is, to be the champion of our church.
What since thou swor'st is sworn against thyself
And may not be performed by thyself,　　　　　195
For that which thou hast sworn to do amiss
Is not amiss when it is truly done,
And being not done, where doing tends to ill,
The truth is then most done not doing it:
The better act of purposes mistook　　　　　200

185. *cased*] F1 ; *chased* Pope ; *chafed* Theobald, edd. ; *caged* Collier conj.　197. *not*]
F1 ; *most* Hanmer ; *yet* Warburton ; *but* Collier ii (MS.).

185. *cased lion*] Theobald's "chafed
lion" was a common phrase (as in *H 8*,
III. ii. 207), and may be right. Some
defend *cased lion* = a lion irritated by
confinement (Steevens). But surely the
point is due to Austria's lion's-skin; a
cased lion is one still wearing his *case* (=
skin), i.e. a live lion. Cf. *T.R.* "the
Lyons case, / Which here he *holds*" (I. iv.
31–2; cf. I. ii. 128–30).
　mortal] deadly.
　188. *but . . . faith.*] "and yet keep my
faith", or "but my faith I may not disjoin (break)."
　189–223. *So . . . weight.*] In this
speech, said T. W. Baldwin (*William
Shakspere's Small Latine*, II, 277),
Shakespeare follows exactly the form
of ratiocinatio prescribed by Erasmus
for "argumentatio perfectissima".
Pandulph propounds the doctrine of
equivocation, hated by Protestants,
for which cf. *Ham.*, v. i. 148, *Mac.*, II.
iii. 10–13.
　193. *champion*] "The King of France
was styled the Eldest Son of the Church

and the Most Christian King"
(Wright).
　196–9. *For . . . it*] Tilley (p. 511)
quoted the proverb "An unlawful
Oath is better broken than kept", with
many Shakespearean uses, as *2 H 6*,
v. i. 182.
　197–9. *Is . . . it*] "is *not amiss* (i.e.,
becomes right) when it is *done truely*
(that is, as he explains it, not done at
all) ; and being *not done*, where it would
be a *sin* to *do it*, the *truth* is *most done*
when you *do it not*" (Ritson). In *truly*
(l. 197), *truth* (l. 199) there are quibbles
on the meaning "righteous(ness)",
"faithful(ness)".
　200–2. *The . . . direct*] Cf. *Ham.*, II. i.
66: "By indirections find directions
out", where *indirections* and *directions*
parallel *falsehood* and *truth* as here.
"When we have turned aside from the
straight path the best thing to do is not
to retrace our steps but to take another
turning which is a short cut to the
direction we ought to go" (Wilson,
comparing *Ham.*, v. ii. 398).

K

Is to mistake again; though indirect,
Yet indirection thereby grows direct,
And falsehood falsehood cures, as fire cools fire
Within the scorched veins of one new-burn'd.
It is religion that doth make vows kept,   205
But thou hast sworn against religion:
By what thou swear'st against the thing thou swear'st,
And mak'st an oath the surety for thy truth!
Against an oath the truth thou art unsure
To swear—swears only not to be forsworn!—   210
Else what a mockery should it be to swear?
But thou dost swear only to be forsworn,
And most forsworn, to keep what thou dost swear.
Therefore thy later vows against thy first
Is in thyself rebellion to thyself;   215
And better conquest never canst thou make
Than arm thy constant and thy nobler parts
Against these giddy loose suggestions:
Upon which better part our prayers come in,

---

208. *truth!*] F3 (*truth:*); *truth*, F1, edd.   209. *oath*] F1; *oath*. Heath, edd.
210. *swear—*. . . *forsworn!—*] This ed.; *sweare*, . . . *forsworne*, F1.   *swears*] F1;
swear Rowe iii.   214. *later*] F1; *latter* F3.   *vows*] F1; *vow* Dyce ii.

---

203. *And . . . cures*] Tilley (p. 147) quoted the proverb "One Deceit (falsehood) drives out another."

fire cools fire] Cf. *Gent.*, II. iv. 193, *Cor.*, IV. vii. 54, *Rom.*, I. ii. 47, *Caes.*, III. i. 171. Tilley (p. 215) quoted the proverb "One Fire drives out another."

205. *It . . . kept*] Cf. *LLL.*: "It is religion to be thus forsworn" (IV. iii. 363), and cf. these two treatments of perjury.

206. *against religion*] = "irreligiously", or "against the interests of religion (i.e. siding with heretics)".

207. *By . . . swear'st,*] By the truth (faithfulness) which you swear to John (you commit yourself) against your own truth (integrity).

208–10. *And . . . forsworn!—*] "(Having forsworn thy truth) thou hast the effrontery to make an oath the pledge of thy truth!" (l. 208). Ll. 209, 210 are sarcastic (especially *art unsure*): "Thou art unlikely to swear the truth (if thy oath runs) against an (earlier) oath:— (He) swears only to avoid being forsworn (who has heard the like)!" Our punctuation is less confusing than that of the *textus receptus* and closer to F1.

210. *swears*] Usually taken as second person. The form (= swear*est*) is used elsewhere by Shakespeare, but the syntax is then un-English. We prefer *swears* as third person. Elliptic exclamation was common—cf. *A Knacke to Know an Honest Man* (1596): "*Eta serua vostra fettisima seruidore siniore.* / *For:* Speakes in parables." (sig. Cᵛ).

215. *Is*] "*Therefore* (to put) *thy later vows*, whence the singular verb" (Moberly); "singular on account of 'rebellion'" (Wright).

218. *giddy*] foolish.

suggestions] temptations (Furness).

If thou vouchsafe them. But if not, then know   220
The peril of our curses light on thee
So heavy as thou shalt not shake them off,
But in despair die under their black weight.
Aust. Rebellion, flat rebellion!
Bast.   Will't not be?
Will not a calve's-skin stop that mouth of thine?   225
Lew. Father, to arms!
Blanche.   Upon thy wedding-day?
Against the blood that thou hast married?
What, shall our feast be kept with slaughter'd men?
Shall braying trumpets and loud churlish drums,
Clamours of hell, be measures to our pomp?   230
O husband, hear me! ay, alack, how new
Is "husband" in my mouth! even for that name,
Which till this time my tongue did ne'er pronounce,
Upon my knee I beg, go not to arms
Against mine uncle.
Const.   O, upon my knee,   235
Made hard with kneeling, I do pray to thee,
Thou virtuous Dolphin, alter not the doom
Forethought by heaven!
Blanche. Now shall I see thy love: what motive may
Be stronger with thee than the name of wife?   240
Const. That which upholdeth him that thee upholds,
His honour: O, thine honour, Lewis, thine honour!
Lew. I muse your majesty doth seem so cold,
When such profound respects do pull you on.

---

224. *Will't*] F1 (*Wil't*); *Wilt* Capell.   231. *ay,*] F1; *ah!* Theobald ii.   235–8. *O
. . . heaven!*] Pope; three lines F1 (ending *kneeling,* | *. . .* Daulphin, | *. . .
heauen.*|).

222–3. *heavy . . . black*] Transferred
epithets; *heavy curse, black curse* are
implied.

224. *Will't not be?*] "Is everything in
vain?"—Onions compared *Rom.*, IV. v.
11, *1 H 6*, I. v. 33.

229. *braying trumpets*] Probably a recent coinage; cf. *Answer to the Vntruthes*
(1589), by D. F. R. de M.: "braieng
trumps" (sig. H₂ᵛ); cf. *R 2*, I. iii. 135;

Ham., I. iv. 11.
   churlish drums] Cf. II. i. 76.
   230. *measures*] melodies.
   237–8. *Thou . . . heaven!*] Protestants
held "it is impossible for any of the
elect to fall away"; the Roman
Catholics "Men cannot bee saued,
though they bee predestinate, vnlesse
they keepe Gods commaundements."
   244. *respects*] considerations.

Pand. I will denounce a curse upon his head.   245

K. Phi. Thou shalt not need. England, I will fall from
        thee.

Const. O fair return of banish'd majesty!

Elea. O foul revolt of French inconstancy!

K. John. France, thou shalt rue this hour within this
        hour.

Bast. Old time the clock-setter, that bald sexton time,   250
        Is it as he will? well then, France shall rue.

Blanche. The sun's o'ercast with blood: fair day, adieu!
        Which is the side that I must go withal?
        I am with both: each army hath a hand;
        And in their rage, I having hold of both,   255
        They whirl asunder and dismember me.
        Husband, I cannot pray that thou mayst win;
        Uncle, I needs must pray that thou mayst lose;

---

246. *I will*] F1 ; *I'll* Pope.   249. K. John.] Eng. F1.

<hr/>

246. *fall from*] forsake.

248. *O . . . inconstancy!*] Delius compared *1 H 6*: "Done like a Frenchman: turn, and turn again!" (III. iii. 85).

249. *France . . . hour.*] Cf. *1 H 6*: "France, thou shalt rue this treason with thy tears" (III. ii. 36).

within this hour] in a short time (common phrase). Possibly there was an emblem (figuring Time or Death) with the motto "Thou shalt rue this hour within this hour", in the popular "Ut hora, sic fugit vita" class.

250–1. *Old . . . rue*] The sexton was in charge of the church clock, and dug the graves. The mattock and hourglass of Father Time are also alluded to. Shakespeare plays on a popular quibble, as in Greene's *Quip* (1592): "the Courtiers comfort, Time, an herb that many stumble on . . . [makes] a snaile . . . as swift as a swallow", "they lookte so proudly . . . that they stumbled on a bed of Rue, that grewe at the bottome of the banke where the Time was planted" (sigs. A₃, A₃ᵛ). The last page of Greene's *Mamillia*, Pt II (writ-

ten by 1583) shows that Tilley's proverb "Rue and thyme grow both in one garden" (p. 577) was pre-Shakespearean. Read: "If it is only a question of time (thyme), then France shall rue, because rue and thyme go together (grow in the same garden)."

252. *The . . . blood*] i.e. the red heat of *the glorious sun* (III. i. 3) is not an omen of joy at all. Cf. *Ham.*, I. i. 117, and Chapman's *Bussy*: "O, my heart is broken . . . / My sun is turn'd to blood" (v. iv. 131–5).

254–62. *I . . . play'd*] John and Lewis (the same men as here) put the pope in a like dilemma: "[Papa] dixit: Heu mihi, quia in hoc facto ecclesia Dei non potest euadere confusionem. Si enim Rex Angliae vincitur, in ipsius confusione confundimur . . . Si dominus Lodouicus vincitur, quod Deus auertat, in ipsius laesione laeditur Romana ecclesia. . . Et in fine dixit, quod melius vellet mori, quam aliquod malum vobis accideret" (M. Paris, p. 379).

256. *dismember*] Cf. II. i. 508.

Father, I may not wish the fortune thine;
Grandam, I will not wish thy wishes thrive: 260
Whoever wins, on that side shall I lose;
Assured loss before the match be play'd.

Lew. Lady, with me, with me thy fortune lies.

Blanche. There where my fortune li'es, there my life dies.

K. John. Cousin, go draw our puissance together.   265

[*Exit Bastard.*

France, I am burn'd up with inflaming wrath;
A rage whose heat hath this condition,
That nothing can allay, nothing but blood,
The blood, and dearest-valued blood, of France.

K. Phi. Thy rage shall burn thee up, and thou shalt turn   270
To ashes, ere our blood shall quench that fire:
Look to thyself, thou art in jeopardy.

K. John. No more than he that threats. To arms let's hie!

[*Exeunt.*

---

263. *lies*] F1; *lives* Capell.   264. *li'es*] Fleay; *liues* F1.   265. S.D.] Pope; om.
F1.   268. *allay*] F1; *allay't* Capell conj.   269. *The blood*] F1; *The best*
Walker.   *dearest-valued*] Theobald; no hyphen F1.

259. *fortune*] better fortune.

261–2. *Whoever . . . play'd*] Cf. the proverb "Uncertain life, but certain misery".

264. *li'es*] Fleay quoted many examples of dropped medial *v*. The only probable example we know for *lives* (N.B. noun not verb as in *John*) is in T. D.'s *Life of the Dutches of Suffolke* (1631): "in your hands it lies, / Either to comfort, or confound our liues" (sig. E). Cf. IV. ii. 57, note.

266–73. *France . . . threats.*] Cf. W. Clever's *Flower of Phisicke* (1590): "There is a choller burning in itselfe, and conuerted to ashes" (sig. H₂). John says: "I am burned up with

inflaming choler (*wrath*, *rage*) which can only be allayed (quelled) by blood. [Here he remembers that *the humours allay each other*, and adds] And I don't mean the humour blood in my own body, but the blood of France— the blood of Philip." Cf. R. W.'s *Tancred and Gismund* (ed. 1592): "this heart hath felt the fire/That cannot els be quencht but with his bloud" (sig. E₄); *3 H 6*, II. i. 79–80; *Rom.*, I. i. 90–1.

267. *condition*] quality.

272. *jeopardy*] Derived by Wright from French "jeu parti", a game where the risk was evenly divided— a sense which would connect with ll. 261–2.

SCENE II.—[*Plains near Angiers.*]

Alarums, excursions. Enter the BASTARD, *with* AUSTRIA'S *head.*

Bast. Now, by my life, this day grows wondrous hot;
  Some airy devil hovers in the sky,
  And pours down mischief. Austria's head lie there,

    Enter KING JOHN, ARTHUR, *and* HUBERT.

  While Philip breathes.

K. John. Hubert, keep this boy. Philip, make up: 5
  My mother is assailed in our tent,
  And ta'en, I fear.

Bast.   My lord, I rescued her;
  Her highness is in safety, fear you not:
  But on, my liege; for very little pains   9
  Will bring this labour to an happy end. [*Exeunt.*

Scene II

Scene II.] Scaena Secunda. F1; III. Pope; IV. Hanmer; *Act* III *Scene* I. Donovan. Plains . . . Angiers.] Malone; om. F1. S.D.] Allarums, Excursions: Enter Bastard with Austria's head. F1. 4. S.D.] Enter Iohn, Arthur, Hubert. F1; after *breathes* l. 4 Capell. 5. *Hubert*] F1; *There* Hubert Pope; Here, *Hubert* Keightley. *keep*] F1; *keep thou* Tyrwhitt. 10. S.D.] Rowe; Exit. F1.

S.D. *Austria's* head.] A head was a stock property owned by most companies. In the *T.R.* Philip, having won Austria's lion's-skin, presents this to Blanche, who commands him "To weare the same as earst thy Father did" (i. iv. 46); and perhaps Philip ought to wear it in the rest of *John*. In *The Famous History of . . . Fauconbridge* Richard's bastard son wears the lion's-skin in honour of his father (cf. Introduction, p. xxiii).

2–3. *Some . . . mischief.*] "i.e. A thunderstorm threatens. According to the demonologists there were devils of air, fire, water, and earth . . . those of the air being specially responsible for tempests and thunderstorms" (Wilson). But the tense of the verb is queer. Perhaps Shakespeare means: "this *battle* grows wondrous *fierce*; some *invisible* devil is pouring down (providing) *hard fighting*". With *pours down* cf. iv. ii. 109,

and *LLL.*: "Thus pour the stars down plagues for perjury" (v. ii. 395); for *day* = battle, cf. ii. i. 314, 393; v. iii. 1, etc.

4. *breathes*] recovers his breath (cf. *1 H 4*, i. iii. 102).

5. *make up*] advance, hurry to the fore.

6–7. *My . . . her;*] A curious conflation. Arthur was captured at Mirabeau while besieging Eleanor, who was in a tower when the town fell to John (Hol., 164). The tower becomes a tent, and Faulconbridge, not John, gets the credit for the rescue (one of John's most determined exploits).

7. *ta'en, I fear.*] Shakespeare felt unsure about facts, and pretended that his character was unsure. Holinshed (164, ii) mentions that the authorities disagreed whether Eleanor was captured or only besieged. Cf. ii. ii. 14, iv. ii. 123–4, v. iii. 3, v. vi. 23, notes.

Alarums, excursions, retreat. Re-enter KING JOHN, ARTHUR, *the*
    BASTARD, HUBERT, *with* ELEANOR *and Lords.*

K. John. [*To Eleanor.*] So shall it be; your grace shall stay
    behind
        So strongly guarded. [*To Arthur.*] Cousin, look not sad:
        Thy grandam loves thee; and thy uncle will
        As dear be to thee as thy father was.
Arth. O, this will make my mother die with grief!   15
K. John. [*To the Bastard.*] Cousin, away for England! haste
    before:
        And, ere our coming, see thou shake the bags
        Of hoarding abbots; imprison'd angels
        Set at liberty: the fat ribs of peace
        Must by the hungry now be fed upon: 20
        Use our commission in his utmost force.
Bast. Bell, book, and candle shall not drive me back
        When gold and silver becks me to come on:
        I leave your highness. Grandam, I will pray—
        If ever I remember to be holy—   25
        For your fair safety; so, I kiss your hand.
Elea. Farewell, gentle cousin.

11.] F1; *Scene* IV. Pope; V. Hanmer; III. Capell; *Act* III *Scene* I. Donovan.
11. S.D.] This ed.; Alarums, excursions, Retreat. Enter Iohn, Eleanor, Arthur,
Bastard, Hubert, Lords. F1.   S.D. [To Eleanor.] Hanmer; om. F1.   12. *So*]
F1; *More* Lettsom conj.; *And* Sisson.   12. S.D.] Pope; om. F1.   16. S.D.] Pope;
om. F1.   18–19. *imprison'd . . . liberty*] F1; *set at liberty Imprison'd angels* Walker
conj.   20. *now*] F1; *War* Warburton conj.   21. *his*] F1; *its* Rowe.   22–3.
back/ . . . on:] This ed.; *back,/ . . . on.* F1.   27. *gentle*] F1; *my gentle* Pope.

12. *So*] Eleanor may have asked for
a specific number of men, cf. l. 80
below (Marshall).

17. *shake the bags*] "Shake-bag" was
cant for thief, scoundrel (cf. *O.E.D.*
and the character "Shakebag" in
Arden of Feversham). John's order is to
ruffianize it among the abbots; the
word implies consciousness of wrong-
doing (cf. III. iii. 175, note).

18. *angels*] The usual pun; cf. II. i.
590, note.

20. *hungry*] Malone compared *Psalms*,
cvii, *Luke*, 1. 53.

22. *Bell . . . candle*] "A form of excommunication ending with the
words, 'Do to (close) the book, quench
the candle, ring the bell!'" (Tilley,
p. 42).

24. *I . . . highness.*] The F1 stop after
on may mean that this line should follow quickly, to imply "When gold
beckons me—I leave your highness"
(spoken facetiously, viz. *commodity* before loyalty).

26. *so . . . hand.*] It is not likely
that Faulconbridge, contemptuous of
formalities, would kiss the queen's
hand. He only says "I take my leave"
in the "I kiss your feet, your humble
servant" jargon. Cf. I. i. 154–6, 240,
notes.

K. John.   Coz, farewell.   [*Exit Bastard.*
Elea. Come hither, little kinsman; hark, a word.
                                        [*She takes Arthur aside.*
K. John. Come hither, Hubert. O my gentle Hubert,
　　We owe thee much! within this wall of flesh   30
　　There is a soul counts thee her creditor,
　　And with advantage means to pay thy love:
　　And, my good friend, thy voluntary oath
　　Lives in this bosom, dearly cherished.
　　Give me thy hand. I had a thing to say,   35
　　But I will fit it with some better tune.
　　By heaven, Hubert, I am almost asham'd
　　To say what good respect I have of thee.
Hub. I am much bounden to your majesty.
K. John. Good friend, thou hast no cause to say so yet,   40
　　But thou shalt have; and creep time ne'er so slow,
　　Yet it shall come for me to do thee good.
　　I had a thing to say, but let it go:
　　The sun is in the heaven, and the proud day,

27. S.D.] Pope; om. F1.   28 S.D.] Malone; om. F1.   36. *tune*] F1; *time*
Pope.   37. *I am*] F1; *I'm* Pope.   40. *so yet,*] F1; *so—yet—* Pope.

28. *hither*] here. Regular for "to this place" in 1590.

30. *We . . . much*] Referring to Hubert's service in bringing about the Lewis-Blanche match (Wilson). But the usefulness of the match has gone: Hubert's support of John in the last battle is probably meant (cf. l. 33 n.).

30–1. *within . . . creditor*] "intended to recall the part which the First Citizen [Hubert], the soul within the walls of Angiers, had played while the two kings stood disputing without" (Wilson, p. xlvii). The commoner phrasing was "these walls of flesh" (plural); cf. *Tit.*, IV. ii. 99, *R 2*, III. ii. 167, Glapthorne's *Ladies Priviledge* (1640), sig. H₂ᵛ.

32. *advantage*] = interest; opportunity (cf. III. iii. 151).

33. *voluntary oath*] Cf. Intro., p. xli.
35. *hand*] Cf. III. i. 118, note.
35–6. *I . . . tune*] Cecropia similarly

manipulated her temptations in Sidney's *Arcadia* (1590): "I had a thing to say to you, but it is no matter . . . [she] staied indeede, thinking *Philoclea* would have had a female inquisitivenesse of the matter" (p. 377).

36. *tune*] Pope's *time* could easily be misread as *tune*, would agree with *time* (l. 41) and John's next speech. But *tune* (= style, *O.E.D.* tune, 4) is here idiomatic, as in *Mac.*, "the self-same tune and words" (I. iii. 88), *Ado*, "do you speak in the sick tune?" (III. iv. 42). Read: "But I will adorn my words (or, fit my purposes) when I can say it in better style (i.e. not only speak, but give)."

39. *much bounden*] greatly indebted. A frequent phrase in epistles dedicatory (archaic).

41–2. *and . . . come*] and however slowly time creeps forward, my *opportunity* shall come.

Attended with the pleasures of the world,   45
Is all too wanton and too full of gauds
To give me audience: if the midnight bell
Did, with his iron tongue and brazen mouth,
Sound on into the drowsy race of night;
If this same were a churchyard where we stand,   50
And thou possessed with a thousand wrongs;
Or if that surly spirit, melancholy,
Had bak'd thy blood and made it heavy, thick,
Which else runs tickling up and down the veins,
Making that idiot, laughter, keep men's eyes   55
And strain their cheeks to idle merriment,
A passion hateful to my purposes;
Or if that thou couldst see me without eyes,

---

49. *on into*] F1; *One unto* Theobald; *one into* Variorum 1821; *On! into* Delius conj.
race] F1; *ear* Collier conj.; *face* Sisson.   53. *heavy, thick,*] F1; hyphened Pope.
54. *tickling*] F1; *trickling* Rowe.

---

46. *gauds*] showy ornaments (Steevens); "gaudy spring" was a poetic
cliché.

48. *iron tongue*] Cf. *MND.*, v. i. 372.
brazen] "used with a sub-reference
to its metaphorical sense of shameless,
unabashed" (Deighton).

49. *on*] F1 *on* could = "on" or "one".
To an Elizabethan 1 a.m. could be
midnight: cf. *Ham.*, 1. i. 39 and 1. ii.
198; *John a Kent*: "The houre is one at
midnight" (M.S.R., l. 298). Malone
compared the *one-on* quibble in *Gent.*,
ii. i. 1–2. But here *on* is surely the primary sense, even if confusion was possible.

race] "course" is the usual gloss.
Keightley[*Shakespeare-Expositor* (1867),
p. 223] compared Spenser's Night,
who must "run her timely race"
(*F.Q.*, i. v. 44). Spenser had helped to
familiarize the cliché *drowsy night.*—
Sisson thinks the *r* in *race* may be a
broken *f*. Both *face* and *ear* agree with
the face-images of the speech. But *race*
may = huge compass (derivation unknown) as in "whom hell it selfe com-
plaines to keep within her race" [*Rare
Triumphes of Loue and Fortune* (1589),

sig. A₂]. Read: "If, at dead of night,
the passing-bell were sounding on and
on into the drowsy, vast stillness of the
night".

51. *possessed*] "wholly taken up with
. . . with an allusion to the 'possession'
of a man by an evil spirit" (Deighton).

52. *melancholy*] ill-temper, sullen-
ness. Melancholy was thought due to
the thickening of the blood, and *vice
versa* as here.

54. *tickling*] tingling; tickling to
laughter. So in *The Returne of the Renowned Caualiero Pasquill* (1589): "I
needed no Minstrill to make me mer-
rie, my hart tickled of it selfe" (sig.
C₂ᵛ); Furness noted the same pun in
Spenser's *Muiopotmos* (1590).

55. *idiot, laughter*] Cf. Dekker, *Old
Fortunatus*: "cheekes, / Wrinckled with
Idiot laughter" (iii. i).

56. *strain*] stretch; constrain.

57. *passion*] emotion.

58–61. *Or . . . words;*] So in Mas-
singer's *Duke of Milan*: "O you
Powers, / That can convey our
thoughts to one another / Without
the aid of eyes or ears, assist me"
(v. i).

Hear me without thine ears, and make reply
Without a tongue, using conceit alone,   60
Without eyes, ears, and harmful sound of words;
Then, in despite of brooded watchful day,
I would into thy bosom pour my thoughts:
But, ah, I will not. Yet I love thee well;
And, by my troth, I think thou lov'st me well.   65
Hub. So well, that what you bid me undertake,
Though that my death were adjunct to my act,
By heaven, I would do it.

K. John.   Do not I know thou wouldst?
Good Hubert, Hubert, Hubert, throw thine eye
On yon young boy; I'll tell thee what, my friend,   70
He is a very serpent in my way;
And wheresoe'er this foot of mine doth tread,
He lies before me: dost thou understand me?
Thou art his keeper.

Hub.   And I'll keep him so
That he shall not offend your majesty.   75
K. John. Death.
Hub.   My lord?
K. John.   A grave.
Hub.   He shall not live.
K. John.   Enough.
I could be merry now. Hubert, I love thee.
Well, I'll not say what I intend for thee:

62. *brooded*] F1; *broad-ey'd* Pope.   68. *I would do it*] F1; *I'd do't* Theobald.
75–6. *That . . . Death.*] One line Walker conj.   76. *Death . . . Enough.*] One line
Steevens; separate lines F1.   *lord?*] Rowe; *Lord.* F1.

60. *conceit*] conception, thought, imagination.

62. *brooded*] brooding. The sense, not the form, has puzzled edd. The vigilance of brooding birds was Steevens's explanation (comparing *L'Allegro*: "Where brooding Darkness spreads his jealous wings") : *young Arthur* might be thought as defenceless as a chick. The night-death-thick blood, day-life-fresh blood contrasts make the word effective.

71. *He . . . way*] Carter compared

Genesis, xlix. 17: "Dan shall be a serpent by the way".

76. *Death.*] In Holinshed John gives way to his counsellors, but Shakespeare makes him alone responsible for the idea of murder.

My lord?] Cf. iv. ii. 230.

77. *I . . . thee.*] Other villains expressed love of their "tools" thus; cf. *The Alchemist*: "*Lungs*, my *Lungs!* / I loue thee." (ii. iii) ; *The Revengers Tragædie* (1607): "Thou art a pretious fellow, faith I loue thee" (ii. ii).

Remember.—Madam, fare you well:
I'll send those powers o'er to your majesty.   80
Elea. My blessing go with thee!
K. John.   For England, cousin, go:
Hubert shall be your man, attend on you
With all true duty. On toward Calais, ho!   [*Exeunt.*

SCENE III.—[*The French King's Pavilion.*]

Enter KING PHILIP, LEWIS, PANDULPH, *and Attendants.*

K. Phi. So, by a roaring tempest on the flood,
A whole armado of convicted sail
Is scatter'd and disjoin'd from fellowship.
Pand. Courage and comfort! all shall yet go well.
K. Phi. What can go well, when we have run so ill?   5
Are we not beaten? Is not Angiers lost?
Arthur ta'en prisoner? divers dear friends slain?
And bloody England into England gone,
O'erbearing interruption, spite of France?
Lew. What he hath won, that hath he fortified: 10
So hot a speed with such advice dispos'd,
Such temperate order in so fierce a cause,

---

82. *attend*] F1; *to attend* F3.   83. *Calais*] Rowe iii; Callice F1.

Scene III

Scene III.] F1; V. Pope; VI. Hanmer; IV. Capell; II. Donovan.   The . . .
Pavilion.] As Malone; om. F1; the *French* Court. Theobald.   S.D.] Enter
France, Dolphin, Pandulpho, Attendants. F1.   2. *armado*] F1; *Armada*
Theobald iii.   *convicted*] F1; *collected* Pope; *conjuncted* Maxwell conj. (*N. & Q.*,
28 Oct. 1950).   12. *cause*] F1; *course* Hanmer.

1. *flood*] open sea.
2. *armado*] More common than the form "armada" in 1590; cf. Armado in *LLL.*
convicted] "defeated" (usual gloss). We prefer the Cowden Clarkes' "condemned, doomed to perdition". The 1588 Armada was smitten by a tempest, popularly believed (in England) the work of God, who had doomed the foes of the true faith. The *T.R.* echo bears this out: "Thus hath the God of

Kings with conquering arme / Dispearst the foes to true succession" (I. vii. 1–2).
5. *run*] "a double meaning, *run our course* and *run away*" (Smith).
11–12. *So . . . cause*] As *such advice dispos'd* goes with *Such temperate order*, *So hot a speed* would go with *so fierce a course*. But *cause* (= dispute, quarrel) often quibbles on *course*: cf. v. ii. 30, and *Alchemist*, III. i ("The *sanctified cause* / Should haue a *sanctified course*").

   Doth want example: who hath read or heard
   Of any kindred action like to this?
K. Phi. Well could I bear that England had this praise   15
   So we could find some pattern of our shame.

          Enter CONSTANCE.

   Look, who comes here! a grave unto a soul;
   Holding th' eternal spirit, against her will,
   In the vild prison of afflicted breath.
   I prithee, lady, go away with me.   20
Const. Lo! now—now see the issue of your peace!
K. Phi. Patience, good lady! comfort, gentle Constance!
Const. No!—I defy all counsel, all redress,
   But that which ends all counsel, true redress:
   Death! death, O amiable, lovely death!   25
   Thou odoriferous stench! sound rottenness!
   Arise forth from the couch of lasting night,

---

14. *kindred action*] Theobald; hyphened F1.   17. S.D.] F1; Enter Lady *Constance*, her Hair dishevel'd. Capell; after l. 19 Dyce.   17. *here!*] F1 (*heere?*). 18. *spirit*] F1; *sprite* Fleay.   21. *Lo! now—now*] This ed.; *Lo ; now : now* F1; *Lo, now! now* Capell.   24–5. *redress :|Death! death,*] As Pope; *Redresse :|Death, death,* F1; *redress,|Death, Death ;* Theobald, edd.

16. *pattern*] example.

17–19. *Look . . . breath.*] Some take *spirit* = *soul*, with *her* alluding to *soul*. We take *eternal spirit* = the Holy Ghost, held in Constance's soul, which is held in the vile body of her afflicted life (= *breath*). Cf. note on *1 Corinthians*, xv. 45 in an old Bible: "Christ is called a Spirite . . . Adam is called a liuing soule, by reason of the soule which is the best part in him." Note how *spirit* mediates between *soul* and *breath* (cf. i. i. 17, III. i. 154, III. iii. 146, etc.).

19. *vild prison*] body (popular cliché). Cf. *Tarltons Newes* (1590): "After thy breath hath left thy bodye, and thy soule is set free from this vile prison of earth" (p. 4); *Celestina* (1596): "the poore soule which must . . . passe out of his vile prison" (p. 203).

23. *defy*] renounce, disdain.

25–36. *Death . . . me!*] Cf. *Rom.*, III. ii. 73–85 for the style, IV. v. 35–40 for

the imagery. Apostrophe of Death was a popular poetic figure, cf. Harington's *Orlando Furioso* (1591): "Come death & close mine eyes, & stop my breath" (Bk xxxiii, st. 58).

25. *lovely*] Could mean "amorous" (cf. *Shr.*, III. ii. 126).

27. *Arise . . . night*] Cf. *Zepheria* (1594): "From forth dead sleep of everlasting dark; / Fame, with her trump's shrill summon, hath awaked / The Roman NASO" [ed. Arber (1904), p. 155]. A *couch* is any place of rest: here *lasting night* is the couch. Shakespeare means Hell, where Death is at rest since he cannot function. *Everlasting night* was the more usual cliché—as in *Soliman and Perseda* (Death says) "I will not downe to euerlasting night / Till I haue moralliz'd this Tragedie" (Kyd, p. 165); "To send them down to euerlasting night" (Kyd, p. 220). Note the fitting

Thou hate and terror to prosperity,
And I will kiss thy detestable bones
And put my eyeballs in thy vaulty brows,   30
And ring these fingers with thy household worms,
And stop this gap of breath with fulsome dust,
And be a carrion monster like thyself:
Come, grin on me, and I will think thou smil'st,
And buss thee as thy wife. Misery's love,   35
O, come to me!

K. Phi.   O fair affliction, peace!

Const. No, no, I will not, having breath to cry:
O, that my tongue were in the thunder's mouth!
Then with a passion would I shake the world;
And rouse from sleep that fell anatomy   40
Which cannot hear a lady's feeble voice,
Which scorns a modern invocation.

Pand. Lady, you utter madness, and not sorrow.

Const. Thou art holy to belie me so!—
I am not mad: this hair I tear is mine;   45

---

34. *smil'st*] F1; *smilest* Cambridge.   35. *buss*] F1; *kiss* Pope.   42. *modern*] F1;
mother's Heath.   44. *holy*] F1; *not holy* F4; *unholy* Variorum 1773; *too holy*
Maxwell conj. (*N. & Q.*, 28 Oct. 1950).

cumbrousness of *forth from* instead of
the usual *from forth.*

28. *prosperity*] Carter compared
Ecclesiasticus: "O Death, how bitter is
the remembrance of thee to a man that
... hathe prosperitie" (xli. 1); cf. *Job*:
"in his prosperitie the destroyer shal
come vpon him" (xv. 21).

32. *stop*] stop up.
fulsome] nauseous.

34. *grin . . . smil'st*] A *grin* is fixed,
showing the teeth; a *smile* vivacious,
with the play of the features.

35. *buss*] kiss wantonly.

39. *shake the world*] "The sorowes of
the graue haue compassed me about:
the snares of death ouertooke me.
(But) in my trouble did I call vpon the
Lorde.... Then the earth trembled...
the mountaines moued and shooke,
because he was angry.... The Lorde
also thundred in the heauen" (*Psalms*,
xviii. 5–13).

40. *fell anatomy*] fierce, cruel skele-
ton.

42. *modern*] trite, ordinary [Steevens,
citing "wise saws and modern instances" (*AYL.*, II. vii. 156)].

invocation] supplication; incantation
(*O.E.D.* 1, 2).

44. *holy*] Constance's venom needs a
disrupted line. Read: "You are a good
churchman (but inhuman) to tell this
lie about me (viz. to pretend I am mad,
therefore not responsible for my un-
christian wish): Preach (l. 51) some
philosophy to make (= render;
prove) me mad and you will be made a
saint." Suicides were rejected by the
Church, but madness took away responsibility for oneself; *holy* and
canonis'd thus go together (ll. 44, 52).

45–8. *I . . . mad:*] J. C. Bucknill [*Mad
Folk of Shakespeare* (1867), p. 281] compared *Tw.N.*, IV. iii. 1, *Oth.*, II. iii.
118.

My name is Constance; I was Geoffrey's wife;
Young Arthur is my son, and he is lost!
I am not mad: I would to heaven I were!
For then 'tis like I should forget myself:
O, if I could, what grief should I forget!   50
Preach some philosophy to make me mad,
And thou shalt be canoniz'd, cardinal;
For, being not mad but sensible of grief,
My reasonable part produces reason
How I may be deliver'd of these woes,   55
And teaches me to kill or hang myself:
If I were mad, I should forget my son,
Or madly think a babe of clouts were he.
I am not mad; too well, too well I feel
The different plague of each calamity.   60
K. Phi. Bind up those tresses. O, what love I note
In the fair multitude of those her hairs!
Where but by chance a silver drop hath fall'n,
Even to that drop ten thousand wiry friends
Do glue themselves in sociable grief,   65
Like true, inseparable, faithful loves,
Sticking together in calamity.
Const. To England, if you will.
K. Phi.   Bind up your hairs.
Const. Yes, that I will; and wherefore will I do it?

64. *friends*] Rowe iii; *fiends* F1.   68.] F1; [Giving some of her hairs to the wind. Rann.

48–9. *I . . . myself:*] Tilley (p. 229) quoted the proverb "He is a Fool that forgets himself."

53. *sensible*] capable.

55. *deliver'd of*] "= delivered from" (Wilson). But cf. ll. 93–8, where *Grief* is a child-substitute. Constance described Death as a lover (ll. 25–36, 40) and now talks of giving birth to (being *deliver'd of*) her Grief-child; the *babe of clouts* (l. 58) also belonging to this madly sane sequence. Cf. *R 2*, II. ii. 62 ("midwife to my woe").

58. *babe of clouts*] "rag doll" (usual gloss). But "(person) of clouts" was an idiom for "inferior (person)": cf.

Mother Bombie: "I had as liefe haue one [a husband] of clouts" (Lyly, III, 224); *Rare Triumphes of Loue and Fortune* (1589): "a maister of clowtes" (sig. C₃). Shakespeare may intend the figurative sense too, for in ll. 93–8 Grief becomes the inferior substitute.

64. *wiry*] "strong, and with a reference to the likeness between hair and wire" (Deighton); "wire" was a popular metaphor for hair (cf. Sonnet 130).

68. *To . . . will.*] Cf. Introduction, p. xli.

69. *Yes . . . will;*] "(You will not do a little thing like invade England to please me but) I will bind up my hair to

I tore them from their bonds and cried aloud,   70
"O that these hands could so redeem my son,
As they have given these hairs their liberty!"
But now I envy at their liberty,
And will again commit them to their bonds,
Because my poor child is a prisoner.   75
And, father cardinal, I have heard you say
That we shall see and know our friends in heaven:
If that be true, I shall see my boy again;
For since the birth of Cain, the first male child,
To him that did but yesterday suspire,   80
There was not such a gracious creature born.
But now will canker-sorrow eat my bud
And chase the native beauty from his cheek
And he will look as hollow as a ghost,
As dim and meagre as an ague's fit,   85
And so he'll die; and, rising so again,
When I shall meet him in the court of heaven
I shall not know him: therefore never, never
Must I behold my pretty Arthur more.
Pand. You hold too heinous a respect of grief.   90
Const. He talks to me that never had a son.
K. Phi. You are as fond of grief as of your child.

76. *And*] F1 ; *Oh* Pope.   78. *true*] F1 ; om. Pope.   *I shall*] F1 ; *I'll* Walker conj.
79. *male child*] Pope; hyphened F1.   81. *born*] F1 (*borne*).   85. *ague's fit*] As
F1 ; *ague-fit* Dyce ii.

please you"; "*I will*" resumes "*you
will*", bracketing an invasion of England and the tying of her hair as
equally simple.

76. *And*] i.e. "As for you (I have not
finished with you yet)". Having in-
sulted Philip obliquely (ll. 68–75), she
turns on Pandulph again to condemn
his mad philosophy.

77. *see . . . heaven*] The Anglican
Church also accepted this doctrine,
but it was disputed: cf. P. S., *Christal
Glasse for Christian Women* (1591), sig.
Cvff.

78. *If . . . again;*] Constance makes
the popular objection that our friends
may change after we knew them (ll.

82–6), that sight and normal powers of
recognition are not enough, but that
sight without recognition is valueless.

80. *suspire*] breathe.

81. *gracious*] godly, holy.

83. *native*] natural.

88–9. *never . . . more*] Instead of
pretty Arthur she will see a *hollow
ghost* which she will not recognize. Cf.
Marlowe's *Edward the Second* (1594):
"I shall neuer see / My louely *Pierce*,
my *Gaueston* againe" (sig. F3).

90. *heinous*] wicked; terrible.

91. *He . . . son.*] Cf. *3 H 6*, v. v. 63,
Mac., IV. iii. 216 (Tilley, p. 99).

92. *fond of*] foolishly tender (about);
eager for, desirous of.

Const. Grief fills the room up of my absent child,
      Lies in his bed, walks up and down with me,
      Puts on his pretty looks, repeats his words,   95
      Remembers me of all his gracious parts,
      Stuffs out his vacant garments with his form;
      Then have I reason to be fond of grief?
      Fare you well: had you such a loss as I
      I could give better comfort than you do.   100
      I will not keep this form upon my head,
      When there is such disorder in my wit.

      O Lord! my boy, my Arthur, my fair son!
      My life, my joy, my food, my all the world!   104
      My widow-comfort, and my sorrows' cure!   [*Exit.*
K. Phi. I fear some outrage, and I'll follow her.   [*Exit.*
Lew. There's nothing in this world can make me joy:
      Life is as tedious as a twice-told tale
      Vexing the dull ear of a drowsy man;
      And bitter shame hath spoil'd the sweet word's taste, 110

---

98. *grief?*] F1; *Grief.* Rowe.   101.] F1; [Tearing off her head-cloaths. Pope; [Dishevelling her hair. Dyce ii.   105. *sorrows'*] F1 (*sorrowes*).   107.] F1; *Scene* VI. Pope; VII. Hanmer.   110. *word's*] F1; *world's* Pope.

93. *Grief . . . child,*] Malone compared "Perfruitur lachrymis, et amat *pro conjuge luctum. Lucan.* lib. ix."

93–100. *Grief . . . do.*] Some edd. think Shakespeare remembers the death of his son Hamnet (*ob.* 1596).

98. *grief?*] *?* often = *!* in F1; but frenzied Constance loves to triumph in her logic, and a question here withers all retort.

101–2. *form . . . disorder*] Cf. III. i. 179, which suggests that *form* here = order, not a head-dress; i.e. Constance again disorders her hair.

104. *My . . . world!*] The four metaphors of this line were familiar from love-poetry. In II. ii. 53–4 Constance also applied a courtly lover's comparisons to her son. This suggests that a particular fixation was meant.

108. *Life . . . tale*] Malone compared *Psalms,* xc. 9, *Mac.,* v. v. 24–8; Noble added *Wisdom,* ii. 1 ("Our life is short and tedious"); cf. *Ecclesiasticus,* xxii

("6. A tale out of time is as musicke in mourning: but wisedome knoweth the seasons of correction and doctrine. 7. Who so teacheth a foole, is as one that . . . waketh one that sleepeth. . . . 10. Who so telleth a foole of wisdome, is as a man which speaketh to one that is asleepe"). Cf. IV. ii. 18–20, where *time unseasonable* appears too.

110. *word's*] "The *sweet word* is *life*" (Malone). Dyce called this "sheer foolishness", and Pope's *world's* has stood. But if *sweet word's taste* = enjoyment of (the praise of) one's achievements [sweet word(s) = praise, flattery was common] then F1 means: Hearing his life-story told a second time (looking back after having lived it) *his very successes* are his bitterest shames when he recalls that he has now failed so miserably. See also G. Baldini, *Letterature Moderne,* II (1951), 555–60.

That it yields nought but shame and bitterness.
Pand. Before the curing of a strong disease,
 Even in the instant of repair and health,
 The fit is strongest; evils that take leave,
 On their departure most of all show evil.   115
 What have you lost by losing of this day?
Lew. All days of glory, joy and happiness.
Pand. If you had won it, certainly you had.
 No, no; when fortune means to men most good
 She looks upon them with a threat'ning eye. 120
 'Tis strange to think how much King John hath lost
 In this which he accounts so clearly won:
 Are not you griev'd that Arthur is his prisoner?
Lew. As heartily as he is glad he hath him.
Pand. Your mind is all as youthful as your blood. 125
 Now hear me speak with a prophetic spirit;
 For even the breath of what I mean to speak
 Shall blow each dust, each straw, each little rub,
 Out of the path which shall directly lead
 Thy foot to England's throne; and therefore mark. 130
 John hath seiz'd Arthur; and it cannot be
 That, whiles warm life plays in that infant's veins,
 The misplac'd John should entertain an hour,
 One minute, nay, one quiet breath of rest.
 A sceptre snatch'd with an unruly hand 135
 Must be as boisterously maintain'd as gain'd;

---

133. *misplac'd John*] *mis-plac'd*-Iohn F1. *an*] F1; *one* Collier ii (MS.). 134.
One] F1; *A* Rowe.

112–15. *Before . . . evil.*] "This passage unquestionably refers to the medical doctrine of crises which was universally prevalent" [Bucknill, *Medical
Knowledge of Shakespeare* (1860), p. 134].

114–15. *evils . . . evil*] Shakespeare
follows the proverbs grouped together
by Tilley (p. 28) as "When Bale is
highest boot is next."

119–20. *No . . . eye.*] For the "false
Fortune's frown" *sententia* cf. *Pilgr.*:
"Whilst as fickle Fortune smil'd / Thou
and I were both beguil'd" (Sonnets,
vi), *Troil.*, I. iii. 22–8.

128. *dust*] grain of dust.

rub] In bowls, an obstacle hindering
the bowl's course; hence, obstacle.

135–8. *A . . . up*] J. W. Cunliffe [*Influence of Seneca* (1893)] compared *Hercules Furens*: "rapta sed trepida manu /
sceptra obtinentur. omnis in ferro est
salus. / quod ciuibus tenere te inuitis
scias, / strictus tuetur ensis. alieno in
loco / haut stabile regnum est" (ll.
345–9). Here (said Cunliffe) *obtinentur
= servantur =* Shakespeare's *maintain'd.* Perhaps *haut stabile* led Shakespeare to the biblical parallel (cf.
l. 137, note).

136. *boisterously*] violently, roughly.

And he that stands upon a slipp'ry place
Makes nice of no vild hold to stay him up:
That John may stand, then, Arthur needs must fall;
So be it, for it cannot be but so.   140
Lew. But what shall I gain by young Arthur's fall?
Pand. You, in the right of Lady Blanche your wife,
May then make all the claim that Arthur did.
Lew. And lose it, life and all, as Arthur did.
Pand. How green you are and fresh in this old world!   145
John lays you plots; the times conspire with you;
For he that steeps his safety in true blood
Shall find but bloody safety and untrue.
This act so evilly borne shall cool the hearts
Of all his people, and freeze up their zeal,   150
That none so small advantage shall step forth
To check his reign, but they will cherish it;
No natural exhalation in the sky,
No scope of nature, no distemper'd day,
No common wind, no customed event,   155
But they will pluck away his natural cause
And call them meteors, prodigies and signs,
Abortives, presages, and tongues of heaven,
Plainly denouncing vengeance upon John.

146. *you plots*] F1; *your plots* Malone conj.   152. *reign*] F1; *rein* Capell conj.
154. *scope*] F1; *scape* Pope.   156. *his*] F1; *its* Pope.

137. *slipp'ry place*] "Surely thou hast set them [the wicked] in slipperie places, (and) castest them downe into desolation. 19. Howe suddenly are they destroyed, perished (and) horribly consumed" (*Psalms*, lxxiii).

138. *Makes . . . up:*] Is not fussy how vilely he supports himself.

140. *So be it*] Amen. In the Genevan Bible *amen* is always *so be it*, also in some catechisms etc. Pandulph thus pretends submission to Providence (i.e. his *prophetic spirit*, i.e. Church interests).

146. *lays you plots*] Ethic dative. "To lay a plot for" could = teach, prescribe a course for, as in P. Barrough's *Methode of Phisicke* (1583), epistle to Burghley: "[I would be a fool] to lay

a plot for your Honor, from whence you may deriue an example of gouernment". The sense *teach* goes with *green* (l. 145), and *plots* (= traps, schemes) with *conspire*.

147–8. *For . . . untrue*] Noble compared *Genesis*, ix. 5, 6 ("Whoso shedeth mans blood, by man shall his blood be shed . . .").

149. *borne*] A quibble on *born* (having such an evil birth) and *borne* (carried out): cf. *Mac.*, III. vi. 3.

151. *advantage*] opportunity.

153. *exhalation*] meteor.

154. *scope*] "circumstance within the limits of nature's operations" (Wright).

158. *Abortives*] Abortions of nature.

Lew. Maybe he will not touch young Arthur's life,   160
    But hold himself safe in his prisonment.
Pand. O, sir, when he shall hear of your approach,
    If that young Arthur be not gone already,
    Even at that news he dies; and then the hearts
    Of all his people shall revolt from him,   165
    And kiss the lips of unacquainted change,
    And pick strong matter of revolt and wrath
    Out of the bloody fingers' ends of John.
    Methinks I see this hurly all on foot:
    And, O, what better matter breeds for you   170
    Than I have nam'd! The bastard Faulconbridge
    Is now in England ransacking the church,
    Offending charity: if but a dozen French
    Were there in arms, they would be as a call
    To train ten thousand English to their side,   175

170-1. *O, . . . The*] As F1; *O!—what . . . nam'd—the* Maxwell conj. (*N. & Q.*, 28 Oct. 1950).   173. *a dozen*] F1; *twelve* Pope.

164–8. *and . . . John.*] "To pick out of (one's own) fingers' ends" = to use one's mother-wit about [cf. *Gammer Gurton's Needle*: "I picke not this geare, hearst thou, out of my fingers endes; / But he that hard it told me" (v. ii); *Greenes Newes* (1593) by B. R.: "my wife . . . had picked out at her fingers endes the whole drift of my pretence" (sig. F3)]. Shakespeare departs from this use. Perhaps he knew the *Heroicall Devises* of C. Paradin (1591; S.R. Aug. 1590) in which a full-page picture of a hand with needles under the finger-nails and blood streaming forth is explained: When Dionysius the Tyrant was expelled, his daughters were ravished, then put to death "by driuing sharpe needles, or pinnes vnder the nayles of their fingers" (p. 126). Shakespeare has a tyrant-revolt context, alters a set phrase, and ll. 166, 167–8 seem to follow Paradin.

166. *And . . . change*] As in the parallel of iv. ii. 5–8 revolt is "stain", here it is "rape" (equivalent images: Introduction, p. lxii); *unacquainted change* (l. 166) = *long'd-for change* (iv. ii. 8).

The subaudition is "Ravish the lips of virgin change".

167. *matter*] corrupt matter, pus; argument. Cf. iv. i. 64, v. ii. 85.

169. *hurly*] tumult.

170–1. *O . . . The*] Maxwell wants *what* subject and *better matter* object of *breeds*, not intransitive *breeds* [N.B. Cf. Jonson's *Alchemist*: "No clime breeds better matter" (Prologue)].

173. *charity*] good-will (I. John). Or perhaps alluding to the Roman Catholic cry that closing the monasteries ends all charity. Onions quoted E. K. (gloss on Spenser) that "sweete Saint Charitee" was "the Catholiques comen othe".

174. *call*] decoy. Birds were often caught by placing a decoy in a net, then imitating their calls.

175. *train*] "attract, draw on" (usual gloss). The verb was influenced by the substantive *train* = treachery, guile, trap. After *call* this suggests "a decoy to trap 10,000 English into treachery": Shakespeare's comment is there behind Pandulph's words (cf. notes on iii. ii. 17, v. i. 20, v. vii. 46).

Or as a little snow, tumbled about,
Anon becomes a mountain. O noble Dolphin,
Go with me to the king: 'tis wonderful
What may be wrought out of their discontent,
Now that their souls are topful of offence.   180
For England go; I will whet on the king.
Lew. Strong reasons makes strange actions. Let us go:
If you say ay, the king will not say no.   [*Exeunt.*

177. *O*] F1; om. Pope.   179–80. *discontent,* . . . *offence.*] As Knight; *discontent,*
. . . *offence,* F1; *Discontent.* . . . *Offence,* Rowe.   182. *makes*] F1; *make* Capell.
strange] F1; *strong* F2, edd.

176–7. *Or* . . . *mountain.*] "*Bacon,* in
his history of *Henry* VII. speaking of
Perkin's march, observes, that *their*
snow-ball *did not gather as it rolled*"
(Johnson). So in Savile's *Tacitus*
(1591): "vindex first stirred the stone,
which rowling along tumbled Nero
out of his seate" (p. 7). A commonplace.
 177. *Anon*] Immediately.
 180. *topful*] brimful; cf. *Mac.,* I. v. 43.
offence] John's offence, or their own

offending thoughts. Intentional ambiguity (cf. l. 175).
 182. *strange*] Cf. the last speeches of
Acts I and II: that strong motives de-
flect us into strange courses is a basic
theme in *John.* The strangeness (foolishness) of invading England emerges
in II. i. 23–30, III. iii. 1–3, 68, v. vii.
112–18. *Strong reasons* causing strange
action reappear in IV. ii. 40–1.
 actions] deeds; military engage-
ments.

ACT IV

SCENE I.—[*A Room in a Castle. Coals burning in a brazier.*]

Enter HUBERT *and Executioners.*

Hub. Heat me these irons hot; and look thou stand
　　Within the arras: when I strike my foot
　　Upon the bosom of the ground, rush forth
　　And bind the boy which you shall find with me
　　Fast to the chair. Be heedful: hence, and watch.　　5
First Exec. I hope your warrant will bear out the deed.
Hub. Uncleanly scruples! fear not you; look to't.
　　　　　　　　　[*The Executioners withdraw.*
　　Young lad, come forth; I have to say with you.

Enter ARTHUR.

ACT IV

Scene i

Act IV *Scene* I.] F1; *Act* III *Scene* III. Donovan.　　A ... Castle.] Staunton; om.
F1.　　Coals ... brazier.] Wilson; om. F1.　　S.D.] F1; ... two *Attendants.*
Malone, edd.　　6. First Exec.] Cambridge; Exec. F1.　　7. *scruples! fear not*
you;] Rowe iii; *scruples feare not you:* F1.　　7. S.D.] This ed.; om. F1; Exeunt
Attendants. Malone.

Scene] Various locations have been proposed—Northampton (Capell), Dover (Halliwell), Canterbury (White), Tower of London (Wilson). But Shakespeare probably gave no thought to this.—For the source of the scene cf. Appendix A (2).

S.D. Executioners] "tormentors" in Holinshed (p. 165). *John* and *T.R.* assign the "execution" to Hubert; *T.R.* calls Hubert's helpers *Attendants* (1. xii. 12), but Shakespeare's "Executioners" suggests their role in Holinshed.

　1. *irons*] Cf. iv. i. 39, 59, 61, 67, 74, 81, 119, 124. Shakespeare uses *iron* =

(*a*) iron metal, (*b*) searing-iron. Two searing-irons are needed.

　3. *bosom*] Cf. v. ii. 28, iii. i. 171–2.

　7. *Uncleanly*] Improper.—Smith read F1 as "Let no unbecoming scruples frighten you". Or we might read: "Uncleanly scruples! fear not! (*To the last speaker*).—You: look to't. (*To the other two*)." *T.R.* has three attendants.

S.D.] The illustration in Theobald ii shows why the *exit* could be omitted. The irons are heated on-stage. And the man behind the *arras* (curtain to the inner stage) could be visible watching, not really "off".

Arth. Good morrow, Hubert.
Hub.   Good morrow, little prince.
Arth. As little prince, having so great a title   10
          To be more prince, as may be.—You are sad.
Hub. Indeed, I have been merrier.
Arth.   Mercy on me!
          Methinks nobody should be sad but I:
          Yet, I remember, when I was in France,
          Young gentlemen would be as sad as night,   15
          Only for wantonness. By my christendom,
          So I were out of prison and kept sheep,
          I should be as merry as the day is long;
          And so I would be here, but that I doubt
          My uncle practises more harm to me.   20
          He is afraid of me and I of him:
          Is it my fault that I was Geoffrey's son?
          No, indeed, is't not; and I would to heaven
          I were your son, so you would love me, Hubert.
Hub. [*Aside.*] If I talk to him, with his innocent prate   25
          He will awake my mercy, which lies dead:
          Therefore I will be sudden and dispatch.
Arth. Are you sick, Hubert? you look pale to-day.
          In sooth, I would you were a little sick,
          That I might sit all night and watch with you: 30

18. *be as*] F1; *be* Pope.   23. *No*] F1; om. Pope.   *is't*] F1; *it's* F2.   25. S.D.]
Rowe; om. F1.

9. *Good morrow*] Good morning. *T.R.*
makes the time *euening* (1. xii. 14). The
sad, long night (iv. i. 15, 30, 45–7) is
not only a symbol of darkness (blindness). It is early morning; Arthur perhaps enters in his night-shirt from bed,
returning back to bed at the end (iv. i.
129, note).

10–11. *As . . . be*] "Considering my
great title . . . I am at present as little a
prince as may be" (I. John). Or:
"True, I am a little prince—in so far as
anyone having so great a claim to be a
great prince may be 'little prince'"
(quibbling on physical and feudal
stature).

15. *Young gentlemen*] Holinshed more
than once calls Arthur a "yoong gentleman" (p. 165); Shakespeare means
"young gentlemen such as I".

16. *for wantonness*] through a whimsical affectation.

By my christendom] "= *As I am a
Christian!*" (*O.E.D.*). Malone took
christendom = baptism, as in *All's W.*,
i. i. 190.

17. *kept sheep*] Cf. *3 H 6*, ii. v.
1–54.

18. *as . . . long*] A proverb; so *Ado*, ii.
i. 52 (Tilley, p. 140).

19. *doubt*] fear.

25. *prate*] prattle.

I warrant I love you more than you do me.
Hub. [*Aside.*] His words do take possession of my bosom.
Read here, young Arthur.   [*Showing a paper.*
                    [*Aside.*] How now, foolish rheum!
Turning dispiteous torture out of door!
I must be brief, lest resolution drop   35
Out at mine eyes in tender womanish tears.—
Can you not read it? is it not fair writ?
Arth. Too fairly, Hubert, for so foul effect:
Must you with hot irons burn out both mine eyes?
Hub. Young boy, I must.
Arth.   And will you?
Hub.   And I will.   40
Arth. Have you the heart? When your head did but ache,
I knit my handkercher about your brows,
The best I had, a princess wrought it me,
And I did never ask it you again;
And with my hand at midnight held your head,   45
And, like the watchful minutes to the hour,
Still and anon cheer'd up the heavy time,
Saying, "What lack you?" and "Where lies your grief?"
Or "What good love may I perform for you?"

31. *do*] F1; om. Vaughan conj.   32. S.D.] Capell; om. F1.   33. S.D.
[Showing a paper.] As Rowe iii; om. F1.   S.D. [Aside.] Rowe iii; om. F1.
33–4. *rheum! . . . door!*] F1 (*rheume? . . . doore?*).   37. *fair*] F1; *fairly* Keightley
39. *hot*] F1; om. Pope.

31. *I warrant*] Cf. l. 6, John's murderous warrant.

32. *bosom*] Cf. l. 3: Arthur's words
strike into Hubert's bosom.

33. *rheum*] Arthur's words take *room*
in Hubert's bosom (l. 32), so that no
room for the idea of torture remains
(l. 34). The quibble on *rheum* (= tears)
supports the conceit.

33–4. *rheum! . . . door!*] F1 *?* may = *!*
or *?* in both cases.

34. *dispiteous*] merciless.

37. *fair writ*] "clearly written"; or
"clear writing".

38. *effect*] meaning, purpose.

42. *knit*] tied. As Arthur speaks
Hubert's *brows* are probably *knit*.

The image plays on the blinding-
theme.

43. *wrought*] embroidered.

46. *watchful . . . hour*] "the minutes
that watch the progress of the hour"
(On.). But this may be a parenthood
image (cf. ll. 24, 50): *midnight* and
watchful resume III. ii. 47, 62, and
minutes-hour may resume *brooded* (III.
ii. 62, note), viz. minutes = the brood
or chicks of the hen-hour.

47. *Still and anon*] Continually.

48. *Where . . . grief?*] A set phrase; cf.
If You Know Not Me (1605): "*Winch:*
Oh, I am sicke. / *Con.* Where lyes your
greife?" (sig. F₄).

49. *love*] loving deed.

Many a poor man's son would have lien still   50
And ne'er have spoke a loving word to you;
But you at your sick-service had a prince.
Nay, you may think my love was crafty love,
And call it cunning: do, and if you will.
If heaven be pleas'd that you must use me ill,   55
Why then you must. Will you put out mine eyes?
These eyes that never did nor never shall
So much as frown on you.

Hub.   I have sworn to do it;
And with hot irons must I burn them out.

Arth. Ah, none but in this iron age would do it!   60
The iron of itself, though heat red-hot,
Approaching near these eyes, would drink my tears
And quench this fiery indignation
Even in the matter of mine innocence;
Nay, after that, consume away in rust,   65
But for containing fire to harm mine eye.
Are you more stubborn-hard than hammer'd iron?
And if an angel should have come to me

---

52. *sick-service*] Delius; no hyphen F1.   58. *I have*] F1; *I've* Pope.   63. *this*]
F1; *his* Capell, edd.   64. *matter*] F1; *water* W.W. (*Parthenon*, 16 Aug. 1862).
66. *eye*] F1; *eyes* Dyce ii.   67. *stubborn-hard*] Theobald ii; no hyphen F1.

55–6. *If . . . must*] Tilley (p. 486) quoted the proverb "What Must be must be", and *Rom.*, iv. i. 21.

60. *this iron age*] this cruel world. As metals were thought to degenerate (from gold to silver to iron etc.) so the one-time "golden age" had coarsened. A traditional phrase. Cf. iii. i. 5, note.

61. *The iron*] That an inanimate weapon could be more humane than its wielder was a popular conceit: "Seemed, the senselesse yron did feare, / Or to wrong holy eld did forbeare" (Spenser's *Shepheardes Calender*).

heat] heated.

63. *this fiery indignation*] "the indignation *thus* produced by the iron being made red-hot for such an inhuman purpose" (Malone); or *indignation* may simply = wrath (as in ii. i. 212).

Walker thought that *this* and *his* were often confused in Shakespeare, citing this line and v. ii. 145 in *John*.

64. *matter*] substance; exudation. H. Constable's *Diana* contains a curious parallel: "Thyne eye a fire is both in heate and light, / Myne eye of teares a river doth become; / O that the matter of myne eye had might / To quench the flames that from thyne eye doe come" [*Harleian Miscellany*, ix (ed. 1812), p. 493, from an early MS. Instead of *matter* the printed text (1592) read *water*].

67. *hammer'd iron*] "iron beaten into strongest consistency by the hammer" (Deighton).

68. *angel*] "Sapience" was thought the essential quality of angels, who were also the announcers of decrees of the Deity.

And told me Hubert should put out mine eyes,
I would not have believ'd him,—no tongue   70
But Hubert's.
Hub.   Come forth!   [*Stamps.*

The Executioners come forth, with a cord, irons, etc.

                         Do as I bid you do.
Arth. O, save me, Hubert, save me! my eyes are out
Even with the fierce looks of these bloody men.
Hub. Give me the iron, I say, and bind him here.
Arth. Alas, what need you be so boist'rous-rough?   75
I will not struggle, I will stand stone-still.
For heaven sake, Hubert, let me not be bound!
Nay, hear me, Hubert, drive these men away,
And I will sit as quiet as a lamb;
I will not stir, nor winch, nor speak a word,   80
Nor look upon the iron angerly:
Thrust but these men away, and I'll forgive you
Whatever torment you do put me to.
Hub. Go, stand within; let me alone with him.
First Exec. I am best pleas'd to be from such a deed.   85
                              [*Exeunt Executioners.*
Arth. Alas, I then have chid away my friend!
He hath a stern look, but a gentle heart:
Let him come back, that his compassion may
Give life to yours.
Hub.   Come, boy, prepare yourself.
Arth. Is there no remedy?

70-1. —*no . . . Hubert's.*] This ed.; *no tongue but* Huberts. F1; *a tongue but* Hubert's.
Pope; *no . . . Hubert's*— Steevens conj.   71. S.D.] This ed.; om. F1; Re-enter
Officers with a Cord, the Irons, *&c.* Capell, edd.   71. *do.*] F1; *do.* [Stamps, and
the men enter. Pope; om. Theobald ii.   75. *boist'rous-rough*] Theobald; no
hyphen F1.   77. *heaven sake*] F1; *heav'n's sake* Theobald ii, edd.   85. S.D.]
Cambridge; om. F1; Exit. Pope.

70-1. *no . . . Hubert's.*] i.e. I would
not have believed *any* tongue but
Hubert's; *no* is a double negative.

77. *heaven sake*] A distinct form; the
"s" of "heaven's" was dropped before
the following "s".

79. *as . . . lamb*] Pre-Shakespearean proverb (Tilley, p. 366).

80. *winch*] Variant of *wince*, as in
Ham., III. ii. 256 (Q₂).

81. *angerly*] angrily.

84. *let . . . him.*] "leave me to deal
with him alone" (Wright, comparing
Tw.N., II. iii. 146).

Hub.   None, but to lose your eyes.   90
Arth. O heaven, that there were but a mote in yours,
  A grain, a dust, a gnat, a wandering hair,
  Any annoyance in that precious sense!
  Then, feeling what small things are boisterous there,
  Your vild intent must needs seem horrible.   95
Hub. Is this your promise? go to, hold your tongue.
Arth. Hubert, the utterance of a brace of tongues
  Must needs want pleading for a pair of eyes:
  Let me not hold my tongue, let me not, Hubert!
  Or, Hubert, if you will, cut out my tongue,   100
  So I may keep mine eyes: O, spare mine eyes,
  Though to no use but still to look on you!
  Lo, by my troth, the instrument is cold
  And would not harm me.
Hub.   I can heat it, boy.
Arth. No, in good sooth; the fire is dead with grief,   105
  Being create for comfort, to be us'd
  In undeserv'd extremes; see else yourself:
  There is no malice in this burning coal;
  The breath of heaven hath blown his spirit out
  And strew'd repentant ashes on his head.   110

---

90. *to*] F1; om. Vaughan. 91. *mote*] F1 (*moth*). 108. *in this burning*] F1; *burning in this* Z. Grey. 109, 110. *his*] F1; *its* Pope.

91. *mote*] Upton compared *Matthew*, vii. 3. So *Luke*, vi. 41. Mote and moth could stand for each other.

92. *A . . . hair*] Cf. III. iii. 128.

a gnat] Suggested by *moth* (l. 92), as in *LLL.*, IV. iii. 161–6.

93. *precious sense*] Sight was thought the principal sense; cf. III. i. 5, and *LLL.*, V. ii. 446.

94. *boisterous*] intractable, hence irritating.

97–8. *the . . . eyes:*] "the words used by a pair of tongues must necessarily plead inadequately for", or "the words of a pair of tongues must needs be used to plead when two eyes are at stake" (the latter an appeal to "argue it out between us").

99. *let me not*] (*a*) Repetition; (*b*) = do not stop (*let*) me (pleading).

102. *Though . . . you!*] "I pray you (said she) even by these dying eies of mine (which are onely sorrie to dye, because they shall lose your sight)" (Sidney's *Arcadia*, p. 297).

105. *dead with grief*] Cf. l. 128, note (the rumour that Arthur *died of grief*).

107. *In . . . extremes*] "In cruel deeds which I have not deserved", with a quibble on *in extremes* (Latin *in extremis*) = in one's last agony (cf. *O.E.D.*, extreme, 4, 2).

108. *malice*] power to harm.

burning] glowing.

109. *breath of heaven*] air; divine influence.

110. *repentant ashes*] Referring to the ceremonial manner of Jewish repentance (Carter, citing *Job*, xlii. 6, etc.). Deighton compared *R 2*, V. i. 46–9.

Hub. But with my breath I can revive it, boy.

Arth. And if you do, you will but make it blush
And glow with shame of your proceedings, Hubert:
Nay, it perchance will sparkle in your eyes;
And, like a dog that is compell'd to fight,   115
Snatch at his master that doth tarre him on.
All things that you should use to do me wrong
Deny their office: only you do lack
That mercy which fierce fire and iron extends—
Creatures of note for mercy lacking uses!   120

Hub. Well, see to live; I will not touch thine eye
For all the treasure that thine uncle owes:
Yet am I sworn and I did purpose, boy,
With this same very iron to burn them out.

Arth. O, now you look like Hubert! all this while   125
You were disguis'd.

Hub.   Peace; no more. Adieu.
Your uncle must not know but you are dead.
I'll fill these dogged spies with false reports:
And, pretty child, sleep doubtless and secure

---

119. *extends*] F1; *extend* Pope.   120. *mercy lacking*] This ed.; *mercy, lacking* F1; hyphened Pope, edd.   121. *eye*] F1; *eyes* ed. 1735.   122. *owes*] F1; *owns* Pope. 126. *disguis'd*] F1; *disguisèd* Dyce.

114. *sparkle in*] send out sparks into.

115-16. *And . . . on.*] Tilley (p. 419) quoted the proverb "A Man may cause his own dog to bite him", comparing *2 H 6*, v. i. 151-2, *H 5*, II. ii. 83.

116. *Snatch*] Snap, bite.

tarre] urge; so *Ham.*, II. ii. 379.

118. *office*] proper function.

120. *Creatures . . . uses!*] Creatures = anything created, animate or inanimate. Pope rounds off a sense already clear (taking *uses* = customs). But F1 also means: "(How strange that) Creatures of note for mercy (such as Hubert) (should be) lacking in their ability to use (mercy)!" (Cf. *O.E.D.*, use, 10b: "The power of using some faculty").

121. *Well, . . . live;*] "*Well*, take you thought how *to live*" (Capell). The idiom "See to do" puzzled some edd. in view of the blinding context.

I . . . eye] *LLL.*, IV. iii. 183-4 and many other rhymes show that, as now, *I* and *eye* were pronounced alike.

122. *owes*] owns. Also quibbling on "owes me" (cf. III. ii. 30-42, 78).

128. *dogged*] cruel; with play on "dogging" = hot on the trail.

false reports] "[Hubert] caused it to be bruted abroad through the countrie, that the kings commandement was fulfilled, and that Arthur also through sorrow and greefe was departed out of this life" (Hol., 165, ii).

129. *sleep*] May mean "*always* sleep", or "go back *now* to sleep" (cf. IV. i. 9, note).

doubtless and secure] "free from fear and care", or (in view of l. 131 *not*) "certain and assured".

That Hubert, for the wealth of all the world, 130
Will not offend thee.

Arth. O heaven! I thank you, Hubert.

Hub. Silence; no more. Go closely in with me:
Much danger do I undergo for thee. [*Exeunt.*

SCENE II.—[*The Court of England.*]

Enter KING JOHN, PEMBROKE, SALISBURY, *and other Lords.*

K. John. Here once again we sit, once again crown'd,
And look'd upon, I hope, with cheerful eyes.

Pem. This "once again", but that your highness pleas'd,
Was once superfluous: you were crown'd before,
And that high royalty was ne'er pluck'd off, 5
The faiths of men ne'er stained with revolt;
Fresh expectation troubled not the land
With any long'd-for change or better state.

Sal. Therefore, to be possess'd with double pomp,
To guard a title that was rich before, 10
To gild refined gold, to paint the lily,

Scene II

Scene II] F1; *Act* IV *Scene* I. Donovan. The . . . England.] Pope; om. F1.
S.D.] Enter Iohn, Pembroke, Salisbury, and other Lordes. F1; King *John* upon
his Throne, . . . discovered. Kemble. 1. *again*] F3; *against* F1. 8. *long'd-for change*] long'd-for-change F1. 10. *guard*] F1; *gard* Halliwell.

132. *closely*] secretly.

Scene II

1. *again*] Yet *against* (as in F1) was a
variant of *again* (*O.E.D.*, against, C).

2. *cheerful eyes*] Dramatic irony after
IV. i.

4. *superfluous*] Shakespeare may recall M. Paris: "Reuersus itaque Cantuariam Rex cum Regina sua . . .
coronati sunt ambo ibidem, vbi
Archiepiscopus Cantuariensis copiosas
eis, ne dicam superfluas, ministrauit
expensas" (p. 275).

crown'd before] This is John's *fourth*
coronation (Z. Grey).

8. *long'd-for change*] Cf. III. iii. 166,
note.

9. *pomp*] ceremony.

10. *guard*] ornament a garment with
trimming [a sense continued in *rich* =
splendid (of dress)]; defend.

11. *gild . . . gold*] To "gild gold" was
a common phrase, as in Sidney's *Arcadia*, p. 467.

11–12. *lily . . . violet*] These flowers
were associated for their opposite
qualities: "let lillies wither on the
stalke and weare violets in thy hand,
the one faire and vnsauory, the other
blacke but of sweete verdure" [R.
Greene, *Ciceronis Amor* (1589), sig. G2].
Note the climax: (*a*) from part-perfect
to wholly perfect (gold has to be refined, the lily and violet are only half-
perfect); (*b*) motion upwards [gold

To throw a perfume on the violet,
To smooth the ice, or add another hue
Unto the rainbow, or with taper-light
To seek the beauteous eye of heaven to garnish,   15
Is wasteful and ridiculous excess.

Pem. But that your royal pleasure must be done,
This act is as an ancient tale new told,
And, in the last repeating, troublesome,
Being urged at a time unseasonable.   20

Sal. In this the antique and well-noted face
Of plain old form is much disfigured;
And, like a shifted wind unto a sail,
It makes the course of thoughts to fetch about,
Startles and frights consideration,   25
Makes sound opinion sick and truth suspected,
For putting on so new a fashion'd robe.

Pem. When workmen strive to do better than well
They do confound their skill in covetousness;
And oftentimes excusing of a fault   30

---

26. *suspected*] F1; *suspect* Anon. conj. *ap.* Cambridge.   29. *covetousness*] F1;
covetize Capell conj.

---

within the earth (cf. III. i. 5, note),
flowers and ice (on the earth's surface),
rainbow, sun].

14–16. *or . . . excess*] Edd. compared
"to burn daylight" (*Rom.*, I. iv. 43,
Wiv., II. i. 54) = to do the superfluous.
Tilley (p. 641) quoted the proverb
"To set forth the Sun with a candle
(taper)". Perhaps also a glance at
primitive eclipse ritual: "the Ro-
MAINES beganne to make a noyse
with basons and pannes . . . to call her
[the moon] againe, and to make her
come to her light, lifting vp many
torches lighted" [Plutarch's *Lives* (ed.
1595), p. 270]. John fears an eclipse of
himself.

15. *eye*] Cf. III. i. 5, IV. ii. 2, notes.
18–19. *This . . . troublesome*] Cf. III.
iii. 108, note.
21. *well-noted*] familiar; much observed.
22. *form*] order (cf. III. i. 179, III. iii.
101–2).

disfigured] *disfigur'd* would read
better.
23–4. *like . . . about*] Cf. *Ephesians*, iv.
14: "wauering and caryed about with
euerie winde of doctrine".
24. *fetch about*] change their tack.
26. *sick . . . suspected*] A natural transition, since houses with the plague were
"suspected places".
27. *robe*] See l. 10, note. The attack
on ceremony inevitably veers to "vest-
ment", the deepest issue. J. W. Allen
(*History of Political Thought in the 16th
Century* (1941), p. 213] showed why
Elizabeth's government regarded an
attack on ceremony as one on royal
supremacy. John's nobles here indirectly attack *his* supremacy.
28–9. *When . . . covetousness*] Malone
compared *Lr.*, I. iv. 371, Sonnet 103.
"Confound" = mingle indistinguish-
ably; waste, consume; destroy. Alluding to the proverb "He that coveteth
all, loseth all."

Doth make the fault the worse by th' excuse:
As patches set upon a little breach
Discredit more in hiding of the fault
Than did the fault before it was so patch'd.

Sal. To this effect, before you were new crown'd,   35
We breath'd our counsel: but it pleas'd your highness
To overbear it, and we are all well pleas'd,
Since all and every part of what we would
Doth make a stand at what your highness will.

K. John. Some reasons of this double coronation   40
I have possess'd you with, and think them strong;
And more, more strong than lesser is my fear,
I shall indue you with: meantime but ask
What you would have reform'd that is not well,
And well shall you perceive how willingly   45
I will both hear and grant you your requests.

Pem. Then I, as one that am the tongue of these,
To sound the purposes of all their hearts,
Both for myself and them, but, chief of all,
Your safety, for the which, myself and them,   50

---

31. *worse*] F1; *worser* Maxwell conj. (*N. & Q.*, 28 Oct. 1950).   37. *it*] F1;
'*t* Anon. conj. *ap.* Cambridge.   *we are*] F1; *we're* Pope.   42. *than*] F1 (*then*);
when Tyrwhitt, edd.   50. *safety*, . . . *which*, . . . *them*,] This ed.; *safety:* . . .
which, . . . *them* F1.   *them*] F1; *they* Pope.

32–4. *As . . . patch'd.*] "no man
pieceth an olde garment with a piece
of newe clothe: for that that shuld fil it
vp, taketh awaye from the garment,
and the breache is worse" (*Matthew*,
ix. 16; cf. *Mark*, ii. 21, *Luke*, v. 36) [G.
Colton, *Shakspeare and the Bible* (1888),
p. 38]. Genevan bibles note that the
example refers to a *ceremony*.

33. *fault*] defect.

37. *we . . . pleas'd*] "Salisbury concludes politely . . . the nobles are well
pleased since their will must corre-
spond with his" (Wilson, taking *make
a stand at* (l. 39) = pause, stop short
at).—Or is Salisbury ironic ["make
a stand at" = conflict with (*O.E.D.*,
stand, 4)]?

39. *will*] wishes; commands.

42. *than lesser*] "reasons stronger

than my fear is less, or as strong as my
fear is little . . . comparing the degree
of two things . . . entirely different in
kind" (White). In F1 *then* often =
"than".

43. *indue*] supply.

48. *sound . . . purposes*] "express . . .
proposals", or "proclaim (as with a
trumpet) . . . intentions". The alter-
natives in IV. ii. 10, 37–9, 48, 63 rise
to barely concealed threatening.

49–50. *but . . . safety*] "The F. pauses
before and after these words give them
a sinister emphasis that is almost a
threat" (Wilson).

50. *them*] Condemned as ungram-
matical. But if *them* stands for "they"
(whether due to repetition of l. 49, or
the form *them(selves)* after *myself*), we
expect "our", not *their*, in l. 51. If *my-*

Bend their best studies, heartily request
Th' enfranchisement of Arthur: whose restraint
Doth move the murmuring lips of discontent
To break into this dangerous argument:
If what in rest you have in right you hold,   55
Why then your fears, which, as they say, attend
The steps of wrong, should move you to mew up
Your tender kinsman, and to choke his days
With barbarous ignorance, and deny his youth
The rich advantage of good exercise?   60
That the time's enemies may not have this
To grace occasions, let it be our suit
That you have bid us ask his liberty;
Which for our goods we do no further ask
Than whereupon our weal, on you depending,   65
Counts it your weal he have his liberty.

Enter HUBERT.

---

55. *rest*] F1 ; *wrest* Steevens conj.   56–7. *then . . . should*] F1 ; *shou'd . . . then* Pope.
63. *ask*] F1 ; *ask*, Rowe iii.   64. *goods*] F1 ; *good* Pope.   *further*] F1 ; *farther*
Collier.   67. S.D.] As F1 ; after l. 67 Johnson, edd.

---

self and *them* are governed by *for* we
can assume a subject "They" for
Bend (l. 51), suggested by *these, their,
them, them* (ll. 47–50). The subject *I*
(l. 47) of *request* (l. 51) would thus be
further obscured, but l. 50, with the
subject-confusion of l. 51, then emphasizes the identity of interests that is
Pembroke's theme (as in IV. ii. 64–6).

51. *Bend . . . studies*] "direct their (or
our) best efforts" (Smith).

55. *rest*] Steevens' *wrest* = an act of
seizure or violence. Wright thought *in
rest* = "in quiet possession". Both have
found backers and critics.—We think
rest = the (not uncommon) aphetic
form of "arrest". But cf. p. 152, l. 12.

56–7. *then . . . should*] Pope's transposition is needless: the syntax is correct for an indirect question (Wright).

57. *move*] Perhaps the *v* was dropped
to pronounce *mo'e* (cf. III. i. 264, note),
playing on *mo'e* and *mew*—John's
fears *force* him to use *force* against

Arthur (they are in a similar position).
mew up] coop up, imprison.

60. *exercise*] Not only martial exercise, but the practice of all gentlemanly
qualities. Edd. compare *AYL.*, I. i. 5–
22, 72–80.

62. *grace occasions*] take the stigma
from attack, or fault-finding.

62–3. *suit . . . liberty*] Cf. Introduction, p. xiii. "The custom of asking
and granting *suits* at these seasons [i.e.
coronations], was once general"
(Capell).

63. *That . . . ask*] Ambiguous: "let
his liberty be the suit *which* you have
told us to ask", or "let it be our suit
that (it may be given out that) *you* asked
us to ask for his liberty."

64. *our goods*] our own good.

65. *whereupon*] in so far as.

67. S.D.] John grants the suit as
soon as Hubert's entry assures him
Arthur is dead. To bring on Hubert
later than F1 changes John's tac-

K. John. Let it be so: I do commit his youth
　　　　To your direction. Hubert, what news with you?
　　　　　　　　　　　　　　　　　[*Taking him apart.*

Pem. This is the man should do the bloody deed:
　　　　He show'd his warrant to a friend of mine.   70
　　　　The image of a wicked heinous fault
　　　　Lives in his eye; that close aspect of his
　　　　Do show the mood of a much troubled breast;
　　　　And I do fearfully believe 'tis done,
　　　　What we so fear'd he had a charge to do.   75

Sal. The colour of the king doth come and go
　　　　Between his purpose and his conscience,
　　　　Like heralds 'twixt two dreadful battles set:
　　　　His passion is so ripe, it needs must break.

Pem. And when it breaks, I fear will issue thence   80
　　　　The foul corruption of a sweet child's death.

K. John. We cannot hold mortality's strong hand:
　　　　Good lords, although my will to give is living,
　　　　The suit which you demand is gone and dead:
　　　　He tells us Arthur is deceas'd to-night.   85

---

68. S.D.] Capell; om. F1.　73. *Do*] F1; *Does* F4; *Doth* Dyce.　78. *set*] F1; *sent* Theobald.

tical surrender into mere weakness.

it be so] Cf. III. iii. 140.

71. *heinous fault*] monstrous offence. A common tag (cf. *Faerie Queene*, III. viii. 36).

76. *The . . . go*] In the old *King Leir* (1605) Ragan, reading a letter, is thus described: "See how her colour comes and goes agayne, / Now red as scarlet, now as pale as ash:" (sig. E⁵).

78. *heralds*] Wilson thought the coloured coats of heralds are meant. —John's alternate paleness and redness declare his *purpose* (to kill Arthur) and his (regard for the dictates of) *conscience* (to refrain)—as heralds come and go to declare the wishes of two powers ready to fight.

set] Edd. now take with *battles* (= armies in battle array). White insisted that "*coming and going*, could not be compared to any thing *set*". But *set*

may = stationed to perform duties (*O.E.D.*, set, 45; as *set sentries*), referring to *function*, not *place.*

79–81. *His . . . death.*] "the rancor which king Henrie the sonne had conceiued . . . was so ripened, that it could not but burst out . . . the sooner to powre out his poison which he had sucked before" (Holinshed, life of Henry II, 86, i). The impostume image recurs in l. 101.

82. *We . . . hand:*] Cf. the cliché "to shake hands with death" = to die (*O.E.D.*, shake, 9a; *3 H 6*, I. iv. 102). He means (*a*) We (the king) cannot save anyone from Death; (*b*) We (mankind) cannot hold Death's hand (without dying, i.e. we must all die). Cf. v. ii. 22.

84. *gone and dead*] "dead and gone" was the cliché: cf. *1 H 6*, I. iv. 93, *2 H 6*, II. iii. 37, *Ham.*, IV. v. 29.

Sal. Indeed we fear'd his sickness was past cure.

Pem. Indeed we heard how near his death he was,
　　　Before the child himself felt he was sick:
　　　This must be answer'd, either here or hence.

K. John. Why do you bend such solemn brows on me?　　90
　　　Think you I bear the shears of destiny?
　　　Have I commandment on the pulse of life?

Sal. It is apparent foul-play; and 'tis shame
　　　That greatness should so grossly offer it:
　　　So thrive it in your game! and so, farewell.　　95

Pem. Stay yet, Lord Salisbury; I'll go with thee,
　　　And find th' inheritance of this poor child,
　　　His little kingdom of a forced grave.
　　　That blood which ow'd the breadth of all this isle
　　　Three foot of it doth hold: bad world the while!　　100
　　　This must not be thus borne: this will break out
　　　To all our sorrows, and ere long I doubt.　　[*Exeunt Lords.*

K. John. They burn in indignation. [*Enter a Messenger.*]
　　　I repent:
　　　There is no sure foundation set on blood,
　　　No certain life achiev'd by others' death.　　105

99. *ow'd*] F1; *own'd* Pope.　　102. S.D.] Capell; Exeunt F1.　　103.] F1;
Scene III. Pope.　　103-5. *They . . . death.*] F1; Aside. Rowe iii.　　103. S.D.]
This ed.; Enter Mes. F1 (after *repent:*; after l. 105 Johnson, edd.).

89. *answer'd*] accounted or atoned for.

here or hence] on earth or in heaven; cf. III. i. 113, v. iv. 29.

91. *Think . . . destiny?*] Alluding to the Fates, i.e. Atropos, who cut the thread of life.

93. *apparent*] obvious.

94. *grossly offer*] plainly, flagrantly attempt or dare.

95. *So . . . game*] "*So thrive it* with you *in your game* as your game deserves" (Capell). Or perhaps: "May you have the like fortune."

98. *forced*] = (*a*) brought about by violent means; (*b*) artificially or carefully raised (of soils). Vaughan compared a similar use, referring to a tomb, in North's Plutarch.

99-100. *That . . . hold:*] Following

the conventionalized monarch's epitaph. Cf. that of Henry II: "And yet while all the earth could scarse my greedie mind suffice, / Eight foot within the ground now serues, wherein my carcase lies" (Hol., 116, ii).

100. *bad . . . while!*] It's a bad world while such things are suffered. Cf. IV. iii. 116, *R 3*, III. vi. 10.

101. *break out*] Cf. l. 80.

103. S.D.] The F1 entrance can be defended: John does not dare to ask at once for more bad news.

I repent] Cf. note to IV. ii. 208-14. The line ("They are indignant *therefore* I repent") suggests that John repents his policy, not his crime; cf. IV. ii. 220, note.

104-5. *There . . . death.*] Cf. Appendix A, p. 166.

M

[*To the Messenger.*] A fearful eye thou hast: where is that
    blood
That I have seen inhabit in those cheeks?
So foul a sky clears not without a storm:
Pour down thy weather: how goes all in France?

Mess. From France to England. Never such a power   110
For any foreign preparation
Was levied in the body of a land.
The copy of your speed is learn'd by them;
For when you should be told they do prepare
The tidings comes that they are all arriv'd.   115

K. John. O, where hath our intelligence been drunk?
Where hath it slept? Where is my mother's care,
That such an army could be drawn in France,
And she not hear of it?

Mess.   My liege, her ear
Is stopp'd with dust: the first of April died   120
Your noble mother; and, as I hear, my lord,
The Lady Constance in a frenzy died
Three days before: but this from rumour's tongue
I idly heard; if true or false I know not.

K. John. Withhold thy speed, dreadful occasion!   125
O, make a league with me, till I have pleas'd
My discontented peers! What! mother dead!

106.] F1; *Scene* III. Kemble.   106. S.D.] As Rowe iii; om. F1.   110. *England.*]
Roderick, edd.; *England*, F1.   115. *comes*] F1; *come* F4, edd.   117. *care*] F1;
ear Walker conj. *ap.* Dyce.

109. *weather*] tempest.

110. *From . . . England.*] "All *in*
France goes *from* France *to* England"
(Roderick).

113. *copy*] example. Cf. Introduction, p. lxv.

116–17. *O, . . . slept?*] Malone compared *Mac.*: "Was the hope drunk, /
Wherein you dress'd yourself? hath it
slept since," (I. vii. 35–6).

116. *intelligence*] spies.

117. *care*] The first letter is broken in
F1. Some thought it an "e", but Furness showed that it was a "c".

119–20. *her . . . dust*] Death stopping

the ears of men is a biblical image.

120. *first of April*] Cf. Introduction, p. xvii.

121–4. *and . . . not.*] She died three
years before (Constance in 1201,
Eleanor in 1204). Perhaps Shakespeare remembered that Constance
died three somethings before, and the
messenger's disclaimer (ll. 123–4) indicates *Shakespeare's* uncertainty: cf. III.
ii. 7, note.

124. *idly*] without paying proper
attention.

125. *occasion*] Cf. Introduction, p.
lxi.

How wildly then walks my estate in France!
Under whose conduct came those powers of
    France
That thou for truth giv'st out are landed here?   130
Mess. Under the Dolphin.

Enter the BASTARD *and* PETER *of Pomfret.*

K. John.   Thou hast made me giddy
With these ill tidings.—Now, what says the world
To your proceedings? do not seek to stuff
My head with more ill news, for it is full.
Bast. But if you be afeard to hear the worst,   135
Then let the worst unheard fall on your head.
K. John. Bear with me, cousin; for I was amaz'd
Under the tide: but now I breathe again
Aloft the flood, and can give audience
To any tongue, speak it of what it will.   140
Bast. How I have sped among the clergymen
The sums I have collected shall express.
But as I travaill'd hither through the land
I find the people strangely fantasied;
Possess'd with rumours, full of idle dreams,   145
Not knowing what they fear, but full of fear.
And here's a prophet, that I brought with me
From forth the streets of Pomfret, whom I found

131. S.D.] As F1; after *tidings* l. 132 Johnson, edd.

128. *wildly*] chaotically.
walks] proceeds (cf. I. i. 172,
note).
131. S.D. Pomfret] Pontefract.
137. *amaz'd*] Cf. IV. iii. 140, note.
138. *Under the tide*] "Thy wrathful
displeasure goeth ouer me: and the
feare of thee hath vndonne me. They
came rounde about me dayly lyke
water: and compassed me tegeather
on euery syde. My louers and frends
hast thou put away fro me: and hyd
mine acquaintance out of my sight"
(*Psalms*, lxxxviii. 16–18, Book of Common Prayer); "all thy waues and thy

floods are gone ouer me" (*Psalms*, xlii.
7).
139. *Aloft*] Not used elsewhere by
Shakespeare as a preposition.
141. *sped*] fared; succeeded; hastened.
143. *travaill'd*] Travel and travail
were only differentiated after Shakespeare who here means *toiled* and
journeyed.
144–5. *I . . . dreams*] Cf. Intro., p. xiv.
145. *idle dreams*] A cliché, as in
Faerie Queene, I. i. 46, II. vi. 27, *Meas.*,
IV. i. 65.
146. *Not . . . fear*] Cf. *Mac.*, IV. ii. 20.

With many hundreds treading on his heels;
To whom he sung, in rude harsh-sounding
    rhymes,   150
That, ere the next Ascension-day at noon,
Your highness should deliver up your crown.
K. John. Thou idle dreamer, wherefore didst thou so?
Peter. Foreknowing that the truth will fall out so.
K. John. Hubert, away with him; imprison him: 155
And on that day at noon, whereon he says
I shall yield up my crown, let him be hang'd.
Deliver him to safety, and return,
For I must use thee.   *[Exit Hubert with Peter.*
              O my gentle cousin,
Hear'st thou the news abroad, who are arriv'd?   160
Bast. The French, my lord: men's mouths are full of it.
Besides, I met Lord Bigot and Lord Salisbury,
With eyes as red as new-enkindled fire,
And others more, going to seek the grave
Of Arthur, whom they say is kill'd to-night   165
On your suggestion.
K. John.   Gentle kinsman, go,
And thrust thyself into their companies.
I have a way to win their loves again;
Bring them before me.
Bast.   I will seek them out.
K. John. Nay, but make haste: the better foot before!   170

---

150. *harsh-sounding*] Pope; no hyphen F1.
om. F1.   165. *whom*] F1; *who* Pope.
Rowe iii; with l. 165 F1.

159. S.D.] Theobald (after l. 159);
166. *On . . . suggestion.*] New line

149. *on*] at.
150. *sung*] declared in verse (*O.E.D.*,
sing, 12). Shakespeare probably read
M. Paris on the Children's Crusade
(during John's reign): "Quidam enim
puer . . . per ciuitates vadens & castella
in regno Francorum, quasi a Domino
missus, cantillabat gallice modulando
. . . . sequebantur eum infiniti" (p.
324).
153. *dreamer*] A dreamer could be a
recognized prophet, as in B. & F.'s
Women Pleased: "Diviners, Dreamers,
Schoolemen, deep Magitians" (ed.

1647, p. 37); but John is contemptuous. H. F. Brooks refers me to *Caes.*:
"He is a dreamer; let us leave him:
pass." (I. ii. 24.)
158. *safety*] safe custody.
163. *With . . . fire*] Tilley (p. 214)
quoted the proverb "As red as
Fire".
165. *whom*] Confusion of construction with "whom they say (report)
killed".
170. *the . . . before*] Already proverbial (Tilley: p. 234) when used by
Shakespeare in *Tit.*, II. iii. 192.

O, let me have no subject enemies,
When adverse foreigners affright my towns
With dreadful pomp of stout invasion!
Be Mercury, set feathers to thy heels,
And fly like thought from them to me again.   175
Bast. The spirit of the time shall teach me speed.   [*Exit.*
K. John. Spoke like a sprightful noble gentleman.
Go after him; for he perhaps shall need
Some messenger betwixt me and the peers;
And be thou he.
Mess.   With all my heart, my liege. [*Exit.* 180
K. John. My mother dead!

Re-enter HUBERT.

Hub. My lord, they say five moons were seen to-night:
Four fixed, and the fift did whirl about
The other four in wondrous motion.
K. John. Five moons?
Hub.   Old men and beldams in the streets 185
Do prophesy upon it dangerously:
Young Arthur's death is common in their mouths:
And when they talk of him, they shake their heads
And whisper one another in the ear;
And he that speaks doth gripe the hearer's wrist,   190
Whilst he that hears makes fearful action,
With wrinkled brows, with nods, with rolling eyes.

---

171. *subject*] As F1; *subjects* F2.   180. S.D.] Rowe; om. F1.   182.] F1;
Scene IV. Pope.   182. S.D.] Re-enter Capell; Enter F1.

174. *Be Mercury*] E. I. Fripp [*Shake-speare Studies* (1930), p. 106] compared Ovid's *Metam.*, 1. 671 ff.

175. *like thought*] "As swift as thought" was proverbial (Tilley, p. 663) as in *Lucr.*, 1. 1216, *LLL.*, IV. iii. 330.

177. *sprightful*] spirited. Punning on l. 176 (*spright* being a contraction of *spirit*).

182. *five moons*] So Holinshed. (Appendix A, p. 152.)

183. *fift*] Common variant of *fifth*.

185–202. *Old . . . death.*] Shakespeare amplifies Holinshed's comment on Arthur's death "For the space of fif-teene daies this rumour incessantlie ran through both the realmes of Eng-land and France" (165, ii).

185. *beldams*] grandmothers; hags.

186. *prophesy*] "used not so much in the sense of foretelling the future events predicted by this phenomenon as in that of commenting upon and expounding the phenomenon itself, making it the text of a dangerous dis-course" (Wright).

I saw a smith stand with his hammer, thus,
The whilst his iron did on the anvil cool,
With open mouth swallowing a tailor's news;   195
Who, with his shears and measure in his hand,
Standing on slippers, which his nimble haste
Had falsely thrust upon contrary feet,
Told of a many thousand warlike French
That were embattailed and rank'd in Kent: 200
Another lean unwash'd artificer
Cuts off his tale and talks of Arthur's death.

K. John. Why seek'st thou to possess me with these fears?
Why urgest thou so oft young Arthur's death?
Thy hand hath murd'red him: I had a mighty cause 205
To wish him dead, but thou hadst none to kill him.
Hub. No had, my lord! why, did you not provoke me?
K. John. It is the curse of kings to be attended
By slaves that take their humours for a warrant
To break within the bloody house of life,   210
And on the winking of authority
To understand a law, to know the meaning
Of dangerous majesty, when perchance it frowns
More upon humour than advis'd respect.
Hub. Here is your hand and seal for what I did.   215

205. *I had*] F1; *I'd* Vaughan.   *a*] F1; om. Steevens.   *mighty*] F1; om. Pope.
207. *No had*] F1; *Had none* Rowe iii, edd.

197. *slippers*] "tailors generally work barefooted" (Malone).
198. *contrary*] Accent on second syllable.
200. *embattailed*] set in order of battle.
203. *Why . . . fears?*] Cf. II. ii. 11–18.
207. *No had*] Arrowsmith (*ap.* Furness) showed that constructions such as *No had?*, *No does?*, *No will?*, were common, as in "the whole world Yields not a workman that can frame the like. *Fort.* No does?" (Dekker's *Old Fortunatus*, II. i).
provoke] incite.
208. *It . . . to*] An idiom = Kings are cursed (condemned) to.
208–14. *It . . . respect.*] Holinshed

says that Hubert did not murder Arthur because he thought the command due to John's "heat and furie . . . and that afterwards, vpon better aduisement*, he would both *repent* himselfe so to haue commanded, and giue them small thanke that should see it put in execution" (165, ii). Cf. IV. ii. 103.
212. *To*] Influenced by *To*, l. 210.
214. *humour*] moodiness. This follows Holinshed's hint of *heat and furie* (cf. l. 208, note).
215. *Here . . . did.*] Cf. *R 2*, v. vi. 34 ff. (Deighton). For the Davison allusion cf. Introduction, p. xxviii; for the murder-blinding confusion Appendix B, p. 168.

K. John. O, when the last accompt 'twixt heaven and earth
　　　Is to be made, then shall this hand and seal
　　　Witness against us to damnation!
　　　How oft the sight of means to do ill deeds
　　　Make deeds ill done! Hadst not thou been by,　　　220
　　　A fellow by the hand of nature mark'd,
　　　Quoted and sign'd to do a deed of shame,
　　　This murther had not come into my mind;
　　　But taking note of thy abhorr'd aspect,
　　　Finding thee fit for bloody villainy,　　　225
　　　Apt, liable to be employ'd in danger,
　　　I faintly broke with thee of Arthur's death;
　　　And thou, to be endeared to a king,
　　　Made it no conscience to destroy a prince.
Hub. My lord—　　　230
K. John. Hadst thou but shook thy head or made a pause
　　　When I spake darkly what I purposed,
　　　Or turn'd an eye of doubt upon my face,
　　　As bid me tell my tale in express words,　　　234
　　　Deep shame had struck me dumb, made me break off,
　　　And those thy fears might have wrought fears in me:
　　　But thou didst understand me by my signs
　　　And didst in signs again parley with sin;

220. *Make*] F1; *Makes* Theobald, edd.　　　*deeds ill*] F1; *ill deeds* Capell conj.
Hadst] F1; *for hadst* Pope; *Hadest* Capell.　　　229. *Made*] F1; *Mad'st* Pope.
230. *lord*—] Rowe iii; *Lord.* F1.　　　234. *As*] F1; *Or* Pope.　　　238. *sin*] F1; *sign*
Collier MS.

216. *accompt*] account. This variant
is used also in *Wint.*, II. iii. 197, *Mac.*,
v. i. 42, etc.
　　220. *Make*] Plural influenced by
means, deeds.
　　ill done] unskilfully performed. John
equates the *evil deed* (l. 219) and *in-
efficient doing* to suggest that sin is intel-
lectually untenable. He submits to
accepted values since they pay best:
cf. IV. ii. 103, v. vii. 82, notes, v. i. 5.
　　222. *Quoted*] Noted.
　　226. *liable*] fit.
　　227. *broke with*] confided to.
　　229. *conscience*] matter of conscience.
　　230. *My lord*—] Cf. III. ii. 76.

232-4. *darkly . . . express*] Cf. Introduction, p. xxix.
　　234. *As*] Which (Vaughan); Such
as (Abbott, sect. 280).
　　238. *signs . . . sin*] Sin and *sign* were
punned upon in Middleton's *Tricke to
Catch the Old-One* (1608): "Henceforth for euer I defie, / The Glances of
a sinnefull eye, / Wauing of Fans,
which some suppose, / Tricks of
Fancy, Treading of Toes, / . . . Taking
false Phisicke, and nere start, / To be
let blood, tho signe be at heart" (sig.
H₃ᵛ). In Tourneur's *Revengers Tragædie*
(1607) "sin" is spelt "signe" (sig.
E₄ᵛ).

Yea, without stop, didst let thy heart consent,
And consequently thy rude hand to act   240
The deed, which both our tongues held vild to name.
Out of my sight, and never see me more!
My nobles leave me, and my state is brav'd,
Even at my gates, with ranks of foreign powers:
Nay, in the body of this fleshly land,   245
This kingdom, this confine of blood and breath,
Hostility and civil tumult reigns
Between my conscience and my cousin's death.

Hub. Arm you against your other enemies,
    I'll make a peace between your soul and you.   250
Young Arthur is alive: this hand of mine
Is yet a maiden and an innocent hand,
Not painted with the crimson spots of blood.
Within this bosom never ent'red yet
The dreadful motion of a murderous thought;   255
And you have slander'd nature in my form,
Which, howsoever rude exteriorly,
Is yet the cover of a fairer mind
Than to be butcher of an innocent child.

K. John. Doth Arthur live? O, haste thee to the peers, 260
Throw this report on their incensed rage,
And make them tame to their obedience!
Forgive the comment that my passion made
Upon thy feature; for my rage was blind,
And foul imaginary eyes of blood   265
Presented thee more hideous than thou art.

247. *reigns*] F1 ; *reign* Hanmer.

240. *to*] Cf. Abbott, sect. 349 (*to* inserted after *let*). Vaughan thought *to*
could = *too* here, which is more probable than Furness's "take the infini-
tive 'to act' as directly dependent on
the verb 'consent' ".
    245. *fleshly land*] His own body.
    246. *confine*] territory; prison.
    247–8. *Hostility . . . death*] Cf. IV. ii.
76–8.
    254–5. *Within . . . thought*] But cf.
III. ii. 76, IV. i. 123.
    255. *motion*] impulse, inclination.

    261. *Throw*] i.e. as water, to quench
their rage.
    265–6. *And . . . art*] After l. 264 the
foul *imaginary* (= imaginative) eyes
seem to be John's. But as the foul blood
which John had thought disfigured
Arthur's eyes now turns out to be
imaginary (= unreal), Arthur's eyes
might be meant. And the *image* of the
blinding is visible in Hubert's eye (IV.
ii. 71), viz. Hubert's guilty eyes *reflecting* his crime might present him more
hideous, etc. (Cf. *imaginary* in *O.E.D.*).

O, answer not, but to my closet bring
The angry lords with all expedient haste.
I conjure thee but slowly: run more fast!　　　[*Exeunt.*

SCENE III. —[*Before the Castle.*]

Enter ARTHUR, *on the walls.*

Arth. The wall is high, and yet will I leap down:
　　Good ground, be pitiful and hurt me not!
　　There's few or none do know me: if they did,
　　This ship-boy's semblance hath disguis'd me quite.
　　I am afraid; and yet I'll venture it.　　　　　5
　　If I get down, and do not break my limbs,
　　I'll find a thousand shifts to get away:
　　As good to die and go, as die and stay.
　　　　　[*He leaps, and lies momentarily in a trance.*
　　O me! my uncle's spirit is in these stones:
　　Heaven take my soul, and England keep my bones!　　10
　　　　　　　　　　　　　　　　　　　[*Dies.*

Enter PEMBROKE, SALISBURY, *and* BIGOT.

Sal. Lords, I will meet him at Saint Edmundsbury:
　　It is our safety, and we must embrace
　　This gentle offer of the perilous time.

Scene III

Scene III] F1; V. Pope; II. Donovan.　　Before . . . Castle.] Capell; om. F1;
A Prison. Rowe.　　8. S.D.] This ed.; om. F1; Leaps down. Rowe, edd.
9. *spirit*] F1; *sprite* Fleay.

　　1. *leap*] Shakespeare read various
theories about Arthur's death, two
being: "proouing to clime ouer
the wals of the castell, he fell" (Hol.
165, ii); "leaping into the ditch thinking to make his escape" (Foxe, 250,
i).
　　7. *shifts*] stratagems; changes of
clothing. A common pun, as in *2 H 6*:
"My shame will not be shifted with my
sheet" (II. iv. 108).
　　8. S.D.] Our S.D. follows the *T.R.*,
which probably imitated *John* here:
cf. Appendix C, p. 175.

　　10. *Heaven . . . bones!*] Rushton
[*Shakespeare's Testamentary Language*
(1869), pp. 4–5] noted the resemblance
to the regular opening of wills, e.g.
Shakespeare's own: "ffirst I Comend
my Soule into the handes of god my
Creator . . . And my bodye to the
Earth whereof yt ys made."
　　11. *Saint Edmundsbury*] Shakespeare
conflates the nobles' pilgrimage to St
Edmundsbury where they "vttered
their complaint of the kings tyrannicall maners" in 1214, and the Dauphin's landing (1216).

Pem. Who brought that letter from the cardinal?

Sal. The Count Melun, a noble lord of France;   15
Whose private with me of the Dolphin's love
Is much more general than these lines import.

Big. To-morrow morning let us meet him then.

Sal. Or rather then set forward; for 'twill be
Two long days' journey, lords, or ere we meet.   20

Enter the BASTARD.

Bast. Once more to-day well met, distemper'd lords!
The king by me requests your presence straight.

Sal. The king hath dispossess'd himself of us:
We will not line his thin bestained cloak
With our pure honours, nor attend the foot   25
That leaves the print of blood where'er it walks.
Return and tell him so: we know the worst.

Bast. Whate'er you think, good words, I think, were best.

Sal. Our griefs, and not our manners, reason now.

Bast. But there is little reason in your grief;   30
Therefore 'twere reason you had manners now.

Pem. Sir, sir, impatience hath his privilege.

16. *with me*] F1; *warrant* Wilson conj.; *notice* Sisson.   17. *general than these*] F1; *than these gen'ral* Hanmer.   24. *thin bestained*] Rowe; hyphened F1.   32, 33. *his*] F1; *its* Pope.

15. *Count Melun*] Cf. Introduction, pp. xiii, xviii, n. 4.

16. *private*] Though *private* = "privacy, private affairs, etc." is found, this is the only use = private communication.

17. *general*] comprehensive.

20. *or ere*] before (as in *Mac.*, IV. iii. 173).

21. *Once more*] Cf. IV. ii. 162 (Delius). *distemper'd*] ill-tempered. Faulconbridge probably means "deranged", i.e. making their disloyalty a disease.

24. *line*] "(*a*) furnish a lining to, (*b*) reinforce" (Wilson).

25–6. *nor . . . walks.*] Cf. III. ii. 72, IV. ii. 57.—A commonplace? Cf. E. Daunce, *Briefe Discourse* (1590): "Mac-

chiauel . . . maintaineth that where the Pope and Cardinals set footing, they leaue most fearefull printes of confusion" (sig. D₂ᵛ). So in the *Psalms*: "That thy foote may be dipped in the blood . . . of the enemies" (lxviii. 23); "the mighty people . . . haue reproched the footsteppes of thine Anointed" (lxxxix. 50–1).

28. *good words*] Cf. *T.R.* "Good words sir sauce, your betters are in place" (I. ii. 129). Faulconbridge means "it would be best to speak fair words," and "it would be best not to speak so fiercely" (cf. *O.E.D.*, good, 7b).

29. *reason*] talk.

30. *But . . . grief;*] Cf. III. iii. 43.

Bast. 'Tis true, to hurt his master, no manners else.
Sal. This is the prison. [*Seeing Arthur.*] What is he lies here?
Pem. O death, made proud with pure and princely beauty!
    The earth had not a hole to hide this deed.   36
Sal. Murther, as hating what himself hath done,
    Doth lay it open to urge on revenge.
Big. Or, when he doom'd this beauty to a grave,
    Found it too precious-princely for a grave.   40
Sal. Sir Richard, what think you? You have beheld.
    Or have you read, or heard? or could you think,
    Or do you almost think, although you see,
    That you do see? could thought, without this object,
    Form such another? This is the very top,   45
    The heighth, the crest, or crest unto the crest,

33. *manners*] This ed.; *mans* F1; *man* F2, edd.   34. S.D.] Pope; om. F1.   40. *precious-princely*] Capell; no hyphen F1.   41. *You have beheld.*] Fleay; *you haue beheld*, F1; *have you beheld*, F3, edd.   42. *read, or heard?*] Capell; *read, or heard*, F1.   42–4. *think, . . . think, . . . see?*] Pope; *thinke? . . . thinke, . . . see?* F1, edd.   45. *This is*] F1; *'tis* Pope.

33. *to . . . master*] For the "iracundia sibi nocet" proverb see Tilley (p. 14), *Ecclesiasticus*, i. 27.

manners] *mans* is nonsense. The contiguous play on *manners* suggests "man's" (a possible spelling of *manners*, with the *-er* suspension), copied unintelligently from the MS. to make a familiar phrase [as in Holinshed: "to his naturall brother, and to no man else" (146, ii)]. Perhaps a play on "good manners" (as in ll. 29, 31), and "customary mode of acting or behaviour" (*O.E.D.*, manner, 3), i.e. the only quality (or good manners) that impatience has is to hurt its master.

35. *death . . . proud*] Death's pride in exceptional victims was a common conceit.

40. *grave*] "The bodies of princes were not buried in the ground, but embalmed and placed in a sepulchre or vault" (Wilson).

41. *You have beheld.*] You have had a good look. The syntax seems to have confused the edd.

42–4. *Or . . . see?*] We take as two *or . . . or* (= either . . . or) constructions. The speech revolves round *thinking* and *seeing*. *Reading* and *hearing* anticipate thinking (l. 42), and two degrees of thought follow (ll. 42–4). Perhaps an echo of legal interrogatories (cf. III. i. 73), which often tried thus to cover all the possibilities: "*Imprimis*, whither do you know, or haue you herd, seene or red that...".

43. *almost*] Used to intensify a rhetorical question (On.); = with difficulty (Vaughan, comparing *R 3*, III. v. 34).

44. *That*] The relative, though the conjunction is possible. Read: "Have you either read or heard (of the like)? could you either conceive, or do you get near the verge of conceiving, even with the aid of your eyes, that which you actually see before you?"

46. *heighth*] Variant of "height". *crest*] Crests were not generally used, and a "crest unto the crest" not at all in John's time [C. W. Scott-Giles, *Shakespeare's Heraldry* (1950), p. 42].

Of murther's arms: this is the bloodiest shame,
The wildest savagery, the vildest stroke,
That ever wall-ey'd wrath or staring rage
Presented to the tears of soft remorse.   50

Pem. All murthers past do stand excus'd in this:
And this, so sole and so unmatchable,
Shall give a holiness, a purity,
To the yet unbegotten sin of times;
And prove a deadly bloodshed but a jest,   55
Exampled by this heinous spectacle.

Bast. It is a damned and a bloody work;
The graceless action of a heavy hand,
If that it be the work of any hand.

Sal. If that it be the work of any hand!   60
We had a kind of light what would ensue:
It is the shameful work of Hubert's hand,
The practice and the purpose of the king:
From whose obedience I forbid my soul,
Kneeling before this ruin of sweet life,   65
And breathing to his breathless excellence
The incense of a vow, a holy vow,
Never to taste the pleasures of the world,
Never to be infected with delight,

---

54. *sin of times*] F1; *sins of Time* Pope.   60. *hand!*] F1 (*hand?*).   66. *his*] F1;
this Rowe.

49. *wall-ey'd*] with glaring eyes (so
Tit., v. i. 44), literally an eye with a
discoloured iris. *O.E.D.* (wall-eyed, 2)
notes that the adjective could be applied specifically to jealousy (John's
motive).

50. *remorse*] pity.

51–4. *All . . . times*] Cf. A. Colynet,
True History (1591): "yee that are
famous for any notorious wickednes,
reioyce, for your infamy is iustified by
the raging cruelty of . . . Dominican
Fryers" (p. 402), *Lr.*, II. iv. 259–60.

52. *sole*] unique.

54. *times*] future times.

55. *And . . . jest*] Cf. *Arden of Feversham*: "My death to him is but a
merryment, / And he will murther me
to make him sport" (sig. E).

56. *Exampled by*] Compared with.

58. *heavy*] wicked, grievous.

61. *light*] inkling.

63. *practice*] machination.

64–72. *From . . . revenge.*] The idea
may come from K. Philip's reactions:
"seeking reuenge of his death . . .
swearing that he would not ceasse to
pursue the warre against king Iohn,
till he had depriued him of his whole
kingdome" (Hol., 167, i). But the
elaborate *vow* copies the new Revenge
Tragedy. Cf. also Appendix A, p. 165.

67. *The . . . vow*] "Prayer" or *vow* =
"incense" was a common figure [cf.
Psalms: "Let my prayer be directed in
thy sight (as) incense" (cxli. 2)].

69. *infected*] "as though *delight* in
such circumstances would be a disease,

Nor conversant with ease and idleness,   70
Till I have set a glory to this hand,
By giving it the worship of revenge.

Pem. ⎫
Big. ⎭ Our souls religiously confirm thy words.

Enter HUBERT.

Hub. Lords, I am hot with haste in seeking you:
    Arthur doth live; the king hath sent for you.   75
Sal. O, he is bold and blushes not at death.
    Avaunt, thou hateful villain, get thee gone!
Hub. I am no villain.
Sal.   Must I rob the law? [*Drawing his sword.*
Bast. Your sword is bright, sir; put it up again.
Sal. Not till I sheathe it in a murtherer's skin.   80
Hub. Stand back, Lord Salisbury, stand back, I say;
    By heaven, I think my sword's as sharp as yours.
    I would not have you, lord, forget yourself,
    Nor tempt the danger of my true defence;
    Lest I, by marking of your rage, forget   85
    Your worth, your greatness and nobility.
Big. Out, dunghill! dar'st thou brave a nobleman?
Hub. Not for my life: but yet I dare defend

---

71. *hand*] F1; *head* Farmer.   74.] F1; *Scene* VI. Pope.   78. S.D.] Pope; om. F1.

something that would pollute him"
(Deighton).

71. *glory*] splendour (?). Or an
aureole, with which early painters
adorned hands, might be meant
(Fleay).

hand] Mason thought this Arthur's
hand. But Salisbury probably means
his own, which he lays on his sword as
on a cross (cf. *Ham.*, I. v. 160), so that
worship = honour, dignity.

76. *death*] the murder which he has
committed.

79. *Your . . . again.*] Malone compared *Oth.*: "Keep up your bright
swords, for the dew will rust them"
(I. ii. 59).

84. *tempt*] put to the test; venture
upon, risk; entice, solicit.

true defence] "*Honest* defence; defence
in a *good cause*" (Johnson); skilful defence, good swordsmanship (Davies).
A quibble.

85. *marking*] observing; aiming a
blow at (cf. *O.E.D.*, mark, 12, 13).

87. *Out . . . nobleman?*] Cf. Marlowe's
Edward the Second: "Away base vpstart,
brau'st thou nobles thus." (sig. G₂ᵛ).
Rushton [*Shakespeare Illustrated* (1867),
I, 64] showed that villein service included the carrying of dung for the
lord, whence such jibes. Wilson de-
duced that Hubert is not of noble birth
(cf. Introduction, p. xxxvii).

88–9. *Not . . . emperor*] So Dekker's
Match Mee in London (1631): "*King.*
'Shart doe I lye! doe you braue me!
you base Peasant? / *Mart.* No my

My innocent life against an emperor.

Sal. Thou art a murtherer.

Hub.   Do not prove me so: 90
Yet I am none. Whose tongue soe'er speaks false,
Not truly speaks; who speaks not truly, lies.

Pem. Cut him to pieces!

Bast.   Keep the peace, I say.

Sal. Stand by, or I shall gall you, Faulconbridge.

Bast. Thou wert better gall the divel, Salisbury: 95
If thou but frown on me, or stir thy foot,
Or teach thy hasty spleen to do me shame,
I'll strike thee dead. Put up thy sword betime—
Or I'll so maul you and your toasting-iron
That you shall think the divel is come from hell.   100

Big. What wilt thou do, renowned Faulconbridge?
Second a villain and a murtherer?

Hub. Lord Bigot, I am none.

Big.   Who kill'd this prince?

Hub. 'Tis not an hour since I left him well:
I honour'd him, I lov'd him, and will weep   105

90. *not*] F1; *but* Keightley.

Lord, but I must guard my life against an Emperor" (sig. C).

90–1. *Do . . . none.*] "Do not make me a murderer by compelling me to kill you; I am *hitherto* not a murderer" (Johnson). Singer took *prove* = provoke.

91–2. *Whose . . . lies.*] Cf. W. Segar's *Booke of Honor and Armes* (1590): "who soeuer being offered iniurious speach, shall say to the offerer thereof *Thou liest*, or thou saiest not truelie, doth therby repulse the iniurie, and force the Iniurer to challenge" (sig. B₂ᵛ). In ll. 81–6 Hubert suggests that he will *fight*, Bigot scornfully rejects the challenge as an inferior's *brave* (l. 87) or impudence, which makes Hubert give the lie direct (cf. *AYL.*, v. iv. 94 ff.).

93. *Cut . . . pieces!*] The nobles pretend they are too far above Hubert to need to consider his claim to a duel—a grave insult.

94. *by*] aside.
gall] hurt.

95, 100. *divel*] Cf. ii. i. 567, note.

97. *spleen*] fiery temper.
do me shame] treat me shamefully like an inferior, as you have done Hubert.

99. *toasting-iron*] "Iron" was slang for "sword". Z. Grey compared *H 5*: "I will wink and hold out mine iron. It is a simple one; but what though? it will toast cheese" (ii. i. 8–10). Perhaps the mockery of Salisbury's sword is in allusion to his nickname: "Salisburie . . . surnamed Long Espée", "William Longspée earle of Salisburie base brother to king Iohn" (Hol., 150, ii, 179, i).

102. *Second*] Support; act as second to. The ambiguity is placatory, granting the *right to duel* (by implication), which was previously denied (cf. notes on ll. 91, 93).

My date of life out for his sweet live's loss.
Sal. Trust not those cunning waters of his eyes,
For villainy is not without such rheum;
And he, long traded in it, makes it seem
Like rivers of remorse and innocency.   110
Away with me, all you whose souls abhor
Th' uncleanly savours of a slaughter-house;
For I am stifled with this smell of sin.
Big. Away toward Bury, to the Dolphin there!   114
Pem. There tell the king he may inquire us out.

                                        [*Exeunt Lords.*

Bast. Here's a good world! Knew you of this fair work?
Beyond the infinite and boundless reach
Of mercy, if thou didst this deed of death,
Art thou damn'd, Hubert.
Hub.   Do but hear me, sir—
Bast. Ha! I'll tell thee what;   120
Thou'rt damn'd as black—nay, nothing is so black;
Thou art more deep damn'd than Prince Lucifer:
There is not yet so ugly a fiend of hell
As thou shalt be, if thou didst kill this child.
Hub. Upon my soul—
Bast.   If thou didst but consent   125

---

110. *innocency*] F1; *innocence* Pope.   116.] F1; *Scene* VII. Pope.   117–19.]
Pope; two lines F1 (ending *mercie,*/ . . . *Hubert.*/).   124–6. *child.* . . . *If* . . . *act,*]
As Rowe; *childe.* . . . *If* . . . *Act:* F1; *child*— . . . —*If* . . . *act.* Maxwell (*N. & Q.,*
28 Oct. 1950).

106. *date*] duration.
live's] life's.
109. *traded in*] accustomed to; driving a trade in.
112. *uncleanly*] Stronger than in IV. i. 7, perhaps = the "unclean flesh" sacrifices of the Old Testament (*Leviticus*, v, etc.); *savours* and *smell* may also be biblical: "The Lorde looke vpon you and iudge: for ye haue made our sauour to stinke before Pharaoh . . . ye haue put a sword in their hand to slay vs" (*Exodus*, v. 21; cf. *Genesis*, xxxiv. 30).
116. *Here's . . . world!*] Common exclamation = "It's a bad world!" Cf. IV. ii. 100.

117–19. *Beyond . . . Hubert.*] "Thy mercie, O Lord, (reacheth) vnto the heauens" (*Psalms*, xxxvi. 5).
121–4. *Thou'rt . . . child.*] That blackness = damnation was not disputed ["Damn'd as thou art" said to Othello (I. ii. 63); "Damn'd as he is" said of Aaron (*Tit.*, v. iii. 124)]. The white angel Lucifer was thrown into deepest hell, i.e. blackest, i.e. ugliest (cf. *Isaiah*, xiv, *Luke*, x).
123. *ugly*] "The emphasis upon Hubert's ugliness (cf. 4. 2. 220–25, 266) suggests that the actor who played him possessed uncomely features" (Wilson).

To this most cruel act, do but despair;
And if thou want'st a cord, the smallest thread
That ever spider twisted from her womb
Will serve to strangle thee; a rush will be a beam
To hang thee on; or wouldst thou drown thyself,   130
Put but a little water in a spoon,
And it shall be as all the ocean,
Enough to stifle such a villain up.
I do suspect thee very grievously.

Hub. If I in act, consent, or sin of thought,   135
Be guilty of the stealing that sweet breath
Which was embounded in this beauteous clay,
Let hell want pains enough to torture me!
I left him well.

Bast.   Go, bear him in thine arms.
I am amaz'd, methinks, and lose my way   140
Among the thorns and dangers of this world.
How easy dost thou take all England up

---

129. *Will . . . beam*] F1; *Will . . . be/A beam* Steevens.   *serve to*] F1; om. Pope.
130. *thyself*] F1; om. Steevens conj.   142–3. *up . . . royalty!*] F1 (*vp, . . . Royaltie?*);
up! . . . Royalty, Theobald, edd.

126. *do but despair*] "only despair is left for you" (I. John). Despair was sinful, as the Cave of Despair shows (*Faerie Queene*, Bk 1, canto ix).

127–33. *And . . . up.*] Vaughan suggested an allusion to the superstition that criminals are less immune to ill fortune than others, citing from Holinshed (744, i, Life of Richard III) an example of "drowning in a small puddle", which Holinshed thought God's judgement.

130. *hang*] A reference to Judas's hanging himself after betraying Christ? (Delius).

133. *up*] Intensive.

134. *I . . . grievously*] Holinshed says of Arthur's death "king Iohn was had in great suspicion" (165, ii), "king Philip . . . tooke the matter verie greeuouslie" (166, i), and Shakespeare adapts to Hubert. This "very grievously" is unique in Shakespeare (cf. Bartlett's *Concordance*).

135. *If . . . thought*] Cf. IV. ii. 254, note. Hubert echoes the "general confession" in use before Holy Communion: "wee knowledge and bewaile our manifolde sinnes and wickednesse, which we from tyme to tyme most grieuously haue committed, by thought, word, and deede."

137. *embounded*] enclosed.

140. *amaz'd*] bewildered. This word was connected with *maze* = labyrinth.

140–1. *lose . . . world*] Thorns = riches, and losing one's way among thorns is a biblical commonplace. *Proverbs*, xxii. 3–5, *Matthew*, xiii. 22 have been compared. This resumes the commodity motif.

142. *How . . . up*] Here *take up* must refer to l. 139; and Hubert's innocence is suggested since the body does not bleed near its supposed murderer (cf. J. Masefield: *William Shakespeare*, p. 83). But *take up* = "levy, raise in arms"

From forth this morsel of dead royalty!
The life, the right and truth of all this realm
Is fled to heaven; and England now is left   145
To tug and scamble, and to part by th' teeth
The unow'd interest of proud swelling state.
Now for the bare-pick'd bone of majesty
Doth dogged war bristle his angry crest
And snarleth in the gentle eyes of peace: 150
Now powers from home and discontents at home
Meet in one line; and vast confusion waits,

147. *proud swelling*] F1; hyphened Pope.

as well (cf. *2 H 4*, IV. ii. 26), anticipating ll. 145–54.

142–3. *How . . . royalty!*] The speech
quibbles on the identity of king and
country (cf. II. i. 91, 202, notes). In
l. 142 *England* = (*a*) the nation, (*b*)
Arthur. The *right* that has *fled to heaven*
(l. 145) = (*a*) the nation's law and
order (cf. II. i. 86–8), (*b*) Arthur's soul.
Theobald's removal of F1 *?* (= *!*) to
l. 142 destroys the quibble, which
shows Faulconbridge *almost* recognizing Arthur's right. The idea of England
taken up *From forth* Arthur's body
parallels that of his soul *fled to heaven*
(from his body).

144. *The . . . truth*] Alluding to the
words of Jesus (*John*, xiv. 6)? The
sovereign was traditionally the *life* of
his land, but Faulconbridge does not
necessarily recognize Arthur's claims
here: he says that *sovereignty* has departed, since Arthur's death will cause
revolt from John.

145, 148, 151, 155. *now . . . Now*]
Such summaries of the state of things
were common in the moralities (cf.
Introduction, p. lxxi), e.g. Bale's *King
Iohan*: "now maye we realmes con-
founde / Our holye father, maye now
lyue at hys pleasure / . . . He is now
able, to kepe downe Christe and hys
gospell / . . . Now shall we ruffle it . . . /
. . . now maye we synge Cantate"
(M.S.R., ll. 1702–9).

146. *scamble*] scramble.

147. *unow'd interest*] (*a*) *unowned* title

or right; (*b*) the accruing interest or
power of the nobles *unowed* to a king.
For the owe-own pun cf. IV. i. 123.

148. *bone*] The common dissention
figure, as in Dekker's *Newes from Hell*
(1606): "the *Diuell* . . . has . . . throwne
heresies (like bones for dogges to gnaw
vpon) amongst the Doctors" (sig.
B₂), and *Troil.*, I. iii. 391–2.

151. *Now . . . home*] Here *from home, at
home* may = "out of their element", "in
their element" (cf. v. vii. 115; *O.E.D.*,
home, 11c, 12). This would emphasize
disorder, viz. nobles uniting *unnaturally*
with the rabble (taking *powers* =
nobles, as in *H 8*, II. iv. 111). But many
take *powers from home* = "armies from
abroad". There was much talk in 1590
of Roman Catholic "discontents" joining the feared invaders. Cf. the same
ambiguity in v. i. 8–9, and *T.R.*: "The
multitude (a beast of many heads) /
Doo wish confusion to their Soue-
raigne; / The Nobles blinded with
ambitions fumes, / Assemble powers to
beat mine Empire downe, / And more
than this, elect a forren King" (II. ii.
124–8).

152. *Meet . . . line*] "When in one
line two crafts directly meet" (*Ham.*,
III. iv. 210) has been compared.
Schmidt glossed as "go the same way."
Wilson added "The image involved is
not clear, but I suggest that of two
knights meeting at full tilt". But
"meeting in one line" could have the
opposite sense, as in *The Proceedings of*

N

As doth a raven on a sick-fall'n beast,
The imminent decay of wrested pomp.
Now happy he whose cloak and ceinture can   155
Hold out this tempest. Bear away that child
And follow me with speed: I'll to the king.
A thousand businesses are brief in hand,
And heaven itself doth frown upon the land.   [*Exeunt.*

---

155. *ceinture*] F1 (*center*); *cincture* Pope.   159. S.D.] Rowe; Exit. F1.

---

the Earle of Leycester for . . . Sluce (1590): Leicester tried to reconcile all his allies, "to recure all seditious wounds, and to drawe all in one line to the reliefe of this beseiged Towne" (sig. B₂). It all depends whether *powers* and *discontents* (l. 151) are friends or not.

154. *wrested*] Some think that Faulconbridge now "wavers in his allegiance", recognizing John's authority as *wrested* (usurped from Arthur). We think Shakespeare continues the ambiguity of ll. 142 ff., that Faulconbridge talks of England first, of John only secondly, i.e. Arthur's death will cause revolt (cf. l. 144, note). Read: "Now armies from abroad and discontents at home join forces; and an all-embracing chaos, like a raven hovering above a dying beast, awaits the imminent general dissolution consequent upon the wresting of power from John."

155. *cloak . . . ceinture*] "Let it be unto him as the cloke that he hath vpon

him: and as the gyrdle that he is alway gyrded withall" (*Psalms*, cix. 19, in *Book of Common Prayer*). Shakespeare follows the common protection-image, as in *Isaiah*, xi. 5, xxii. 21, lix. 17, etc. J. C. Maxwell suggests (privately) that *ceinture* = "centre" and "ceinture", as in *1 H 6*, ii. ii. 6 ("the middle centre of this cursed town").

156. *this tempest*] "SVb eadem tempestate conuenerunt ad colloquium apud sanctum Eadmundum Comites & Barones Anglie" (M. Paris, p. 337). Cf. v. i. 17, 20, etc. (the common war-tempest image).

158. *brief*] "Rife; common; prevalent: often used of epidemic diseases" (*O.E.D.*).

159. *And . . . land.*] "the generall scourge wherewith the people were afflicted, chanced not through the princes fault, but for the wickednesse of his people, for the king was but the rod of the Lords wrath" (Hol., 173, ii). Cf. v. ii. 84.

ACT V

SCENE I. [*The Court of England.*]

Enter KING JOHN, PANDULPH, *and Attendants.*

K. John. Thus have I yielded up into your hand
    The circle of my glory.   [*Giving the crown.*
Pand.   Take again [*Giving back the crown.*
    From this my hand, as holding of the pope,
    Your sovereign greatness and authority.
K. John. Now keep your holy word: go meet the French,   5
    And from his holiness use all your power
    To stop their marches 'fore we are inflam'd.
    Our discontented counties do revolt;
    Our people quarrel with obedience,
    Swearing allegiance and the love of soul   10

ACT V

Scene 1

Act V Scene I.] Rowe; Actus Quartus, Scaena prima. F1; *Act* IV *Scene* III. Donovan. The . . . England.] Pope; om. F1.   S.D.] Enter King Iohn and Pandolph, attendants. F1; King *John,* . . . discovered. Kemble.   2. S.D. [Giving the crown.] Pope; om. F1.   2. *Take*] F1; *Take't* Lettsom conj. 2. S.D. [Giving back . . .] Capell; om. F1.   3. *From this*] F1; *This from* Heath. 7. *'fore*] F1; *for* J. M. Mason [*Comments* (1785), p. 160].

1–4. *Thus . . . authority.*] For the source cf. Introduction, p. xiv; for the motivation, p. xxvii.

    2. *circle . . . glory*] For *crown* = *glory* cf. *R 2,* III. iii. 90; for *glory* = *circle* cf. *1 H 6,* I. ii. 133–7; for the magic of the circle cf. *AYL.,* II. v. 60, v. iv. 34.

    3. *pope,*] Shakespeare probably took l. 4 as vague object of "Take" and "holding".

    7. *'fore*] Mason emended since "the nation was already as much inflamed as it could be".—Shakespeare probably intended *for* and *'fore,* taking *we* =

England or John, *inflam'd* = sick or roused.

    8. *counties*] shires. Some edd. interpret "nobles", but Shakespeare only used the word in this sense in "Italian" plays. Smith noted that military organization was in counties, comparing *Kent,* l. 30. Cf. IV. iii. 151, note.

    10. *love of soul*] *Faerie Queene* has been compared: "love of soule doth love of bodie passe / No lesse than perfect gold surmounts the meanest brasse" (IV. ix. 2). Schmidt (*Lex.,* soul) cited examples where the soul is "the seat of real, not only professed, sentiments".

To stranger blood, to foreign royalty.
This inundation of mistemp'red humour
Rests by you only to be qualified:
Then pause not; for the present time's so sick
That present med'cine must be minist'red   15
Or overthrow incurable ensues.
Pand. It was my breath that blew this tempest up,
    Upon your stubborn usage of the pope;
But since you are a gentle convertite
My tongue shall hush again this storm of war,   20
And make fair weather in your blust'ring land.
On this Ascension-day, remember well,
Upon your oath of service to the pope,
Go I to make the French lay down their arms.   [*Exit.*
K. John. Is this Ascension-day? Did not the prophet   25
Say that before Ascension-day at noon
My crown I should give off? Even so I have:
I did suppose it should be on constraint;
But, heaven be thank'd, it is but voluntary.

Enter the BASTARD.

Bast. All Kent hath yielded: nothing there holds out   30

11. *stranger blood*] Theobald; hyphened F1.   29. *heaven*] F1 (*heau'n*).

12–13. *This . . . qualified:*] Alluding to the physiology of humours, in which, if one humour preponderated (making an *inundation*), it had to be *qualified* (abated) to restore health (H. Belden); *mistemp'red* = disordered.

14–15. *present . . . present*] existing . . . immediate.

15. *present . . . minist'red*] Medical cliché: "*Gangrena* . . . comes . . . because the inflamation was not defended . . . the aboundance of humours . . . choake and extinguish the naturall heate . . . except present helpe be ministred [mortification will follow]" [*The Sclopotarie of Iosephus Quercetanus* (1590), sig. K₃]. Cf. v. i. 7, 12.

17. *breath*] Cf. III. iii. 127.
this tempest] Cf. IV. iii. 156.
18. *stubborn*] Cf. *wilfully* (III. i. 68),

and Holinshed: "The pope perceiuing that king Iohn continued still in his former mind (which he called obstinacie)" (171, ii).

19. *convertite*] convert.

20–1. *My . . . land*] Make fair weather = (*a*) be conciliatory, (*b*) pretend that something is better than it is. Also *fair weather* was a cliché for pacification (cf. *O.E.D.*, weather). Shakespeare comments on Pandulph's hypocrisy, as in III. iii. 175.

21. *blust'ring*] blowing violently (of winds); threatening bluffingly; agitated.

28–9. *I . . . voluntary*] Holinshed says that John "voluntarilie submitteth himselfe" (186, ii).

30–6. *All . . . friends.*] Cf. Appendix A, p. 166.

But Dover Castle; London hath receiv'd,
Like a kind host, the Dolphin and his powers;
Your nobles will not hear you, but are gone
To offer service to your enemy;
And wild amazement hurries up and down　　　　35
The little number of your doubtful friends.
K. John. Would not my lords return to me again
After they heard young Arthur was alive?
Bast. They found him dead and cast into the streets,
An empty casket, where the jewel of life　　　　40
By some damn'd hand was robb'd and ta'en away.
K. John. That villain Hubert told me he did live.
Bast. So, on my soul, he did, for aught he knew.
But wherefore do you droop? why look you sad?
Be great in act, as you have been in thought;　　　　45
Let not the world see fear and sad distrust
Govern the motion of a kingly eye!
Be stirring as the time, be fire with fire,
Threaten the threat'ner, and outface the brow
Of bragging horror: so shall inferior eyes,　　　　50
That borrow their behaviours from the great,
Grow great by your example and put on
The dauntless spirit of resolution.
Away, and glister like the god of war

---

35. *hurries*] F1; *harries* Staunton conj.　　40. *jewel of life*] F1; *jewel, life,* Pope.
53. *spirit*] F1; *sprite* Fleay.

---

35. *amazement*] bewilderment.

hurries] Transitive, with *up and down* adverbial (Wright); intransitive with *up and down* prepositional (Delius). Cf. *The Golden Age*: "Feare and amazement hurry through each chamber" (Heywood, III, 23).

40. *jewel of life*] i.e. the soul; cf. *Mac.*, III. i. 68: "mine eternal jewel"; *2 H 6*, III. ii. 409: "A jewel, lock'd into the woefull'st cask". Or Shakespeare may mean "the jewel *that is* life".

44–61. *But . . . nigh!*] Shakespeare follows M. Paris: John's advisers "Dixerunt enim grunniendo & derisionibus multiplicatis subsannando: Ecce vigesimus quintus Rex in Anglia:

ecce iam non Rex, nec etiam regulus, sed Regum opprobrium . . . Heu miser & seruus vltimae conditionis, ad quam seruitutis miseriam deuolutus es? Fuisti Rex, nunc fex . . . Et sic iram prouocantes . . . [irae] scintillas excitarunt" (pp. 352–3).

45. *act . . . thought*] Cf. IV. iii. 135.

46. *sad*] grave, serious; sorrowful, despondent.

48. *stirring*] energetic.

49. *outface*] Cf. II. i. 97, note.

50. *bragging*] threatening (*O.E.D.*, brag, 3).

53. *dauntless . . . resolution*] The cliché was "undaunted resolution".

54. *glister*] Cf. *Ven.*, 273–6.

When he intendeth to become the field: 55
Show boldness and aspiring confidence!
What, shall they seek the lion in his den,
And fright him there? and make him tremble there?
O, let it not be said: forage, and run
To meet displeasure farther from the doors,   60
And grapple with him ere he come so nigh!

K. John. The legate of the pope hath been with me,
And I have made a happy peace with him;
And he hath promis'd to dismiss the powers
Led by the Dolphin.

Bast.   O inglorious league!   65
Shall we, upon the footing of our land,
Send fair-play orders and make comprimise,
Insinuation, parley and base truce
To arms invasive? shall a beardless boy,
A cock'red silken wanton, brave our fields,   70
And flesh his spirit in a warlike soil,
Mocking the air with colours idlely spread,

---

60. *farther*] F1; *further* Steevens.   61. *come*] F1; *comes* ed. 1735.   67. *fair-play orders*] Ed. 1735; *fayre-play-orders* F1.   70. *cock'red silken*] Fleay; hyphened F1.
72. *idlely*] F1; *idly* Hanmer, edd.

55. *become*] adorn.

57. *the lion*] John bore the English lion in his arms. If Faulconbridge wears the lion-skin this symbolizes his ascendancy here (cf. III. ii. 1, note).

59. *forage*] "range abroad", "seek for prey" have been suggested; cf. *LLL.*, IV. i. 94, *H 5*, I. ii. 110.

63. *happy*] propitious, favourable; dexterous, skilful.

65–73. *O . . . arms!*] Armada rhetoric. Cf. *Cornelia* (1594): "Shall we then, that are men and Romains borne,/Submit vs to vnurged slauerie?/ Shall Rome that hath so many ouerthrowne / Now make herselfe a subiect to her owne? / O base indignitie: a beardles youth . . ." (Kyd, p. 138).

66. *upon . . . of*] standing upon.

67. *fair-play orders*] Cf. IV. ii. 93–5, v. ii. 118. "Orders" probably = arrangements, measures, though

Schmidt takes it = stipulations.

comprimise] This variant form of compromise was Shakespeare's favourite.

68. *Insinuation*] Self-ingratiation.

70. *cock'red*] pampered.

wanton] spoilt child.

brave] "the ordinary sense of 'defy,' with a side reference to the meaning of the adjective 'brave,' showy, or splendid; as if 'to brave our fields' signified to display his finery in our fields" (Wright).

71. *flesh*] initiate or inure to bloodshed (On.), as in *Lr.*, II. ii. 50. But the senses "inflame" (cf. *2 H 4*, I. i. 149), "gratify" (cf. *All's W.*, IV. iii. 19) are also present.

72. *idlely*] carelessly. An expressive variant of *idly*, once common.— Shakespeare repeats the image in *Mac.*: "the Norweyan banners flout the sky" (I. ii. 50) (Johnson).

And find no check? Let us, my liege, to arms!
Perchance the cardinal cannot make your peace;
Or if he do, let it at least be said   75
They saw we had a purpose of defence.

K. John. Have thou the ordering of this present time.

Bast. Away, then, with good courage! yet, I know,
Our party may well meet a prouder foe.   [*Exeunt.*

SCENE II.—[*The Dauphin's Camp at St Edmundsbury.*]

Enter, in arms, LEWIS, SALISBURY, MELUN, PEMBROKE, BIGOT,
and Soldiers.

Lew. My Lord Melun, let this be copied out,
And keep it safe for our remembrance:
Return the precedent to these lords again;
That, having our fair order written down,
Both they and we, perusing o'er these notes,   5

---

74. *cannot*] F1; *can't* Pope.

Scene II

Scene II] F1; *Scene* IV. Donovan.   The . . . Edmundsbury.] Theobald; om. F1.
S.D.] Enter (in Armes) Dolphin, Salisbury, Meloone, Pembroke, Bigot,
Souldiers. F1.

77. *Have . . . time.*] "Ipso eodem tempore, Rex Iohannes . . . qui quendam armigerum Falconem imposuerat custodie cuidam in Marchia Walliae, sciens illum nullum facinus abhorrere, vocauit ipsum vt in Barones baccharetur. Erat autem ruptarius nequissimus, Neuster natione, & spurius" (M. Paris, p. 311).

78. *yet*] "now as always"; or "none the less", viz. "(Though I am heartening you) *yet* (this is unnecessary since) our side (*party*) may well cope with a more spirited (*prouder*) foe."

Scene II

1–63. *My . . . mine.*] Shakespeare dramatizes the lament of the barons after John's submission to *Rome* (Introduction, p. xvi), whence the dis-

courtesy of Salisbury's grief after the barons' submission to *Lewis*. In Holinshed (186, ii, 48) the *stranger* (l. 27) is the pope.

1. *this*] Shakespeare conflates the lords' pilgrimage to St Edmundsbury of 1214 and the landing of Lewis in 1216. No reform document is ascribed to either occasion by Holinshed, but the climax of these years was Magna Carta (1215), signed to restore old liberties to the nobles (cf. *our right*, l. 21). Holinshed implies that Lewis subscribed to Magna Carta: "[Lewis] tooke an oth to mainteine and performe the old lawes and customes of the realme" (191, ii).

3. *precedent*] original. Some take = first draft (as in *R 3*, III. vi. 7).

4. *fair order*] Cf. III. i. 176–7, note.

May know wherefore we took the sacrament
And keep our faiths firm and inviolable.
Sal. Upon our sides it never shall be broken.
 And, noble Dolphin, albeit we swear
 A voluntary zeal and an unurg'd faith   10
 To your proceedings; yet believe me, prince,
 I am not glad that such a sore of time
 Should seek a plaster by contemn'd revolt,
 And heal the inveterate canker of one wound
 By making many. O, it grieves my soul,   15
 That I must draw this metal from my side
 To be a widow-maker! O, and there
 Where honourable rescue and defence
 Cries out upon the name of Salisbury!
 But such is the infection of the time,   20
 That, for the health and physic of our right,
 We cannot deal but with the very hand
 Of stern injustice and confused wrong.
 And is't not pity, O my grieved friends,
 That we, the sons and children of this isle,   25
 Was born to see so sad an hour as this;
 Wherein we step after a stranger, march
 Upon her gentle bosom, and fill up

---

10. *and an*] F1; *and* Pope; *an* Capell.   13. *contemn'd*] F1; *condemn'd* Heath.
16. *metal*] F1 (*mettle*). 26. *Was*] F1; *Were* F2. 27. *stranger, march*] F1;
hyphened Hanmer.

6–7. *May . . . inviolable.*] At St Edmundsbury the nobles "receiued a solemne oth vpon the altar" that they would force John to confirm their rights "vnder his seale, for euer to remaine most stedfast and inuiolable" (Hol., 183–4).

12–15. *I . . . many.*] A Tudor commonplace, as in *The Book of Homilies*: "rebellion is an vnfit and vnwholesome medicine . . . far worse than any other maladies and disorders that can be in the body of a commonwealth" (Homily against Wilful Rebellion).

13. *contemn'd revolt*] Wright compared "despised arms" (*R 2*, ii. iii. 95).

19. *Cries out upon*] Exclaims against; or (more probably) appeals to; cf.

AYL., ii. vii. 70, iv. iii. 151 (Wright).

21–3. *right . . . wrong*] "play upon *right* (that which is due) . . . [and] *right* (that which is morally good) as opposed to *wrong* (that which is morally evil) makes the sentence difficult" (Deighton).

22. *We . . . hand*] "in such extremitie of despaire they [the barons in 1216] resolued with themselues to seeke for aid at the enimies hands" (Hol., 190, i).

27. *stranger, march*] Theobald took *stranger* = adjective, comparing *R 2*, i. iii. 143, *march* = martial music. But cf. next note.

27–8. *march . . . bosom*] Cf. iii. i. 172, iv. i. 2–3; *R 2*, ii. iii. 92–3.

Her enemies' ranks—I must withdraw and weep
Upon the spot of this enforced cause—   30
To grace the gentry of a land remote,
And follow unacquainted colours here?
What, here? O nation, that thou couldst remove!
That Neptune's arms, who clippeth thee about,
Would bear thee from the knowledge of thyself—   35
And cripple thee—unto a pagan shore,
Where these two Christian armies might combine
The blood of malice in a vein of league,
And not to spend it so unneighbourly!
Lew. A noble temper dost thou show in this;   40

30. *spot of*] F1; *spot, for* Pope.   36. *cripple*] F1; *grapple* Pope, edd.; *gripple*
Steevens conj.   39. *to spend*] F1; *mis-spend* Hanmer.

29. *I . . . weep*] So Chettle's *Hoffman*
(1631): "I must withdraw, and weepe,
my heart is full" (sig. E4v).

30. *Upon . . . cause*] Spot = (a) stain,
disgrace (as v. vii. 107), (b) place;
Upon = (a) because of, (b) on; cause
= (a) course, (b) cause (cf. III. iii. 12,
note).

31. *grace*] adorn; do honour to.

33–9. *What . . . unneighbourly!*] M.
Paris quotes the pope's letter to the
barons saying that their revolt en-
dangered the Crusade (p. 385), and
discusses plans for the Crusade (pp.
357, 362).

34. *That . . . about*] Fripp [*Shakespeare
Studies* (1930), p. 100] compared Ovid,
Metam., I. 13, II. 270; *clippeth* = em-
braceth, surroundeth.

35. *bear*] F1 *beare* = bear (after *remove*, l. 33), bare (heralding *cripple*,
l. 36). For the same pun cf. *Meas.*:
"Would bark your honour from that
trunk you bear, / And leave you
naked" (III. i. 70–1), Middleton's *Mad
World* (1608): "She gets but her allow-
ance, thats bare one" (sig. Bv).

from . . . thyself] (away,) so that
thou wouldst not know thyself. Smith
compared *Ant.*: "poison'd hours had
bound me up / From mine own knowledge" (II. ii. 94–5). Wilson glossed
"i.e. to self-forgetfulness". Cf. *The

Two Noble Ladies*: "my father who did
change his name, / and kept him from
the knowledge of himselfe" (M.S.R.,
ll. 2056–7).

36. *cripple*] "Grapple" assumes the
variant "gripple" (never used by
Shakespeare) corrupted to *cripple*. But
cripple (= disable) makes sense.
"Nation" = (a) Englishmen, (b) England. Read: "O Englishmen, that you
could depart! That Neptune . . . would
strip England of its people (so that it
would no longer recognize itself without them), bearing them to a pagan
shore, and actually cripple the *nation* in
this separation of people and land (if
this would only cure it)!" The "separation of people and land" idea precedes in l. 31 and the "disease must
cure disease" commonplace in ll. 12–
15, 20–3. Shakespeare follows the proverb "A desperate Disease must have a
desperate cure" (Tilley, p. 158). Cf.
also *Lucr.*: "Who, like a late-sack'd
island, vastly stood, / Bare and un-
peopled in this fearful flood" (ll. 1740–
1).

38. *malice*] Cf. II. i. 251.

vein] "(a) blood-vessel, (b) mood,
humour" (Wilson).

39. *to*] For Shakespeare's insertion
of *to* cf. Abbott, pp. 248–52, and I. i.
135, IV. ii. 212, 240, v. ii. 31, 139–42.

And great affections wrastling in thy bosom
Doth make an earthquake of nobility.
O, what a noble combat hast thou fought
Between compulsion and a brave respect!
Let me wipe off this honourable dew,   45
That silverly doth progress on thy cheeks:
My heart hath melted at a lady's tears,
Being an ordinary inundation;
But this effusion of such manly drops,
This shower, blown up by tempest of the soul,   50
Startles mine eyes, and makes me more amaz'd
Than had I seen the vaulty top of heaven
Figur'd quite o'er with burning meteors.
Lift up thy brow, renowned Salisbury,
And with a great heart heave away this storm: 55
Commend these waters to those baby eyes
That never saw the giant world enrag'd,
Nor met with fortune other than at feasts,

41. *affections*] F1; *affection* Pope.   42. *Doth*] F1; *Do* Hanmer, edd.   43. *hast thou*] F4; *hast* F1.   56. *baby eyes*] Capell; hyphened F1.   57. *giant world*] Theobald; hyphened F1.

41. *affections*] passions, viz. loyalties. Perhaps we should read *affection's*.
wrastling] Variant of "wrestling".
42. *earthquake*] Cf. *Tamburlaine*, Pt 1: "windy exhalations / Fighting for passage, tilt within the earth" (I. ii); this was the usual explanation of earthquakes.
43-4. *O . . . respect!*] Cf. *Wint.*, v. ii. 80, also the old *King Leir* (1605): "Oh, what a combat feeles my panting heart, / 'Twixt childrens loue, and care of Common weale!" (sig. A₄ᵛ), and W. Fulke's *Sermon of Faith* (1574) "if God him selfe seeme to wrestle wyth vs . . . hys purpose is in thys most noble combate . . . to geue vs strength" (sigs. Dᵛ, D₂).
44. *brave*] fine; courageous.
respect] discrimination (viz. a combat between a recognition of a personal compulsion, and a fair consideration of the motives for and against revolt).
46. *progress*] Perhaps the noun, viz.

"makes a progress": Salisbury's tears symbolize his *honour*, which, having won the sovereignty in his nature, makes a (royal) procession. Cf. II. i. 339-40.
48. *inundation*] Recalls v. i. 12.
50. *This . . . soul*] Cf. *Lucr.*, l. 1788 (Malone), *3 H 6*, II. v. 85 (Wright).
55. *great heart*] your great heart, full as it is; or your great-heartedness.
heave] = utter (a groan) (cf. *AYL.*, II. i. 36, *Lr.*, IV. iii. 27); thrust away.
56. *Commend*] Do not hide your face (l. 54), but express your passions unashamedly (l. 55): *recommend* such tears (through *your* shedding them) to those baby eyes.—Lewis thus approves of Salisbury's tears. But the opposite is possible too: Do not be dejected (l. 54); thrust this passion behind you with your great-heartedness (l. 55), and commit (or leave) these tears to those baby eyes (but *abandon them yourself*)—.
58. *fortune . . . at feasts*] The popular "bountiful Fortune" image.

Full warm of blood, of mirth, of gossiping.
Come, come; for thou shalt thrust thy hand as deep   60
Into the purse of rich prosperity
As Lewis himself: so, nobles, shall you all,
That knit your sinews to the strength of mine.

Enter PANDULPH.

And even there, methinks, an angel spake:
Look, where the holy legate comes apace,   65
To give us warrant from the hand of heaven,
And on our actions set the name of right
With holy breath.
Pand.   Hail, noble prince of France!
The next is this: King John hath reconcil'd
Himself to Rome; his spirit is come in,   70
That so stood out against the holy church,
The great metropolis and see of Rome.
Therefore thy threat'ning colours now wind up,
And tame the savage spirit of wild war,
That, like a lion foster'd up at hand,   75
It may lie gently at the foot of peace,
And be no further harmful than in show.
Lew. Your grace shall pardon me, I will not back:

---

59. *warm of*] F1; *of warm* Heath, edd.   64.] F1; *Scene* III. Pope.   64. S.D.]
Enter Pandulpho. F1; He sees *Pandulph* coming at a distance. Hanmer; after
l. 64 Halliwell; after *breath* l. 68 Dyce.   68.] F1; *Scene* III. Enter *Pandulph.*
Hanmer.   77. *further*] F1; *farther* ed. 1735.

59. *Full warm*] *Full* is an intensive;
warm (= friendly, loving, heated) continues the Fortune imagery of II. i. 391,
II. ii. 54–61.
　of] with.
　blood] emotion, passion; the fleshly
nature of man ["the fire i' the blood"
(*Tp.*, IV. i. 53)].
　64. *And . . . spake:*] Wright explained
as a pun on *angel* (the coin) after *purse*,
nobles. "There spake an angel" was a
proverb (Tilley, p. 14, quoted an early
gloss to it: "Ironically spoken oft
times, as if one would say, There spake
Wisdom it self"). The proverb was

often used punningly, as in Middleton's *Famelie of Love* (1608): "*Pur.*
Myne is very currant sir, I can shew
you good gilt. *Dry.* I marry, there
spoke an Angell, guilt's currant" (sig.
H₃).
　67. *set*] "*i.e.* as a seal, carrying on the
metaphor in *warrant*" (Deighton).
　69. *reconcil'd*] "reconciled, both to
God and his church" (Hol., 176, ii;
cf. 178, ii).
　70. *is come in*] has submitted.
　73. *wind*] furl.
　78. *shall*] must.
　back] go back.

I am too high-born to be propertied,
To be a secondary at control,   80
Or useful serving-man and instrument
To any sovereign state throughout the world.
Your breath first kindled the dead coal of wars
Between this chastis'd kingdom and myself,
And brought in matter that should feed this fire;   85
And now 'tis far too huge to be blown out
With that same weak wind which enkindled it.
You taught me how to know the face of right,
Acquainted me with interest to this land,
Yea, thrust this enterprise into my heart;   90
And come ye now to tell me John hath made
His peace with Rome? What is that peace to me?
I, by the honour of my marriage-bed,
After young Arthur, claim this land for mine;
And, now it is half-conquer'd, must I back   95
Because that John hath made his peace with Rome?
Am I Rome's slave? What penny hath Rome borne,
What men provided, what munition sent,
To underprop this action? Is't not I
That undergo this charge? who else but I,   100
And such as to my claim are liable,
Sweat in this business and maintain this war?
Have I not heard these islanders shout out

83. *coal of wars*] F1; *coals of war* Capell conj.

79. *propertied*] made a tool of. So
Tw.N.: "They have here propertied
me" (iv. ii. 101).

83-7. *Your . . . it.*] Tilley (p. 728)
quoted the proverb "A little Wind
kindles, much puts out the fire," and
Shr., ii. i. 135.

83. *kindled . . . wars*] The "blowing
the coals of contention" cliché recurs
in Hol., 204, i, and *H 8*, ii. iv. 77, 92.

84. *chastis'd*] Cf. iv. iii. 159, note.

85, 88-9. *matter, . . . You . . . land*] Cf.
iii. iii. 166-7.

88-9. *right . . . interest*] Lewis "with
frowning looke beheld the legat . . .
disprouing not onelie the right which
king Iohn had to the crowne, but also

alledging his owne interest" (Hol.,
191, i); *interest* = claim, title.

90-100. *enterprise . . . charge*] Shakespeare conflates Lewis's and King
Philip's answers to Pandulph: Philip
"determined not so to breake off his
enterprise, least it might be imputed to
him for a great reproch to haue beene
at such charges" (Hol., 178, ii).

98. *What . . . sent*] Shakespeare was
now reading Holinshed (p. 191) (cf.
note on ll. 88-9), where John's "furnishing the castell of Douer, with men,
munition, and vittels" is also noted.

100. *charge*] = expense (cf. l. 90,
note); burden.

101. *liable*] Cf. ii. i. 490.

"Vive le roi!" as I have bank'd their towns?
Have I not here the best cards for the game   105
To win this easy match play'd for a crown?
And shall I now give o'er the yielded set?
No, no, on my soul, it never shall be said.

Pand. You look but on the outside of this work.

Lew. Outside or inside, I will not return·   110
Till my attempt so much be glorified
As to my ample hope was promised
Before I drew this gallant head of war,
And cull'd these fiery spirits from the world,
To outlook conquest and to win renown   115
Even in the jaws of danger and of death. [*Trumpet sounds.*
What lusty trumpet thus doth summon us?

Enter the BASTARD, *attended.*

Bast. According to the fair-play of the world,
Let me have audience; I am sent to speak:
My holy lord of Milan, from the king   120
I come, to learn how you have dealt for him;
And, as you answer, I do know the scope
And warrant limited unto my tongue.

Pand. The Dolphin is too wilful-opposite,
And will not temporize with my entreaties;   125

---

108. *No, no*] F1; *No,* Pope.   116. S.D.] Rowe; om. F1.   118. S.D.] As
Capell; Enter Bastard. F1.   119–20. *speak:* . . . *king*] F1; *speak,* . . . *King:*
Theobald.   124. *wilful-opposite*] Theobald; no hyphen F1.   125. *entreaties*]
F1; *entreats* Walker.

104. *"Vive le roi!"* . . . *bank'd*] Card-playing terms (cf. Appendix B, p. 169);
Vive is disyllabic.

106. *crown*] The common pun, as in
H 5, 1. ii. 263.

113. *drew*] assembled.

head of war] *head* = armed force is
common, but Shakespeare may here
translate "caput belli" = flower, nuc-
leus of an army.

114. *cull'd*] chose.

115. *outlook*] Cf. *outface* (11. i. 97, v. i.
49) and *outstare* (*Mer.V.*, 11. i. 27 etc.).

116. *jaws* . . . *of death*] So *Tw.N.*,

iii. iv. 396.

118. *fair-play*] Cf. v. i. 67.

119. *I* . . . *speak:*] This clause goes
with the preceding ("Let me have
audience: *for* I am sent") *and* the following ("I am sent . . . from the king").
Similarly, the pause at the end of l. 120
allows *from the king* to go with *I* . . . *him;*
(l. 121) as well as with *I* . . . *speak:*
(l. 119).

123. *limited*] appointed.

124. *wilful-opposite*] stubbornly hostile.

125. *temporize*] compromise.

He flatly says he'll not lay down his arms.

Bast. By all the blood that ever fury breath'd,
The youth says well. Now hear our English king,
For thus his royalty doth speak in me:
He is prepar'd, and reason too he should—   130
This apish and unmannerly approach,
This harness'd masque and unadvised revel,
This unhair'd sauciness and boyish troops,
The king doth smile at; and is well prepar'd
To whip this dwarfish war, this pigmy arms,   135
From out the circle of his territories.—
That hand which had the strength, even at your door,
To cudgel you and make you take the hatch,
To dive like buckets in concealed wells,
To crouch in litter of your stable planks,   140
To lie like pawns lock'd up in chests and trunks,
To hug with swine, to seek sweet safety out
In vaults and prisons, and to thrill and shake
Even at the crying of your nation's crow,

---

133. *unhair'd*] F1 (*vn-heard*).   *troops*] F1; *troop* Capell conj.   135. *this*] F1;
these Rowe, edd.   142. *hug*] F1; *herd* Rowe iii.   144. *crying . . . crow*] F1;
crowing . . . cock Collier MS.   *your*] F1; *our* Rowe ii.

127. *blood . . . fury*] Either noun could be subject or object.

129. *For . . . me:*] Cf. i. i. 3.

132. *harness'd masque*] masque in armour.

133. *unhair'd*] Cf. *beardless* (v. i. 69); *hair* was commonly spelt *heare*.

136. *circle*] compass.

137–48. *That . . . No:*] Armada rhetoric, as in W. Averell's *Exhortation* [in *A Meruailous Combat* (1588)]: "Consider the auncient fame you haue often won in the field . . . where are nowe the noble heartes that haue so much honoured your English land? Shall the enemie thinke they are gone . . .? No, no, they shall I hope finde them redoubled" (sig. E^v).

138. *take . . . hatch*] Cf. i. i. 171, *Lr.*, iii. vi. 76.

139–40. *To . . . planks*] The proverb "Like two Buckets of a well, if one go up the other must go down" (Tilley, p. 69) may lie behind l. 139. Cf. *R 2*, iv. i. 184.

139–42. *To*] Cf. v. ii. 39, note.

140. *litter*] bedding (for animals or men).

141. *To . . . trunks*] *pawns* = articles in pawn (cf. *Wint.*, i. ii. 436); *chests* (= chess) and *trunks* (a kind of billiards) were games, chests involving *pawns*, so he hints that the English *played with* the French.

143. *thrill*] shiver.

144. *crow*] cock, "*your* nation's crow" (Douce, since *gallus* meant cock and Frenchman). Furness thought cock did not = France till after Shakespeare. But cf. G. Lynne's *Beginning . . . of all Popery* (1548), sig. E4, B. Aneau's *Alector* (1560), *passim*, for cock = France. Z. Grey compared *1 H 6*, i. iv. 43 (Talbot = the "scarecrow" of the French). Or is the crow as omen meant? Omens could be *for* one side,

Thinking this voice an armed Englishman;   145
Shall that victorious hand be feebled here,
That in your chambers gave you chastisement?
No: know the gallant monarch is in arms
And like an eagle o'er his aery towers,
To souse annoyance that comes near his nest.   150
And you degenerate, you ingrate revolts,
You bloody Neroes, ripping up the womb
Of your dear mother England, blush for shame:
For your own ladies and pale-visag'd maids
Like Amazons come tripping after drums,   155
Their thimbles into armed gauntlets change,

145. *this*] F1; *his* Rowe, edd.   148. *No: know*] F1; *No, no* Lettsom conj.   153.
mother England] Theobald; hyphened F1.   156. *change*] F1; *chang'd* Dyce.

against the other (*R 3*, v. iii. 282–8;
Cym., IV. ii. 348–52): Faulconbridge
mocks French panic at the omen that
supports them.

145. *this*] Cf. IV. i. 63, note.

voice] John Newnham talks of the
"crie or voice" of a crow [*Nightcrowe*
(1590), sig. A₃]. Or is *voice* a verb?
("Thinking this *announces* an armed
E.", i.e. the crow anticipates carrion.)

148. *No: know*] Cf. v. ii. 108.

149. *eagle*] The French are crows
(l. 144): cf. *Cor.*, III. i. 138, *Troil.*, I. ii.
263 for the traditional comparison of
crows and eagles.

aery] nest or brood of a bird of prey.

towers] (In falconry) "to rise in
circles of flight till she reaches her
'place'" (On.), hence "soar".

150. *souse*] Usually glossed as "swoop
upon, a hawking term". But hawking
souse was constructed with *on*, *upon*, or
drwn. Though the hawking sense is
there, the sense "smite" (also common) is there too.

151–3. *And . . . England*] Armada
commonplaces, as in G. D.'s *Briefe Discoverie* (1588): "he that will not sticke
to rippe vp the wombe, and to teare
and rake out the bowels of his owne
mother, he that will endeuour to bring
in an inuasion, to the vtter spoyle,
ruine, and depopulation of his deare

countrye: . . . what impietye, will hee
leaue vnattempted?" (sig. H₂).

151. *revolts*] rebels.

154–8. *For . . . inclination.*] Armada
commonplaces, as in A. Marten's *Exhortation, To Stirre vp the Mindes of all
Her Maiesties Faithfull Subiects, to defend
their Countrey* (1588): "Conuert your
ploughes into speares, and your sithes
into swordes. Turne your boules into
bowes, and al your pastimes into mus-
ket shot" (sig. E); cf. Hol., 61, ii, and
Joel, iii. 10, *Micah*, iv. 3; also L.
Wright's *Display of Dutie* (1589):
"changing their trapt Mules, into
bard horses: sylken cotes, into arming
corslets: golden hats, into steeled helmets . . . dauncing in chambers, into
marching in the field" (sig. B₃ᵛ).

156–7. *thimbles . . . needl's*] Fifty
years later the Parliamentary Army
was nicknamed "the Thimble and
Bodkin Army", since even thimbles
and bodkins were accepted for the
cause.

156. *armed*] Perhaps Shakespeare
thinks of leather thimbles, or the plates
over the fingers of gauntlets. Furness
noted that "many forms of the early
thimble were open at the end, thus the
resemblance to an 'armed gauntlet'
was not so unlike."

change] A second present is wanted,

Their needl's to lances, and their gentle hearts
To fierce and bloody inclination.

Lew. There end thy brave, and turn thy face in peace;
We grant thou canst outscold us: fare thee well;   160
We hold our time too precious to be spent
With such a brabbler.

Pand.   Give me leave to speak.

Bast. No, I will speak.

Lew.   We will attend to neither.
Strike up the drums; and let the tongue of war
Plead for our interest and our being here.   165

Bast. Indeed, your drums, being beaten, will cry out;
And so shall you, being beaten: do but start
An echo with the clamour of thy drum,
And even at hand a drum is ready brac'd
That shall reverberate all, as loud as thine: 170
Sound but another, and another shall
As loud as thine rattle the welkin's ear
And mock the deep-mouth'd thunder: for at hand—
Not trusting to this halting legate here,
Whom he hath us'd rather for sport than need—   175
Is warlike John; and in his forehead sits
A bare-ribb'd death, whose office is this day
To feast upon whole thousands of the French.

---

157. *needl's*] F1 (*Needl's*); *Needles* F3; *neelds* Variorum 1778.   159. *There end*]
F1; *There; end* Collier ii.   170. *all,*] F1; *all* Pope, edd.

for two distinct actions, marching and
riding, are described.

157. *needl's*] *Needle* was often monosyllabic.

158. *inclination*] mental tendency,
character; leaning or slanting position
(of a charging knight with lance).

159. *brave*] defiant threat, bravado.

160. *outscold*] Cf. II. i. 191, note.

162. *brabbler*] brawler, quarreller.

163–5. *We . . . here.*] Cf. *R 3*, IV. iv.
149–54.

169. *brac'd*] with tightened skin;
perhaps quibbling on *brace* = pair.

172. *welkin's ear*] Cf. *LLL.*, IV. ii. 5.
Shakespeare usually used *welkin* in
"extravagant" poetry.

173. *deep-mouth'd*] loud and sonor-
ous; cf. *H 5*, v. chor. 11, *Shr.*, Ind. i.
18.

174. *halting*] "wavering, shifting (cf.
I *Kings*, xviii. 21)" (Wilson).

176–8. *and . . . French*] The idiom
differs from the suggested "echo" in
R 2, III. ii. 160–2; cf. *Good Newes from
Fraunce* (written 1591): "Terror and
maiestie sitteth in the forehead of this
christian King" (sig. A₃ᵛ); *The
Famous History of . . . Fauconbridge* (ed.
1635): "such newes that . . . the signi-
fication thereof, sate like characters in
their foreheads, & as it were made
dumb shewes of discontent" (p. 24).

178. *feast*] Cf. II. i. 354, note.

Lew. Strike up our drums, to find this danger out.   179
Bast. And thou shalt find it, Dolphin, do not doubt.   [*Exeunt.*

SCENE III.—[*The Field of Battle.*]

Alarums. Enter KING JOHN *and* HUBERT.

K. John. How goes the day with us? O, tell me, Hubert.
Hub. Badly, I fear. How fares your majesty?
K. John. This fever, that hath troubled me so long,
Lies heavy on me; O, my heart is sick!

Enter a Messenger.

Mess. My lord, your valiant kinsman, Faulconbridge,   5
Desires your majesty to leave the field
And send him word by me which way you go.
K. John. Tell him, toward Swinstead, to the abbey there.
Mess. Be of good comfort; for the great supply
That was expected by the Dolphin here,   10
Are wrack'd three nights ago on Goodwin Sands.

179. *our*] F1; *your* I. John.

Scene III

Scene III.] F1; *Scene* V. Pope; *Act* V *Scene* I. Donovan.   The . . . Battle.] Pope;
om. F1.   S.D.] Alarums. Enter Iohn and Hubert. F1.

180. *find it*] find it with a vengeance.
Cf. M. Hurault's *Discourse vpon the present estate of France* (1588): "Carrie
thither the fire of war, seeing it is there
that thou shouldest finde thine enimies, and thou shalt finde them in
deede" (p. 54).

Scene III

S.D. Alarums.] " 'Alarums' may
possibly represent the decisive battle
of Lincoln . . . when the French and
their English allies were defeated by
William Marshal Earl of Pembroke,
who commanded the army of the boy-
king Henry III . . . we may suppose
this "great supply" [mentioned l. 9] to
be the reinforcements sent by Philip of
France, about three months after the
battle of Lincoln" [Boswell-Stone,

Shakspere's Holinshed (1896), p. 71].

3. *fever*] Holinshed (p. 194, ii) gives
various theories for John's death, fever
and poison (cf. v. vi. 23) among them:
cf. III. ii. 7, note.

8. *Swinstead*] Swinstead (where there
was no abbey) is twenty-five miles from
Swineshead Abbey (where John rested) (Reed, Halliwell). For Shakespeare's source cf. Introduction, p.
xx.

9. *supply*] Cf. v. iii. 1, note. Holinshed says "a new supplie of men was
readie to come and aid Lewes" (p. 201,
i).

10–11. *was . . . Are*] Shakespeare must
be responsible for this confusion of
tense and number: cf. v. v. 13.

11. *wrack'd*] wrecked. The major
chronicles agree that Hubert de Burgh

O

    This news was brought to Richard but even now:
    The French fight coldly, and retire themselves.
K. John. Ay me! this tyrant fever burns me up,
    And will not let me welcome this good news.   15
    Set on toward Swinstead; to my litter straight:
    Weakness possesseth me, and I am faint.   *[Exeunt.*

SCENE IV.—[*Another part of the Field.*]

Enter SALISBURY, PEMBROKE, *and* BIGOT.

Sal. I did not think the king so stor'd with friends.
Pem. Up once again; put spirit in the French:
    If they miscarry, we miscarry too.
Sal. That misbegotten divel, Faulconbridge,
    In spite of spite, alone upholds the day.   5
Pem. They say King John sore sick hath left the field.

Enter MELUN, *wounded.*

Mel. Lead me to the revolts of England here.
Sal. When we were happy we had other names.
Pem. It is the Count Melun.
Sal.   Wounded to death.
Mel. Fly, noble English, you are bought and sold;   10

14. *Ay me!*] F1 (*Aye me,*); *Ah me!* Pope.

Scene IV

Scene IV.] F1; *Scene* VI. Pope; scene contd. Donovan.   Another ... Field.] As
Capell; om. F1.   7. S.D.] F1; Enter *Melun,* led. Capell.

sank the French navy. Shakespeare
may have got his version from R.
Coggeshall (Appendix A, p. 166), not
wishing to glorify Hubert.
    13–14. *The . . . up*] The French are
cold through most of the play: cf. Introduction, p. lxv.
    16. *litter*] "not able to ride, [John]
. . . was faine to be carried in a litter"
(Hol., 194, i). *T.R.* does not name the
litter, but opens II. vi with "Enter
King Iohn carried betweene 2. Lords."

Scene IV

    4. *divel*] Cf. II. i. 567, note.
    5. *In . . . spite*] "against all odds.
Compare *3 Henry VI,* II. iii. 5" (I.
John).
    8. *When . . . names.*] He means (*a*)
When we had other names we were
happy; (*b*) We were happy before we
became rebels; (*c*) When things were
going well with us you gave us other
names. The line veils resentment.
    10. *bought . . . sold*] Foul play has

Unthread the rude eye of rebellion
And welcome home again discarded faith.
Seek out King John and fall before his feet;
For if the French be lords of this loud day
Lewis means to recompense the pains you take   15
By cutting off your heads: thus hath he sworn
And I with him, and many moe with me,
Upon the altar at Saint Edmundsbury;
Even on that altar where we swore to you
Dear amity and everlasting love.   20
Sal. May this be possible? may this be true?
Mel. Have I not hideous death within my view,
Retaining but a quantity of life,
Which bleeds away, even as a form of wax
Resolveth from his figure 'gainst the fire?   25
What in the world should make me now deceive,
Since I must lose the use of all deceit?
Why should I then be false, since it is true

---

11. *Unthread ... eye*] F1; *Untread ... way* Theobald.   *rude eye of*] F1; *eye o,*
rude Hudson ii.   14. *the French be lords*] As F1; *the Prince be lord* Keightley;
French Lewis be lord Donovan.   15. *Lewis*] This ed.; *He* F1, edd.   17. *moe*] F1;
more Rowe.   25. *his*] F1; *its* Pope.

been used (Malone, comparing *R 3*,
v. iii. 306). Tilley (p. 75) gives this as a
proverb = to be tricked.

11. *Unthread*] Cf. *untread* (v. iv. 52).
In *Cor.*, III. i. 123 *thread* (the gates) =
pass through the gates [Steevens compared *Lr.*: "*threading* dark-*ey'd* night"
(II. i. 121)]. Rebellion is thought as
effective as needle and thread together.

rude] Transferred epithet (Malone).

12. *discarded*] After *Unthread* this may
be a quibble on "to card" = to prepare
(wool, etc.) for spinning (by disen-
tangling threads with a "card"); ll.
10–12 then suggest that *faith* (= wool)
is a natural product abused in organ-
ized society.

15. *Lewis*] Wright compared *H 5*,
IV. iv. 82: "the French might have a
good prey of us, if he knew of it." But
in *John* not only concord (*French* and
He), but syntax is queer [*He* (l. 15) =

John]. If we suppose the form "Le" for
"Lewis" (a monosyllable), "He"
would be an easy misreading in Secretary hand.

17. *moe*] more. Common in Shakespeare (e.g. *R 3*, IV. iv. 200, 503).

18. *Saint Edmundsbury*] Shakespeare
follows Holinshed closely, except for
the location at St Edmundsbury:
cf. IV. iii. 11, note, Appendix A,
p. 161.

23. *quantity*] small quantity; cf. *Shr.*,
IV. iii. 112, *2 H 4*, v. i. 69.

24. *form of wax*] Wax images of one's
enemies were melted before a fire,
usually by witches, to destroy the real
persons by sympathy. Shakespeare
hints that Melun is doubly doomed
(by his wounds, by destiny).

25. *Resolveth*] Dissolves.

26–9. *What ... truth?*] Tilley (p. 434)
compared *R 2*, II. i. 5 ff.

27. *use*] profit, advantage.

That I must die here and live hence by truth?
I say again, if Lewis do win the day,   30
He is forsworn if e'er those eyes of yours
Behold another day break in the east:
But even this night, whose black contagious breath
Already smokes about the burning crest
Of the old, feeble and day-wearied sun,   35
Even this ill night, your breathing shall expire,
Paying the fine of rated treachery
Even with a treacherous fine of all your lives,
If Lewis by your assistance win the day.
Commend me to one Hubert with your king: 40
The love of him, and this respect besides,
For that my grandsire was an Englishman,
Awakes my conscience to confess all this.
In lieu whereof, I pray you, bear me hence
From forth the noise and rumour of the field,   45
Where I may think the remnant of my thoughts
In peace, and part this body and my soul
With contemplation and devout desires.
Sal. We do believe thee; and beshrew my soul

30. *do*] F1; om. Pope.   34. *crest*] F1; *cresset* Anon. conj. *ap.* Cambridge.

29. *hence*] Cf. IV. ii. 89, note.

by truth] "by telling the truth" (Furness). Or *truth* may = the Deity, as often at this time.

33. *But . . . breath*] Furness compared *Caes.*, II. i. 265 ("the vile contagion of the night") for "this idea that the night air was dangerous to health".

34. *smokes*] grows misty: cf. "smoke and dusky vapours of the night" (*1 H 6*, II. ii. 27).

crest] helmet. The conjecture "cresset" = beacon.

36. *expire*] Lat. *exspiro*, breathe out.

37–8. *fine . . . fine*] penalty; end. Wright quoted *Ham.*, v. i. 113: "is this the fine of his fines?"

37. *rated*] Perhaps the sense "rebuked, blamed" is implied (Smith); "(*a*) assessed, (*b*) estimated at its true value, exposed" (Wilson).

41. *love of him*] If Hubert was a leading citizen of Angiers (Introduction,

p. xxxvi) he might well be the friend of a French lord.

42. *For . . . Englishman*] One of the two lines identical in *T.R.* (II. v. 28) and *John* (cf. II. i. 528, note). The genealogy is probably wrong (Melun's maternal grandfather is untraceable), but Shakespeare may have associated this Melun with Robert de Melun, Bishop of Hereford, d. 1167.

42–3. *Englishman . . . conscience*] In Foxe (not in Holinshed) Melun mentions England and conscience as motives for his disclosure: "I was one of them, which was sworn to [kill you]. I haue great conscience therof, and therfore I geue you this warning. I pittie poore England, which hath bene so noble a region, that now it is come to so extreme misery" (p. 255, ii; cf. Foxe, p. 258, i).

45. *rumour*] confused din.

49. *beshrew*] Cf. v. v. 14.

But I do love the favour and the form　　　50
Of this most fair occasion, by the which
We will untread the steps of damned flight,
And like a bated and retired flood,
Leaving our rankness and irregular course,
Stoop low within those bounds we have o'erlook'd,　　55
And calmly run on in obedience
Even to our ocean, to our great King John.
My arm shall give thee help to bear thee hence;
For I do see the cruel pangs of death
Right in thine eye. Away, my friends! New flight;　　60
And happy newness, that intends old right!

[Exeunt, leading off Melun.

SCENE V.—[*The French Camp.*]

Enter LEWIS *and his train.*

Lew. The sun of heaven methought was loath to set,
But stay'd and made the western welkin blush,

60. *Right*] F1; *Fight* Capell; *Bright* Collier MS.　　61. S.D.] As Theobald;
Exeunt F1.

Scene v

Scene V.] F1; *Scene* VII. Pope.　The . . . Camp.] Capell; om. F1; Night comes
on; retreat sounded. Donovan.　S.D.] Enter Dolphin, and his Traine. F1.

50. *But*] *If* I do *not* love the favour.
Cf. *Oth.*, III. iii. 91.

favour] appearance, look (as *Lr.*, I.
iv. 260); attraction, charm (as *Ham.*,
IV. v. 188).

52. *untread*] retrace (steps); cf. *Mer.
V.*, II. vi. 10.

damned flight] = *contemn'd revolt* (v.
ii. 13).

53. *bated*] diminished.

54. *rankness*] "Rank . . . signifies *exuberant, ready to overflow*" (Malone).

55. *Stoop*] The nobles will kneel for
pardon.

o'erlook'd] Cf. II. i. 441–5, II. ii. 23.

57. *ocean*] Shakespeare adapts a
commonplace. Cf. J. Prime's *Sermon*
(1585): "*All autoritie is of God*, and

therefore kinglie most of all, euen as all
the waters ishue from the Ocean, but
more immediatlie the great riuers"
(sig. A₆).

60. *Right*] Clearly; immediate
(Steevens); unmistakably (Wilson).

61. *happy*] = (*a*) propitious, (*b*)
appropriate. Read: "A new flight
must be our course; and its newness is
appropriate, seeing it *aims at* the re-
storation of the old (former) right; and
is propitious, seeing it *signifies* old
(ancient) right." Cf. III. i. 196–7, and
v. iv. 8, note.

Scene v

1–2. *The . . . stay'd*] Cf. III. i. 3–4,
note.

When English measure backward their own ground
In faint retire. O, bravely came we off,
When with a volley of our needless shot,   5
After such bloody toil, we bid good-night,
And wound our tott'ring colours clearly up,
Last in the field, and almost lords of it!

Enter a Messenger.

Mess. Where is my prince, the Dolphin?
Lew.   Here: what news?
Mess. The Count Melun is slain; the English lords   10
By his persuasion are again fall'n off,
And your supply, which you have wish'd so long,
Are cast away and sunk on Goodwin Sands.
Lew. Ah, foul shrewd news! beshrew thy very heart!
I did not think to be so sad to-night   15
As this hath made me. Who was he that said
King John did fly an hour or two before
The stumbling night did part our weary powers?
Mess. Whoever spoke it, it is true, my lord.
Lew. Well; keep good quarter and good care to-night: 20
The day shall not be up so soon as I,
To try the fair adventure of to-morrow.   [*Exeunt.*

3. *English*] F1; *th'* English Rowe iii; *the* English Capell, edd.   *measure*] F1;
measur'd Pope, edd.   7. *clearly*] F1; *chearly* Capell conj.; *cleanly* Cambridge conj.
12. *supply*] F1; *supplies* Capell.   13. *Are*] F1; *Is* Halliwell.

3. *English*] Englishmen; cf. *R 2*, iv. i.
137.
    measure] traverse, tread. "The wes-
tern welkin blushes . . . in sympathy
with the discomfiture of the most western race and kingdom. . . . The general and indefinite word 'English' and
the present tense 'measure' seem to me
appropriate to the double meaning"
(Vaughan). Final *e* and *d* were often
confused, but F1 seems sound.
    4. *retire*] Cf. v. iv. 53.
    came we off] retired we from the en-
gagement.
    7. *tott'ring*] Totter (variant of *tatter*)
was associated with *totter* = swing to
and fro (cf. *O.E.D.*). Both "waving"
and "tattered, in rags" may be meant,
for ragged ensigns (*colours*) were no

disgrace but implied hard fighting.
    clearly] "without obstruction from
the enemy" (Collier). The gloss "entirely or totally" is lame, while Collier's agrees with *O.E.D.*, clear, 18:
"Free from encumbering contact; dis-
engaged, unentangled, out of reach,
quite free", and *Tw.N.*: "Let me be
clear of thee" (iv. i. 4).
    12. *supply*] Cf. v. iii. 9, note.
    14. *shrewd*] bad, grievous; *beshrew*
comes from the same root, which =
curse.
    18. *stumbling*] "causing stumbling"
(On.).
    20. *keep . . . quarter*] "guard carefully
the posts assigned to you" (Wright,
comparing *1 H 6*, ii. i. 63).
    22. *adventure*] hazard, chance.

SCENE VI.—[*An open place in the neighbourhood of Swinstead Abbey.*]

Enter the BASTARD *and* HUBERT, *severally.*

Hub. Who's there? speak, ho! speak quickly, or I shoot.
Bast. A friend. What art thou?
Hub.   Of the part of England.
Bast. Whither dost thou go?
Hub. What's that to thee? [*Pause.*] Why, may not I demand
Of thine affairs as well as thou of mine?   5
Bast. Hubert, I think.
Hub.   Thou hast a perfect thought:
I will upon all hazards well believe
Thou art my friend, that know'st my tongue so well.
Who art thou?
Bast.   Who thou wilt: and if thou please
Thou mayst befriend me so much as to think   10
I come one way of the Plantagenets.
Hub. Unkind remembrance! thou and endless night
Have done me shame: brave soldier, pardon me,
That any accent breaking from thy tongue
Should 'scape the true acquaintance of mine ear.   15
Bast. Come, come; sans compliment, what news abroad?

Scene VI

Scene VI.] F1; VIII. Pope; II. Donovan.   An . . . Abbey.] Theobald; om. F1.
S.D.] As F1.   1–5. Hub. . . . *mine?*] As F1; Bast. *Who's . . . shoot.* Hub. *A friend.*
Bast. *What . . . thou?* Hub. *Of . . . go?* Bast. *What's . . . thee?* Hub. *Why . . . mine?*
K. Elze [*Notes on Eliz. Dram.* (1880), p. 65].   2–5.] Hub. *Of . . . go?* Bast. *What
is that to thee?* Hub. '*What's that to thee?*'—*Why may . . . mine?* Vaughan.   4. S.D.]
This ed.; om. F1.   4. *Why,*] This ed.; *Why* F1.   4–5.] Capell; three lines F1
(ending *thee?|. . . affaires,|. . . mine?|*).   *Why . . . mine?*] As F1; Bast. *Why . . .
mine?* Lloyd (*ap.* Dyce ii).   12. *endless*] F1; *eyeless* Theobald, edd.

1–5. Hub. . . . *mine?*] The speech
headings are altered by some since
Faulconbridge is "hot-headed", Hubert "sedate". But this is one of Faulconbridge's laconic moods (cf. i. i.
154–6, note)—his coolness in danger
is not out of character.

4. S.D.] The pause is needed to make
Hubert angry.

Why,] Exclamative, not a question;
why, is often *why* in F1.

6. *perfect*] correct; cf. *2 H 4*, III. i. 88.
7. *hazards*] Cf. i. i. 119.
12. *remembrance*] memory.
endless night] Common cliché: cf.
R 2, I. iii. 177, 222; *Faerie Queene*, III. v.
22; *Tamburlaine*, Pt II, II. iv. 7; Du
Bartas, *Iudith* (tr. T. Hudson, 1584),
p. 81. "Endless" was a common intensive (cf. the last lines of *The Spanish
Tragedy*).

14. *accent*] word, speech.

Hub. Why, here walk I in the black brow of night,
    To find you out.
Bast.   Brief, then; and what's the news?
Hub. O, my sweet sir, news fitting to the night,
    Black, fearful, comfortless and horrible.   20
Bast. Show me the very wound of this ill news:
    I am no woman, I'll not swound at it.
Hub. The king, I fear, is poison'd by a monk:
    I left him almost speechless; and broke out
    To acquaint you with this evil, that you might   25
    The better arm you to the sudden time,
    Than if you had at leisure known of this.
Bast. How did he take it? who did taste to him?
Hub. A monk—I tell you, a resolved villain—
    Whose bowels suddenly burst out: the king   30
    Yet speaks and peradventure may recover.
Bast. Who didst thou leave to tend his majesty?
Hub. Why, know you not? the lords are all come back,
    And brought Prince Henry in their company;
    At whose request the king hath pardon'd them,   35
    And they are all about his majesty.
Bast. Withhold thine indignation, mighty heaven,

---

25. *To*] F1; *T'* Pope.   29. *monk*— . . . *you*, . . . *villain*—] This ed.; *Monke . . . you,
. . . villaine* F1; *Monk,* . . . *you;* . . . *Villain,* Theobald, edd.   32. *Who*] F1;
Whom Hanmer.   33-4. *not?* . . . *company;*] Theobald, edd.; *not?* . . . *companie,*
F1; *not,* . . . *company?* Malone conj.

17. *black brow*] frowning brow; blackness. Hinting at the malevolence of this night. Cf. *black-brow'd night* (*MND.*, III. ii. 387; *Rom.*, III. ii. 20).

22. *swound*] Later form of *swoon*, with excrescent *d*.

23. *I fear*] Holinshed says that John died through fever *or* poison (cf. V. iii. 3, note): *I fear* betrays Shakespeare's uncertainty (cf. III. ii. 7).

26. *sudden time*] emergency.

28. *taste*] A *taster* ate part of every dish set before his master, to detect poison.

29. *A . . . villain*—] The usual punctuation suggests "A monk, as I've already told you." But (*a*) would Hubert show impatience with his superior? (*b*) Hubert has not told Faulconbridge about the *tasting*; (*c*) *I tell you* draws attention to the monk's resolution. We take *I tell you* = "I dare be sworn," as in *Err.*, IV. iv. 7, *Wint.*, III. ii. 114, etc.

30. *bowels . . . burst out*] Shakespeare follows J. Foxe (Introduction, p. xiv).

32. *tend*] take care of, look after; wait or attend upon.

35. *pardon'd*] Holinshed says Melun's speech moved the nobles to make peace with Henry III (after John's death); Foxe, like Shakespeare, gives it an immediate effect—the nobles returned to John, and so "were a great number of them pardoned" (p. 256, i).

And tempt us not to bear above our power!
I'll tell thee, Hubert, half my power this night,
Passing these flats, are taken by the tide;   40
These Lincoln Washes have devoured them;
Myself, well mounted, hardly have escap'd.
Away before: conduct me to the king;
I doubt he will be dead or ere I come.   [*Exeunt.*

SCENE VII.—[*The Orchard in Swinstead Abbey.*]

Enter PRINCE HENRY, SALISBURY, *and* BIGOT.

P. Hen. It is too late: the life of all his blood
Is touch'd corruptibly, and his pure brain,
Which some suppose the soul's frail dwelling-house,
Doth by the idle comments that it makes
Foretell the ending of mortality.   5

Enter PEMBROKE.

Pem. His highness yet doth speak, and holds belief
That, being brought into the open air,
It would allay the burning quality
Of that fell poison which assaileth him.
P. Hen. Let him be brought into the orchard here.   10

Scene VII

Scene VII.] F1; IX. Pope; III. Donovan.   The . . . Abbey.] Theobald; om. F1.
2. *corruptibly*] F1; *corruptedly* Capell.

38. *tempt*] put to the test. So L.
Wright's *Display of Dutie* (1589): "God
. . . neuer fayleth his children in necessity: nor suffereth them to be tempted
aboue their power" (sig. Eᵛ). Carter
compared *1 Corinthians*: "God . . .
shall not suffer you to be tempted
aboue your strength: but shall with the
temptation make a way, that ye may
be able to beare it" (x. 13, Bishops'
Bible; cf. *Genesis*, iv. 13).

39–42. *I'll . . . escap'd*] Shakespeare
follows M. Paris (Introduction, p.
xv); cf. v. vii. 61–4.

43. *Away before*] Lead the way.

Scene VII

1. *life*] essence, or vitality.
2. *touch'd*] infected.
corruptibly] causing corruption.
pure] clear. Halliwell noted that
Deloney imitated these lines in his
Lamentable Death of King Iohn [in
Strange Histories (1602)]: the poison
distempered John's "pure vnspotted
braine".

3. *some suppose*] The location of the
soul was disputed, but the brain was
thought to house the "reasonable
soul".

4. *idle comments*] nonsensical remarks.

Doth he still rage?   [*Exit Bigot.*

Pem.   He is more patient
Than when you left him; even now he sung.

P. Hen. O vanity of sickness! fierce extremes
In their continuance will not feel themselves.
Death, having prey'd upon the outward parts,   15
Leaves them invisible, and his siege is now
Against the mind, the which he pricks and wounds
With many legions of strange fantasies,
Which, in their throng and press to that last hold,
Confound themselves. 'Tis strange that death should
    sing.   20
I am the cygnet to this pale faint swan
Who chants a doleful hymn to his own death
And from the organ-pipe of frailty sings
His soul and body to their lasting rest.

---

11. S.D.] Capell; om. F1.   16. *invisible*] F1; *insensible* Hanmer; *invincible*
Steevens conj.; *invasible* Wilson conj.; *enfeebl'd* Maxwell conj. (*N. & Q.*, 18 Feb.
1950); *unusable* Sisson.   17. *mind*] Rowe iii; *winde* F1.   20. *Confound*] *Coun-*
found F1.   21. *cygnet*] Rowe iii; *Symet* F1.

11. *rage*] rave.

13–17. *sickness . . . mind*] Mrs Bone
refers me (privately) to Holinshed:
"through anguish of mind, rather
than through force of sicknesse, he departed this life" (p. 194, i).

15–17. *Death . . . mind*] Cf. H.
Chettle's *Hoffman*: "How cold thou
art; death now assailes our hearts, /
Hauing triumph't ouer the outward
parts" (sig. E₃).

16. *invisible*] The invisibility of death
was a commonplace: Malone compared *Ven.*, 1004 (Death is called "invisible commander") and took *invisible*
as adverb; but "invincible" or "unusable" might well have been misread.

18. *legions*] Goes with the images of
war and of *numberlessness*.

fantasies] fancies; whims.

19. *press*] Malone compared *H 8*:
"many maz'd considerings did throng,/
And press'd in with this caution" (II.
iv. 183–4), and *Lucr.*, 1301.

last hold] Possibly so called because
the mind was often located in the
heart, as in W. Clever's *Flower of
Phisicke* (1590): "the minde and the
heart mutually inhabite one with another" (sig. Kᵛ). The heart would be
pricked by the trembling caused by the
dying man's fancies. Cf. l. 3, note.

20. *Confound*] Confuse; destroy.

21. *cygnet*] Did Shakespeare write
"Sycnet"?

swan] Cf. *Mer.V.*, III. ii. 44, *Lucr.*,
1611. Tilley (p. 644) quoted the proverb "Like a Swan, he sings before his
death." Ovid's "carmina iam moriens
canit exequialia cygnus" (*Metam.*,
xiv. 430) has been compared.

23. *organ-pipe*] W. Vallans explained
"swan-song" in 1590: "The Philo-
sophers say it is because of the spirit,
which, labouring to passe thorow the
long and small passage of her necke,
makes a noise as if she did sing" ["To
the Reader" in *A Tale of Two Swannes*
(1590), ed. Hearne].

Sal. Be of good comfort, prince; for you are born   25
　　　To set a form upon that indigest
　　　Which he hath left so shapeless and so rude.

Enter Attendants, and BIGOT, *bringing in* KING JOHN *in a chair.*

K. John. Ay, marry, now my soul hath elbow-room
　　　It would not out at windows nor at doors.
　　　There is so hot a summer in my bosom,   30
　　　That all my bowels crumble up to dust:
　　　I am a scribbled form, drawn with a pen
　　　Upon a parchment, and against this fire
　　　Do I shrink up.
P. Hen.   How fares your majesty?
K. John. Poison'd, ill fare; dead, forsook, cast off: 35
　　　And none of you will bid the winter come
　　　To thrust his icy fingers in my maw,
　　　Nor let my kingdom's rivers take their course
　　　Through my burn'd bosom, nor entreat the north
　　　To make his bleak winds kiss my parched lips   40
　　　And comfort me with cold. I do not ask you much,

---

28. S.D.] Capell; Iohn brought in. F1.　28–9. *elbow-room . . . doors.*] This ed.; *elbow roome, . . . doores,* F1; *elbow-room; . . . doors.* Pope, edd.　35. *fare*] F1; *fate* Pope.　41. *I . . . you*] F1; *I ask not* Pope.

---

26. *form*] Holinshed marvels how soon England under Henry III was "from a troubled fourme reduced to a flourishing and prosperous degree: chiefelie by the diligent heed . . . of the king himselfe" (p. 203, ii); *form* = order.

26–7. *indigest . . . rude*] Ovid's "rudis indigestaque moles" (*Metam.*, I. 7) was a familiar tag, e.g. R. H. in *A Sermon* (1589) called his book "this my *Rudis indigestaque moles*" (sig. A₅).

28–9. *Ay . . . doors.*] i.e. "now *that* my soul". John wants to die quickly, but now that his soul does not need to labour for passage (cf. l. 23, note) it prefers to stay. Some think Shakespeare alludes to the superstition that it is easier to die out of doors, taking *windows, doors* literally; but surely the

mouth is imagined as *windows* etc. of the body (cf. *this wall of flesh*, III. ii. 30).

33. *parchment*] Cf. Chapman's *Alphonsus*: "Mine entrails shrink together like a scroll / Of burning parchment" (IV. ii. 9–10) (Bagley).

35. *ill fare*] For the same pun cf. *Ham.*, III. ii. 97–100.

36–41. *And . . . cold.*] Much imitated, closest in B. and F.'s *Wife for a Month* (ed. 1647, sig. 6H₃ᵛ). Shakespeare may follow *Faerie Queene*, II. vi. 44. Malone compared *Lusts Dominion* (1657) ("Written by Christofer Marloe"): "the cold hand of sleep / Hath thrust his Icie fingers in my brest" (sig. D₅ᵛ); so earlier: "Deaths frozen hand hold's Royal *Philip*'s heart" (sig. B₅ᵛ).

37. *maw*] throat; belly.

39. *north*] north wind.

I beg cold comfort; and you are so strait,
And so ingrateful, you deny me that.
P. Hen. O that there were some virtue in my tears
That might relieve you!
K. John.   The salt in them is hot.   45
Within me is a hell; and there the poison
Is as a fiend confin'd to tyrannize
On unreprievable condemned blood.

Enter the BASTARD.

Bast. O, I am scalded with my violent motion,
And spleen of speed to see your majesty!   50
K. John. O cousin, thou art come to set mine eye:
The tackle of my heart is crack'd and burn'd,
And all the shrouds wherewith my life should sail
Are turned to one thread, one little hair;
My heart hath one poor string to stay it by,   55
Which holds but till thy news be uttered;
And then all this thou seest is but a clod
And module of confounded royalty.
Bast. The Dolphin is preparing hitherward,

49.] F1; *Scene* X. Pope.   49. S.D.] As F1 (Enter Bastard.).   51. *eye*] F1; *eyes*
Keightley.   58. *module*] F1; *model* Hanmer.

42. *cold comfort*] poor comfort
(idiom), as in *Shr.*, IV. i. 33.
strait] narrow, i.e. niggardly.
44. *virtue*] power, efficacy.
45. *The . . . hot.*] John does not
simply reject Henry's tears as *hot* (i.e.
unpleasant). He recalls the medical
theory that *salt* is essential to preserve
the *blood* from corruption, and rejects
tears quibblingly (his blood cannot be
saved even by salt).
46. *Within . . . hell*] The biblical idea
that the sinner has a hell within him
was commonplace, as in R. Some's
Godly Sermon (1580): "his sinnes had so
galled his heart, that he felt . . . a gree-
uous hell within him" (sig. B₃). This
idea (not in John's but in Shakespeare's mind) is reinforced through
the legal *unreprievable, condemned* (l. 48).

49. *scalded*] heated, burnt.
50. *spleen*] Cf. II. i. 448, note.
51. *set*] close (after death).
52. *tackle*] Wright compared *3 H 6*,
V. iv. 18. Perhaps Shakespeare follows
Isaiah: "Thy tackling is loosed . . ."
(xxxiii. 23, Bishops' Bible. The Genevan Bible called this chapter "The
destruction of them, by whome God
hath punished his Church", and commented on v. 23: "Hee derideth the
. . . enemies of the Church, declaring
their destruction, as they that perish
by shipwracke").
53. *shrouds*] ropes of the mast.
54. *thread*] The thread spun by the
Fates?
55. *string*] The physiology of "heartstrings" was generally accepted.
58. *module*] counterfeit, image.

Where God He knows how we shall answer him;   60
For in a night the best part of my power,
As I upon advantage did remove,
Were in the Washes all unwarily
Devoured by the unexpected flood.   [*The King dies.*

Sal. You breathe these dead news in as dead an ear.   65
My liege! my lord!—But now a king, now thus.

P. Hen. Even so must I run on, and even so stop.
What surety of the world, what hope, what stay,
When this was now a king, and now is clay?

Bast. Art thou gone so? I do but stay behind   70
To do the office for thee of revenge,
And then my soul shall wait on thee to heaven,
As it on earth hath been thy servant still.
Now, now, you stars that move in your right spheres,
Where be your powers? show now your mended
     faiths,   75
And instantly return with me again,
To push destruction and perpetual shame
Out of the weak door of our fainting land.
Straight let us seek, or straight we shall be sought;
The Dolphin rages at our very heels.   80

Sal. It seems you know not, then, so much as we:

---

60. *God*] Walker; *heauen* F1.   64. S.D.] Rowe; om. F1.   74. *right*] F1;
bright Pope.

60. *God*] Cf. III. i. 81, note.
61–4. *For . . . flood.*] Cf. v. vi. 39–44.
Shakespeare follows M. Paris (Introduction, p. xv), but *the best part of my
power* (l. 61) follows Holinshed: "a
great part of his armie" (194, i)—for
this *T.R.* reads "the most of all our
men" (II. vi. 50).
62. *upon advantage*] to seize an advantage.
65. *dead news*] deadly, terrible news.
66. *now . . . now*] "but even now
worth this, / And now worth nothing"
Mer.V., I. i. 35–6).
68–9. *What . . . clay?*] "For what
suerty is in stone or timber? What
strength? Nor is any house for the gorgeousnes the safer" [L. Humfrey,

Nobles or of Nobilitye (1563), sig. T₈ᵛ)].
Moralist commonplace.
68. *stay*] prop, support (On.); continuance in a state (as Sonnet 15).
69. *clay*] Cf. the "Kings are clay"
proverbs.
72. *And . . . heaven*] But cf. ll. 103–5.
74. *stars*] Various edd. thought that
Faulconbridge addresses John's stars
—"John's fortune had broken faith
with him" (Wright). But Shakespeare
may follow M. Paris (Introduction,
p. xvii), with *stars* = nobles (who move
round the king as stars round a sun).
Cf. *Per.*, II. iii. 39–40 ("Had princes
sit, like stars, about his throne, / And
he the sun"), *H 8*, IV. i. 54.
78. *door*] Cf. v. i. 60, v. ii. 137.

The Cardinal Pandulph is within at rest,
Who half an hour since came from the Dolphin,
And brings from him such offers of our peace
As we with honour and respect may take,   85
With purpose presently to leave this war.

Bast. He will the rather do it when he sees
Ourselves well sinew'd to our defence.

Sal. Nay, 'tis in a manner done already,
For many carriages he hath dispatch'd   ·   90
To the sea-side, and put his cause and quarrel
To the disposing of the cardinal:
With whom yourself, myself and other lords,
If you think meet, this afternoon will post
To consummate this business happily.   95

Bast. Let it be so: and you, my noble prince,
With other princes that may best be spar'd,
Shall wait upon your father's funeral.

P. Hen. At Worcester must his body be interr'd;
For so he will'd it.

Bast.   Thither shall it then: 100
And happily may your sweet self put on
The lineal state and glory of the land!
To whom, with all submission, on my knee
I do bequeath my faithful services
And true subjection everlastingly.   105

Sal. And the like tender of our love we make,
To rest without a spot for evermore.

---

88. *sinew'd*] F1; *sinewèd* Dyce.   89. *'tis*] F1; *it is* Pope.   91. *sea-side*] As F2; no
hyphen F1.   97. *princes*] F1; *nobles* K. Elze [*Notes on Eliz. Dram.* (1880),
p. 66].

82. *The ... rest*] Unhistorical. Shake-speare emphasizes John's spiritual in-dependence.

84. *such . . . peace*] Lewis, after the loss of his supply (v. v. 12), "inclined the sooner vnto peace ... he tooke such offers of agreement as were put vnto him" [Hol., 201, ii, noted by A. S. Cairncross, *Problem of Hamlet* (1936), p. 141].

85. *respect*] self-respect.

90. *carriages*] With the impedimenta of his army.

99–100. *At ... it.*] Cf. Intro., p. xii.

101. *happily*] propitiously; content-edly; fittingly, appropriately.

102. *lineal*] Cf. II. i. 85.—"As the heir of a crowned king, Henry had a better title than John; just as Henry V's was better than his father's" (Wil-son). Cf. I. i. 40, note.

106. *tender*] offer.

P. Hen.   I have a kind soul that would give thanks
          And knows not how to do it but with tears.

Bast.   O, let us pay the time but needful woe,   110
          Since it hath been beforehand with our griefs.
          This England never did, nor never shall,
          Lie at the proud foot of a conqueror,
          But when it first did help to wound itself.
          Now these her princes are come home again   115
          Come the three corners of the world in arms
          And we shall shock them! Nought shall make us rue
          If England to itself do rest but true!   [*Exeunt.*

---

108. *give*] *give you* Rowe, edd.   110. *time*] *time :* F1.   118. S.D.] F1; Exeunt,
bearing in the Body. Capell.

---

108. *kind*] proper, appropriate;
loving.

give thanks] Henry's temporary in-
sufficiency is expressed in an imperfect pentameter.

110–11. *O . . . griefs.*] "Let us now
indulge in sorrow, since there is
abundant cause for it. England has
been long a scene of confusion, and its
calamities have anticipated our tears"
(Malone); "As previously we have
found sufficient cause for lamentation,
let us not waste the present time in
superfluous sorrow" (Steevens). The
F1 colon, bringing a pause after *time*,
brackets *give (you) thanks* (l. 108) and
pay the time.

woe . . . griefs] lamentation . . . suf-
ferings.

111. *beforehand*] Wilson glosses as a
"commercial metaphor", since "to
be beforehand" = to draw money in
advance (*O.E.D.*, 1d).

115. *home*] Cf. IV. iii. 151, V. iv. 12.
116. *three . . . world*] "the four *corners*

of the world" (*Isaiah*, xi. 12) and "the
three *parts* of the world" (cf. *Ant.*, IV.
vi. 6, *Caes.*, IV. i. 14) were both
clichés = the whole world. Furness
thought *three* corners means that England was the fourth ["that utmost
corner of the west" (II. i. 29)]. *T.R.*
(II. ix. 54) supports him, taking the
three to be the pope, France, Spain.

117. *shock*] meet force with force,
throw into confusion.

117–18. *Nought . . . true!*] Armada
pamphleteers (citing *Matthew*, xii. 25,
Mark, iii. 24, *Luke*, xi. 17) popularized
this watch-word. Cf. G. D.'s *Briefe
Discoverie* (1588): "our realme . . . was
neuer conquered by any, so long as it
was true within it selfe" (sig. R₃ᵛ);
G. B.'s *Fig for the Spaniard* (1591): "If
England feare God, and be true within
it selfe, it may boldly bid a fig for the
Spaniard" (sig. B₃ᵛ); also *3 H 6*, IV. i.
40, *The True Tragedie of Richard Duke of
Yorke* (1595), sig. D₃ᵛ ,*T.R.*, II. ix.
45–6.

Appendix A

HOLINSHED AND COGGESHALL

(1) Holinshed

The sources of *John* were discussed in the Introduction, where Shakespeare's debts to his minor sources were outlined in full. A detailed comparison of the play and Holinshed, the principal source, was not possible there: we now subjoin extracts from the chronicle, covering the story as Shakespeare used it. Some of Shakespeare's purely verbal debts are not included, however: these can be traced through the footnotes.

A.D. 1191. Richard I "had instituted his nephue Arthur duke of Britaine to be his heire and successour" (Hol., 129, ii).

1199. Richard I died. He "ordeined his testament...

"Vnto his brother Iohn he assigned the crowne of England, and all other his lands and dominions, causing the Nobles there present to sweare fealtie vnto him..." (155, ii–156, i). Cf. *John*, II. i. 191–4.

"IOhn the yoongest son of Henrie the second... so soone as his brother Richard was deceassed, sent Hubert archbishop of Canturburie, and William Marshall earle of Striguill (otherwise called Chepstow) into England, both to proclaime him king, and also to see his peace kept, togither with Geffrey Fitz Peter lord cheefe iustice, and diuerse other barons of the realme, whilest he himselfe went to Chinon where his brothers treasure laie, which was foorthwith deliuered vnto him by Robert de Turneham: and therewithall the castell of Chinon and Sawmer and diuerse other places, which were in the custodie of the foresaid Robert. But Thomas de Furnes nephue to the said Robert de Turneham deliuered the citie and castell of Angiers vnto Arthur duke of Britaine. For by generall consent of the nobles and peeres of the countries of Aniou, Maine, and Touraine, Arthur was receiued as the liege and souereigne lord of the same countries.

"For euen at this present, and so soone as it was knowne that king Richard was deceassed, diuerse cities and townes on that side of the sea belonging to the said Richard whilest he liued, fell at ods among themselues, some of them indeuouring to preferre king

Iohn, other labouring rather to be vnder the gouernance of Arthur duke of Britaine, considering that he seemed by most right to be their cheefe lord, forsomuch as he was sonne to Geffrey elder brother to Iohn . . ." (157, i, ii).

"Now whilest king Iohn was thus occupied in recouering his brothers treasure, and traueling with his subiects to reduce them to his obedience, queene Elianor his mother . . . trauelled as diligentlie to procure the English people to receiue their oth of allegiance to be true to king Iohn . . ." (157, ii).

John established himself in England: ". . . this was doone cheeflie by the working of the kings mother, whom the nobilitie much honoured and loued. For she being bent to prefer hir sonne Iohn, left no stone vnturned to establish him in the throne, comparing oftentimes the difference of gouernement betweene a king that is a man, and a king that is but a child. For as Iohn was 32 yeares old, so Arthur duke of Britaine was but a babe to speake of. In the end, winning all the nobilitie wholie vnto hir will . . ." (158, i).

"Surelie queene Elianor the kings mother was sore against hir nephue Arthur, rather mooued thereto by enuie conceiued against his mother, than vpon any iust occasion giuen in the behalfe of the child, for that she saw if he were king, how his mother Constance would looke to beare most rule within the realme of England, till hir sonne should come to lawfull age, to gouerne of himselfe . . ." (158, i). Cf. ii. i. 122–3.

"When this dooing of the queene was signified vnto the said Constance, she doubting the suertie of hir sonne, committed him to the trust of the French king, who receiuing him into his tuition, promised to defend him from all his enimies . . ." (158, i, ii).

"In the meane time . . . queene Elianor, togither with capteine Marchades entred into Aniou, and wasted the same, bicause they of that countrie had receiued Arthur for their souereigne lord and gouernour. And amongst other townes and fortresses, they tooke the citie of Angiers, slue manie of the citizens, and committed the rest to prison . . ." (158, ii).

"Whilest these things were a dooing in England, Philip K. of France hauing leuied an armie, brake into Normandie. . . . In an other part, an armie of Britains . . . tooke the citie of Angiers, which king Iohn had woon from duke Arthur, in the last yeare passed. These things being signified to king Iohn, he thought to make prouision for the recouerie of his losses there, with all speed possible . . ." (160, i).

". . . king Philip made Arthur duke of Britaine knight, and receiued of him his homage for Aniou, Poictiers, Maine, Touraine, and Britaine. Also somewhat before the time that the truce should expire . . . the two kings . . . came togither personallie, and communed at full of the variance depending betweene them. But the French king shewed himselfe stiffe and hard in this treatie, demanding the whole countrie of Veulquessine to be restored vnto him . . . Moreouer, he demanded, that Poictiers, Aniou, Maine, and Touraine, should be deliuered and wholie resigned vnto Arthur duke of Britaine.

"But these, & diuerse other requests which he made, king Iohn would not in any wise grant vnto . . ." (160, ii). Cf. II. i. 151–5.

"All this while was William de Roches busilie occupied about his practise, to make king Iohn and his nephue Arthur freends, which thing at length he brought about, and therevpon deliuered into king Iohns hands the citie of Mauns which he had in keeping. . . But in the night folowing, vpon some mistrust and suspicion gathered in the obseruation of the couenants on K. Iohns behalfe, both the said Arthur, with his mother Contance . . . fled awaie secretlie from the king, and got them to the citie of Angiers, where the mother of the said Arthur refusing hir former husband the earle of Chester, married hir selfe to the lord Guie de Tours . . . by the popes dispensation. The same yere, Philip bastard sonne to king Richard, to whome his father had giuen the castell and honor of Coinacke, killed the vicount of Limoges, in reuenge of his fathers death . . ." (160, ii). Cf. II. ii. 14, note, III. ii. 3.

1200. King John and King Philip "came eftsoones to a communication betwixt the townes of Vernon and Lisle Dandelie, where finallie they concluded an agreement, with a marriage to be had betwixt Lewes the sonne of king Philip, and the ladie Blanch, daughter to Alfonso king of Castile the 8 of that name, & neece to K. Iohn by his sister Elianor.

"In consideration whereof, king Iohn, besides the summe of thirtie thousand markes in siluer, as in respect of dowrie assigned to his said neece, resigned his title to the citie of Eureux, and also vnto all those townes which the French king had by warre taken from him, the citie of Angiers onelie excepted. . . The French king . . . receiued of king Iohn his homage for all the lands, fees and tenements which at anie time his brother king Richard, or his father king Henrie had holden of him, the said king Lewes (sic) or any his predecessors, the quit claims and marriages alwaies excepted. The king of England likewise did homage vnto the French king for Britaine, and againe (as after you shall heare) receiued homage for the same countrie, and for the countie of Richmont of his nephue Arthur . . ." (161, i, ii).

"By this conclusion of marriage betwixt the said Lewes and Blanch, the right of king Iohn went awaie, which he lawfullie before pretended vnto the citie of Eureux, and vnto those townes in the confines of Berrie . . . likewise vnto the countrie of Veuxin or Veulquessine . . . the right of all which lands, townes and countries was released to the king of France by K. Iohn, who supposed that by his affinitie, and resignation of his right to those places, the peace now made would haue continued for euer. And in consideration thereof, he procured furthermore, that the foresaid Blanch should be conueied into France to hir husband with all speed . . ." (161, ii). Cf. ii. i. 416–560.

"King Iohn being now in rest from warres with forren enimies, began to make warre with his subiects pursses at home, emptieng them by taxes and tallages, to fill his coffers, which alienated the minds of a great number of them from his loue and obedience . . ." (161, ii).

John dealt severely with the white monks. "The cause that mooued the king to deale so hardlie with them was, for that they refused to helpe him with monie, when . . . he demanded it of them towards the paiment of the thirtie thousand pounds which he had couenanted to pay the French king . . ." (162, i). Cf. iii. ii. 16–23.

"About the moneth of December, there were seene in the prouince of Yorke fiue moones, one in the east, the second in the west, the third in the north, the fourth in the south, and the fift as it were set in the middest of the other, hauing manie stars about it, and went fiue or six times incompassing the other, as it were the space of one houre, and shortlie after vanished awaie . . ." (163, i). Cf. iv. ii. 182–5.

1202. "In the yeare 1202 king Iohn . . . and the French king met togither, neere vnto the castell of Gulleton, and there in talke had betweene them, he commanded king Iohn with no small arrogancie, and contrarie to his former promise, to restore vnto his nephue Arthur duke of Britaine, all those lands now in his possession on that side the sea, which king Iohn earnestlie denied to doo, wherevpon the French king immediatlie after, began war against him, . . . he besieged the castell of Radepont for the space of eight daies, till king Iohn came thither, and forced him to depart with much dishonor . . ." (164, i).

Arthur led an army against the English and won a small victory. "Queene Elianor that was regent in those parties being put in great feare with the newes of this sudden sturre, got hir into Mirabeau a strong towne, . . . Arthur following the victorie, shortlie after followed hir, and woone Mirabeau, where he tooke his grandmother within the same, whom he yet intreated verie honorablie, and with great reuerence (as some haue reported.) But other write far more trulie, that she was not taken, but escaped into a tower, within the which she was straitlie besieged . . ." (164, ii). Cf. III. ii. 5–8.

"King Iohn . . . was maruellouslie troubled with the strangenesse of the newes, and with manie bitter words accused the French king as an vntrue prince, and a fraudulent league-breaker: and in all possible hast speedeth him foorth, continuing his iournie for the most part both day and night to come to the succour of his people. To be briefe, he vsed such diligence, that he was vpon his enimies necks yer they could vnderstand any thing of his comming, or gesse what the matter meant . . ." (164, ii). Cf. III. i. 266–70, II. i. 79.

Arthur's force was routed "and Arthur with the residue of the armie that escaped with life from the first bickering was taken, who being herevpon committed to prison, first at Falais, and after within the citie of Rouen, liued not long after as you shall heare . . ." (164, ii).

"It is said that king Iohn caused his nephue Arthur to be brought before him at Falais, and there went about to persuade him all that he could to forsake his freendship and aliance with the French king, and to leane and sticke to him being his naturall vncle. But Arthur like one that wanted good counsell . . . made a presumptuous answer . . ." (165, i).

"Shortlie after king Iohn comming ouer into England, caused himselfe to be crowned againe . . . and then went backe againe into Normandie, where immediatlie vpon his arriuall, a rumour was spred through all France, of the death of his nephue Arthur. True it is that great suit was made to haue Arthur set at libertie, as well by the French king, as by William de Riches a valiant baron of Poictou, and diuerse other Noble men of the Britains, who when they could not preuaile in their suit, they banded themselues togither, and . . . began to leuie sharpe wars against king Iohn in diuerse places, insomuch (as it was thought) that so long as Arthur liued, there would be no quiet in those parts: wherevpon it was reported, that king Iohn through persuasion of his councellors, appointed certeine persons to go vnto Falais, where Arthur was kept in prison, vnder the charge of Hubert de Burgh, and there to put out the yoong gentlemans eies.

"But through such resistance as he made against one of the tormentors that came to execute the kings commandement (for the other rather forsooke their prince and countrie, than they would consent to obeie the kings authoritie heerein) and such lamentable words as he vttered, Hubert de Burgh did preserue him from that

iniurie, not doubting but rather to haue thanks than displeasure at
the kings hands, for deliuering him of such infamie as would haue
redounded vnto his highnesse, if the yoong gentleman had beene
so cruellie dealt withall. For he considered, that king Iohn had resolued vpon this point onelie in his heat and furie (which moueth
men to vndertake manie an inconuenient enterprise, vnbeseeming
the person of a common man, much more reprochfull to a prince,
all men in that mood being meere foolish and furious, and prone
to accomplish the peruerse conceits of their ill possessed heart ...)
and that afterwards, vpon better aduisement, he would both repent
himselfe so to haue commanded, and giue them small thanke that
should see it put in execution. Howbeit to satisfie his mind for the
time, and to staie the rage of the Britains, he caused it to be bruted
abroad through the countrie, that the kings commandement was
fulfilled, and that Arthur also through sorrow and greefe was departed out of this life. For the space of fifteene daies this rumour incessantlie ran through both the realmes of England and France ..."
(165, i, ii). Cf. IV. i.

"But when the Britains were nothing pacified, but rather kindled
more vehementlie to worke all the mischeefe they could deuise, in
reuenge of their souereignes death, there was no remedie but to signifie abroad againe, that Arthur was as yet liuing and in health.
Now when the king heard the truth of all this matter, he was nothing displeased for that his commandement was not executed. . .
But now touching the maner in verie deed of the end of this Arthur,
writers make sundrie reports. . . Some haue written, that as he
assaied to haue escaped out of prison, and proouing to clime ouer
the wals of the castell, he fell into the riuer of Saine, and so was
drowned. . . But some affirme, that king Iohn secretlie caused him
to be murthered . . . verelie king Iohn was had in great suspicion,
whether worthilie or not, the lord knoweth . . ." (165, ii). Cf. IV. ii.
249–69, IV, iii. 1–10.

1203–4. John gathered huge sums in subsidies. "Neither were the
bishops, abbats, nor any other ecclesiasticall persons exempted, by
meanes whereof he ran first into the hatred of the clergie . . ." (167,
i). Cf. III. ii. 16–23.

1204. "King Philip vnderstanding that king Iohn remained still
in England, rather occupied in gathering of monie amongst his
subiects, than in making other prouision . . . thought now for his
part to lose no time. . . With this swiftnesse of speed, he brought also
such a feare into the hearts of most men, that he wan all the countrie of Normandie . . ." (167, i, ii).

"About this time queene Elianor the mother of king Iohn departed this life, consumed rather through sorow and anguish of mind, than of any other naturall infirmitie . . ." (167, ii–168, i). Cf. iv. ii. 116–21.

1206. King John, making an expedition in France, "entred into Aniou, and comming to the citie of Angiers, appointed certeine bands of his footmen, & all his light horssemen to compasse the towne about, whilest he, with the residue of the footmen, & all the men of armes, did go to assault the gates. Which enterprise with fire and sword he so manfullie executed, that the gates being in a moment broken open, the citie was entered and deliuered to the souldiers for a preie. So that of the citizens some were taken, some killed, and the wals of the citie beaten flat to the ground . . ." (170, i).

"After this it chanced that king Iohn remembring himselfe of the destruction of the citie of Angiers, which (bicause he was descended from thence) he had before time greatlie loued, began now to repent him, in that he had destroied it, and therefore with all speed he tooke order to haue it againe repaired, which was doone in most beautifull wise . . ." (170, ii).

From 1205 onwards King John was in trouble because of the election of the Archbishop of Canterbury. The nominees of John and of the monks of Canterbury were both rejected by Innocent III, who promoted Stephen Langton, only to find that John refused to accept him. Holinshed's marginal gloss ["Stephan Langton chosen archbishop of Canturburie" (171, i)] was transcribed by Shakespeare. Cf. iii. i. 69.

1207. King John wrote to the pope "that he maruelled not a little what the pope ment, in that he did not consider how necessarie the freendship of the king of England was to the see of Rome, sith there came more gains to the Romane church out of that kingdome, than out of any other realme on this side the mountaines. He added hereto, that for the liberties of his crowne he would stand to the death, if the matter so required . . .

"Moreouer, he declared that if he might not be heard and haue his mind, he would suerlie restraine the passages out of this realme, that none should go to Rome, least his land should be so emptied of monie and treasure . . ." (171, i). Cf. iii. i. 73–97.

1208. "The pope perceiuing that king Iohn continued still in his former mind (which he called obstinacie) sent ouer his bulles into England, directed to William bishop of London [and others] . . . commanding them that vnlesse king Iohn would suffer peaceablie the archbishop of Canturburie to occupie his see, and his moonks their abbie, they should put both him and his land vnder the sentence of interdiction, denouncing him and his land plainelie accurssed . . ." (171-2).

King John "in a great rage sware, that if either they or any other presumed to put his land vnder interdiction . . . what Romans soeuer he found within the precinct of any his dominions, he would put out their eies, and slit their noses . . ." (172, i).

The king was cursed by the bishops and, "taking this matter in verie great displeasure, seized vpon all their temporalties, and conuerted the same to his vse . . ." (172, i).

1209. "King Iohn notwithstanding that the realme was thus wholie interdicted and vexed, . . . made no great account thereof as touching any offense towards God or the pope: but rather mistrusting the hollow hearts of his people, he tooke a new oth of them for their faithfull allegiance . . ." (173, i). Cf. IV. ii. 1.

"There liued in those daies a diuine named Alexander Cementarius . . . [who declared] that the generall scourge wherewith the people were afflicted, chanced not through the princes fault, but for the wickednesse of his people, for the king was but the rod of the Lords wrath . . .

"[Cementarius also asserted] that it apperteined not to the pope, to haue to doo concerning the temporall possessions of any kings or other potentats touching the rule and gouernment of their subiects, sith no power was granted to Peter (the speciall and cheefe of the apostles of the Lord) but onlie touching the church . . ." (173, ii–174, i). Cf. III. i. 73-97.

"In the same yeare also, the pope sent two legats into England, the one named Pandulph a lawier, and the other Durant a templer, who comming vnto king Iohn, exhorted him with manie terrible words to leaue his stubborne disobedience to the church, and to reforme his misdooings. The king for his part quietlie heard them . . . when they perceiued that they could not haue their purpose . . . the legats departed, leauing him accursed, and the land interdicted, as they found it at their comming . . ." (175, i). Cf. III. i. 61 ff.

"In the meane time pope Innocent, after the returne of his legats out of England, perceiuing that king Iohn would not be ordered by him, determined . . . to depriue king Iohn of his kinglie state, and so first absoled all his subiects and vassals of their oths of allegiance made vnto the same king, and after depriued him by solemne protestation of his kinglie administration and dignitie, and lastlie signified that his depriuation vnto the French king and other christian princes, admonishing them to pursue king Iohn, being thus depriued, forsaken, and condemned as a common enimie to God and his church. He ordeined furthermore, that whosoeuer imploied goods or other aid to vanquish and ouercome that disobedient prince, should remaine in assured peace of the church . . . not onlie in their goods and persons, but also in suffrages for sauing of their soules . . ." (175, ii). Cf. iii. i. 100–5.

The pope "appointed Pandulph . . . to go into France . . . giuing him in commandement, that repairing vnto the French king, he should communicate with him all that which he had appointed to be doone against king Iohn, and to exhort the French king to make warre vpon him, as a person for his wickednesse excommunicated . . ." (175, ii). Cf. iii. i. 117–19.

1213. "Ye shall vnderstand, the French king being requested by Pandulph the popes legat, to take the warre in hand against king Iohn, was easilie persuaded thereto of an inward hatred that he bare vnto our king, and therevpon with all diligence made his pro-uision. . . Pandulph vpon good considerations thought first to go eftsoones, or at the least wise to send into England, before the French armie should land there, and to assaie once againe, if he might induce the king to shew himselfe reformable vnto the popes pleasure . . ." (176, ii).

King John assembled an army to defend England, "so that if they had beene all of one mind, and well bent towards the seruice of their king and defense of their countrie, there had not beene a prince in christendome, but that they might haue beene able to haue defended the realme of England against him . . ." (176, ii). Cf. v. vii. 112–18.

Pandulph convinced John that he was in a hopeless position. John "vtterlie despairing in his matters, when he saw himselfe con-streined to obeie, was in a great perplexitie of mind . . . oppressed with the burthen of the imminent danger and ruine, against his will, and verie loth so to haue doone, he promised vpon his oth to stand to the popes order and decree. Wherefore shortlie after (in like manner as pope Innocent had commanded) he tooke the crowne from his owne head, and deliuered the same to Pandulph the legat, neither he, nor his heires at anie time thereafter to re-ceiue the same, but at the popes hands . . ." (177, i).

"Then Pandulph keeping the crowne with him for the space of fiue daies in token of possession thereof, at length (as the popes vicar) gaue it him againe . . ." (177, ii). Cf. v. i. 1 ff.

"Pandulph . . . sailed backe into France, & came to Roan, where he declared to king Philip the effect of his trauell, and what he had doone in England. But king Philip hauing in this meane while con-sumed a great masse of monie, to the summe of sixtie thousand pounds, as he himselfe alledged, about the furniture of his iournie,

which he intended to haue made into England . . . was much
offended for the reconciliation of king Iohn, and determined not so
to breake off his enterprise, least it might be imputed to him for a
great reproch to haue beene at such charges and great expenses in
vaine . . ." (178, ii). Cf. v. ii. 65–116.

"An hermit named Peter of Pontfret, or Wakefield as some
writers haue." This gloss introduces a series of events briefly recorded in the play: "There was in this season an heremit, whose
name was Peter, dwelling about Yorke, a man in great reputation
with the common people, bicause that either inspired with some
spirit of prophesie as the people beleeued, or else hauing some notable skill in art magike, he was accustomed to tell what should follow after. And for so much as oftentimes his saiengs prooued true,
great credit was giuen to him as to a verie prophet . . . [but he was]
rather a deluder of the people, and in instrument of satan raised vp
for the inlargement of his kingdome: as the sequele of this discourse
importeth. This Peter about the first of Ianuarie last past, had told
the king, that at the feast of the Ascension it should come to passe,
that he should be cast out of his kingdome. And (whether, to the
intent that his words should be the better beleeued, or whether
vpon too much trust of his owne cunning) he offered himselfe to
suffer death for it, if his prophesie prooued not true. Herevpon being committed to prison within the castell of Corf, when the day by
him prefixed came, without any other notable damage vnto king
Iohn, he was by the kings commandement drawne from the said
castell, vnto the towne of Warham, & there hanged, togither with
his sonne.

"The people . . . thought, that he had much wrong to die, bicause the matter fell out euen as he had prophesied: for the day before the Ascension day, king Iohn had resigned the superioritie of
his kingdome (as they tooke the matter) vnto the pope . . ." (180,
i, ii). Cf. iv. ii. 143–58, v. i. 22–9.

1214. A large section of John's nobles, goaded by the king's in-
fringements upon their ancient rights, were plotting against him.
"The Nobles supposing that longer delaie therein was not to be
suffered, assembled themselues togither at the abbeie of Burie
(vnder colour of going thither to doo their deuotions to the bodie
of S. Edmund which laie there inshrined) where they vttered their
complaint of the kings tyrannicall maners. . ."

The nobles "receiued a solemne oth vpon the altar there, that if
the king would not grant to the same liberties, with others which
he of his owne accord had promised to confirme to them, they
would from thenceforth make warre vpon him, till they had ob-

teined their purpose, and inforced him to grant, not onelie to all these their petitions, but also yeeld to the confirmation of them vnder his seale, for euer to remaine most stedfast and inuiolable ..." (183, ii–184, i). Cf. IV. iii. 11, V. ii. 2, 7.

1215. "The king soone after also, to assure himselfe the more effectuallie of the allegiance of his people in time to come, caused euerie man to renew his homage, and to take a new oth to be faithfull to him against all other persons ..." (184, ii). Cf. IV. ii. 1.

The barons began to make war against King John. "The chiefe ringleaders of this power were these ... Richard earle de Bigot ... G. de Maundeuile earle of Essex ..." (185, i).

The barons captured London, and the remainder of the nobility left John, viz. "William Marshall earle of Penbroke, ... Nicholas earle of Salisburie ..." (185, ii).

The barons "sore lamented the state of the realme, gessing what would follow ...

". . . they said among themselues, Wo be to vs, yea rather to the whole realme that wanteth a sufficient king, and is gouerned by a tyrant that seeketh the subuersion therof. Now hath our souereigne lord made vs subiect to Rome ... [John] of his owne accord voluntarilie submitteth himselfe to become vassall to euerie stranger ..." (186, ii). Cf. V. ii. 1–63.

1216. Because of John's successes the barons appealed for help to the French. "Therefore considering that they were in such extremitie of despaire they resolued with themselues to seeke for aid at the enimies hands ..." (190, i). Cf. V. ii. 22, 29.

To put heart into the English barons, Lewis "sent ouer a certeine number of armed men, vnder the leading of [various French lords including] ... Giles de Melun ... Moreouer the said Lewes wrote to the barons, that he purposed by Gods assistance to ... passe ouer with all speed vnto their succours ..." (190, i, ii). Cf. IV. iii. 15–17.

John, hearing of the alliance of the barons and Lewis, "dispatched a messenger in all hast to the pope, signifieng to him what was in hand and practised against him, requiring furthermore the said pope by his authoritie to cause Lewes to staie his iournie. . . This he needed not haue doone, had he beene indued with such prudence and prowesse as is requisit to be planted in one that beareth rule ... he bare too low a saile, in that he would be so foolified as being a king, to suffer vsurped supremasie to be caruer of his kingdome. . . The pope desirous to helpe king Iohn all that he might (bicause he was now his vassall) sent his legat Gualo into France, to disswade king Philip from taking anie enterprise in hand against the king of England. But king Philip though he was content

to heare what the legat could saie, yet by no meanes would be turned from the execution of his purpose . . ." (190, ii–191, i).

"Lewes on the morrow following . . . came into the councell
chamber, and with frowning looke beheld the legat, where by his
procurator he defended the cause that moued him to take vpon him
this iournie into England, disprouing not onelie the right which
king Iohn had to the crowne, but also alledging his owne interest
. . ." (191, i). Cf. v. ii. 64–116.

Lewis landed at Sandwich and camped there for three days. "In
which meane time there came vnto him a great number of those
lords and gentlemen which had sent for him, and there euerie one
apart and by himselfe sware fealtie and homage vnto him, as if he
had beene their true and naturall prince.

"King Iohn about the same time that Lewes thus arriued, came
to Douer, meaning to fight with his aduersaries by the way as they
should come forward towards London. But yet vpon other aduisement taken, he changed his purpose. . . Therefore furnishing the
castell of Douer, with men, munition, and vittels, he left it in the
keeping of Hubert de Burgh, a man of notable prowesse & vali-
ancie. . . Lewes being aduertised that king Iohn was retired out of
Kent, passed through the countrie without anie incounter, and
wan all the castels and holds as he went, but Douer he could not
win.

"At his comming to Rochester, he laid siege to the castell there. . .
This doone, he came to London, and there receiued the homage of
those lords and gentlemen which had not yet doone their homage
to him at Sandwich. On the other part he tooke an oth to mainteine and performe the old lawes and customes of the realme, and
to restore to euerie man his rightfull heritage and lands, requiring
the barons furthermore to continue faithfull towards him . . ." (191,
ii). Cf. v. i. 30–6, v. ii. 1–7.

"The rumour of this pretended outward courtesie being once
spred through the realme, caused great numbers of people to come
flocking to him" among whom were William Earl of Salisbury,
William Marshall the Younger, and others (191, ii.).

Gualo, the papal legate, returned to England after the landing
of Lewis. He went at once to see John, "of whome he was most
ioifullie receiued, for in him king Iohn reposed all his hope of victorie. This legat immediatlie after his comming did excommunicate Lewes by name, with all his fautors and complices, but speci-
allie Simon de Langton, with bell, booke, and candle, as the maner
was . . ." (192, i). Cf. v. i. 62–5, III. ii. 22.

"About the same time, or rather in the yeare last past as some hold, it fortuned that the vicount of Melune a French man, fell sicke at London, and perceiuing that death was at hand, he called vnto him certeine of the English barons, which remained in the citie, vpon safegard thereof, and to them made this protestation: I lament (saith he) your destruction and desolation at hand, bicause ye are ignorant of the perils hanging ouer your heads. For this vnderstand, that Lewes, and with him 16 earles and barons of France, haue secretlie sworne (if it shall fortune him to conquere this realme of England, & to be crowned king) that he will kill, banish, and confine all those of the English nobilitie (which now doo serue vnder him, and persecute their owne king) as traitours and rebels, and furthermore will dispossesse all their linage of such inheritances as they now hold in England. And bicause (saith he) you shall not haue doubt hereof, I which lie here at the point of death, doo now affirme vnto you, and take it on the perill of my soule, that I am one of those sixteen that haue sworne to performe this thing: wherefore I aduise you to prouide for your owne safeties, and your realmes which you now destroie, and keepe this thing secret which I haue vttered vnto you. After this speech was vttered he streightwaies died.

"When these words of the lord of Melune were opened vnto the barons, they were, and not without cause, in great doubt of themselues . . . so that manie of them inwardlie relented, and could haue bin contented to haue returned to king Iohn, if they had thought that they should thankfullie haue beene receiued . . ." (193, ii). Cf. v. iv.

John decided to fight back against his enemies. "So that hauing gotten togither a competent armie for his purpose, he brake foorth of Winchester, as it had beene an hideous tempest of weather, beating downe all things that stood in his waie . . ." (193, ii).

"Thus the countrie being wasted on each hand, the king hasted forward till he came to Wellestreme sands, where passing the washes he lost a great part of his armie, with horsses and carriages, so that it was iudged to be a punishment appointed by God, that the spoile which had beene gotten and taken out of churches, abbeies, and other religious houses, should perish, and be lost by such means togither with the spoilers. Yet the king himselfe, and a few other, escaped the violence of the waters, by following a good guide. But as some haue written, he tooke such greefe for the losse susteined at this passage, that immediatlie therevpon he fell into an ague, the force and heat whereof, togither with his immoderate feeding on rawe peaches, and drinking of new sider, so increased his sicknesse, that he was not able to ride, but was faine to be carried in a litter . . . the disease still so raged and grew vpon him, that . . . through anguish of mind, rather than through force of sicknesse, he departed this life . . .

"There be which haue written, that after he had lost his armie, he came to the abbeie of Swineshead in Lincolneshire . . . a moonke . . . being mooued with zeale for the oppression of his countrie, gaue the king poison in a cup of ale, wherof he first tooke the assaie, to cause the king not to suspect the matter, and so they both died in manner at one time . . ." (194, i, ii). Cf. v. vi. 39–42, v. vii. 59–64; v. vi. 23–31, v. vii.

John's men "marching foorth with his bodie, each man with his armour on his backe, in warlike order, conueied it vnto Worcester, where he was pompouslie buried in the cathedrall church before the high altar, not for that he had so appointed (as some write) but bicause it was thought to be a place of most suertie for the lords . . ." (194, ii). Cf. v. vii. 99–100, note.

"Here therefore we see the issue of domesticall or homebred broiles, the fruits of variance . . . no greater nor safer fortification can betide a land, than when the inhabitants are all alike minded . . . [this being the real] sinewes of a realme . . ." (195, i). Cf. v. vii. 112–18, v. vii. 88.

Holinshed describes King John: "He was comelie of stature, but of looke and countenance displeasant and angrie, somewhat cruell of nature, as by the writers of his time he is noted, and not so hardie as doubtfull in time of perill and danger . . . he was a great and mightie prince, but yet not verie fortunate, much like to Marius the noble Romane, tasting of fortune both waies . . ." (196, i).

"HEnrie, the third of that name, the eldest sonne of K. Iohn, a child of the age of nine yeres, began his reigne ouer the realme of England the nineteenth day of October, in the yeare of our Lord 1216 . . ." (197, i).

"Immediatlie after the death of his father king Iohn, William Marshall earle of Penbroke, generall of his fathers armie, brought this yoong prince . . . vnto Glocester . . . a great number of the lords and cheefe barons of the realme hasted thither (I meane not onelie such as had holden with king Iohn, but also diuerse other, which vpon certeine knowledge had of his death, were newlie reuolted from Lewes) in purpose to aid yoong king Henrie, to whome of right the crowne did apperteine . . ." (197, i).

Pembroke made an oration in support of Henry. " . . . Wherefore, in so much as euerie man is charged onelie with the burthen of his owne works and transgressions, neither shall the child (as the scripture teacheth vs) beare the iniquitie of his father: we ought therefore of dutie and conscience to pardon this yoong and tender prince ... let vs remooue from vs this Lewes the French kings sonne, and suppresse his people, which are a confusion and shame to our nation: and the yoke of their seruitude let vs cast from off our shoulders ..." (197, i, ii). Cf. ii. i. 179–82, v. vii. 74–80.

The barons "with one consent, proclaimed the yoong gentleman king of England ..." (197, ii).

"It is reported by writers, that amongst other things, as there were diuerse which withdrew the hearts of the Englishmen from Lewes, the consideration of the confession which the vicount of Melune made at the houre of his death, was the principall ..." (197, ii). Cf. v. iv.

1218. A "new supplie of men was readie to come and aid Lewes". Hubert de Burgh, captain of Dover Castle, attacked the French fleet at sea ... "in the end the Englishmen bare themselues so man-fullie, that they vanquished the whole French fleet, and obteined a famous victorie ..." (201, i). Cf. v. iii. 9–11, v. v. 12–13.

"Lewes, after he vnderstood of this mischance happening to his people that came to his aid, began not a litle to despaire of all other succour to come vnto him at any time heerafter: wherfore he inclined the sooner vnto peace, so that at length he tooke such offers of agreement as were put vnto him ..." With the help of the legate Gualo peace was finally effected (201, ii.). Cf. v. vii. 84–95.

"But a maruell it was to consider here at home, in how short a space the state of the English common-wealth was changed, and from a troubled fourme reduced to a flourishing and prosperous degree: chiefelie by the diligent heed and carefull prouision of the king himselfe ..." (203, ii). Cf. v. vii. 26.

(2) COGGESHALL

In some ways iv. i is the climax of *John*. Shakespeare may have known Coggeshall's account of the attempted blinding and death of Arthur, and we therefore reprint it below [from *Radulphi de Coggeshall Chronicon Anglicanum* (1875), ed. Joseph Stevenson].

"Cernentes autem regis consiliarii quod multas strages et seditiones facerent ubique Britones pro Arturo domino suo, et quod nulla firma pacis concordia posset fieri, Arturo superstite, suggesserunt regi quatinus praeciperet ut nobilis adolescens oculis et genitalibus privaretur, et sic deinceps ad principandum inutilis redderetur, ut vel sic pars adversa ab insania sedulae expugnationis conquiesceret et regi se subderet. Exacerbatus itaque indefessa congressione adversariorum, et minis eorum et impropriis lacessitus, praecepit tandem in ira et in furore tribus suis servientibus quatinus ad Falesiam quantocius pergerent, atque hoc opus detestabile perpetrarent. Duo vero ex servientibus tam execrabile opus in tam nobili adolescente committere detestantes, a curia domini regis diffugerunt; tertius vero ad castellum pervenit in quo puer regius a domino Huberto de Burch, regis camerario, diligenter custodiebatur, triplices annulos circa pedes habens. Cumque mandatum domini regis Huberto detulisset, exortus est fletus et planctus nimius inter milites qui custodiebant illum, utpote nimia miseratione super nobili adolescente permoti. Arturus autem diram avunculi sui sententiam super se datam cognoscens, atque de salute propria omnino diffidens, totus effluxit in lacrymas et in lamentabiles querimonias. At cum astaret ille praesens qui a rege missus fuerat ad hoc opus exsequendum, et persona gementi et flenti puero innotuisset, inter lamenta subito concitus surrexit, et manus suae dejectionis ultrices in personam illam violenter injecit, ad milites circumstantes voce lacrymabili vociferans: "O domini mei carissimi! pro Dei amore sinite paulisper, ut me de isto facinoroso ulciscar antequam mihi oculos eripiat; nam hic ultimus omnium existet quem in praesenti saeculo conspiciam." Ad hunc vero tumultum sedandum ocius surrexere milites, et manus utriusque cohibuerunt, atque, ex praecepto domini Huberti, juvenis ille qui advenerat de thalamo illo ejectus est; ex cujus expulsione atque ex assistentium consolatoria collocutione Arturus aliquantulam, sedata cordis moestitia, recepit consolationem.

"Hubertus autem regis camerarius, honestati et famae regiae deferre volens, et indemnitati regis prospiciens, puerum regium servavit illaesum, perpendens quod dominus rex super tali edicto statim poeniteret, ac semper postmodum haberet exosum qui ejus tam crudeli imperio obtemperare praesumpissset (*sic*); quod magis ex subitaneo furore quam ex perpendiculo aequitatis et justitiae emanare credidit. Volens itaque et domini regis iram ad tempus mitigare ac Britonum saevitiam cohibere, fecit per castellum et per totam provinciam divulgari quod sententia regis effectui esset mancipata, et quod dominus Arturus prae cordis tristitia et vulnerum acerbo dolore diem clausisset extremum: quae fama, per xv. dies, per utrumque regnum volitabat incessanter. Denique classicum per vicos et castella, quasi pro anima ejus, pulsatum est; vestes ejus hospitali leprosorum distributae. Divulgatum est etiam quod corpus ejus ad abbatiam de Sancto Andrea, ordinis Cisterciensis, delatum sit, ibique sepultum. Ad tales igitur rumores, Britones non animis sedati sed magis magisque exacerbati, ferocius quam prius, ubi poterant, debacchati sunt; jurantes quod nunquam deinceps ab expugnatione regis Angliae conquiescerent, qui tam detestabile facinus in dominum suum et nepotem proprium exercere praesumpsisset. Sicque factum est quod necesse erat iterum praedicare Arturum adhuc viventem et incolumem, quem ubique diffamaverant mortuum, ut vel sic efferata Britonum ferocitas aliquantulum mitigaretur. Quod cum regi intimatum esset, nequaquam displicuit ei ad praesens quod mandatum ejus exsecutum non esset. Dicebant etiam quidam militum domino regi, nequaquam ulterius milites se inventurum qui castella sua custodirent, si tam infaustum judicium de domino Arturo nepote suo exercere praesumpsisset; nam, si contingeret aliquos deinceps capi milites a rege Franciae, vel ab adversariis suis, similem statim absque miseratione sortirentur vindictam." (pp. 139–41).

Holinshed, in his account of the end of Arthur, refers to Coggeshall in the margin as his authority. Elizabethan chroniclers knew this work well, but it was only available to them in MS. The Waverley *Chronicle*, however, was also unprinted; and modern studies of Shakespeare's sources have shown that printed books do not necessarily tell us the whole story.

As Holinshed condensed Coggeshall we might conclude that any convergence of Coggeshall and *King John*, where Holinshed is silent, argues Shakespeare's debt to Coggeshall. In isolated instances of convergence this argument would scarcely hold. Any single point listed below could be explained as a coincidence, one or two as Shakespeare's conventional technique. But do they carry any cumulative weight? It is not easy to decide. We think they do, but admit that the balance is very evenly poised.

(i) In Shakespeare and Coggeshall Arthur is informed of his fate, and utters lamentable words, before the entry of the executioners, or messenger. He pleads for a delay ["For heaven sake, Hubert, let me not be bound!" (iv. i. 77); "pro Dei amore sinite paulisper"]. *Hubert orders the executioners, or messenger, out of the room.* Arthur is consoled by the compassion of the executioners (iv. i. 85–9), or attending soldiers. Holinshed's conflation omits all these details.

(ii) Shakespeare, who identifies his Salisbury, Pembroke, Bigot, with the nobles of Brittany, makes them swear a solemn vow to revenge Arthur's death (iv. iii. 64–73). Holinshed merely says that

the Britains were nothing pacified, but rather kindled more vehementlie to worke all the mischeefe they could deuise, in reuenge of their souereignes death (165, ii).

Coggeshall repeatedly emphasizes the rage of the nobles (cf. *John*, IV. ii. 103, 261, 268; IV. iii. 21), mentioned only once by Holinshed, and like Shakespeare makes his nobles vow revenge.

(iii) Possible verbal contacts with Shakespeare in the above passage may be noted:

(*a*) The formula "dominum suum et nepotem proprium", "de domino Arturo nepote suo", may have led to Shakespeare's "Thy nephew and right royal sovereign" (I. i. 15).

(*b*) In Coggeshall the murder of Arthur was suggested to John because "nulla firma pacis concordia posset fieri" on account of Arthur. In the play John also weighs "no firm peace" against the death of Arthur:

> There is no sure foundation set on blood,
> No certain life achiev'd by others' death (IV. ii. 104–5)

(*c*) When the nobles were not pacified by the rumour of the death of Arthur "there was no remedie," says Holinshed, "but to signifie abroad againe, that Arthur was as yet liuing and in health" (165, ii). In Coggeshall Arthur is proclaimed alive "ut vel sic efferata Britonum ferocitas aliquantulum mitigaretur". Compare *John*, IV. ii. 261–2, especially "their incensed rage".

(iv) Besides the account of the attempted blinding of Arthur, one or two fugitive Shakespeare–Coggeshall contacts may be suggested.

(*a*) In *John* we read twice that the French supply to aid Lewis was lost on Goodwin Sands (V. iii. 11, V. v. 13). Holinshed, Foxe, M. Paris etc. say that the French navy was defeated by an English force. Only Coggeshall also mentions the storm: "reduxit Dominus super quosdam eorum diffugientes aquas maris, et submersi sunt quasi plumbum" (p. 185).

(*b*) *John*, V. i. 30–6 corresponds closely to Hol., 191, ii (cf. p. 160), but even more so to Coggeshall: "Lodovicus . . . civitatem Cantuariam cum castello in deditionem accepit; postea alia castella Cantiae, praeter solam Doveram munitissimam. Inde Londonias veniens, honorifice a proceribus et civibus susceptus est, et in fidelitatem ejus et homagium omnes pariter juraverunt . . . [Lewis proceeded to Winchester]. Ibi venerunt ad eum fere omnes comites et barones regni, qui eatenus Johanni adhaeserant . . . pauci vero adhuc Johanni pertinaciter adhaeserunt" (pp. 181–2). Note (1) Shakespeare and Coggeshall refer to the *yielding* of Kent—Holinshed says that Lewis "wan all the castels and holds"; (2) Shakespeare's "But Dover Castle" has "But" as a preposition, like Coggeshall's "praeter"—Holinshed's "but" is conjunctive; (3) in Shakespeare and Coggeshall we read of Lewis *being received*, and Shakespeare's "like a kind host" resembles "honorifice"—in Holinshed, Lewis (active) *received* homage; (4) Shakespeare's conclusion of this short summarizing passage about "the little number" of John's "doubtful friends" reminds one of Coggeshall's "pauci vero adhuc Johanni pertinaciter adhaeserunt".

Appendix B

STRUCTURAL INCONSISTENCIES IN *JOHN* AND *THE TROUBLESOME RAIGNE OF IOHN*

From time to time critics have noted "structural inconsistencies" in *John* which, they claim, are due to Shakespeare's hurry while revising the *T.R.* The most important attacks were made by Edward Rose,[1] Prof. Moore Smith,[2] Prof. F. Liebermann,[3] and Prof. J. D. Wilson.[4] As Prof. Wilson summarized the key arguments of his predecessors it is convenient to restrict comment mainly to his case.—Prof. Wilson contends that

there are a number of points common to the two plays which are far clearer in *The Troublesome Reign* than in *King John*, some of them indeed being quite unintelligible in the latter without reference to the former.

If we prefer to date the *T.R.* after *John* it is our duty, of course, to defend *John* against Prof. Wilson's points.

(i) Prof. Wilson finds the Bastard's "insulting parody of the Dauphin's lovemaking . . . both impolitic and excessive".—But as the speech (ii. i. 504–9) is an aside, even in Prof. Wilson's edition, the Bastard scarcely took an impolitic risk with it. And as he was "spoiling for a fight" he is naturally annoyed by the proposed marriage which would bring peace, as Prof. Wilson agreed. What is more, is not the Bastard habitually "excessive"? Rose observed

1. 'Shakespeare as an Adapter' [*Macmillan's Mag.* (1878)]; reprinted in the Introduction to the Praetorius facsimile of *T.R.*, Pt i.
2. See Smith's *King John* (1900), Introduction; and *An English Miscellany presented to Dr Furnivall* (1901), p. 335.
3. See Herrig's *Archiv*, CXLII, 177; CXLIII, 17, 190.
4. The C.U.P. *John*, pp. xxi–xxxiv.

that the *T.R.* had a better reason for the Bastard's behaviour, because Blanche had been previously promised in marriage to him (*T.R.*, I. iv. 121–5). But a "better reason" in the *T.R.* does not make *John* inconsistent, nor even unclear.

Prof. Moore Smith subjoined that the Bastard's threat in the *T.R.* that he will cuckold his rival, the Dauphin, loses point when directed, as by Shakespeare, against Austria.[1] But in fact the lion-lioness quibble, which the editors have so far overlooked, gives the *John* threat a very neat point.[2]

(ii) "Shakespeare never accounts for the poisoning of John."—As this was one of the details of the John story familiar to Elizabethans, we suggest that Shakespeare expected his audience to look forward to the poisoning, therefore motivation was less necessary.[3] In any case, repeated passages describing John's anti-monastic policy (I. i. 48–9, III. ii. 17–23, IV. ii. 141–2) would surely make matters plain.

(iii) In *John*, IV. iii. 11 the English nobles give no reason why they should meet at Saint Edmundsbury.—Our reply is that there are other persons in other Shakespeare plays who do not give reasons for going on their various journeys. Why should reasons always be given?

(iv) Shakespeare's John does not inform us of the reasons for his second coronation (IV. ii. 40–3).—Nevertheless, John's motives are not "unclear", his desire to turn over a new leaf, now that he thinks Arthur dead, being emphasized by his offer of a boon (IV. ii. 43–6). And as the new coronation is lifted straight out of Holinshed (165, i), in a context very close to the source, another argument why Shakespeare states no clear-cut reasons is that Holinshed provided none. If Shakespeare is unclear, the fault is Holinshed's in the first place.

(v) The "glaring inconsistency" that Shakespeare's John suggests the *assassination* of Arthur to Hubert (III. ii. 76), but that Hubert, executing the king's command, has in mind only *blinding* (IV. i. 39), already puzzled Thomas Edwards[4] two hundred and T. P. Courtenay[5] one hundred years ago. In the *T.R.* John delivers Arthur to Hubert with the words:

> *Hubert* keepe him safe,
> For on his life doth hang thy Soueraignes crowne,
> But in his death consists thy Soueraignes blisse (I. ix. 31–3)

1. See *T.R.*, I. iv. 128–30, *John*, II. i. 290–3.   2. See II. i. 291, note.
3. See Introduction, p. xxvii.   4. *Canons of Criticism* (1765), p. 254.
5. *Commentaries on the Historical Plays of Shakspeare* (1840), vol. I, pp. 18–19.

In the *T.R.*, says Wilson, John is obliged "to content himself with putting out his rival's eyes, which would at least render him incapable of ruling"—and this Shakespeare misunderstood, taking John's hinted desire for Arthur's death as an order to murder him, but quite forgetting this order whilst rapidly revising the blinding-scene.

In our opinion, Prof. Wilson misconstrues both plays. Shakespeare, if he differs from the *T.R.* "source-play", must be following Holinshed (p. 165), who shows how the necessity of Arthur's *death* led to an order for his *blinding*, and how Hubert pretended that Arthur *died* after the blinding, as John had intended. In short, we think that Holinshed and Shakespeare (and the *T.R.* too, by the way) interpret John's overt order to blind Arthur as a concealed order to kill him in the process—exactly as Hubert's pretence of Arthur's death indicates. Shakespeare in Act IV, Sc. i has not *forgotten* the earlier order: he still pursues one and the same plan.

(vi) Constance calls Philip and John "perjur'd kings" (III. i. 33), though only Philip has perjured himself by promising her aid. In the *T.R.* Constance curses "the traytors . . . Whose periurie . . . Beleaguers all the Skie with misbeliefe" (I. iv. 208–10), and probably thinks of Philip, Lewis and Austria, while Shakespeare, it is said, took her to mean the two kings.—But "perjured" was sometimes used more loosely than now, in the sense "acting against the law, wrong-doing, false",[1] which would explain this minute "inconsistency". Apart from which, Constance's suggestion that *both* kings are *perjured* (=forsworn), a meaning also present, harmonizes with her vein of exaggeration, and indeed follows up a well-prepared idea.[2]

(vii) Some "obscure expressions" in *John* are explained through the *T.R.*, the two main ones being "and the territories" (I. i. 10), and "bank'd" (v. ii. 104). The former is discussed in our footnote; the latter can now be explained, with the help of a discovery by Mrs F. M. H. Bone (who has generously given permission for its publication here).

Staunton once suggested that "bank'd" was "an allusion to card-playing; and by 'bank'd their towns' is meant, *won their towns, put them in bank*". Furness countered, however, that *O.E.D.* records no such use of "bank" before the nineteenth century. Despite the fact

1. Thus Cassander is reviled as "periurde villaine, homicide vniust" in F. Sabie's *Fissher-mans Tale* (1595), sig. E₂ᵛ, though neither a murderer nor an oath-breaker.

2. "False blood to false blood join'd" (II. ii. 2); "you think *them* false" (II. ii. 27).

that Shakespeare continues at once with a card-playing allusion, Staunton's idea was therefore dropped. Mrs Bone has now found that Shakespeare probably uses a card-playing term immediately before "bank'd":

> Have I not heard these islanders shout out
> "Vive le roi!" as I have bank'd their towns?
> Have I not here the best cards for the game . . . (v. ii. 103–5)

For many early playing-cards had "Vive le roi" and similar expressions inscribed on them.[1] Moreover, Mrs Bone contends, "bank" was known as a card-playing term in other languages in the sixteenth century:[2] since cards and card-terms were nearly all imported in England at that time, and v. ii. 105 definitely mentions card-playing, Staunton's theory can no longer be brushed aside.

If Staunton and Mrs Bone are right, the crux gives us further help with the problem of the precedence of *John* and the *T.R.* (cf. p. lviii). For the *T.R.* also assigns a "vive le roi" speech to Lewis:

> Your Citie Rochester with great applause
> By some deuine instinct layd armes aside:
> And from the hollow holes of Thamesis
> Eccho apace replide *Viue la roy.*
> From thence, along the wanton rowling glade
> To *Troynouant* your fayre *Metropolis,*
> With luck came *Lewes* to shew his troupes of *Fraunce,*
>
> (II. iii. 170–6)

The point of interest is that the sources do not indicate that Lewis proceeded by water up the Thames, as the *T.R.* states: but this

1. H.-R. D'Allemagne's *Les Cartes à Jouer* (2 vols., 1906) reproduces 16th-century French cards, one inscribed "VIVE LE ROY" (II, 445); 17th-century French cards inscribed "VIVE LE ROY", "ET LA COVR" etc. (I. 91); "VIVE LA REYNE" (I. 89). R. Merlin's *Origine des Cartes à Jouer* (1869) reproduces a 16th-century French card inscribed "vive le ro" (Plate 36). W. Gurney Benham's *Playing Cards* (1931) reproduces 17th-century French cards inscribed "VIVE LE ROY", "ET LA COVR", "VIVE LA RAINE", "MAYME LAMOVR" (p. 135).

2. Cf. Florio's *Worlde of Wordes* (1598): "Banco fallito, *a game at cards*" (p. 38); C. Cotton's *Compleat Gamester* (1674): "BANKAFALET, a Game on the Cards" (p. 153).—Passages in T. M.'s *Blacke Booke* (1604) suggest that "bank" was also an English gambling term in Shakespeare's time: "I giue and bequeath to you, old *Bias, Alias, Humfrey Hollow-banke,* true cheating Bowler, and Lurcher, the one halfe of all false Bettes" (sig. F^v); "Moreouer, *Humfrey,* I giue you the lurching of all yong Nouices . . . that are hookt in by the winning of one Twelue-penny Game at first, lost vppon policy, to bee cheated of Twelue-pounds worth-a Bets afterward" (sigs. F^v, F₂); "Your cheating Bowler that will bancke false of purpose, and loose a game of twelue=pence to purchase his Partner twelue shillings in Bettes, and so share it after the Play" (sigs. D₄, D₄^v).

journey might have been suggested by "bank'd their towns" (*John*, v. ii. 104). Editors of *John*, not understanding the card-playing allusion, have similarly explained "bank'd" as "sailed past". As *T.R.*, II. iii. 170 *sqq.* either imitates *John*, v. ii. 103 *sqq.*, or *vice versa*, it is most significant that Shakespeare's "bank'd" and "Vive le roi", if technical, can only be associated with "*Viue la roy*" in the *T.R.* (with a change of meaning);—while the *T.R.* departure from history is most simply explained as a misunderstanding of Shakespeare's two technicalities. However this may be, it can no longer be argued that Shakespeare's "bank'd" is unclear without reference to the *T.R.*[1]

The "inconsistencies" in *John* can all be rejected, we think, on one or more of four counts: (i) Shakespeare's vocabulary was not fully appreciated; (ii) some of the "inconsistencies" are actually subtleties, and the editors and not Shakespeare must be blamed for working too hurriedly; (iii) the sources have been followed—without "misunderstandings"—so that Shakespeare himself did not originate inconsistencies; (iv) various "inconsistencies", laboriously searched for to prove the priority of the *T.R.*, have numerous parallels in Shakespeare's other plays, and would never have been so named if his customary techniques had been compared.

It has not yet occurred to anyone to reverse the "inconsistency" test, but clearly the argument can be turned. Are there not self-contradictions in the *T.R.* which might be due to the priority of *John*?

(i) The age of Arthur.—In the *T.R.*, as in Holinshed, Arthur appears as a young soldier aged sixteen or seventeen: "*Arthur*, bestirre thee man" (*T.R.*, I. v. 136); "Duke *Arthur* . . . To armes in hast" (I. vii. 24–5). In *John* he is a boy aged eight or ten, not more than three feet tall (IV. ii. 100). Shakespeare obviously made Arthur younger so that his helplessness would be more pathetic. Addressed as "pretty Arthur" (III. iii. 89), and "boy" (II. i. 18, 30, 43, 115, etc.) the child of eight or ten cannot complain. But what young warrior of sixteen or seventeen (a less immature age in Shakespeare's time than in ours) would like to be called "Poore helples boy" (*T.R.*, I. iv. 225) or "louely boy" (*T.R.*, I. iv. 232)? In view of the close verbal contact of the plays, the version which altered Arthur's age would have introduced the "pretty Arthur" jargon more naturally than *vice versa*, and unintelligent echoing seems the likeliest explanation of the language of the *T.R.*

(ii) The prophecy of Peter of Pomphret.—In *John*, IV. ii. 151–2,

1. I am indebted to Mrs Bone for the argument of this paragraph.

v. i. 25–7 we find that Peter predicted John's surrender of the
crown "ere the next Ascension-day at noon". The *noon* of the day
does not come from Holinshed or Foxe, both of whom the two play-
wrights probably consulted for the episode.—In Part I of the *T.R.*
the prophecy dates John's "surrender" precisely as Shakespeare:

> ere Ascension day
> Haue brought the Sunne vnto his vsuall height,
> Of Crowne, Estate, and Royall dignitie,
> Thou shalt be cleane dispoyld and dispossest
> (*T.R.*, I. xiii. 184–7)

In Part II it has been forgotten that the *noon* of Ascension day is the
fatal hour, the whole day itself being taken as the time-limit:

> The Diall tells me, it is twelue at noone.
> Were twelue at midnight past, then might I vaunt
> False seers prophecies of no import (*T.R.*, II. ii. 11–3)

> *Peter* King *Iohn*, although the time I haue prescribed
> Be but twelue houres remayning yet behinde
> (*T.R.*, II. ii. 24–5)

Why has "noone" (*T.R.*, II. ii. 11) been dragged in by the hairs?
The writer seems to realize that it has some significance, but to have
forgotten what that significance is. Just as the Duke of York, in the
piracy of *Henry VI*, Part II, builds up an elaborate claim to the
crown on a false assumption which would ironically be sufficient
claim by itself if it were true:[1] so in the *T.R.* an elaborate prophecy
is "planted", its point is forgotten, the prepared "facts" are confused, and then, best of all, *Shakespeare's* threat to hang Peter on
Ascension day at noon (IV. ii. 155–7), a threat not made in the
T.R., is put into execution (*T.R.*, II. ii. 43–5), though the *T.R.* at
this stage envisages another twelve hours before the end of the
danger!

(iii) Old Faulconbridge's attitude to the Bastard.—In the *T.R.*
Robert Faulconbridge reports that his father accepted Philip as his
son (I. i. 122). Yet he continues later that Lady Faulconbridge was
delivered "Sixe weekes before the account my Father made" (I. i.
167)—which contradicts his father's blindness. In *John* we do not
hear that old Faulconbridge ever thought Philip his own son: but
the father's calculation that Philip was born "Full fourteen weeks
before the course of time" (I. i. 113) has some connection with the
"Sixe weekes" of the *T.R.* Here *John* is logical, the *T.R.* self-con-
tradictory.

1. See Prof. P. Alexander, *Shakespeare's Henry VI and Richard III*, p. 62.

(iv) The Bastard's ignorance of his father.—In the *T.R.* Philip asks his mother who his father was (I. i. 325 *sqq.*). In *John* the same question puzzles us less (I. i. 233 *sqq.*), because Philip had not already named his father (*T.R.*, I. i. 278), nor had he done so in the presence of his mother, whom Shakespeare brought on after John's hearing of the dispute.

(v) The behaviour of the citizens of Angiers.—In the *T.R.* the citizens ask for a parley (I. iv. 9–11), though in fact they have nothing to say (I. iv. 51–2). In *John* the citizen asks for audience after the Bastard's proposal to sack Angiers (II. i. 373–96), which seems more natural. Confusion of the sequence of events, as in the *T.R.*, we know to be the hallmark of piratical memorization.

(vi) King Philip's betrayal of Constance.—In the *T.R.* King Philip, while inclining to the proposed reconciliation with John, denies that he betrays Constance, blatantly untrue though it is:

> The King of *Fraunce* respects his honor more
> Than to betray his friends and fauourers (I. iv. 117–18)

He assures Constance very similarly in *John* that she

> shall have no cause
> To curse the fair proceedings of this day:
> Have I not pawn'd to you my majesty? (III. i. 22–4)

Here Philip speaks after the marriage, for Shakespeare took Constance off during the "marriage-proposal" episode (II. i. 416 *sqq.*): and the king seems a less bare-faced liar than in the *T.R.* because he makes vague promises for the future, and is not glossing over his past promises to Constance as he actually breaks them.

Countless other inconsistencies crop up in the *T.R.* Once our suspicions are aroused they stare us in the face. Whereas in the *T.R.* these are *structural*, two conflicting versions of one character or event being apparently conflated, the "inconsistencies" that have been detected in *John* are entirely due to the commentators' failure to consider Shakespeare's regular techniques, or unfamiliar Elizabethan idioms.

Appendix C

THE TEXT OF *THE TROUBLESOME RAIGNE OF IOHN* (1591)

We observed (p. lvi) that the *T.R.* has textual features common in "bad quartos". A short selection will make this clear.

(i) *Omission of exits and entrances*. This also happens in good texts (omission of entrances being much the rarer of the two), but not in the profusion offered by the *T.R.* In i. i. 73 the (first) entrance of the Faulconbridges passes unnoted; so in i. ii. 74 the (first) entrance of Blanche. In i. x. 16 Constance is brought on a second time, though already brought on in i. x. i. In i. i. 60, xii. 28, xiii. 144 etc. exits are unnoted.

(ii) *Speeches without headings*. See ii. i. i, ii. i. 52, ii. ii. 219, ii. iii. 150, ii. iv. i.

(iii) *Ambiguous speech headings*. In i. v the third and fifth speech headings both read "*Philip*": the third standing for Faulconbridge, the fifth for France. Other speech heading variations are perhaps no more extraordinary than those of some good texts (France is *King* in i. ii. i, *K. Philip* in i. ii. 46, *Philip* in i. iv. 14; Pandulph is *Pandulph* and *Legat* in ii. viii; and so on).

(iv) *Descriptive and summarizing directions*. This is an important clue for a decision about the provenance of the text. Some cases can be parallelled in "good" texts, e.g.

Enter *Philip* leading a Frier, charging him to show where the Abbots golde lay (i. xi. i).

Others remind one of "bad quarto" presentation:

Excursions. The Bastard chaseth *Lymoges* the Austrich Duke, and maketh him leaue the Lyons skinne. (i. iii. i)
Excursions. The Bastard pursues *Austria*, and kills him. (i. vi. i)
Excursions. *Elianor* is rescued by *Iohn*, and *Arthur* is taken prisoner. *Exeunt*. Sound victorie. (i. viii. i)

Compare similar compression in the bad quarto of *Romeo*:

They draw, to them enters *Tybalt*, they fight, to them the Prince, old *Mountague*, and his wife, old *Capulet* and his wife, and other Citizens and part them.

she stood there, nonplussed, feeling more helpless than she had ever done in her life before. She shivered. It was cold in the room, the smoke that she had noticed coming from the chimney had promised warmth, but was in fact only arising from a large lump of damp driftwood that smouldered unproductively in the dismal grate

'The house, it is cold.' He spread his hands and shook his head. 'I am a poor housekeeper, I play the piano yes, but the fire to light, no. Tina does it for me when she comes to make lunch but today I thought to surprise her by doing it myself. Since the arrival of Eve's baby, Tina has much to do and I have no wish to become a nuisance to her.'

It was Rachel's turn to take over. Throwing him a mischievous glance, she took his hand, led him to a chair and made him sit in it before she went out of the room. In the back porch she found kindling, coal, a shovel and a zinc bucket. On a shelf in the kitchen cupboard she discovered a hoard of old newspapers and one of Tina's aprons hanging behind the door. Piling everything into the bucket, she returned to the sitting room where he still remained seated, an expression of amusement on his face.

Removing her jacket, she donned the apron, signalled for him to observe what she was doing, then knelt before the grate to gingerly lift out the smouldering log, which she placed on the hearth. Next she riddled out choked cinders and ash which she shovelled into the bucket. Very carefully she piled paper, sticks and small pieces of coal on top of one another, applied a match and in minutes a cheerful blaze was leaping up the lum.

'*Voilà!*' he cried in delight, his strong face sparkling. 'You have many talents, *mein Frau*. Would your admiring fans ever guess, seeing you in your jewels and your finery, that the dazzling young violinist can change herself back into a Cinderella with just the flick of a match?'

She threw him a glance of reproach and he had the grace to look ashamed. 'But of course, I forgot, you are an island girl, you knew these things from the cradle. How fortunate, to be great and yet to be humble, you would survive where I would perish. Now look at us, Vienna sits by the flames warming her pretty little toes, I, too, sit but I have learned how to light fires, and you, you have black hands and soot on your nose.'

He stood up and took one of her dirty hands. 'Come, you will wash, I will make us a hot drink – no, not the famous Oxo of Herr Tam's stories, I make better cocoa. When we have cleaned and warmed ourselves and drunk my lovely cocoa I shall play for you, anything you want to hear, and I promise you won't have to stand outside of my window like the little match girl: you will be inside, warm, and dry and fed – just like my Vienna.'

They laughed, they had a wonderful time. When Tina came puffing in to attend to her belated duties she found the pair of them ensconced together on the couch, heads bent over pages of music scores, which also littered the table and spilled on to the floor and on top of the cat, who, blissfully asleep by the fire, was oblivious to everything.

Tina stared at the cosy hearth. 'Och, Mr Klebb, you've lit the fire!' Her pink pleasant face was dismayed. 'Surely to goodness that is no job for a gentleman!'

'Frau Tina, don't fash yourself,' he grinned, delighted at having the opportunity to air one of Tina's own expressions, 'a gentleman didn't light it, a lady did, this young lady. She got down on her hands and knees and in minutes the blaze was leaping. I observe, I know now how to do it, the burdens of looking after me will be one less.'

'Ach, you have never been any bother to me, Mr Klebb, but wi' Eve just having the baby I canny have her doing too much in the house, so you'll have to excuse me if I am sometimes a wee bittie late in coming over here.'

She couldn't keep the the pride from her voice. Little Matthew John's arrival into the world had caused a great stir of excitement. Tina had never been so rushed as she attended to her daughter, saw to the baby and 'did' for Otto. But she didn't mind. Her life had meaning again, the house was no longer the quiet place it had been since the death of her husband Matthew, and she hummed a lilting, tuneless little tune as she went through to the kitchen to see to Otto's lunch.

'Stay and have some with me,' Otto said to Rachel. 'Tina

always makes too much for me and Vienna is growing fat with all the scraps I give her.'

Rachel barely hesitated before she accepted. She forgot all about her promise to have lunch with Ruth and Lorn at Fàilte, not till the afternoon was halfway through did she remember and by then it was too late.

When Rachel finally appeared after tea, full of apologies and of her time spent with Otto, Ruth looked at Lorn but held her tongue. She had seen that look on Rachel's face before and remembered it only too well. Lorn remembered, too, and turned his head away in shame, not wishing to be reminded of that turbulent affair he had had with Rachel behind Ruth's back.

But Ruth wasn't going to let go so easily. That night, when the children were in bed and it was just herself and Lorn in the house, there was a strange expression in her violet eyes when she faced him. 'It's happening again, Lorn,' she said slowly. 'Rachel has that special glow about her when she's getting up to something she shouldn't – usually wi' a man,' she ended bitterly.

Lorn wriggled uncomfortably. 'Och, come on, Ruthie, how can you say that? She and Otto have a lot in common, that's all, she's missing Jon and has grown tired o' her own company.'

'Ay,' Ruth spoke slowly, thoughtfully, 'just like you and she had a lot in common when I was away and poor Jon had to leave her to her own devices for a while. She tires o' her own company quickly, does Rachel. I wonder if she and Jon had a row and she's not saying anything. Look at the strange way she behaved when she came home, no' saying a word to anyone, just creeping on to the island like a thief in the night.'

'That's it, isn't it, Ruthie?' Lorn's face was flushed, he hadn't liked being reminded of his affair with Rachel and privately he thought that whenever she appeared she always seemed to cause trouble of one sort or another. 'You're still mad at her for no' telling you that she was coming. And another thing,' he hid his discomfort in anger, 'you're beginning to sound like old Behag! Surmising things that might never have happened or are ever likely to happen. Just because Rachel is attractive to men doesny mean that she wants to pounce on everything in trousers, she has too much sense in her head for that.'

He had said all the wrong things. Ruth's face was like thunder. Shaking back her fair hair from her face she said through tight lips, 'Ay, Lorn, you of all people should know how attractive she is to men, and the pair o' you had no sense at all in your heads when you tumbled in the heather for all the world to see! As for trousers! Rachel prefers men in the kilt, they're more available – in every way.' Her face red with temper, she went on, 'When we used to play together as children it was a favourite game o' Rachel's to try and look up men's kilts to see what was going on up there. Not even the old men were safe from Rachel's prying eyes and to this day, whenever she's around, old Colin of Rumhor gives her a wide berth. Maybe he's feart she'll try to find out how he managed to father six children wearing his threadbare kilt when Jon in his perfectly presentable trousers can give her none!'

Normally Lorn would have thrown back his head and laughed uproariously at that, but tonight neither he nor she were in a laughing mood and the pair of them retired to bed in the highest dudgeon to lie back to back, as far from one another as possible.

After that day Rachel was a regular visitor at Tigh na Cladach. In order to get there she had to go through the village of Portcull, on foot or on Ranald's bicycle, or she walked there via the beach. Either way she soon had the curtains twitching and the tongues wagging, but, being Rachel, she held her head high and went on her way regardless.

'Arrogant, aye was, as brazen as her mother and a bit more besides,' sniffed Behag, who, fully recovered from her accident, was very definitely making up for lost time. She might have chosen to prolong her convalescence had it been to her advantage, but on the day that Holy Smoke brought an enormous bunch of daffodils instead of the usual parcel of meat she knew it was time to let go of a good thing.

'As long as he gets them for nothing he'll bring you flowers till the house looks and smells like a funeral parlour,' Kate had said with a smirk.

'It was kind of Mr McKnight to pick the flowers from his own garden,' Behag had said huffily, more in defence of herself than the butcher. 'At least he paid me some attention while I was laid up wi' my ankle – more than I can say for some.'

'Attention!' Kate had hooted derisively. 'The daft bugger was feart you would sue him for your ankle and fine you know it. Don't forget, I was in his shop the day you hobbled in wi' your arms that tight round his neck I thought you would choke the life out o' him. At first I thought maybe you were lettin' your passions run away wi' you and had given in to him at last, but no, we'll have to wait a whilie yet for that to happen. In the meantime you got your money's worth from the poor bodach, and now instead o' steak it's flowers, which I saw him takin' out the kirk, wi' my very own eyes. He'll be robbin' the kirkyard next, just to keep you going, for nothing but weeds grow in that neglected garden o' his.'

Seeing Behag's downcast face, she relented. 'Ach, you were quite right to get as much as you could out the mean sod but don't be too clever if you know what's good for you. Give him an inch and he'll take a mile and if he goes on bringin' you bunches o' second-hand daffodils there might just be a marriage proposal at the end o' it. Holy Smoke aye has his eye on chance and this is a nice wee house you have here, Behag. If he thought he could save a bob or two he would marry you, just to move in here and let his own crofthouse out to the towrists.'

Behag was aghast; in next to no time she was scuttling about as if nothing had ever happened to her ankle. When Holy Smoke appeared next day behind an even larger bunch of flowers, she snatched them from him, and told him that her ankle had 'knitted nicely' and that she would be putting the flowers in kirk in time for the Sabbath as someone had been stealing the floral arrangements from the altar – 'and may the Lord have mercy on his soul,' she had added as a wicked afterthought.

His face on hearing that was a picture and she had wallowed

in the satisfaction of seeing him sprachle away down the brae as fast as his legs would carry him.

Breathing a sigh of relief and feeling that she had escaped his clutches in the nick of time, she returned to the firing line of everyday affairs, and only just in time too. Things were happening on the island, so much so that the activities of Elspeth and Captain Mac, which so far had been disappointingly sluggish, could keep for a while. The 'stranger mannie' and 'that Rachel Jodl' were a much more intriguing pair and so Behag returned to the fray, fully restored to health and her tongue in 'fine fettle' as old Sorcha so aptly put it.

In the midst of all the talk, Otto and Rachel, locked in their own little world of music and magic, were hardly aware of the stir their relationship had engendered, until Tina, who loved them both, decided that it was high time they did.

So one day, 'Mr Otto' as he had become to those who felt that to address him solely by his Christian name was taking too much of a liberty, found himself confronted by a very embarrassed Tina, pink in the face but nevertheless determined to have her say.

'Mr Otto,' she began, keeping her lovely languid eyes firmly fixed on the view of Sgurr nan Ruadh outside the front window, 'I know it is really none o' my business, and if it was just me I wouldny say anything that might hurt you, but I think it is only right you should know that folks are talking about you and Rachel behind your backs.'

'Talking about us, Tina?' he repeated, his brow furrowed in puzzlement.

'Ay, talking about you, Mr Otto.' Nervously she caught a strand of flyaway hair and tucked it into the elastic band that was holding together an untidy ponytail. 'Rhanna is just a tiny wee island and some o' the nosier folk make it their business to take an interest in what other folks are doing. Rachel is a bonny lass and you, Mr Otto, if you don't mind me saying so, are a very striking-looking man and wi' her being married it just doesny seem right for the pair o' you to be seen spending so much time together. I don't know what your wife would have to say if she found out about it but I know what Jon would think if he saw you laughing and enjoying yourselves together the way you do.'

'Tina,' taking her hands he shook his head as he looked down at her from his considerable height, 'my wife I don't have anymore, and even if I did, myself and Frau Rachel have done nothing to be ashamed of. If Herr Jon came here tomorrow he would have no cause for jealousy, I assure you. I am aware of his wife's beauty, what man wouldn't be? But we have much in common, Frau Rachel and I, we laugh because we enjoy the same things, we make good music together but that doesn't mean that we also make love behind the scenes. If people want to talk about the things they make up in their heads then so be it. I will not forbid my little Rachel to come here because to do so would make nasty feelings between us and I will not spoil a young woman's happiness for the sake of the idle tongues. So you see, little Tina, you must not worry anymore about us, there is nothing to worry about.'

Tina, red with shame and discomfiture, was saved further embarrassment by the arrival of both Rachel and Eve. Up the path they came together, fair-haired Eve fully recovered from the birth of her son, raven-haired Rachel, breathless and laughing, having run to catch up with Eve on the road.

Otto was entranced by Eve's baby and as soon as she came over the threshold he took the little boy from her and began to croon to him.

'Look, he listens, he enjoys my terrible singing!' laughed the big man in delight. 'Everyone should have babies, I wanted dozens but, alas, it was not to be . . .'

He caught the warning look on Eve's face but it was too late. Quickly he glanced at Rachel and saw there the stark longings of a young woman who ached to have children but whose arms remained empty.

Later, when it was just he and she alone in the house, he took her face in his gentle hands and gazed deep into her eyes. 'My little one,' he said, his soothing voice low and tender, 'forgive me, I did not know of your yearnings to have children. But you are young, there is plenty of time, before you know it there will be one, two, even three babies in your life. Believe me, it will be so.'

She looked at him for a long time; there was pain in her heart but there was hope as well. This dear wonderful man, with his fierce manner and generous heart, had become her mentor, her friend, and her trusted companion. If he said she would have babies then she believed him.

His hands were warm against her face, she felt the power and the passion that was strong within him. 'Her beloved stranger': in her heart that was how she thought of him, how she would always think of him now. Something so poignant seized her she was shaken by the tug it had on her emotions and she turned her face away from him so that he wouldn't see the sadness staring stark and painful from her eyes.

Part Two

EARLY SUMMER 1967

Chapter Nine

It had been cold and wet during the early part of spring but now, as the days lengthened, they became warm and golden, filled with the promise of new life and hope. Slowly the fresh young grasses and heather shoots emerged from the tangle of winter browns and reds on the hills; roe deer and rabbits feasted on the tender new shoots; lambs gambolled and played in the fields; the skylarks spiralled upwards to hover in the blue yonder, spilling out their trembling notes of ecstatic song.

Green mattresses of machair became covered in thousands of yellow buttercups that danced in the breezes and seemed to drape the earth in sunshine, while acres of tiny white daisies were like patches of snow spread over the landscape. The scent of flowering gorse hung sweetly in the air, drowning the senses like heady wine; the great blue ribbon that was the Sound of Rhanna sparkled and shimmered in the sun, and in the calm shallows, the children on their Easter holidays splashed and danced, grew brown and healthy, and wished that some disaster might overtake the school so that its portals would remain closed for many moons to come.

Dodie's cockerels crowed loudly from dawn till dusk, driving Wullie and Mairi McKinnon so crazy they spent the greater part of each day thinking out ways to rid themselves of the nuisance. Something would have to be done, they told one another, but for the moment they couldn't think what form that something would take, short of braining Dodie and shooting his blasted birds into hell!

Rachel and Otto, oblivious to all but the wonders of a

Hebridean spring, greeted each new day with delight and made the most of every minute.

Jon hadn't arrived as promised. Mamma, he wrote, was feeling weak and shaky after an unexpected bout of flu, but as soon as she was well enough he would be on his way as speedily as was possible.

> I miss you, my darling gypsy. It seems such a very long time since I held you and laughed with you. The days go by very slowly here and the only way I know how to get through them is to keep thinking of you and what it will be like when at last I join you on our beloved island.

Rachel could hear the voice of longing in the writings of her dear, gentle Jon, and when a letter like that came from him, she would sit very still by her window and imagine that he was on the steamer as it sailed into view on an ethereal sea, coming closer and closer to Mara Òran Bay and the harbour.

But the pull of life pulsed strongly in her veins and always, always, her footsteps took her to lonely, enchanting Burg Bay and the beloved stranger who waited for her as eagerly and as impatiently as she waited till it was time to go to him.

She knew she ought to visit her mother more, though Annie never made any particular effort to look pleased when she did go. Rachel wanted to feel close to her mother but always there had been a barrier between them. Annie had never had the ability to communicate easily with her beautiful, gifted daughter. When she was younger, Rachel had been frustrated and hurt by this attitude, but as she grew older her highly developed senses told her that it wasn't an intentional slight but one born of many things that had puzzled and frightened her mother.

It had taken years for her to accept the fact that she had given birth to a defective child. The way to understanding had been slow and painful for her and the death of her husband, Dokie Joe, hadn't helped matters. Rachel had adored her father and had resented Annie's second marriage to big, strapping Torquil Andrew. Then had come Rachel's fame, and Annie faced a further struggle as she tried to cope with a young woman who might have sprung from an alien womb, so divorced was she from the reality of Hebridean life.

Only gradually did Annie come to realize that success and fame had never really gone to her daughter's head, rather she had clung more fiercely to her beginnings than ever and was always proud to tell everyone of her birthplace, no matter how elevated they might think themselves to be.

Even so, in Annie's book, Rachel was Somebody with a capital S and, no matter how hard she tried, she often felt awkward and clumsy when her daughter came to visit and she could never stop comparing her untidy little cottage with the opulent surroundings Rachel must be used to.

She had been horrified when both Jon and Rachel had tried to persuade her to let them build a bigger house for her. 'What would the nosy cailleachs think o' that?' had been her reaction. So Rachel had to content herself with sending her mother enough money to keep her comfortable and this Annie did not object to since she was careful never to 'display her wealth in public' but invested it instead in 'bits and bobs that anyone might possess', putting the biggest portion into the bank for a rainy day.

But there were some lighthearted times to be had in Annie's company. In her younger days she had often been the talk of the island with her 'fleering after men o' all sorts'. She had been merry and quick-tongued, full of laughter and fun and, even now, some of the best ceilidhs were held in her house, especially when Kate was there to add her zestful talk to that of her daughter.

Rachel thought the world of her grandmother and enjoyed the informal atmosphere of her cottage. 'Orderly chaos' was how Kate described it. She never put on airs for anyone: 'take me as you find me' was her motto and that could mean anything, from catching her with a headful of formidable curlers, to finding her up to her elbows in the sink sloshing soapsuds around with gusto.

Quite often too, Tam might be 'having his head sheared' with a pair of ancient sheep scissors, or he might simply be sprawled in his favourite chair, snoring his head off and not liking it one bit if Kate poked him in the ribs to don his jacket for 'the visitors coming to the door'.

'But, Kate,' he would protest, 'you're wearing your curlers – surely that's worse than me no' having on my jacket.'

To which she would ably and unreasonably reply, 'At least I'm wearing something that hasny got holes in them. Look at your socks, Tam McKinnon, holes in them as big as your head, put your shoes on this minute, I won't have folks saying that I'm neglecting you by no' darning your socks.'

'But, Kate, you don't darn my socks. The last time you put a bit mending to them was when old Joe was biding here, you were just showing off when you darned his socks *and* his drawers. I knew fine you would never keep it up when the poor auld bodach left home.'

'Tam McKinnon! I don't darn your socks because I'm too busy *knitting* the damt things. Now, no' another peep out o' you or I'll keep you indoors for a week to do all the mending you aye manage to shirk.'

Rachel never minded these altercations between her grand-parents, she knew well enough that Kate's bark was worse than her bite. Rachel always got a warm welcome from the pair of them and, in their house more than anywhere else, she felt as if she had never been away from home and loved it when Kate smothered her in an apron, dumped a bag of flour on the table and told her to make pancakes. As a child, making pancakes and scones in Kate's gloriously cluttered kitchen had been one of the highlights of her life and she remembered vividly the large table-top littered with bowls of eggs, luggies of milk, pats of butter and most of all, flour, flour, everywhere – on Rachel's hands, her face, her apron; clouds of it dancing in the sunbeams spilling through the window; particles of it making the cat sneeze and fall off her chair; dustings of it covering Tam's cap as he sat reading his paper, perfectly oblivious to everything but yesterday's second-hand news. Then the delicious delight of tearing apart piping hot pancakes to sniff their steamy aroma and eat them running with butter and bramble jam. Neither of them had minded the mess she'd made, not like Annie who lived in a jumble but couldn't be bothered showing her daughter how to bake because it would just make more mess.

Rachel had good reason to love her grandparents, but lately she had neglected everyone in favour of her beloved stranger. Ruth, who had looked forward to a long summer spent in the company of her childhood companion, couldn't hide her displeasure at being given the go-by, and the looks she cast at Rachel whenever they encountered one another in the village were anything but friendly.

But Rachel could no more resist the pull of Tigh na Cladach than she could help breathing. She and Otto had spent some wonderful musical evenings together. She had taken along her treasured Cremonese violin and they had played piano and violin concertos and solo pieces, each of them in their turn sitting back by the fire to listen to the other.

One evening they invited Lorn and Ruth to supper at the shorehouse and after an initial spell of awkwardness Ruth had soon bloomed under the soothing influence of music and song. Lorn was a fine musician in his own right, he could play any tune on his fiddle and it wasn't long before feet were tapping as Scottish reels and strathspeys filled the room. Otto was a perfect host, mannerly and considerate, his strong personality and ability to converse on most subjects putting everyone at ease. When it was time to go home Ruth felt ashamed for thinking the things she had about Otto and Rachel and she didn't even make comment when Lorn's expression said 'I told you so.'

Otto had heard a lot about McKenzie o' the Glen and, wishing to get to know him, had sent an invitation to Laigmhor. Fergus, feeling that he would come under the microscope, wasn't so keen to accept but Kirsteen was curious to meet the man whose name was on everyone's lips and coaxed and persuaded till he agreed to go, if only for the sake of peace. They were accompanied by Phebie and Lachlan and Mark and Megan, who were regular visitors at Tigh na Cladach. It wasn't long before a full-blown ceilidh was in full swing in the shorehouse.

It seemed music and rhythm were inherent in Scottish blood, and Otto was enchanted by the Gaelic songs from Lachlan and the amusing Glasgow ditties that Phebie and Mark sang, their heads close together as they gave it 'laldy', to quote Mark.

Only Fergus refused to take part, his natural reserve making him seem dour and unyielding in the laughing company. He sat by the fire, fiddling with his pipe, wishing it was time to go home but knowing there was little hope of that when Kirsteen was so obviously enjoying herself.

'You're getting to be a bodach before your time,' she hissed at him at one point. He glowered at her and dug a twist of wire deeper into the stem of his pipe, his mind more on the spring lambing than anything else.

Rachel played a medley of tunes on her violin, followed by a haunting and evocative selection of Scottish ballads which seemed to bring the wind sighing into the room and evoked the wild beauty of lonely wide spaces. Her young face was pensive in the lamplight as she became lost in the music. She was wearing a simple white dress that enhanced the tanned skin of her smooth limbs and made her look more than ever a child of light and air and beauty.

Otto watched her entranced, fascinated by her talent, by her dazzling appearance, but most of all by the impression she gave of a being as one with the earth and of the heavens at the same time. She was transcendent yet so vibrantly tangible it was taking all of his willpower to go on treating her as he sensed she wanted to be treated, as someone with the same interests, the same loves as himself, things to be enjoyed without emotional complications getting in the way. She was such a child in many ways but the woman in her couldn't deny her outstanding desirability. Jon was a lucky man; he shouldn't leave her alone for so long . . .

The playing ended. He came back to reality with an effort and, remembering that he was host of the evening, he sat himself down at the piano and performed a solo recital of some of the best-loved composers. It was breathtaking, magnificent; the waves of glorious sound filled the room, effortless and compelling. It was as if he was on stage, giving of his best, his fingers flying over the keyboard without hesitation, his strong face set into lines of concentration as he immersed himself in his playing.

The last notes echoed into an enchanted silence. Everyone was stunned with the magnificence of the performance. It seemed too trite to clap or make any of the usual sounds of appreciation.

Lachlan shook his head as if to reluctantly clear it of the magic that had filled it for the last half-hour. 'Herr Otto Klebb,' he said softly, 'who are you, man? You're no ordinary pianist, that's for certain. You belong on the concert platform – and don't try to tell us otherwise . . .'

Otto jumped up abruptly from his seat. 'Doctor Lachlan, your estimation of me is too high, I have performed on stage, it is true, but not for a long time, no one remembers me now, it was all so long ago. Now, let us drink and be merry – the night, she is young. I have many stories to hear about the islands and I have all the ears for listening.'

Kirsteen laughed. 'You need the old ones for that: the seanachaidhs, Bob the Shepherd, Magnus of Croy, for instance. They're becoming a dying breed but there are still a few of them left on Rhanna, thank goodness.'

'Then we shall have them, we shall have everything that is Scottish and wonderful – but this night is for us and I wish not to waste another minute of it.'

His exuberant personality was very catching and he seemed to fill the whole room with his tremendous vitality. He was attentive and kind and treated the womenfolk with the greatest respect and courtesy. Kirsteen, Megan and Phebie had had their hands kissed on arrival and they blossomed under his charm and his manners.

Fergus had looked surprised when his wife's hand had been seized and kissed. To himself he had thought the action foreign and showy but had to admit that the man was certainly as everyone said, a Presence with a capital P, and more of a mystery man than ever with his musical talents and his appreciation of all things Scottish. Fergus, never a man to feel at ease in social gatherings, applied a match to his pipe and wondered if Donald had checked the lambing fields before going home . . .

'McKenzie of the Glen!' Otto was standing there, two huge glasses of schnapps in his hand. 'I have heard much said of you, many good things,' he grinned, ' others not so good, but we can, none of us, be perfect. It seems, however, there is one field in which you excel. Strong men like Herr Tam McKinnon and Herr Shod the Todd have the envy in their eyes when they speak of it: it seems, according to them, that you can drink every man on this island under the table and never be the worse for it yourself. With that in mind I make a challenge to you, drink with me the schnapps, let me discover for myself this wonderful constitution of an ox I have heard so much about.'

'Havers, man,' Fergus returned succinctly, 'Tam and Todd aye did exaggerate. I am no better and no worse than them and fine they know it.'

Otto's eyes gleamed. He proffered one of the glasses. 'Prove it.'

Fergus caught Lachlan's laughing eyes, he also saw the sympathy in Mark's. Mark didn't dare touch strong liquor – the events of last year had ensured that everyone had discovered the reasons for that – even so he knew how to enjoy himself, and all at once Fergus felt boorish and mean because he could take a good dram knowing that he would waken up next day without the ache of addiction gnawing at his innards.

He looked at Otto. The man was laughing, his keen dark eyes were alive with challenge. Fergus took the offered drink. '*Slàinte!*' he muttered and drank the liquid down in one gulp, never so much as one flicker of an eyelash showing that he thought the stuff terrible and nowhere near as good as a good whisky.

Half an hour and two drams of schnapps later he was glowing from head to foot. His dark, handsome face was just a little flushed and he knew he was in perfect control of every one of his senses, therefore it came as a great shock to him to suddenly find himself singing, the notes soaring out clean and clear, as if from the throat of another being over which he had no control.

The chatter in the room ceased, everyone stared, McKenzie o' the Glen singing! Ay, and singing in a voice that was unexpectedly pure and tuneful, a soft, lilting tenor with a beauty of tone that was a delight to hear. The song he sang was 'Vienna, City of my Dreams', and every word, every intonation was perfect.

A pin could have been heard to drop when he came to the last word, but no one was going to let go so easily: everyone took it up, and the haunting melody filled every space in the room:

> Farewell Vienna mine,
> I'm in the spell of your charms divine,
> Dressed like a queen with lights so gay,
> You are the love of my heart today . . .

Rachel had never heard anything so moving. She hardly dared glance at Otto but couldn't help herself. He sat in his chair, his head thrown back, his eyes black and stark with emotion, she caught her breath, something so poignant twisting in her heart she didn't know she was crying till she tasted the salt tears on her lips . . .

> Farewell Vienna mine,
> Laughter and music and stars that shine,
> Wonderful city where I belong,
> To you I sing my song.

The room was suddenly as silent as it had been when Fergus started to sing. A moist-eyed Otto threw his arm round Fergus's shoulder. 'My friend,' he said huskily, 'I take off to you my hat. That was wonderful, superb . . .'

'Och, c'mon, man,' Fergus was overcome with embarrassment at the other man's flamboyancy, 'there's no need to go that far . . .'

'But there is, there is need to go even further. You and I, McKenzie of the Glen, will have another little glass of schnapps, and then we will sing together the songs of Vienna made so famous by the unforgettable Richard Tauber, yes?'

'No,' Fergus said, but he did. He and Otto stood before the fire and they sang the remainder of the night away, much to the delight and amusement of the rest of the company who joined in when they knew the tunes and kept respectfully quiet when they didn't.

When everyone eventually piled out of the shorehouse into a clear, stark, starry night, Otto was singing 'I Belong to Glasgow' in his cultured Austrian accent while Fergus, whose voice had noticeably degenerated in the last half-hour, was attempting a German drinking song.

'My friend,' Otto gave Fergus an affectionate hug, 'we are both equally drunk and therefore we are both equally master drinkers. Next time I will drink with you the Scottish whisky but first, we must get you home in one piece. I have a feeling your legs won't obey the commands of your head.'

'Problem solved.' Mark, who was the only entirely sober member of the company, took a hold of Fergus and propped him against the wall, where, with Kirsteen on one side of him and Otto on the other, he managed to remain standing while Mark's long legs took him swiftly up the brae to the Manse. Ten minutes later he was back at the shorehouse with Thunder, into whose shabby, draughty interior Fergus was stuffed without ceremony to be driven home in anything but style.

It was a laughing group who helped to extricate his rubbery limbed body from the car and then to carry him into Laigmhor. Once inside the door he threw everyone off and said with great dignity and in an unnaturally high-pitched voice, 'I am per – per – perfectly capable of sheeing myshelf to bed, thank you and goodnight,' only to collapse on the bottom step of the stairs with a loud hiccup.

Kirsteen collapsed down beside him, giggling. 'I have never, never seen him like this and he'll certainly never live it down.' She looked at him. His dark head was lolling on to his chest, one big, strong brown hand was hanging down limply at his side. With another hiccup he began to sing 'Simple Little Melody', and he was still singing when the others somehow got him upstairs between them and into bed where they took off his tie and his shoes before pulling the quilt over him.

'He'll have a beauty of a head come morning,' Lachlan predicted with a grin. 'One thing's for certain, he'll no' forget the night that our Austrian friend challenged him to a schnapps-drinking contest.'

'Ach, I doubt if he'll remember anything about it.' Kirsteen's fair face was sparkling with mischief. 'Only, I'll make sure he does, down to every last little detail.' With love in her blue eyes she stroked the hair from his brow. 'My darling Fergie, he's a man of surprises. I knew he loved Richard Tauber, he always listens to him on the wireless, what I didn't know was how beautifully he could sing, I've never heard the likes from him until tonight.'

'Ay, he was always good at keeping things up his sleeve,' Phebie observed, her plump, pleasant face rosily pink from both her exertions and a good drop of the *Uisge Beatha*, 'and he looks so snug and comfortable lying there I'll be joining him if I don't get to my own bed soon.'

'I could drop you off if you like,' Mark offered, but Lachlan, whose own old car had been laid up for weeks, hastily shook his head.

'It's a fine night, the walk will do us good. I've got a hole in my back where Thunder's springs were digging into it on the road up here. I think I'll revert back to the old ways and get a horse, saddle sores are infinitely preferable to rusty springs and cramp.'

'*You* get a horse, Lachy McLachlan!' Phebie said firmly. 'I'm saving up to get us a decent car, and even if I never learn to drive the damt thing I can aye get somebody who does and we'll wave to you as you ride by on your smelly old steed.'

Laughing they bade goodbye to Kirsteen and went their separate ways at the gate. Megan settled herself beside Mark in Thunder and as they drove back up to the Manse she said thoughtfully, 'You know, Lachlan was right about our mystery man, he does belong on the concert platform, I have a feeling that there is a great deal about him we have still to find out.'

Mark nodded, concentrating hard on manoeuvring Thunder, whose lights left a lot to be desired, along the glen road. 'Ay, he is quite a man, is our Otto, his manners are impeccable and his charm rubs off on everybody. Fergus isn't exactly renowned as a chatterbox but he blossomed tonight under Otto's influence. I've been to quite a few gatherings with McKenzie but it's the first time I've heard him singing with such abandon, he has a fine voice too. He must have practised a lot in the bath, or up on the hill with only the sheep as an audience.'

'There was something about his eyes, something strange,' Megan said slowly, speaking as if to herself, her own gaze staring unseeingly into the velvet black of the night. 'But I can't quite put my finger on it.'

'We are talking about Fergus, aren't we?'

'No, Otto.'

'Well, he consumed a fair amount of hard spirits, anybody's eyes would be glazed and queer after a session like that.'

'No-o, it wasn't that – something else . . . Oh well,' she shrugged herself out of her reverie, 'it doesn't matter, it was a great night, and to think I thought that Otto would remain as unapproachable and as remote as he was when first he came to Rhanna. It just goes to show that first impressions don't count.'

'He was being wary,' Mark decided, turning in thankfully at the Manse gates. 'He likely wanted to size us up before deciding that none of us would be able to fathom who he was and why he came here, both factors which still remain something of an enigma.'

'Rachel, of course, had a lot to do with bringing him out of his shell. She and he are real buddies, I don't suppose . . .'

'No, Megsie, you mustny suppose,' he told her firmly, putting his arm round her and giving her nose an affectionate peck. 'This little nose is a doctor's nose and must on no account be poked in where it doesn't belong – leave that to people like Behag and Elspeth, you can be certain they are already making merry with their gossip and I can't have my new and innocent little wife adding fuel to the flames.'

108

'You're right, of course, you usually are. I *am* getting to be a bit of a cailleach, I suppose that's what comes of living in a close-knit island community.'

He took her arm and led her indoors where they were immediately surrounded by a bevy of canine and feline bodies. When they had laughingly extricated themselves from wet tongues and hairy paws, Mark took his wife into his arms and nuzzled her lips with his.

'You'll never be a cailleach,' he murmured tenderly, 'not until you're at least one hundred and ten years old. And I'm not always right, in fact, I'm often wrong, but on the subject of Otto and Rachel I prefer to give them the benefit of the doubt. Now, how about a nice hot cup of cocoa before bed, my treat?'

'Mmm, sounds good – but bed sounds even better, you could be my hot water bottle, my feet are like ice after just fifteen minutes in poor old Thunder.'

His dark eyes glinted. 'Bed it is, Mrs Mark James, I might just make an excellent hot bottle, but I'm in a wicked mood tonight and somehow I think I'm not going to be very interested in your feet, though they, of course, will warm up with the rest of you, I promise you that.'

His mouth fondled her ear, she shivered and forgot all about Rachel in the pleasure of being the wife of this tall, wonderful man who took his job as minister of Rhanna very seriously but who was first and foremost a husband par excellence.

After seeing the visitors off, Otto came back into the room, his face alight as he strode over to Rachel and took her hands. '*Liebling*,' the endearment caressed her ears, 'it has been a perfect evening, such music, such charming people, so natural and entertaining. The ladies I adore, the men I feel I have known all my life. McKenzie of the Glen has, on the outside, all the rough edges of an uncut diamond – but inside,' he put his hands on his chest, ' he has the heart of gold and the character of steel. He and I, we click. Tomorrow we go fishing in the Fallan river but somehow, I think, he will not remember that in the morning time.'

He sighed as he studied her. Only one lamp burned in the room, she looked shadowy and mysterious, her great dark eyes were luminous in the quiet, secret planes of her face. She was regarding him in that quizzical way he had come to know very well and he sighed for many things, but most of all for the absence of a voice from the throat of such an exquisite creature.

'*Ah, mein Mädchen,*' he whispered, 'only to hear one word from your lips would be, for me, paradise. We speak to one another with our hearts, our eyes, and our music, but I am greedy: I have need to know more of you, your thoughts, your fears, your dreams, and so, tomorrow I begin to learn the language of your hands. Tonight I am too tired to want even to listen to my own voice . . .'

He paused and looked above her head to the window, and without another word he led her over to look outside. A feeling of pure magic stole over them; she put her head on his shoulder and together they watched a huge silver moon rising above the sea, spinning a pathway of crystal light over the sparkling waters, etching the great cliffs of Burg into stark black silhouettes against the star-spangled sky.

'Come, *liebling,*' he said at last, though the softness of his voice did not break the spell. 'Together we will walk through that enchantment. I will pluck moonbeams for your hair and steal a star for us to wish upon.' He laughed. 'Forgive my little fantasies but moontime always makes me feel romantic and weaves the poems in my head. We will go to bed with the wonder of this night held in our hearts, you in your small corner, and I in mine.'

She wanted the night to last forever, she didn't want to go back to the emptiness of An Cala when here, with Otto in the shorehouse, there would be warmth and comfort, love and passion, all the things that were missing from her life just then. She was never more happy, more relaxed than when she was with him and she had to concentrate her thoughts on Jon, how much he meant to her, how she had promised never to betray him again for another man . . .

110

She moved away from the window. Otto went out to the hall and came back with one of his own warm jackets which he tucked round her shoulders. Hand in hand they wandered through the moonlit perfection of a Hebridean night to An Cala, waiting lonely and bare up there on the cliffs above Mara Òran Bay.

Chapter Ten

The minute Rachel stepped over the threshold of An Cala she sensed that the house was no longer empty and unwelcoming, the feeling of life was in the atmosphere, and though it was dark in the little hallway it was a friendly darkness and she wasn't afraid to go further inside to investigate.

It was very quiet. The house wore that cloak of soundless peace that seemed to enclose it after gloaming had departed and night had settled over the countryside. Even so, her heart beat a little faster as she stood there in the deep stillness, and she just about jumped out of her skin when, on the wall beside her, the ornate clock she had brought back from a trip to Germany chimed out the hour of one o'clock.

She stayed very still outside the parlour door while her racing pulse galloped on, bringing in its pounding beat the first small niggle of unease. Then, with an impatient shrug, she put her hand very gently on the doorknob and slowly, slowly, began to turn it. The hinges creaked slightly. She held her breath as bit by bit she pushed open the door.

Not even she was prepared for the sight that met her eyes, for there, sprawled by the dying embers of the fire, was her husband, dead to the world.

Jon! Her heart cried out his name; a few swift steps took her across the room, straight into his arms. He awoke with a start but she gave him no chance to say anything, instead she smothered him with kisses until he broke away, breathless and laughing.

'Let me look at you!' he cried, quickly lighting the oil lamp and retrieving his glasses from the fireside table. Putting them on he held her at arms length. 'More beautiful than ever,' he said, the light of love shining in his eyes. 'Your holiday on Rhanna has done you much good, you are brown and healthy and perfect. Ah, *liebling*.' He sighed, folding her in his arms. 'How I've missed you and counted the days till I could be with you. It has been forever, but we will make up for it, the summer is ours to pass as we will. The decision to come home to Rhanna was arrived at in haste and I had no time to write and let you know when I would be coming.'

She had a thousand questions to ask, and her hands flew so swiftly he laughed and shook his head in some bewilderment. 'You go too quickly for me, or perhaps I am just out of practice. Firstly, I came on this evening's boat, you weren't here so I lit myself the fire and settled down to wait – and wait – and wait.' Tenderly he kissed her nose. 'I think to myself, she is at Ruth's house and will be home soon, then when soon passed I have the idea that there is a ceilidh somewhere and she won't be home till late. But my little wife, she still doesn't come at twelve of the clock and I am tired from the journey – and so, I sleep, and now I wonder, what has kept her out till the little hours of the morning.'

She found it hard to meet his eyes, such honest eyes, brown and gentle and trusting, sometimes she laughingly told him that he looked like a big puppy dog, but she didn't convey that to him tonight, not when she had just come fresh from the arms of another man whose kisses still tingled on her lips. For Otto had indeed walked her home, but he hadn't been able to resist crushing her to his chest and covering her mouth with such bruising kisses she had at first been dismayed before she had responded to him with a passion that equalled his.

'Forgive me, *liebling*,' had been his parting words, 'I told you I would only kiss you when I was tempted beyond endurance: tonight I very much needed to kiss you, and now go home before I lose my control altogether.'

He had walked away quickly, leaving her to stare after him, every fibre in her so thoroughly awakened she had been trembling with emotion. Her legs had felt so shaky, her heart had beaten so quickly, she had had to allow some time to elapse before attempting the climb up the cliff path to An Cala – and now, here was Jon, tugging at heartstrings that were already weak with feelings.

Dear, darling Jon. She was glad, so glad to see him, she felt that somehow he had saved her from herself and she was so genuinely pleased to see him her face was aglow with the relief she felt at having him home at last. But his questions awaited an answer and as quickly as she could she told him that she had indeed been to a ceilidh though she omitted to say where it had taken place. Somehow she wasn't yet ready to tell him about Otto but his next words made that kind of evasiveness very difficult indeed.

'Has it been all fun, *liebling*?' he asked lightly. 'Or have you kept up some violin practice? I know you want to forget the world for a while but you have a very large following out there, I have to be a hard taskmaster and we must work out some sort of schedule in order that you do not allow yourself to become rusty.'

'There is a man – he has come to live at Doctor Megan's old house,' unwillingly her fingers spelled out the words. She paused, wondering if she should tell him the truth about Otto. She had given her word not to say anything to anyone, but Jon was her husband: if anyone could be trusted to hold their tongue he could. She gazed at him; he was waiting, a quizzical half-smile lifting the corners of his mouth. Making a swift decision, she told him everything, ending, 'With him I have had the most wonderful time, he plays his piano, I my violin. So you see, darling Jon, I don't need a schedule to make me work, Otto is my encouragement, he makes everything so happy and pleasurable, it is a joy to be with him.'

Whilst talking about Otto, her face had become more alive, more glowing than ever. Jon saw the light in her eyes and slowly he nodded. 'I see you have everything you need here on Rhanna, all the freedom in the world, friends, family, above all a man who is in tune with your spirit and who makes his music with you.' He gave a rueful shrug. 'Perhaps I make a mistake when I think you must be missing

114

me as I missed you, you – light up when you talk of this man.'

'No, Jon, no!' Frantically she tried to make him understand how lonely she'd been without him but still he seemed unconvinced and in desperation she threw herself at him to kiss him with such eagerness he was soon lost in the sweetness and insistence of her mouth.

When at last he spoke he sounded shaky. 'Oh, *mein* Rachel. Always, always, I melt in your arms. I tell myself one day I will be strong and not give in to you so easily but . . .' he spread his hands, 'I can never resist you and you know it.'

For a long time after that they sat on the rug in front of the fire, holding one another, but she sensed a restlessness in him, his mind wasn't fully on her, he kept glancing towards the door, a strange expression on his thin, aesthetic face.

All at once he got abruptly to his feet and began pacing the room in a worried fashion, then, with his back to her, not meeting the questions in her eyes, he said in a low voice, 'Rachel, I don't know how to tell you this, it will come as a shock and perhaps I should have mentioned it right away, but seeing your happiness I couldn't bring myself to ruin our reunion.'

Scrambling up from the rug she went to him and put her hand on his arm but still he wouldn't look at her and she became angry because the only way she could communicate with him was through her hands, and how could she speak to him in that fashion if he couldn't see what she was doing?

He passed a hand over his eyes in a characteristic gesture. 'I'm sorry, *liebling*, I'm not behaving very well, perhaps, after all, I shouldn't have come . . .'

'Jon!' Pulling on his arm she made him turn to face her. 'What is it?'

'It's – it's – Mamma.' Somehow he got the words to come out. 'She's here, Rachel, upstairs asleep in the little guest room. She insisted on coming with me, she wanted, she said, to see for herself the island that we love so much, she said it was time she saw my wife's birthplace. Also – she felt the change might do her some good as she's been very low since her illness and taking the flu didn't help matters . . .'

He couldn't go on. Rachel gave him no chance anyway, her eyes were like black burning coals in the deathly pallor of her face. At first she had stared in disbelief as he had talked, now she balled her hands into fists and began to beat them against his chest.

NO! NO! NO! The screams of protest filled every space in her pounding skull but only the barest of sobs made themselves heard. To have his mother here, on Rhanna, spoiling everything with her hints and innuendoes, her accusations and her black, glowering glances, was just too much to bear.

No! No! No! Her face crumpled. She subsided against him, shaking her dark head. She couldn't, she wouldn't live under the same roof as that formidable woman who had never accepted her as a daughter-in-law and never would.

'Rachel – oh, my *liebling*,' gently he took her hands and clasped them to his mouth, 'please, don't be so unhappy, it will only be for a little while. Mamma is used to the city, she doesn't like the country and will hate an island even more. A week, ten days at the most.'

It was eternity! Rachel saw the days stretching ahead, filled with Mamma, her demands, her likes, her wants, her needs. Limp as a doll, Rachel pulled her hands out of Jon's grasp and moved away from him.

She went to the door. 'Rachel,' he began, but she was already out of the room. He could hear her going upstairs, and not being very quiet about it – she would waken Mamma and that was the last thing he needed just then.

A great sigh gusted out of his chest. The start of his holiday looked very bleak indeed, with the two women in his life hating the sight of each other and making no effort to hide their feelings, be it in private or from the rest of the world.

By the time he got upstairs the room was in darkness and Rachel was in bed. Very quietly he got undressed and slipped in beside her. It was very peaceful, the sky outside the window was littered with stars and even as he watched, the edge of the

116

full moon came into view, peeping through the muslin curtains as it climbed higher. Gradually the room became filled with its silver light and in a moment of contentment he gazed round at all the familiar things that were so evocative of his times spent at An Cala.

The furnishings were simple. Both he and Rachel had agreed that the house, with only a few exceptions, should look as it might have looked fifty – a hundred years ago. Here in their bedroom there were no exceptions: the bride's kist under the window, the sturdy mahogany wardrobe and dresser, the pewter basin and jug, the enormous brass bed with its wonderfully soft feather mattress, even the very rag rugs on the wooden floor, were as they must have been when An Cala was a working croft and its rooms had rung with children's voices and the sound of tackity boots taking their work-weary owner upstairs to well-earned rest.

Jon loved it all; he knew every nook and cranny, every creak and sigh of the old timbers, even the very smells of plaster and wood and cobwebby cupboards filled with household necessities. There was no fighting the spiders on Rhanna, the minute their webs were intentionally or accidentally wrecked, they immediately set to work, spinning bigger and better ones, so that you soon came to realize how pointless it was to keep brushing their nebulous threads away.

The bright face of the moon stared at him calmly as he lay there watching it. Slowly he turned his head on the pillow to look at Rachel. Moonbeams were spilling on to her tumble of black hair; he could see plainly the glossy sheen on the little curls at the nape of her neck and – his heart accelerated – her naked shoulders were like alabaster against the dullness of the patchwork quilt.

She moved slightly; he felt the heat of her flesh burning through the flimsy satin of her nightdress. Oh God! How he ached to touch her. He had waited so long for this moment of nearness and now this: her back hunched sullenly against him – no sign to let him know if she was awake or asleep, only that brief touch of her thigh letting him know that she was there, in the bed beside him . . .

117

All at once a mighty snore reverberated through the wall, followed by another and then another. Each one was louder than the one before, shattering the silence of the house. Jon couldn't believe his ears. It was the first time that he had slept in such close proximity to his mother, and as he lay on his back, counting each explosive sound, a horrible conviction grew that, between one thing and another, there would be no sleep for him that night.

Beside him Rachel tossed, then she sat up, her whole attitude tense and listening. Mamma had settled down to a steady rhythm of snores. Rachel could picture her lying there on her back, like a mountain, her lips sucking inwards, outwards, in, out, in, out . . . and wasn't there now a whistling accompaniment at the end of each rumble? In, out, whistle, in, out, whistle . . .

Rachel glanced at Jon, he gazed at her, a spurt of laughter escaped him. Two seconds later they had collapsed into one another's arms, Jon helpless with mirth, she so filled with it her stomach ached and she could only find release in little gasps and grunts and funny half-sobs that made her throat ache too. Tears poured unheeded down their faces while they clutched one another in agony. Such laughter generated a lot of warmth and Rachel threw off the quilt, eager to feel the deliciously cold, moonlit air washing over her body.

She was very desirable lying there in the silver-blue light. Her nightdress shimmered, her supple limbs moulded themselves into the feathers. Jon forgot about Mamma, forgot about everything except the beautiful creature lying beside him, half woman, half child. Always he had thought about her in that way: compared to him she was so young, a mere girl of nineteen on their wedding day almost seven years ago.

But tonight she was all woman, all desirable, all tempting in that heavenly light spilling over the bed. She melted into his arms. At first her skin was cool under his hands but soon it burned with heat, the satin material of her nightclothes seemed to merge with her flesh, a combination that drove him so crazy with desire he forgot to be careful and tore away the thin restraining garment. Her breasts sprang out, full and ripe

118

and so deliciously tantalizing he wanted to feel them under his teeth. It was always like this, she could bring out the animal in him with just a mere stirring of her lovely limbs, but tonight she too was awash with an untamed passion, the arms that urged him ever closer were fierce and insistent and with a helpless groan he succumbed.

They bruised one another with their kisses, kisses that went deeper and deeper till their tongues played and fought and brought them both to peaks of greater longings. He nibbled her lobes, she squirmed and pushed his head down to her breasts and made no protest when he gently bit her soft flesh and caressed her nipples with just the tips of his teeth.

'*Liebling*,' he murmured huskily, 'you will always be mine, always.'

Rachel closed her eyes. She had imagined that she would feel oppressed having Mamma in the next room but instead the idea excited her. Here she was, with the old lady's adored son in her arms, doing things to her that were for her alone. Jon loved her no matter what Mamma said or did, and nothing could take that away.

He was trembling with his need for her. His mouth moved down from her breasts to caress the soft flesh of her belly. She writhed beneath him till he gave a little cry of helplessness and pushed her legs apart with a mastery that thrilled every fibre of her being. Once upon a time he had been gentle and rather ineffectual during their lovemaking till he found out that that kind of treatment did nothing at all for someone with her kind of wild passions. Now he allowed himself to be completely free with her, which resulted in a relationship that was pleasurable beyond belief.

Roughly he drove himself into her; his sinewy body rippled under her hands. She bit her lip and allowed herself to climb to the crests with him till he cried out and fell back exhausted, bathed in a dew of sweat. A fiery warmth swept through her body; she felt totally relaxed and wonderfully fulfilled.

Twice more in the course of the night he took possession of her body, and each time they both reached peaks of ecstasy that pulsed in their loins till it seemed that nothing could quench the fires burning within them, and all of it was achieved to the tempo of Mamma's snores in the room next door.

Rachel awoke late next morning. By the time she had washed and dressed it was later still, and when she finally made her way down to the kitchen she was horrified to see that Mamma Jodl had made breakfast and was cosily ensconced beside Jon at the table.

He raised his head to look rather sheepishly at his wife but neither she nor he had any chance to say anything, for Mamma got in there first.

'Ah, Rachel, at last you have decided to join us. Jon could not wait for you to attend to his needs – a man must eat a good breakfast, and so I have the search in the cupboards – but . . .' she spread her plump hands and shrugged, 'no food there for a man like Jon. Where is the cold ham? I ask myself. And the cheese, it is fit only for *kinder*, too mild, too without taste; the bread it is too soft; the coffee, it is not in existence – and so, I have to go against my will and make the tea with the funny smell and the eggs with the shells that have still the hen's *schmutz* upon. Yaa!' she lifted her broad shoulders in an expressive shrug and glowered scornfully at her boiled egg.

Mamma didn't have good English; she used her hands and her eyebrows to get over her many points – and in any case, most of the time she was displeased about something and only needed to grimace or utter 'yaa!', which was her favourite expression of disgust, to put over her opinions.

As she rose from her seat to fetch the bowl of eggs, Rachel was struck afresh by her size. Every bone in her body was heavy and big, her discontented face was large-jawed but handsome nonetheless. She had enormous feet, and legs like tree trunks; her well-corseted hips and stomach produced a trimness which only served to emphasize the magnificence of her bosom which swelled out in front of her like a great feather bolster. It was quite a daunting experience to see those vast proportions sailing towards one and Rachel never

120

could make up her mind whether to duck or hastily dodge out of the way.

She seemed to fill every space in the kitchen, and Rachel's resentment at having her here at An Cala boiled in her breast. The kitchen was Jon and Rachel's favourite room, they had painted and papered it in sunshiny shades of lemon and white. The farmhouse dresser, the wooden chairs, the well-scrubbed table, the worn but wonderfully comfortable armchairs, even the brass fender and coal box, had all come from an old crofthouse in Nigg and blended well with the general decor. When Rachel and Jon were at An Cala together they lit the fire in the homely hearth and used the kitchen as a place to eat and relax in.

To Rachel, Mamma's presence in this room was a violation of everything that was private and precious in her life and she had to force herself to go to the table and watch as Mamma's big hand scooped an egg from the bowl to place on Jon's plate, after which she turned to her daughter-in-law.

'The *schmutz* eggs – you want?' she asked in a flat voice.

Rachel shook her head and reached for one of the delicious oatcakes that Tina had recently given her.

Mamma scrutinized the girl's face. 'Like a bird, you eat – no wonder you are thin and pale of the skin. The eyes, they are black underlining, your mouth, it has the swelling lips. They are the only part of you with the fat that should not be.'

Rachel met Jon's eyes, they flashed their secrets to one another. Mamma intercepted the look but chose to ignore it, instead she went on, 'The sleep good you escaped, I too did not sleep well, all night I turn and toss about, and mostly I lie with my eyes open, hearing the noisiness of a strange house.'

Jon choked, Rachel rushed round to thump his back, her lips brushed his ear, he looked up at her and again their eyes sent out their messages.

As soon as the meal was over Mamma began immediately to gather up the dishes and pile them up on the draining board. She was already taking over, Rachel thought bitterly, before we know it she'll be telling us when to go to bed, when to get up . . .

'There is no hot water in the tap,' Mamma complained loudly.

121

'This morning I look also for the bathroom, there is none to find, so I take my wash in cold water from a jug in my room. Last night there were no lights to find, only an oil lamp and candle.' She emitted a noisy sigh. 'It is so different from Hamburg: there I have all the things I am used to having.'

'Of course it's different from Hamburg, Mamma,' Jon explained patiently. 'It is an island, many of the houses here don't have electricity, we are lucky, we have a generator which hadn't been cranked last night but I will see to it this morning.'

'You have plenty of money,' Mamma pointed out stubbornly. 'You could have the electricians put in.'

A faint smile touched Jon's mouth. 'Piped all the way under the Atlantic ocean? No, Mamma, I think Rachel and I are not that rich. As for hot water, there is a back-boiler behind the fire here, when I have had a chance to light it you shall have all the hot water you need.'

'That is all very well, Jon,' Mamma was growing a bit red, 'but what good is hot water without the bath, the washstand? I am a woman who is used to having the clean person.'

Jon remained calm; Rachel had always found his courteous manner towards his mother extraordinary. She had asked him once how he managed it and he had replied, 'It is the only way to live with her. Look at how you and she war with one another, she believes the young should respect her at all times – and of course – she *is* my mother,' he had added, as if that explained everything.

'We fully intend to build a bathroom, Mamma,' he told her soothingly. 'Our trouble is we are never here long enough to see to such things. Not only that, Rachel and I like to be as natural as possible when we're here and don't mind the odd little inconveniences.'

'Little inconveniences! Pah! And is it natural to go to a *hütte* in a field to perform there the needs of the body. This morning I go there, I sit, I jump off my sit when a large hairy *kuh* bellows at my elbow and when I step outside I stand in *kuh dung*!'

Rachel hid a smile, Jon too had difficulty keeping a straight face. 'We call it the wee hoosie here, Mamma, and if you shut the little gate in the fence the cows won't come in.'

'The comedy I do not find!' Mamma snapped. 'You were never like this when you live with me in Hamburg, Jon.' She looked meaningfully at Rachel who stared back and would have stuck out her tongue if it had been anyone else but Mamma. 'You have there all the cultures, all the good tastes, it is not civilized to stand in *kuh dung* and wash from a cold water basin. Myself, I will not go to a *hütte* in the fields again!'

Then you'd better stock up on syrup of figs, Rachel thought gleefully. As my mother used to say, 'you'll get constipation and cramp if you keep it in.'

'And what about the bath?' Mamma wailed. 'How am I going to give myself the wash, tell me that, Jon?'

Jon looked embarrassed. 'We, Rachel and I, use a zinc tub, Mamma. We set it here in front of the fire, fill it with hot water and lock the door.'

There was a pregnant silence as each of them became immersed in their individual thoughts.

Vivid pictures flitted through Rachel's head. A whale, she decided, lowering itself into a fish kettle.

Jon's face grew as red as his mother's as he imagined her getting stuck in the tub, leaving in her wake a great tidal wave that filled the kitchen, with himself and Rachel wading through the flood to go to her assistance . . . an appalling vision.

'The humility, the indignity,' Mamma whispered with unchar-acteristic lack of fire. 'I will not do it – I cannot.'

Rachel felt sorry for her – but not sorry enough. She knew Otto had a bathroom at Tigh na Cladach but she certainly didn't want her mother-in-law poking her nose in there.

Jon was kinder, however. 'My friend Anton, he has a nice bathroom at Croft na Ard; I am sure he and Babbie will not mind letting you have the use of it.' He was growing tired of the subject and wanted to ask his mother outright why she had come to Rhanna when she must have known how different it would be to anything she had been used to, but, conditioned to a lifetime of subservience, he held his tongue. He was greatly relieved to

123

see that his suggestion met with her approval, though he worried about how the Büttgers would react to his request.

'I will go over there later today and ask them about it.' His words came out rather woodenly but Mamma didn't notice. Mollified, she filled a kettle and put it to heat on the stove for the dishes. Meanwhile Rachel, who was determined to let the other woman see that it was still her kitchen, made tracks to the table to clear it, leaving Jon to gather together kindling and coal in order to get the fire going and thus provide Mamma with her desired hot water.

The dishes done and the sink thoroughly cleaned, Mamma peeled off her apron. 'I go now into town,' she declared with determination. 'Proper food you must get, Jon, if you are to keep up your strength to live the way of the heathens. First, the *Bäckerei*, pastries, yes, good solid bread; then the *Fleischerei*, red meat with blood running. You always needed blood running in your meat, Jon; from boytime I give you it to make you strong.'

Jon sighed. Here we go again, he thought, explanations! For her, on Rhanna, always there will be the explanations that will not be allowed to sink in.

'Mamma,' he began a trifle wearily, 'there is a butcher on the island but there is no bakery – and it isn't a town. Portcull is a small village with only a few shops; the women do a lot of their own baking, though Merry Mary does get in things like bread and rolls and a few stodgy cakes.'

'Stodge! I will not have the stodge, no, I will tell this happy Mary to serve to me the apfelstrudel, and if that she has not got I go from there to here till I find.'

Jon gave up. Once Mamma set her mind on something it was useless to try and make her change it. She went to don her hat and coat, each of which was trimmed with grey fur, right down to the hem of the long coat.

Jon gave her directions to the village and off she swept, a string message bag clutched in one hand, a large leather handbag in the other. At the gate she turned and executed a regal wave and then marched down the road as if she had been doing it all her life.

124

'She has certainly recovered from her attack of flu,' Rachel observed rather sarcastically.

'Perhaps it is the island air,' Jon hazarded, not relishing further discussions about his mother.

But Rachel wasn't in a mood for argument, she was thinking of Otto: he would be wondering what had happened to her when she didn't turn up at Tigh na Cladach. She looked at Jon, dare she suggest that they both go over there so that she could introduce them to one another? But Jon had other ideas: she had forgotten his promise to Mamma over the question of a bath.

'Come, *liebling*.' He took her in his arms and kissed her hair. 'It is a lovely morning, a walk on the shore will do us good and then we will pay a visit to Anton. If Mamma doesn't have somewhere to go and bathe we will never hear the end of it.'

She went to get her jacket. Mamma! Mamma! Mamma! Was that all she was going to hear for the next week or two? What Mamma wanted, the kind of things she needed to make her happy: because keeping Mamma happy was of paramount importance to both Jon and herself, otherwise they could forget any ideas of domestic harmony at An Cala. An Cala! The Gaelic for a safe and peaceful harbour! Rachel had to smile; she wondered how her mother-in-law would get on at Portcull – the villagers ought to have had some sort of warning of her impending arrival . . .

'I wonder how she will get on with the islanders.' Jon voiced his wife's thoughts. 'She'll never make herself understood, not only that, she is only familiar with German currency and won't be able to tell the difference between a mark and a shilling. She'll argue, she'll get red in the face – and she will start shouting.'

'And she'll make enemies,' Rachel predicted. She hoped to herself that Mamma would meet Grannie Kate: Kate could sort anyone out, no matter their nationality. If the man in the moon himself came down to Rhanna, Kate would be able to deal with him and not take too long about it either. Rachel felt better; she hoped Behag and Elspeth might bump into Mamma as well. Behag would shrivel her with just one glower and Elspeth would beat her into the ground with a few painful lashings of her razor-sharp tongue.

Rachel grinned. She went to take Jon's arm, smiles begat smiles, and by the time they reached Mara Òran Bay they were in such high spirits they raced one another along the silver-white sands and into little coves that were private and sheltered and just made to be lingered in when it became imperative to steal a few laughing kisses.

Chapter Eleven

As it happened, Mamma took Rhanna by storm, completely disconcerting everyone she met, and as that included some of the less staid inhabitants, she was destined to make her mark in a way that would always be uniquely hers and hers alone.

In the first instance she bumped into Dodie, literally. With his head down because he was crying and didn't want anyone to see, he came loping swiftly along the road, the tails of his greasy old raincoat flying behind him, his fists screwed into his eyes, so blinded by tears he couldn't see where he was going and cared less. Full tilt into Mamma he careered, and the impact stopped him so thoroughly in his tracks he staggered backwards, shaking his head as if to clear it, all the wind knocked out of his sails.

Dodie was not in the best of moods: he had just had a terrible argument with Wullie McKinnon over the subject of his cockerels. At first it had been an amicable enough encounter, Wullie had strolled into Croft Beag, going over in his mind what to say to the old man that wouldn't offend him too much because it was an easy enough matter to bring him to a state of tears. So Wullie had been lost in thought when he encountered Dodie, and Dodie, taking his neighbour's mild manner as an indication that the rift between them had healed, had been very courteous and attentive, showing Wullie his vegetable and flower plots and the patch of richly manured ground where he grew the juicy sticks of rhubarb that were his pride and joy.

He had also hastened to make Wullie a strupak and it was while they were ensconced in the kitchen, drinking tea and eating the pancakes that soft-hearted Mairi had handed in earlier, that the visitor had gradually brought the talk round to poultry.

'Your hens will be laying well the now, Dodie,' Wullie had begun obliquely, maintaining an unnatural politeness in view of his reasons for being there.

'Oh ay, indeed they are,' Dodie agreed eagerly, dunking his pancake into his tea and quickly stuffing the soggy particle into his mouth before it disintegrated into his cup. 'Every morning I go to the hen hoosie to see how many eggs my hens have had.'

'Ach, hens don't have eggs,' Wullie said scornfully, 'they *lay* them.'

'They have eggs,' Dodie persisted, 'and then the eggs have chickens – tis the natural way o' things.'

'But eggs don't have chickens, chickens just come out o' the eggs, Dodie,' an exasperated Wullie cried.

'Ay,' Dodie said patiently, feeling that his visitor needed to be humoured, 'the same way as a calf comes out o' Ealasaid.'

Wullie tried another tactic. 'Cockerels don't lay eggs, do they, Dodie? They just strut about all day, treading the hens and yelling their heads off. They're no' really much good to anyone, all they do is make a God-awful racket and eat up all the food.'

Dodie sighed. 'Ach, but, Wullie, you were brought up on a croft, surely you know the only way that hens can have chickens is to be treaded by the cockerels.'

He spoke to Wullie as if to a child who needed the facts of life explained to him carefully and gently.

'*One* cockerel, Dodie.' Wullie was losing some of his cool; he brushed away a drip from the end of his nose with an agitated hand. '*One* cockerel is all it takes to father hundreds o' chickens.' He paused – he was beginning to sound like the old eccentric. 'To fertilize hundreds o' *eggs*,' he amended hastily. 'Six is just a waste o' time and a buggering nuisance into the bargain.' His temper was rising and he stood up, unable to sit still for a moment longer. 'I'll get rid o' them for you in no time, just a wee twist and it will all be over, you don't even have to watch.'

Dodie was horrified; he had never been able to bring himself to kill anything, far less his beloved chickens, who had proliferated unchecked when he had lived in his lonely cottage up on the hill.

Holy Smoke had already offered to thraw the cockerels' necks and string them up in his shop, affably saying he would share the proceeds with Dodie. He had been rubbing his hands together at the time, an action peculiar to him when talking about money.

Dodie had simply turned tail and run from the scene to tell the story to the first person he met. 'He calls himself a man o' God,' he had sobbed, 'when he is nothing but a heathen goin' round killing poor, defenceless animals.' And now, here was Wullie McKinnon, uttering the self-same murderous words as the butcher man. In panic Dodie had risen to his feet to order Wullie out of his house and never to darken his door again.

'I'll be back!' Wullie had yelled. 'And next time it will be wi' a shotgun! I'll do more than scare the shit out o' these bloody birds o' yours! I'll blast the lot to kingdom come and think o' the deed wi' pleasure when I'm lying sleeping in my bed for the first time in months.'

Dodie had been really scared then, and in his fright he had taken to his heels, straight to the village to tell his woes to someone. That the first person he bumped into should be Mamma was, to his simple mind, just a continuation of his experiences with Wullie, and he backed away from this large, strange woman, the tears coursing in dirty rivulets down his sunken cheeks.

She was so taken aback she began to rant at him in German while he babbled back in Gaelic. To make matters worse, Dodie's pet lamb had followed him into the village and, being a ram lamb, it was only too ready for a bit of fun and games. It charged straight for Mamma and playfully butted her in her stiffly corseted rear. She shrieked, Dodie's nose frothed with fear and for the second time that day he took to his heels and galloped away, the lamb gambolling behind him.

Mamma stared after them. In no time at all they had disappeared from view and she blinked, feeling that she might have imagined the whole episode – had not her stinging backside given her a grim reminder that it had all really happened. But Mamma was made of stern stuff: in next to no time she had girded her loins and was able to take stock of her surroundings. Jon had

129

certainly been correct in telling her that only a few shops serviced the village, but some was better than none and, fully recovered from her experiences with Dodie, she made purposeful tracks for the nearest shop.

Into Merry Mary's she charged, going straight to the head of the little queue and completely ignoring Kate McKinnon who had been first in line and who was rendered speechless for at least thirty seconds.

'You have for me the pastries?' Mamma demanded of Merry Mary. 'I am liking fresh my apfelstrudel; for me the stodge I do not want, it chokes up the system.'

Mamma used a very peremptory tone – after her encounter with Dodie she was taking no chances with anyone else, her idea being that if you got in there first you would show them who was the boss. In Mamma's book anyone who stood at the business side of a counter must be made to understand that the customer was always right and they existed to serve and no questions about it.

Merry Mary was completely taken aback: one minute she had been having a nice cosy blether with her customers, the next she was suddenly faced with this huge monument of a woman with a face on her that would have floored Goliath himself. The little English woman could only stare open-mouthed but Kate, who had recovered her powers of speech, had enough to say for the two of them. Tapping Mamma on one formidable shoulder, she said ominously, 'And just who do you think you are, madam? Barging in here in front o' everybody without as much as a by-your-leave?'

Mamma chose to deal with the first part of the question and ignore the rest. 'I am Frau Helga Jodl,' she intoned proudly, pulling herself up to her full, impressive height and thrusting out her considerable bosom, much to the enjoyment of Robbie Beag who admired well-upholstered women. 'I am *mutter* of Jon Jodl who is married to Rachel Jodl, the famous violinist.'

It was typical of Mamma: very seldom had she praised Rachel to her face, but if she could capitalize on her name she never

130

hesitated to do so. In this instance she hoped that it would intimidate this rather fierce-looking woman whose own generous bosom had further blossomed in the last few minutes.

'Oh, is that so,' Kate nodded conversationally, 'our very own Rachel, eh? I hope she will teach you some of our manners while you are here, for though I say it myself, Rachel aye did have good manners and her being famous hasny altered matters in that respect.'

'Rachel! Manners!' Mamma spat. 'Pah! I have yet to see these manners you speak about, she is not showing them to me since her marriage to my son. She cannot speak, no, but her eyes, they send the rude messages. She has not the respect for her elders, she has the solkiness, she . . .'

'She is my granddaughter,' Kate finished Mamma's sentence in her own words, her sparking eyes sending out dangerous signals of anger yet controlled.

In the face of such righteous ire Mamma hadn't a leg to stand on. She backed off, wishing with all her mighty might that she was back home in Hamburg where the shopkeepers scurried to her bidding, which meant that she was always served and on her way home before anyone else. Taking a deep breath, she turned her back on Kate and was about to address Merry Mary once more when a voice, even more forbidding than Kate's, spoke at her elbow.

'Just a minute, just a minute! Who said you could go first, Mrs Whatever? I was here before you and I am no' waiting a damt minute longer to get served, so just you get out o' the way at once and let me in there before I am forced to take action.'

Mamma turned to see the round face of Aggie McKinnon, who was related to Kate through marriage, glaring at her. If there had been a contest on physical proportions between the two, Aggie would have won hands down, not only was she as rotund as an elephant, she towered above the other woman to such a degree that Mamma was dwarfed by her.

Aggie was normally a sweet-natured, placid soul who liked to agree with everyone for the sake of peace. In common with most of the islanders she enjoyed a good chin-wag and usually

131

never minded if she was last out of whatever shop she happened to be in, but this morning she was in a hurry. She had already wasted a lot of precious time picking Barra McLean's brains for a recipe concerning spicy buns, the island bus would be coming along any minute and she was anxious to catch it so that she could get home and listen to *Morning Story* on the new-fangled radio her Merchant Navy husband had just brought back from America. So, all in all, she considered that she had every right to contest her place in the queue and it was now her turn to draw herself up to her alarming height and thrust out her vast bosom till it was almost touching that of Mamma's.

The two battle-axes faced one another, nostrils flared, guns at the ready; the rest of the shop settled back to watch with the greatest of interest, eager to see who would fire off first. But the promising battle never got off the ground for at that crucial moment the bus arrived at the harbour, the squealing of its brakes being the only indication it needed to let everyone know it was there.

Aggie, her message bag only half filled, shot Mamma a look that promised a revival of the argument at a later date and out of the shop she stomped in high dudgeon.

'It's no' often Aggie is in such a hurry,' Merry Mary observed.

'Ach, she wanted to catch the bus,' Barra explained. 'She likes to listen to *Morning Story* on the wireless and Colin Mor has brought her a fine new one from America.'

Mamma pricked up her ears at mention of the bus: she was beginning to believe that she had landed in a place that might have been Mars, so lacking did it appear to be in modern amenities.

'There is a bus on this island?' she enquired excitedly, visualizing herself being transported to the nearest town, where she could get down to her shopping in earnest.

'Ay, you could call it a bus – at least –' Kate purported a great show of doubt and, addressing herself to her contemporaries, she went on in some puzzlement, 'I've often wondered – is it a bus?'

'It *might* be a bus!' came the chorus.

'Or it might be the Loch Ness monster in person,' Jim Jim said with a grin, 'the way it lumbers along on dry land wi' its bones sticking into every one o' *my* bones.'

'If Erchy would wash the damt thing we could maybe see if it says "bus" on it,' Robbie hazarded, putting on a great display of helpfulness.

'Pah! The comedy I do not find!' Mamma spat. 'I would like to know please' – it was the first time she had used the word 'please' – 'if it goes to a town where I can buy the better food.'

It was Mamma's bad luck that the only sobering influence present in Merry Mary's shop that day wasn't in a mood to be helpful. Barra normally tried to keep the peace, but Mamma Jodl's belligerent attitude had seriously affected her reasoning nature and she was the first to speak.

'A town, you say?' She nodded thoughtfully. 'Well, there is the Clachan of Croy – though I wouldny call that a town . . .'

'No,' Kate chimed in, her face perfectly composed, 'it is more in the nature o' a small city – a very noisy place, I never go there myself unless I can help it.'

'A – city.' Lovingly, Mamma rolled the word round her tongue and without ado she gathered up her bags and went bustling away outside to the waiting bus.

Everyone looked after her, round-eyed.

'You shouldny have done that, Kate,' Barra reproved. 'I admit I was going to have a wee bit fun wi' her but I wouldny have went that far.'

Robbie supported his wife's words, 'No, it wasny very nice to do that to a stranger – and a furriner into the bargain.'

But Kate was unrepentant. 'Ach, it serves the bossy besom right – and just think – she'll get to see the island in style and will experience firsthand the delights o' our island bus.'

Very determinedly, Mamma walked the short distance to the harbour, boarded the bus, and settled herself behind the driver's seat. To supplement his income, Erchy had purchased the vehicle some years ago, and, with the aid of a local-government subsidy, he managed to make a fair profit, especially in the tourist season when trips round the island were in reasonably high demand. Visitors' cars weren't allowed on the island because of the narrow and often dangerous roads and also because of the difficulty of shipping them over on the steamer.

So people like Erchy had quite a monopoly over the question of transport, though he was apt to bemoan his lot and make out that running the bus didn't pay and that he was presented with considerable difficulties when it came to maintaining the vehicle. Any servicing it got was carried out by himself at the side of his cottage. Tam said he didn't know the difference between a spark plug and a bolt, and there might have been some truth in that, for Erchy was anything but mechanically minded, but he cheerfully upheld the view that any sort of bus was better than none and no one needed to use it if they didn't want to.

He knew fine, of course, that people *would* use it whether they liked it or no as few of them owned a car, which presented a great deal of problems when it came to getting from A to B. All things considered, Erchy and his ramshackle bus were in near-constant demand, except, of course, for when he had to exchange his bus driver's role for that of the island postman, or even occasionally for a 'funeral assistant', when he was called on to drive a dearly departed to the kirkyard in the elegant Rolls Royce that Todd the Shod had won in a competition some years ago and which he hired out to wedding and funeral parties. Over the years people had become used to Erchy in all his various guises and the topic of how he kept his bus tacked together had grown stale with the passing of time.

Thus Mamma found herself on a lumpy, hard bench, surrounded by faces she didn't know and which didn't interest her anyway. The well near the driver's seat was a jumble of parcels and boxes as Erchy hated cramming up his post van with the more bulky items, since it meant he had to waste time searching through them every time he came to a stop. It was far easier to carry them on the bus, and it didn't matter if they were accompanied by the odd creel of fish or a sack or two of rabbits. The bus had become quite a favourite rendezvous for those interested in the barter system and many a fresh salmon,

134

poached from Burnbreddie's river, had been furtively exchanged for some other ill-gotten gain. Erchy himself had often accepted a few rainbow trout in lieu of a fare and he was quite happy to add the tag of bootlegger to his various other titles.

There was always a distinct odour of fish in the bus. It hung in the air to mingle disagreeably with other smells of mothballs, mints, tobacco, whisky, sweat and stale beer. Mamma wrinkled her nose in disgust and sat fretting for the driver to appear so that she would catch the shops in Croy before they shut.

But Erchy was in no hurry, he was too busy discussing football with some local lads who had been to the mainland to see some of the last matches of the season and who were only too anxious to tell him about their experiences, both in and out of the football grounds. When he finally appeared, to take his place behind the wheel, he was whistling cheerily and was so carried away with good humour he peered into his mirror and shouted, 'Ride a pink pig on the highway to Nigg!' followed by, 'Bums ahoy on the road to Croy!'

The menfolk merely grinned at his nonsense but one or two of the womenfolk expressed their disapproval in loud snorts while Aggie, who had not yet forgiven Erchy for mistaking her mouth for a post box, glared at his reflection in the mirror and hunched herself dourly into her seat.

Mamma tapped Erchy on the shoulder with a none too gentle finger and requested that he drop her off at Croy, to which he grinned and sang, 'Croy, Croy! The next best thing – to Troy.'

The bus started up. They were moving off when a flying figure waved them down and in came a stringy-looking, garrulous visitor, wearing baggy shorts under a cracked and roomy waterproof. She plumped herself down beside Mamma and immediately began to talk, too taken up with describing some adventure she'd had to notice Mamma's lack of response.

'Just one moment.' Erchy was up again, tying the door with a piece of dirty string. 'Canny be too careful.' He smirked and settled himself once more behind the wheel. The vehicle emitted a series of groans, wheezes and two alarming bangs before it condescended to heave itself out of a pothole, whereafter it

135

proceeded sedately along the front, leaving in its wake a hideous-smelling cloud of diesel fumes.

Erchy was a somewhat erratic driver. On perfectly good stretches of road he would bowl along at a gentle pace suited to his vehicle's temperamental mechanism, but once out on the open road, which for most of his route consisted of narrow little winding ribbons, a change would come over him, and today was no exception.

Through the village of Portcull, past the Schoolhouse, the Manse and the Kirkyard, he was the Erchy that everyone knew – placid, smiling, easy-going to a fault – but as soon as he hit the narrow cliff road to Nigg a grimness settled over his countenance, his mouth became a tight line and his eyes calculating slits in his screwed-up face.

It was as if he saw the road as a challenge to his driving abilities, for no sooner had he come to the first warning sign than he was hanging over the wheel, his foot rammed hard on the accelerator. Round hairpin bends he screeched, scattering the sheep, turf and loose stones flying from under the wheels to go bouncing and whizzing down to the rocky shores far below.

The garrulous visitor was exclaiming in the loudest of voices about the scenery. She had introduced herself to the bus as, 'Viv, botany, geology, history, Creag an Ban cottage, second on the right, B&B, Nigg,' and thenceforth had appointed herself unofficial tour guide. She obviously knew the island well; every passing-place, every patch of heather, every boulder had a story to tell. Ring marks, cup marks, glacial features, duns, forts, ruins of every sort, alpine plants, rare flowers – she rhymed them all off with expertise, her voice wobbling in her throat with every bump. She gave not a blink, nary a pause as Erchy not so much guided the bus along the road as pointed it and hoped for the best.

The islanders were used to such roads: they had lived with them all of their lives. The days of horse-drawn traffic had been far more alarming than the deceptive safety of Erchy's bus, so they listened with half an ear to 'Viv, Creag an Ban, B&B, Nigg,' as they dozed, sucked mints or sent odoriferous clouds of pipe smoke into the already choked atmosphere.

But Mamma was new to it all and Mamma was scared. Viv was in raptures over the scenery. 'Oh, look, just look down there!' she cried, pointing to the sea foaming into rocky coves far below. 'The water! Have you ever seen such colour? So vivid! So ultramarine!'

Mamma was beyond making any sort of response; her heart had long ago leapt into her throat and there it stayed as they plummeted down the braes, spun round tortuous twists and curves and climbed up impossibly steep hills, with sometimes a hairpin bend at the top to complicate matters further.

It seemed a miracle that the vehicle ever made it to the top of those daunting slopes but somehow it sobbed and panted its way to victory.

At one point they met Rab McKinnon ambling along in his tractor. Erchy emitted an explosive curse and just about rammed his brakes through the floor in his efforts to slow down. The vehicle shuddered, every joint took the strain, but miraculously it lumbered to a halt in time to allow Rab to potter unhurriedly into the nearest passing-place.

Erchy drew alongside and for fully five minutes he and Rab blethered about subjects ranging from farming and fishing to the weather, and more football.

Mamma could barely contain herself; wildly she glanced round at her fellow passengers. The only muscles that moved were those necessary to the masticating of mints, the sucking in and blowing out of pipe smoke; there were no signs of agitation on any of the faces with the exception of Aggie's as she wondered if she was going to make *Morning Story* or not.

Aggie caught sight of Mamma's bewildered countenance and moved uncomfortably. She was sorry now for her outburst in the shop – after all, the woman was new to the island, her English wasn't very good and everything must be very strange to her. No one had really given her a chance to explain herself, though it was just a pity she had got off to such a bad start. She wondered why Jon's mother had come on the bus: she had said something to Erchy about Croy but why on earth would she want to go to such an isolated spot? There was nothing at Croy except a few houses and the ruins of the old Abbey, but perhaps she was like the Viv creature – interested in historic buildings – though she didn't give the impression of being anything else but a rather impatient visitor who didn't like to be kept waiting for anything.

Oh well, it takes all types, thought Aggie before opening her mouth to give her lungs full throttle, 'Are you two plannin' on exercising your jaws all day? Some o' us would like to get home, Erchy McKay, and if you don't get goin' this minute I'll report you to the authorities!'

Aggie had no earthly idea what sort of senior body was involved with the running of Erchy's bus but it sounded good and had the effect of making him withdraw his head immediately and slam the vehicle into gear.

Rab took his pipe from his mouth to give everyone a languorous wave and seemed completely unconcerned when he was enveloped in a cloud of exhaust fumes.

A few minutes later Aggie alighted from the bus and off she went towards a little white crofthouse sitting atop a grassy knoll, her fat, rolling gait carrying her to her door in an apparently effortless fashion. She was no more than thirty, fighting fit despite her girth, and ever since her marriage to Colin Mor it had been a joke among the menfolk that he had been the only man brave enough ever to have taken her on and survived.

Several more passengers were decanted at various spots along the way, together with a few parcels. The creel of fish was deposited at Annack Gow's cottage; one sack of rabbits went to an old crofter who would later skin them and sell them to his neighbours, much to the annoyance of Holy Smoke who felt that he and he alone should be the sole purveyor of fresh meat in the district.

Old Johnny Sron Mor, named so because of his enormous nose, met the bus at the turn-off to Croy and into his hands Erchy delivered the second sack of rabbits destined for the population of hungry cats that Johnny had gathered around him over the years. Money changed hands, another exchange of news took place, Johnny 'aying' and 'oching' while Erchy delivered some titbits of gossip.

Mamma boiled over. She was the only one left on the bus now and as she sat there listening to the two men gabbling away in the Gaelic, she was more than ever convinced that she had not only landed on foreign shores, she had also unwittingly involved herself in a situation that was like nothing she had ever experienced in her life before, and was never going to experience again if she could help it.

'I wait to go to Croy!' she boomed. 'I wish to get to this place before one of the clock and I command that you take me – NOW!'

Up until then there were few people in Mamma's life who had ever failed to obey her demands. But then she had never had to reckon with Hebridean islanders whose idea of speed was to think about it first before deciding if it was worth all the effort.

Most of all, she had never had to reckon with Erchy, who, renowned for taking life easy, had been known to read the papers and have a nap in his post van, and all in the busy round of his working day. Erchy enjoyed guessing the contents of folk's mail and he thrived on gossip. He was thriving now on Johnny Sron Mor's account of a fight between two neighbours, and the face he turned back into the bus to look at Mamma was pained in the extreme. It was with the greatest reluctance that he bade Johnny good day and set his bus rather grudgingly on the bumpy road to Croy.

Chapter Twelve

Kate was in her garden, half-heartedly tackling a flourishing patch of dandelions which Tam had promised to annihilate two weeks ago. Kate wasn't in the least bit interested in weeding but had chosen this spot near her gate so that she could watch for the return of Erchy's bus. Ever since she had sent Mamma on her wild-goose chase, her conscience had been bothering her, and on returning home from Merry Mary's she had partaken of a hasty lunch before going out to the garden armed with her hoe. It was a rusty apology for a garden implement – Tam had said he would make her a fine new one 'whenever he had a spare moment' but, as yet, the spare moment had not presented itself – so in between bobbing up to look over the wall, she was kept busy battering the head of the hoe back on to its pole, with the result that the dandelions were given a further reprieve while she alternately cursed Tam, the weeds, the midgies, and the advent of Mamma Jodl on to the island.

But Kate never stayed in a bad mood for long. Despite the midgies it was a fine day, calm and warm; the Sound of Rhanna was blue and serene; the slopes of Sgurr nan Ruadh wore a furring of fresh new green; little trails of mist floated in and out of the corries; Sgurr na Gill was blue in the distance and wore a fluffy cloud cap on its highest peak. The skylarks were trilling in the fields behind her house; a curlew bubbled out its haunting song from the shore; the sparrows were perched on her washing line, looking for all the world like a row of fancy little pegs as they preened themselves and twittered to one another.

A figure was coming along the road from the direction of Port Rum Point, an unfamiliar figure to Kate, and she watched its approach with interest while pretending to examine an exuberant waterfall of purple aubretia growing on her wall. The figure came nearer and soon proved to be none other than Herr Otto Klebb whom Kate, much to her chagrin, had never had any opportunity to speak to as he was apt to keep strictly within the boundaries of Tigh na Cladach and Burg Bay.

'Tis yourself, Mr Klegg,' she greeted cheerily. 'A fine day, is it not?'

To that he made no reply, instead he said rather sourly, '*Mein Frau*, the name is Klebb, K–L–E–B–B, Klebb. A cleg, I believe, is the Scottish name for a large biting insect, known elsewhere as a horsefly.'

'Och well,' Kate replied without hesitation, 'if the cap fits – wear it.'

Otto wasn't used to Kate's ready tongue and he was not amused. 'I assure you, good lady, I neither bite nor suck blood, so the cap, it will not fit.'

Looking at his large, strong teeth, Kate wasn't too sure. She wasn't taken with his surly manner either and, stepping back a pace, she surveyed him for a few moments before throwing down her hoe and stomping away up her path, tossing back, 'If you'll be excusin' me, Mr – er – Otto, I have left Tam's dinner on the stove.'

'Stop, Frau McKinnon!' he roared. Kate stopped dead in her tracks.

'It is Frau McKinnon, is it not? Frau Kate McKinnon?'

Kate retraced her hasty steps, more out of curiosity than of a desire to commune further with this big bear of a man with his dour face and bad manners.

'Ay,' she nodded warily, 'it is Kate McKinnon, no other, and if you don't mind me saying so, I am used to gentlemen treating me with respect. No' even my Tam, in all the years we've been wed, has ever shouted at me the way you shouted, and if you wereny a stranger on Rhanna, and if my very own mother hadny taught me the manners I have on me now, I wouldny have thought twice about just walkin' away and leavin' you in the lurch. You furriners are all the same when it comes to bad manners: we had

141

one in the shop earlier, a German like yourself, a battering ram she was, just charged in and . . .'

'Frau McKinnon,' Otto's voice was clipped, 'I tell this to Frau Tina, I tell it to you: I am an Austrian, not a German, I . . .'

'Same difference,' Kate returned smartly, 'at least, where rudeness is concerned.'

Otto had the grace to look ashamed. 'The apology I give; I am not myself since my head swells to twice its size in the night and greets me with much pain when I wake.'

Kate nodded knowingly. 'Oh ay, Tam has that same problem after a night on the tiles. We were all after hearing the ceilidh at the shorehouse last night. Todd said he couldny sleep for it and my Angus thought he heard McKenzie o' the Glen bawling and singing outside your house at some God-forsaken hour. Of course,' her eyes twinkled, 'I told Angus it couldny be, Fergus McKenzie only ever sings when he thinks he's alone on the hill, nothing on earth could make him raise his voice in the company o' other human beings.'

An appreciative grin banished Otto's dourness. 'The schnapps, Frau Kate, yes, the schnapps could do it . . .' he hesitated and looked towards the house, 'I wonder, if perhaps you are not too busy . . .'

Kate frowned then her face cleared. 'Ach, of course, Mr Otto, you would like a good strong cuppy to clear your head.' She knew there was more to it than that but being Kate she was wily enough not to enlarge on the subject there at the gate, 'in full view o' the world,' as her daughter Nancy would have said.

She made to go indoors with her unexpected visitor then remembered Mamma Jodl. 'Away you go ben the room,' she said to Otto. 'Up the lobby and second on your left – I'll no' be a minute.'

Going back to the gate, she made a hasty assessment of the scene. There was no sign of the bus but her son, Wullie, was coming along, a gloomy expression on his face. Like his mother he was always a mite too ready with his tongue; also, like her, he had a conscience and he was now regretting his indelicate handling of Dodie over the affair of the cockerels.

142

'Have you seen Dodie?' was his greeting as he came up to the gate. 'I told him I would shoot his bloody cockerels and I've no' seen him since. He'll likely be hidin' somewhere, greetin' his eyes out. I was comin' to look for him anyway but Mairi says I'll no' get any tea the night if I don't find the old bugger and bring him back.'

'Ach, Mairi!' snorted Kate, who often found it hard to be patient with her ineffectual daughter-in-law. 'Surely you'll no' let a simple sowel like her boss you about. As for Dodie, he'll come home when his belly starts rumbling and no' before. Meanwhile, my lad, you can make yourself useful by biding here at my gate and keeping a look-out for the bus coming back: I am busy entertaining a special guest but want a word wi' Erchy when he comes.'

'But, Mother,' Wullie protested, 'I have more to do wi' my time than stand here like a haddie watching for the damt bus.'

His words were spoken into thin air: Kate had already disappeared into the house to 'entertain her special guest'. Her son was left to fume and fret and furiously wipe away the drips from his nose, the idea never entering his head to disobey his mother, for even though he was a grown man, if she took it into her head to chase him with a broom or swipe him over the face with a dish cloth, she wouldn't think twice about it – as he had learned to his cost over the years.

And right well did Kate treat her visitor. Hospitality was only one of the many social graces she didn't stint on, in fact, despite her blunt tongue and often intimidating ways, she was renowned for her kindness and was always one of the first to provide home baking for any local function, be it in aid of church funds, the lifeboat sale of work, or any other of the numerous events that took place on the island.

She plied Herr Otto Klebb with tea till it was almost coming out his ears; she piled his plate high with tattie scones, buttered oatcakes, girdle scones and anything else she could lay her hands on. Altogether she lavished him with loving care and attention, not because she had wholly forgiven him for his

143

earlier brusqueness – she would smart over that for a good while to come and might even cast it up to him if she felt it was warranted – but simply because to her keen gaze he looked pale and drawn and in need of her administrations.

Also – and this was the big one – her instincts told her that he hadn't just sought her out to sit in her kitchen drinking tea – oh no – he had come to tell her something or ask her something or even confide something to her, though she hoped fervently that the last was not the case. With her open, honest nature she found it very difficult to hold on to a confidence, as she herself would have been the first to admit.

While he was enjoying his strupak, she filled a large mug with more scalding tea from the seemingly ever-productive teapot, threw some scones on to a plate and rushed outside to thrust them into Wullie's surprised hands. 'Here, take this,' she ordered, 'and don't let anyone see you supping tea outside my gate like a tink. Inside the wall wi' you, my lad – and remember – wave Erchy down and don't let him get away till I have had a word wi' him.'

'But, Mother . . .' Wullie began, but she had disappeared once more and with a sigh of resignation, keeping one furtive eye open, Wullie ate his strupak to the echoing blasts of Dodie's cockerels from further along the village.

When Kate returned, her visitor was sitting back, wiping his mouth with a large, snowy white hanky, 'Frau Kate, that was *wunderbar*. I congratulate you on your culinary prowess. May I now ask that you sit down and have with me the chat. It will not take long but the things I have to say are of great importance to me. You are the one I seek as I have heard of the greatness of your knowledge pertaining to the history of the people on this island.'

Kate's bosom swelled. Like her husband and his cronies before her she fell under the spell of Herr Otto Klebb; she forgot about his previous rudeness – the manners he presented to her now were impeccable, his magnetic eyes were upon her, mesmerising, captivating.

She thought to herself, this is it. She sat down opposite him and waited.

For quite a few moments there was silence. He had closed his eyes; he was so quiet and faraway she thought he had forgotten her and was therefore all the more startled when his eyes suddenly flew open and without hesitation he said, 'Frau Kate, what would you say if I told you I am a McKinnon, the same as yourself?'

Kate was stunned, so much so she couldn't say anything at first, far less comment on the question he had just delivered with the force of a sledgehammer. She sat back in her chair and took several deep breaths, then, true to form, she nodded and said cheerily, 'Ach well, Mr Otto, you wouldny be the first to come into my house and tell me that. Only last year I was able to give all sorts of information about the McKinnons to a fine wee English woman whose ancestors came from the island of Mull. She went away from Rhanna wi' stars in her eyes and though I say it myself I made her time here so happy I wouldny be surprised if she comes back to visit me one o' these days.'

'Frau Kate,' Otto spoke sternly, 'I am not here for the fairy tales! My roots are here on this island of Rhanna.' Leaning forward, he looked her straight in the eye. 'My grandmother was born and bred here; she lived in Croy on the north eastern shores. Her house, it was thatched; her parents made their living on land and on sea. When she was seventeen she became pregnant by a young man from the same village. Her parents, they were scandalised – they sent her away to live with relatives in Canada. There my mother was born. My grandmother never came back to her native lands, she never married: she couldn't forget her "dear young McKinnon" as she called him. Fortunately she was an adventurer, she loved to travel, and she took her daughter to many places in the world. My mother grew up, she too enjoyed to travel: she met my father in Germany. He took her back to his native Austria and there they married . . .'

He had forgotten Kate; he was lost in the story as it unfolded from his memory. His voice was soft, husky, as he went on, 'I was born in Vienna. My grandmother, she lived with us. All

145

through the years of my boytime she tells me about this island and of the young years she spent here. She never forgot, she described it all so clearly: the ocean, the hills, the purple of heather in autumn, the miles and miles of golden beaches. She spoke of the summer shielings when she and the other young people of the island went up into the hills to mind the cattle. She sings to me the songs they sang, the stories they tell to one another when the gloaming steals over the hills and the sea is growing dark; she tells me how boys and girls sleep together, the bedclothes swaddled in such a way that they could not make contact with one another – they were trusted by their elders to behave in the proper way and few of them broke that trust. My grandmother was one of the few: when I am older she tells me of her love for a McKinnon boy. In here . . .' he placed a hand over his heart, 'she aches for this boy and he for her, but they are too young, they know their parents will not consent to their marriage – and so . . .' he spread his hands, 'you know the rest. My mother is begun, the young girl who was my grandmother is sent far away over the sea but she never forgets her beginnings. When she is old and her eyes are growing blind I see the tears in them as she remembers, and there am I, the young man now, my own heart yearning for an island I have never seen but vow to visit one day. She also said I got my gift for music from my grandfather, the young Magnus McKinnon. He writes songs for her, he plays an old fiddle, he sits by the sea and he serenades the girl he wishes to marry, and then one day she goes away and he and she never see one another again – and then she dies and leaves with me a legacy of music and memories that are as much an ache in my heart as they were in hers when she was alive and telling to me her wonderful tales.'

He had brought a breath of pure romance into the homely cluttered room. Kate, her own eyes blinded by tears, buried her face into her apron and gave herself up to a 'good greet'.

'Ach, Mr Otto, that was beautiful just,' was her shaky verdict when she had recovered sufficiently to trust herself to speak. 'Never in all my days have I heard the likes . . .' She raised a tear-stained face. 'It will be Magnus of Croy that the lassie left behind. Och, it is sad, sad, to think o' the heartache he and she suffered over the years, for he never wed either. Many's the time I've listened to him talk o' his bonny Sheena; he said he never could love anyone the way he loved her. Even yet I've seen his eyes grow misty and faraway when he talks o' the old days. I'm no' a body that is easily taken in by daft talk, Mr Otto, but when Magnus gets going wi' his tales o' the summer shielings and how himself and Sheena used to walk hand in hand over the heather braes, talking and singing, I just want to listen to him all day, for he is one o' the finest seanachaidhs on the island. After Sheena went away he buried himself in his stories and music, and if you go over to Croy you'll hear his music long before you come to his cottage . . .'

She paused to stare at Otto in wonder as the full import of his revelations began to sink in. 'He is your maternal grandfather, your very own flesh and blood – tis no wonder you love music for he is full o' it . . .' She shook her head and looked at him, her eyes sparkling suddenly. 'I wouldny be surprised if I myself sprung from that particular McKinnon line for is not my very own granddaughter Rachel brimful o' musical gifts . . .'

She was completely carried away, so much so she forgot that she was a Uist McKinnon and that it was more likely Tam, Rhanna born and bred, who might have passed on any talents. But a notion like that would never have occurred to Kate, for when it came to music she maintained that Tam had bricks in his head, so untuned was he to melody and song.

'Ah, Rachel,' Otto said with a smile, 'when I heard she was a McKinnon, I think of my grandmother telling me of all my Rhanna kinsfolk and it pleases me to know that this beautiful young woman is one of those I have waited so long to meet.'

Kate frowned. 'You seem always to think o' your grandmother in connection wi' Rhanna. What about your mother? Did she never hanker to know more about her Scottish connections?'

Otto sighed. 'There a generation was skipped. My mother was a society beauty. She flitted from one bright light to the next; it was beyond her to sit still for any length of time: my grandmother's breath would have been wasted on her. No, I was the beneficiary of those memories, I was hungry all the time to know more, on every word I hung. My mother had not the time for me, she was a creature of gaiety and laughter; it was my father and my grandmother between them who encouraged my passion for music. I was still a boy when my mother died; my lovely, special grandmother led me into manhood, she guided and counselled me – without her I would be nothing. I still hear her voice, as soft as the Scottish mists I see here on the hills. She was the last of my family to die; my wife lives but she is no more in my heart. We part amicably, we were never in love but tolerated one another for as long as we could. There were no children – and so— '

A wistful smile touched his face. 'I retrace my grandmother's journey, back over the sea. I wish first to know her beloved soil and so I follow her footsteps, I tread the earth she has trod. I rise up very early one morning when no one is about and I make the long tramp to Croy, there I sit on the heather and I gaze out to sea, feeling in my heart that I am looking at it through my grandmother's eyes. Tina has already told me of one Magnus McKinnon of Croy and has described to me where he lives, I find his house, I look and I wonder, "have I at last come to my grandfather's house?" It is early, there is no music, there is no life, and so next I seek the house of my great-grandparents, but there is only a ruin. The dry, grey ribs of the roof stick into the sky, the thatch hangs in tatters into rooms that once rang with the joy and the laughter of a young girl who used to live there. But it is not dead: for me, she is everywhere. Inside the ruin I find the fireplace where the family once sat; in the rubble there are some rusty pots and pans; on a small broken table there is an old bible, the pages are damp and stuck together but on the flyleaf there is an inscription, very faded but still discernible. It is in the language of the Gael . . . I have it here for you to decipher . . .'

Reaching into an inside pocket, he withdrew the ancient book. It was falling apart but the gold tooling was still there on the threadbare spine. Kate took it, her hands trembling in case she should further damage the treasure. The brown leather casing was cracked and barely held together by the binding and she held her breath as she turned it over and looked at the inscription on the parchment-like flyleaf.

'My specs, Mr Otto,' she whispered, almost as if the very breath from her voice might turn the fragile pages into dust. 'On the wee table by the fire.'

He handed them to her, she perched them on the end of her nose and stared at the spidery writing. 'It is very old Gaelic, Mr Otto, but I can still make it out. It says, "to Sheena, on her twelfth birthday, blessings be with you all the days of your life, from your mother and father, 14th June 1882." '

'Sheena,' Otto spoke the name with reverence, 'it was her bible. I'll cherish it always: she held it, she must have read it by the flickering light of a crusie. She told me about crusies, the fuel that was used was fish oil, they were crude and primitive but they served their purpose.'

'Ay, indeed they did, Mr Otto. Some o' the old folk still use them to this day only they don't burn fish oil anymore. Old Magnus has several hanging from his fireplace – och, but you'll have to go and visit him! I can just see his face, the pair o' you will have that much to talk about, so many years to catch up on. It will be a bonny day for him when his very own grandson walks through his door, and himself thinking all these years that there was no kin left in the world to call his own.'

She jumped to her feet. 'This calls for a dram! I canny remember when last I felt so wobbly and queer inside. Fancy! Old Magnus wi' a real flesh-and-blood grandson. He never even knew that he was a father, for Sheena's parents never spoke o' it. No' till their dying day did they mention their lassie's name again, but it was her who was in their hearts and on their lips when they drew breath for the very last time.'

She poured two generous drams, gulping hers down without as much as a grimace. When Otto hesitated over his she tilted the glass to his lips, laughingly telling him he needed a hair of the dog and to get it down like a man.

But several things were puzzling her, and the questions came tumbling out. Why, for instance had he left it so long to unveil his secret? And why did he choose her to tell it to when the island teemed with all sorts of McKinnons.

'I canny understand why you didny tell Rachel first. You and she have been seeing a lot o' one another.'

'The answer to that is simple, *mein Frau*: you are the senior member of her family, it was your place to be told first. Naturally I wanted to tell you and Herr Tam together but he wasn't here and I couldn't waste any more time – also . . .' he cleared his throat and went on tactfully, 'you have lived more years than our little Rachel, the memories in your head go back a long time. You would hear things from your parents about the folk they knew in the old days.'

'Oh, ay, right enough,' she nodded, 'they often spoke o' Neil and Ishbel and the heartache they brought on themselves by sending their own lassie away but never telling anyone why she had gone, just that they thought she would have a better life wi' relatives o' theirs abroad. They never mentioned Canada; Magnus kept asking but they would never say and in the end he just buried himself in his croft and his music.'

She gave Otto a mischievous look. 'They were dark horses – like yourself, hoarding all their wee secrets, for you have still to tell me why you didny say right away that you were a McKinnon. Were you sizing us up, Mr Otto, checking first to make sure we were a worthy clan to belong to?'

He gave a wry smile. 'You have a devious mind, Frau Kate, but this time you do not guess the truth. I waited because I wanted to make sure I would be accepted. My grandmother tells me many times about the islanders' mistrust of strangers who bulldoze their way in when they have only newly set foot on the land. So, I wait, I get to know Herr Tam, I meet others and have with them the ceilidhs and the drams. I make my music with Rachel, people become aware of me, they wish to get to know me better, gradually I become accepted and then I know it is time to show to everyone my true colours.'

Kate grinned. 'Ay, and bonny colours they are too.' She extended one large, capable hand. 'Welcome to Rhanna, Mr Otto, and a bloody great genuine welcome to a bloody great family . . .' Refilling their glasses, she raised hers to the ceiling and shouted, 'To the McKinnons! *Slàinte Mhath!*'

Following her example with exuberance, he repeated the toast, adding, 'And here's to the clan gathering of all the McKinnons, here on Rhanna! It will be the finest, the biggest, in all of the Hebrides!'

'A clan gathering?' Kate's eyebrows shot up, her face sparkled with interest.

'A clan gathering, Frau Kate, but please leave the arranging to me – though of course I will need your help in spreading the news of it around the island.'

Kate, who always made full use of 'Highland Telegraph', looked suitably modest. 'Ach, you can rely on me for that, Mr Otto, just you say the word and I'll . . .'

At that moment Wullie came rushing in to convey to his mother that Erchy's bus had just come into view. She stayed long enough to tell Otto to make himself at home and to be sure and put the cork back in the whisky bottle before he left, then she made haste to follow Wullie outside in time to flag Erchy down as he approached her gate.

'What have you done wi' the big German wifie?' she demanded as soon as he had swung the door open on its one rusty hinge.

Erchy scratched his head. 'Done wi' her? None o' the things I would have liked to do wi' her, that's for sure. She nearly brained me wi' her handbag when I suggested she wouldny find much to suit her in Croy, so I just left the besom to it. The last time I saw her she was sprachlin' along the track towards Croy Beag.'

'You'll have to go back.' Kate was clambering on to the bus as she spoke. 'The daft cailleach thinks there's a city out there on the moors and if we don't find her she might drown herself in a peat bog.'

'A city?' The look Erchy gave Kate suggested she was altogether mad. 'What way would she be thinkin' there's a city at Croy?'

'Because I told her.' Kate's reply was succinct. 'Just get goin'

151

and ask no questions for once in your life. Wullie, you come wi' me, you might be needed in case o' an emergency.'

'There will be an emergency if I don't find Dodie,' Wullie grumbled, 'and wi' the luck I'm havin' these days the emergency could easily be me.'

Nevertheless he got in beside his mother, consoling himself that anything was better than tramping for miles in search of Dodie when he might just come upon him from the comparative comfort of Erchy's bus.

But Erchy wasn't for giving in to Kate so easily. 'I'm no' going back to Croy,' he stated stubbornly. 'The Portvoynachan lot are waitin' for me at the harbour and I'm no' changin' my route just for the sake o' thon bossy big wifie. Everybody knows I'm a stickler for timetables and I'll no' have my reputation ruined for anybody.'

'Reputation!' Kate snorted. 'The only reputation you have is for scaring the shat out your passengers, and if you're no' doin' that you're either snoozin' or readin' in your post van! You can pick up the Portvoynachan folk later; just tell them there's an emergency in Glen Fallan for that's the way we'll be going. It's the quickest route back to Croy and the road goes right to the clachan once you get past Croft na Beinn.'

Erchy gave in. When Kate made up her mind about something she usually got her way – and he didn't dare say that this mad notion of hers would cost her. Unbeknown to her he had recently borrowed ten pounds from Tam and had no intention of paying it back for some time to come. So if he did this favour for Kate, and she somehow found out about the loan, she couldn't very well hold it up to him in the face of his undoubted magnanimity.

Feeling very martyred and extremely hard done by, he tied up his door, vented his feelings by revving up with unnecessary vigour thus causing an extra large emission of diesel fumes and trundled along to the harbour to inform his would-be passengers that he had been 'commissioned' to do an extra run to Croy, which would only take ten minutes at the most and that he would be back 'in two flicks o' a lamb's tail.'

'The way he drives I wouldny be surprised at that!' Malky of Rumhor commented, venting his disgust by spitting energetically on to the cobbles and rubbing it in with the toe of one stoutly booted foot.

Chapter Thirteen

In between outcrops of rock and great clumps of flowering gorse, Mamma glimpsed Erchy's bus dipping and diving, climbing and clawing its hazardous way back over the cliff road to Glen Riach and Burnbreddie.

The journey from Nigg to Croy Beag had been a hair-raising one for Mamma, who had imagined that there was not another road on earth that could possibly be worse than the one they had traversed from Portcull to Nigg. But there she had been wrong. The way through Glen Riach and the lands of Burnbreddie had been gentle and pleasurable. In those rolling silvan pastures Mamma had felt a deep appreciation for nature's bounteous glories, which, for her, was unusual, as the countryside had hitherto never stirred a response in her heart beyond wishing that she could get out of it as speedily as possible since 'all that space' made her feel insecure. But she had had to admit to herself that there was something about the serenity of the purple-blue hills of Glen Riach that caught her imagination.

The great undulating green and amber mattress that was the Muir of Rhanna also brought a sense of peace to her soul. Here the shaggy blonde Highland cows browsed peaceably amongst the heathery knolls, and in the distance, glimpsed between gaps in the rocky coastline, was the sea, unbelievably blue and beautiful, stretching on and forever into hazy infinity.

Despite the bumps and rattles of Erchy's bus she had been lulled into a sense of deep tranquillity that made the shock of the last part of the journey all the more terrifying. Quite suddenly it seemed, they left the moors behind as the vehicle plunged down a near-perpendicular pass between the hills and

154

the sea. Just as suddenly they came to a sharply rising slope up which they crawled at a snail's pace, enveloped by diesel fumes and the stench of red-hot metal.

Up, down! Up, down! The lie of the land became predictable but never monotonous. One minute Mamma's heart was in her throat, the next it had plummeted to her stomach. Looming ahead was a great lump of jagged rock and Mamma's feet were rammed down hard on an imaginary brake – not for one minute did she think anything could get through the impossibly narrow gap, far less a bus. But without hesitation Erchy plunged through the crack, known locally as The Wedge for obvious reasons. After that the road became ever narrower till it was little more than a track winding above the cliffs. Down below, the sea boomed into subterranean caverns, great sprays of white foam burst over reefs and rocks and washed the black, slippery feet of basalt crags sticking up out of the waves.

At this point the roar of the ocean filled Mamma's ears. It echoed and reverberated in every cranny of the bus. Erchy, who had recovered his good humour soon after leaving Johnny Sron Mor at Nigg and who had, incredibly it seemed to his one and only passenger, cheerfully whistled the rest of the treacherous miles away, informed Mamma that the road at this point was built on top of a vast underground sea-cave which was reckoned to have eroded the rock for at least two miles inland at a conservative estimate, for nobody had ever dared explore further.

'There was no air, you see,' he went on chattily, dodging a lamb that had leapt into his path in search of its sure-footed mother, who was browsing amongst the rocks above the cliffs. 'It was a long time ago and they were using these paraffin torches. Two miles in and the lads were pantin' and gaspin' for air, the torches went out, the tide was comin' in, and they would never have made it back if they hadny left a piper at the entrance. To the skirl and blast o' the bagpipes they at last came tumbling out and no one has gone in since, though some say the caves at Dunuaigh, where the monks hid from the Vikings, join up wi' this one, which in recent years has come to be known as

Big Ben because o' the boom it makes at high tide. If you look over there to your right you'll see one o' the blow holes where the water comes spoutin' out from the force o' the waves.'

Sure enough, some distance away, a great spray of water was jetting into the air. It was an exciting, magnificent place to be, and if Mamma had witnessed it in different circumstances, she might have been more appreciative. As it was she was too busy 'gaspin' and pantin'' for air herself to pay much heed to Erchy and his tales. She was tired of the whole episode and was wishing with all her shaky heart that she hadn't made this perilous journey, shops or no shops, city or no city.

As they left Big Ben behind, the way became gentler, and Mamma was just getting her breath back when ahead loomed another gigantic rock with only a tiny arched aperture leading to the other side.

'Gregor's Gap,' Erchy threw over his shoulder, enjoying enormously his impromptu role as tour guide. 'Poor old Gregor lost his life here one dark winter's night. He had been having a wee bit o' a ceilidh wi' one o' his neighbours and might have had one too many. Whatever the way o' it, he missed the road and drove his tractor right into the rock and both himself and the machine went rolling down to the sea far below. It was sad, right enough, because he was normally a canny sort o' man and had been riding this road ever since the days o' horses and carts but, of course, an engine is no match for a good horse that would take a body home blindfolded over any sort o' road.'

Mamma made no reply; she cared nothing for the unknown Gregor who, in her opinion, had diced with death and had only gotten what he deserved. She was sick and tired of Erchy and his gory tales and when he at last brought his bus to a halt outside a five-barred gate, she could hardly wait to be rid of him and his dreadful contraption.

'Tell me, where is this place of Croy?' she demanded over the roar of the red-hot engine.

Erchy scratched his head and treated her to a puzzled grimace. 'Over there.' He pointed vaguely. 'You can just see the tops o' the houses from here. You have to go through that gate –

and don't forget to shut it or Johnson o' Croynachan will have something to say if his cattle get out – and follow the track which takes you right to the clachan.'

Mamma made to squeeze past him but he stayed her by blocking her path. 'If you don't mind me sayin' so, you'll no' find much o' anything over yonder – unless, of course, you have relatives who'll let you bide wi' them till . . .'

'Let me through at once.' Mamma brandished her handbag, swinging it in such a way that it caught Erchy on the side of the head, so that the only things he saw for quite a few moments were stars.

When he recovered his equilibrium Mamma was already off the bus and making her determined way through the gate.

'How will you get back?' he yelled. 'The folk hereabouts only have tractors and pony carts and I'll no' be back this way for another three days!'

To his amazement he imagined that she shouted something about getting a taxi, but he was in no mood to pursue the matter further. Let the old bitch discover for herself the problems of getting about in this part of the island. It was bad enough for people who were born and bred here but a townie like herself simply had no idea of the difficulties involved, and bloody well serve her right if she got her arse soaked in a peat bog in the course of her travels!

With the feeling that he had done his duty as a good honest citizen of the island he revved up and drove away, his ruffled feathers gradually settling at the thought of the dram he would most certainly receive if he called in at old Meggie's on the way back to Portcull.

Mamma was fuming as she stomped along the track to the village. She could hardly believe that any road, in any part of the world, could stop at a five-barred gate leading on to the moors. But then, she had never experienced any of the roads in Scotland, never mind those on a Hebridean island. The roads on Rhanna had certainly been up-graded – if one could call the re-surfacing of the existing narrow tracks an improvement.

Funds had not stretched to the more remote hamlets, with the result that Croy, which was divided into Croy Beag (little Croy) and Croy Mor (big Croy), had been left to its own devices, though the road did go as far as Croy Mor from the Glen Fallan side.

Unfortunately for Mamma, she was on the Croy Beag side and her dismay on reaching the small handful of houses perched on a cliff overlooking the ocean was considerable.

Here there was a sense of timelessness. Some of the houses still had thatched roofs; peat smoke hung lazily above the chimney pots; chickens poked and pried around the houses and spilled over into the heather; great shaggy Highland cows browsed and ambled about, so that wherever you looked you saw huge horns sticking out of gorse bushes or the feathery rear ends of hens lancing up out of the wild flowers growing in the ditches.

Acres of buttercups and daisies smothered the green of the machair, blazing yellow and white all the way to the edge of the cliffs where they merged with the azure of the sky and the dark, deep blue of the sea.

It was a small world of perfection, yet it was vast. The ocean rolled off into horizons unlimited, misty islands floated on the edge of the world, gulls, puffins, kittiwakes, and terns tumbled and dived in the great bowl of the sky and out on the distant waves white-winged yachts drifted on the dream-like reaches.

Mamma, however, was in no mood to appreciate the scenery. The suspicions that had beset her on reaching the five-barred gate were now a near-certain reality. There was no city of Croy, nothing even resembling a town existed on this island, she was stuck here in the middle of nowhere with no shops, no transport, very little in the way of creature comforts, and it was hot, hotter than she had imagined a Scottish island could be. She had long ago peeled off her fur-trimmed coat and hat but even so she sweated – and her stomach was starting to rumble. She had a delicate constitution, she wasn't yet fully recovered from the virus that had struck her down in Germany, she needed to take food regularly or she could get dizzy, or faint, or do any of the dozen and one things she usually did to get attention – especially to get Jon's attention. But Jon wasn't here, nobody was here who could possibly understand how delicate she was, how much she needed unrestricted care and comfort – how much she needed to make herself understood in a land that was so far removed from her beloved Hamburg.

A bent old bodach was coming along the track. In one hand he carried a milk pail and a three-legged stool, in the other was a Harry Lauder walking stick, as full of curves and twists as the roads that the bodach had trod all his life. He leaned on it heavily, his gnarled old fingers clutching it so tightly they looked as if they might have been moulded into the wood. He had a thatch of white hair, nut-brown skin, a wonderfully wise face, blue, blue eyes and, when he opened his mouth to smile politely at Mamma, one tooth set in the middle of his otherwise toothless mouth.

This was ninety-seven-year-old Magnus of Croy – respected, well-loved, a highly regarded member of the island community, storyteller, bard, musician, teacher, friend, a comfort to children and adults alike, a sympathetic ear to those in need of guidance, a font of wisdom to anyone who wanted advice on any subject, because his grasp on world affairs and general knowledge was legendary. All of his life he had studied music and books and newspapers, none of which had ever had the chance to gather dust in his house as even now, in his remarkable old age, he sought learning and retained what he had learned as easily as any man half his age.

Mamma did not return his smile; she had not yet learned her lesson. If she had played her cards right she would undoubtedly have been invited in to the old man's homely, comfortable cottage, to rest and partake of a strupak of tea and scones; as it was she saw him as just another eccentric 'foreigner' and showed scant gratitude when, after a very mannerly salutation, he enquired if he could help her at all.

'Help! There is no help on this island!' she snarled impatiently. 'I come to look for the city of Croy, I find there is none, my feet, they are on fire! My head, it is spinning! I need to find someone of intelligence who can understand what I am saying.

On this island there are only those who make the comedies and frighten me to my grave! I must have a car to take me to the house of An Cala but that is an order too tall for a backward place like this!'

Magnus drew himself up, he had never been able to suffer fools gladly and this large woman, with her handsome, scowling face, gave every indication of being one of the most ignorant persons he had ever yet encountered in all the years of his long life. Nevertheless he was Scottish, hospitality was inherent in him. Only a slight coldness in his keen blue eyes indicated his contempt for her attitude, and he was big enough and tolerant enough to be able to say kindly, 'If you would care to rest in my house for a wee whilie I will get one o' my neighbours to take you home. He doesny have a motor car but he has a fine fast tractor which would get you over to Glen Fallan in no time . . .'

'A tractor! Pah!' Mamma, her face red, interrupted him most rudely and in her excitement she began to speak rapidly in German. Magnus looked at her, he was buggered if he was going to help her now, and to even things up he lapsed into Gaelic and, flapping his fingers, he indicated a track which snaked its way over the moors towards the Glen Fallan hills.

Mamma stared horrified. She was wishing that she hadn't been so hasty in her condemnation of the neighbour's tractor, but it was too late to change her mind: Magnus had gathered up his stool and his milk pail and was off to milk his cow, never deigning to give her so much as a backward glance.

With a great self-pitying sigh, Mamma heaved herself up from the boulder on which she had been sitting and began trudging along the mossy path that Magnus had indicated. Peaty brown burns burbled at her feet, bumblebees and heath moths flitted and droned in amongst the tiny wild flowers that starred the carpets of lichens and mosses growing over the stones; the sweet scents of warm grasses and heather hung agreeably in the sun-filled hollows.

Mamma took a deep breath – these smells, they were good, she decided, and, just for a moment she found herself comparing them with the fumes of traffic she had become so used to in cities.

160

The water of the little streams also had a clean, fresh smell; the sound of it purling over the stones had a special kind of music to it, as if it had gathered on its way the secrets of hidden places and was whispering them to the low, caressing breezes as they passed each other by.

Mamma gave herself a mental shake. Such nonsense! She must be losing her senses. This great, lonely, wild place was her enemy. Her legs were itchy and sore where horseflies and midgies had bitten them. She hadn't known such pests as midgies existed till she had come to this God-forsaken island and the sooner she could leave all of such horrors behind the better it would be for her.

Still, the water looked tempting and her feet were hot and aching. She could do worse than stop for a minute to cool her burning flesh. A few minutes later she was sitting on a rock, her outer layers laid carefully over the bare branches of a dead bush, her shoes and stockings beside her, her feet planted firmly in a little moorland burn. The water slid over her ankles, ice cold, deliciously soothing. The sun had broken through a layer of cloud and beat down warmly on her back. It was a completely new experience for Frau Helga Jodl: she who had always been surrounded by people was now sitting alone in a great expanse of amber moors, divested of garments she had only ever before removed in the privacy of her own home; the curlews were bubbling out their golden song in the heather; the skylarks were spilling out their trembling notes above; and a corncrake sent out its sharp, imperative call from some hidden secret place.

But Mamma was not going to give in so easily to such pure and simple pleasures: every fierce, city-fied fibre in her resisted the delights of this vast, perfumed wilderness. She wanted only to wallow in self-pity. She told herself that she was abandoned and alone in an empty, lifeless desert – birds were just birds, they didn't count, flowers she could buy anywhere in any shop in any city or town, water was only natural when it came out of a tap – and only gypsies and the simple-minded took off their shoes and stockings to dip their feet in a wandering stream.

161

The last thought made her hastily withdraw her own feet from the water, dry them as best she could in the grass and quickly don her stockings and shoes. A movement behind made her turn round to find herself looking up the wet and gleaming nostrils of a cream-coloured Highland cow whose enormous curved horns were outlined against the sky. Beside the cow stood a sturdy calf, front legs spread, head lowered as he stared with unblinking curiosity at the human object that was so obviously fascinating his mother.

For the umpteenth time that day Mamma's heart leapt into her throat. She shrieked and, scrambling upright, she stopped only long enough to gather up her precious hat and coat before backing off from both cow and calf and walking rapidly away. But as fast as she walked so too did the mischievous cow and her frisky offspring, who, every so often, took it into his head to butt playfully at the air and kick up his heels.

'I say to you, go!' Mamma commanded at one point, standing her ground and frantically waving her arms about. The cow also stood her ground, and, lowering her head, she emitted a series of grumbling bellows while her calf watched, his wet nose dripping health, his fur-fringed lips also dripping, in this case the slobbering residue of his mother's milk quickly snatched from her teat while she was communing with Mamma in her own particular language.

For the second time that day, Mamma wielded her handbag, this time in the direction of the cow, who stepped back a pace but who was not for relinquishing this unexpected game which had intruded into an otherwise perfectly ordinary day.

Desperately Mamma's gaze panned the landscape. Nothing! Just miles and miles of heather moor and then more of the same – but wait! There was something else! Smoke, drifting, billowing, perhaps a chimney – and where there were chimneys there had to be a house, and any house with chimneys that smoked had to contain human life of some sort. In those fraught moments she didn't care what sort of humans might live there. People were people when all was said and done and what did it matter if they spoke in that queer singing language that had beset her ears since leaving Portcull. She would find comfort, shelter, perhaps even food. She would be pleasant, she would be grateful, she would get there as quickly as she could, even though her feet were once more giving her hell.

She set off, the cow and her calf following along at her back, like two large dogs who expected a bone at the end of their travels. They mooed, they drooled, they skipped, and gambolled and played. They urinated in great steaming waterfalls, and they released alarmingly huge portions of manure, whose porridge-like consistency created semi-liquid platters that were immediately pounced on by armies of dung-flies that seemed to appear from nowhere.

Mamma was heartily sick of her unwanted followers, yet, strangely, by the time she topped a rise and saw distinct signs of habitation in the distance, she was no longer afraid of the animals, seeing them instead as nothing more than a nuisance who had taken a fancy to her and who had, for the last half mile . . . she had to admit it . . . made her smile against her will with their sly good humour, their natural curiosity, and their unstinting passion for following faithfully in her footsteps.

When finally she arrived at the tink encampment it was hard to know who was the most surprised. She had imagined she was making for some sort of village. From a distance the tink tents had looked like little houses and, as she drew nearer, her mouth had fairly watered at the savoury smells drifting towards her on the breezes. Her face as she stood on the edge of the camp was a picture: shock, horror, dismay all registered on her countenance at one and the same time. She couldn't decide whether to stay and make the most of the situation, or to turn tail and run, cows or no cows. But thirst, fatigue and hunger were powerful persuaders; here there was sustenance, here there was rest – and if she was lucky she might just satisfy all of her needs without being robbed or having her throat cut or a combination of the two. For to her uneducated city eyes the travellers looked a rough and ready bunch with not one jot of civilized veneer on their suspicious country faces to

163

suggest that they were possessed of any social graces in their make-up.

So she stood and stared and openly displayed her hostility, her disgust – and – let it be said – her contempt. She looked just what she was, a big, domineering, city-bred, well-dressed woman who gave the impression of having lived in a land of plenty all of her days and who was used to getting her own way how and when she wanted it. If she felt apprehension or fear she kept it well buried, for in reality Mamma was an exceedingly tough lady who had seldom suffered anything worse than occasional and convenient bouts of severe hypochondria.

It wasn't every day that the tink camp was visited by a lady of Mamma's physical grandeur and all too obvious opulence. The rings on her fingers gleamed, the necklace at her throat glinted fire, she most certainly had not purchased her dress at a jumble sale and her handmade shoes, though dusty and rimmed with cow dung, were made of the finest leather decorated with fancy buttons and silver buckles.

It was not surprising, therefore, that the travellers gaped and stared and eyed one another in questioning doubt, but they appeared harmless enough and big, bold Mamma felt it safe to delve further into the interior, where she got the biggest surprise of all. At the heart of the camp was the fire and seated beside it was Stink the Tink fixing his rabbit snares – and beside him was Dodie, calm and quiet now that he had a large mug of broth clutched in his hands, made by Stink's wife Alana in a great black pot over the embers at the edge of the fire.

Dodie, who had never received anything other than kindness from the tinks, had reached the camp long before the bus had made it to Croy Beag. All of his life he had travelled the highways and byways, and he was familiar with every shortcut on Rhanna. Those on the Muir of Rhanna he knew like the back of his hand, and in his fear of Wullie, his terror of Mamma, he had simply headed for a place where he knew he would receive a welcome and something to fill his stomach.

In his wildest dreams he had never thought to encounter the 'wild furrin wifie' in this least likely of places, and when she

164

came striding over to the fire to stare at him with as much surprise on her face as was registered on his, he rose clumsily to his feet, spilling his soup all over himself in his fright. His lamb, curled up cosily beside the fire, didn't give the intruder a second glance but Dodie was all too conscious of what it had already done to Mamma and he stared at her in abject dread, adrenaline pumping as he prepared himself for take-off.

But Stink was his usual unruffled self. Having listened with half an ear to Dodie's babbled account of his morning encounters, he guessed that the unexpected visitor was the 'wild furrin wifie', but with her red sweating face and her look of exhaustion, she didn't seem all that intimidating to him.

'Will you be sitting yourselves down,' he directed, looking up from his snares to include Mamma in the invitation. Patting the smoke-blackened upholstery of a broken-down car seat, he went on, 'Here ye are, missus, this is for you,' and, raising his voice he roared, 'Alana, be putting out some more soup for the lady! My hands are dirty and not fit to be serving food.'

Mamma accepted the invitation gratefully. If she had been asked to park herself on a chamber pot she might have done so, so much did her tired legs quake and her empty stomach rumble. Pausing only long enough to flick her hanky half-heartedly over the sooty car seat, she sank down into it with the look of one who was sampling the most luxurious armchair in the land.

A red-haired, merry-faced woman emerged from one of the tents to ladle steaming-hot soup into two mugs, one of which she passed to Dodie, the other to Mamma, with hands that looked filthier than those of her husband. She had just spent a morning feeding her children, feeding her husband, tending the fire, airing the bedding, gathering fuel, which included dead heather shoots and ancient cow's dung, and had just gone into her tent to wash when Stink's orders had reached her ears. But Mamma didn't even notice her hands: she was too intent on getting food into her mouth to care very much about anything else.

Alana, whose arm was round Dodie's bent back, soothing away his fears as if he was one of her children, nodded sympathetically and observed, 'Tis hungry you are indeed, missus. We don't see many fine ladies like yourself in this part o' the island – but then, it's a nice day for a walk over the moors – as long as you know where you are going.'

Fortified and rested, Mamma was recovering some of her mettle. 'The walk I did not take willingly – I try to find the city, the city of Croy. I come on the bus, I suffer much pain, and when I arrive I look and look for this city but it is not there . . .'

'The city o' Croy?' Stink blinked and glanced meaningfully at his wife. He looked worried. Perhaps Dodie was right after all: they could be dealing with a mad woman here. He wondered which was the best course of action, to humour her or to see her out of the vicinity as quickly as possible . . .

The matter was taken out of his hands, however, when several of the womenfolk, curiosity getting the better of their reserve, came over to arrange themselves round the fire, and some of the men did likewise, Aaron parking himself on a boulder right next to Mamma's car seat.

When Little Lady Leprechaun came leaping into the scene, Mamma simply gaped. Despite having made a good recovery from her experiences she was still at the stage where her stunned mind was unable to take any more surprises and she could be forgiven at this point for wondering if a sense of normality would ever return to her life again.

Lady Leprechaun was used to people staring at her and she didn't bat one eye at the look of wonder on the visitor's face, instead she poured tea and handed it to Mamma along with a huge doorstep of bread spread with margarine and treacle. The offerings were gratefully received. If Jon had been present, he too would have stared at the sight of his big, fastidious Mamma tucking into bread and treacle and downing great volumes of black tea from a smoke-begrimed tin mug.

The womenfolk plied her with questions. In her halting English she told of her encounter with Kate in 'Happy Mary's', her subsequent 'ride into hell' in a 'mad bus with an equally mad driver', her search for the city of Croy, and her meeting with a senile old man with a 'curly walking stick' who had pointed the way into the wilderness where, footsore and weary, she had been chased by two mad cows for 'so many miles I lose count.'

As one, the tinks turned to gaze at the 'two mad cows' who were peacefully grazing their way back to more familiar territory.

'It would be a joke,' Aaron decided. 'Kate McKinnon is full o' mischief and never means half of what she says. The old man would be Magnus o' Croy, one o' the wisest folk o' these parts . . .'

'Bejabers and bejasus!' Paddy burst out rudely. 'The whole business is nothing but a bloody farce and we're just wastin' our time listening to the like o' such nonsense. Magnus would have helped ye if ye'd let him, missus, and just who do ye think ye are, comin' in about our camp and belittling a man whose boots ye should have kissed!'

Mamma was not intimidated, glowering long and hard at the rough-looking Irishman she thrust out her bosom and intoned, 'I am Frau Helga Jodl, *mutter* of Jon Jodl and mother-in-law of Rachel, the world famous violinist.'

Paddy's eyes narrowed, a gleam of interest shone in their black depths. Her words had reminded him afresh of Rachel and her precious violin and his voice was smooth when he said, 'Indeed, is that right, now? Tis no wonder that the stamp o' a fine lady is upon you and if you'll allow me the honour o' seeing you home I'll just go and hitch up old Shamrock and give the trap a bit o' a clean. We can't have a lady like yourself mucking up her skirts, can we now?'

Mamma watched Paddy's retreating back and felt slightly uneasy but not as uneasy as Aaron, who knew that Paddy's conciliatory gesture was only a means of using Jon's mother for his own shady ends.

Mamma, safely settled in the trap, was quite upset when she saw Paddy heading her way with Dodie in tow. It had been bad enough sitting next to the aptly named Stink at the fire but at least he was well enough kippered in smoke for his smells not to make themselves too apparent. Dodie was a different matter entirely: one didn't have to be rubbing shoulders with him to notice his lack of personal hygiene and when it became obvious that he was also to get a lift home in the trap she squeezed herself as far as possible against the side of the seat and surreptitiously retrieved her hanky in order to prepare herself for what was to come.

But Dodie's objections to having her as a travelling companion were even stronger than hers. When he realized what was happening he simply could not stop a tide of terror rising within him. 'Ach no,' he babbled to Paddy, 'I dinna want to go in the trap. I'll just walk home wi' Curly, he's no' used to horses and will maybe shat himself wi' fright if he's made to go against his will . . .'

'Just you be gettin' in, Dodie.' Paddy gave the old man a none too gentle push. 'It's no' Curly you're thinkin' of, it's yourself, because I know fine you're feart o' the wifie.' Raising his voice for Mamma's benefit he went on, 'She's a lady and ladies don't bite – except . . .' He made a horrible grimace accompanied by a few ape-like postures. '. . . when they turn into gorillas and tear you from limb to limb.'

Paddy was the only one of the travellers that Dodie neither liked nor trusted as, whenever he got the opportunity, he took great pleasure in trying to frighten the old man. Temporarily forgetting Mamma, and in his hurry to get away from Paddy, Dodie fell into the trap, sprawling against a loudly protesting Mamma who hastily applied her hanky to her nose and let blast a stream of vitriolic German into one of Dodie's large, hairy lugs.

Without ceremony Paddy seized hold of Curly and threw him in to join the rest of the passengers. The terrified lamb bleated loudly and lifting his tail he sprayed his master's legs with a good dollop of little round droppings.

Paddy took the reins, Shamrock flexed his sturdy hocks, rolled his eyes, and with an effort began to trundle the trap along the mossy, rutted track that led past the Monk's tombs of Dunuaigh towards Croynachan and Glen Fallan.

Squashed in her seat, Mamma endeavoured to avoid the

wild-eyed Curly and to keep her distance from Dodie. He, meanwhile, not daring to speak or look at her, made every effort to keep *his* distance from *her*, all the time wishing to himself – wickedly – that she would be the next recipient of his adored lamb's frequent and plentiful offerings of little round, hard balls of dung.

Chapter Fourteen

Glen Fallan undoubtedly boasted the best stretch of road on the island and Erchy took full advantage of the fact. He bowled along at a steady pace and was somewhat annoyed to see Elspeth in the distance, waving her hanky in such an imperious manner it was obviously a signal for him to stop. He screeched to a halt beside her and in she climbed. When she instructed him to drop her off at Slochmhor, there was nothing in her manner to suggest that she was quite delighted at having this opportunity to 'save her legs' as she hadn't expected to see the bus today.

'This isny an official run and I'm in a hurry,' Erchy grumbled. 'The Portvoynachan lot are waitin' for me at the harbour and I have no time to spare.'

Elspeth glanced meaningfully at Kate and Wullie. 'I see,' she said stonily. 'Those and such as those, eh, Erchy McKay? Things are indeed changing on this island. There was a time when nobody thought twice o' giving a helping hand to their neighbours but of course,' she sniffed and stuck her sharp nose in the air, 'sillar is all that counts wi' some people and it's a true enough saying that money is the root o' all evil. I have seen— '

'Ach, let her in!' Kate intervened impatiently. 'We're just wasting time gabbling away about nothing. You sit by Wullie and me, Elspeth, and take no more heed o' the man, he's in no mood to see reason and would waste an hour just arguing for the sake o' it.'

Rather haughtily Elspeth took a seat behind Kate and Wullie, assuming an attitude that suggested she had no wish to communicate with anybody in her present ruffled state.

170

But Kate had never been one to let opportunity slip through her fingers, she took a positive delight in other folk's affairs and had been itching for a long time to know more of Elspeth's. The sour-faced housekeeper of Slochmhor had been keeping a very low profile of late and nobody had been able to find out very much about her affair with Captain Mac, not even Behag whose devotion to Elspeth's every move, via the medium of her 'spyglass', had become quite a talking point among her neighbours.

Kate's interest wasn't quite as intense as that, nevertheless she saw no harm in trying to pierce Elspeth's armour of secrecy.

'You'll no' have so much time to spare these days, Elspeth,' she began chattily, poking Wullie in the ribs when he dared to snigger. 'Only the other day Phebie was saying she doesny see near so much o' you now that you and Captain Mac are busy plannin' to set up home together.'

Elspeth treated the back of Kate's head to a positively poisonous glare. 'Phebie never said the words! She knows better! Herself and Lachlan have never indulged in common chit-chat, especially when members o' the household are under threat from idle gossips. As for Captain Mac, he has been dividing his time between his sister on Hanaay and his cousin Gus here on Rhanna and, of course, he is away wi' the trawlers whenever he has the chance. I myself have seen very little o' him, we have our own lives to lead and are too busy to be bothered wi' very much else.'

'Ach, my, and here was me thinkin' the passions were just leapin' in your veins, Elspeth,' said the incorrigible Kate while at her elbow Wullie snottered profusely in his efforts to choke back the laughter. 'It just goes to show you are what you aye said you were, a one-man woman who can never forget Hector marching home from the sea to crush you in his arms and smother your lips wi' red hot kisses. I mind o' those days fine, he was a man o' few words – but they say that the silent ones are the worst and long spells at sea breeds fantasies and longings that have to be spent on somebody. Ay, Hector might no' have been much to look at but he was a man and these

171

wee, thin ones are the worst when it comes to lust in the marriage bed.'

She had hit a sensitive nerve, the only thrilling times in Elspeth's austere marriage to Hector had been when, sodden with drink and past all human reasoning, he had forcibly taken possession of her gaunt body. In spite of herself she had loved every rough, exciting minute of those brutish experiences whose aftermath had seen her praying half-heartedly to the Lord to forgive her for such sinful enjoyments.

But she didn't need the likes of Kate McKinnon to remind her of things that were best forgotten. Inwardly she fumed and vowed afresh to turn the tables on the Kates and the Behags of this world and to show them a thing or two that would 'shock the breeks off them.'

Oh ay, her turn would come, indeed it would. The future held some purpose for her, meantime she felt better in the knowing that she hadn't risen to the bait dangled by Kate McKinnon. She had not succumbed to her usual rigid denials and above all, and most importantly to her at this time, she had conducted herself with dignity and had not given this awful McKinnon woman one jot of satisfaction over the question of herself and Captain Mac. Let them pant and drool and watch her through their spyglasses, let idle old Behag break her ankles – and maybe her neck as well – in her endeavours to find out what was going on in the lives of other people. When Elspeth's turn came, and indeed it was coming very soon, the old bitch would maybe lose her eyesight into the bargain when at last all was revealed . . . something – at this point she squeezed her fists together and closed her eyes – something not one of them would ever have bargained for in all the years of their gossiping existence . . .

Slochmhor hove into view. A spot of red burning high on each taut cheek, Elspeth stood up and removed herself from the bus, every muscle, every bone, bristling with pride and self-respect.

'Here, you forgot the fare!' Erchy yelled after her.

'My good man,' she intoned haughtily, 'this is not your day for the Glen Fallan run. Officially neither you nor your bus are here, therefore, officially, neither am I. I dislike people who

172

say one thing and conveniently forget it when the question o' sillar arises, so take yourself and your disgraceful bus out o' my sight, you each spoil the landscape and do no good at all for the environment.'

With that she was off, scuttling towards Slochmhor's gate, her head high, her bony shoulders thrown back, paying no heed at all to Erchy's yelled insults concerning her state of meanness.

'Ach God!' Kate threw herself against Wullie and the pair of them erupted into guffaws of unrestrained mirth.

'Elspeth was aye a match for you any day, Erchy,' Kate gasped, wiping her streaming eyes and paying no heed to Erchy's oaths, which, in any case, were drowned out by the echoing roar of the engine as the bus zoomed through the narrow opening of Downie's Pass.

It was just past this point that they saw a pony and cart looming in the distance. As it drew closer, it soon proved to be Shamrock with Paddy at the reins and Dodie and Mamma ensconced in the back.

'Would you look at the old bugger!' Wullie cried, craning his neck to get a better view of the cart. 'Being driven home in style, no doubt wi' food in his belly and plenty o' sympathy inside his head.'

'And there's that bossy, big German wifie!' Kate added. 'A bit green about the gills but hale and hearty just the same. After me worrying about the old witch and goin' to all this bother to fetch her.'

Erchy exploded. '*You* went to all the bother! I'll have you know I have upset my whole afternoon's routine just to please you, Kate McKinnon! I have tholed cheek and insults and went hundreds o' miles out o' my way and I haveny even had my dinner yet!'

'Ach, stop havering,' Kate said calmly. 'I know fine you aye stop at old Meggie's or Aggie's on the way back from Croy. Meggie is aye good for a dram and a plate o' mince and tatties and Aggie's broth pot is never off the stove. And seeing you have come this far you may as well go on to Croft na Beinn. I've no' seen Nancy for a long time and I have some news to

173

tell her that will bring the sparkle back to her eyes, for she's no' been too well this wee whilie back.'

Up until that point Erchy had had every intention of turning the bus and heading back the way he had come but the chance of a tea and pancake strupak at Nancy's homely table was too good an opportunity to miss – and if it was accompanied by some juicy piece of news so much the better. The Portvoynachan lot would have grown tired of waiting anyway and would have managed to make their way home without him.

With a fresh surge of vigour he blithely drove on to Croft na Beinn where Wullie and his mother quickly disembarked.

'You'll be in a hurry to get back to the harbour, Erchy,' Kate imparted with a sprite in her eye, 'so we'll no' keep you a minute longer. You've done your good deed for the day but then, I aye knew your heart was bigger than your head – though only just.'

Erchy's face fell, but he had his pride and would never for one moment push himself in where he wasn't wanted. Nevertheless, he was determined to salvage something from the wreckage of his day, but when he broached the subject of fares to Kate, adding something about the cost of fuel, she merely grinned broadly and told him smartly he could deduct it from the interest due on Tam's loan.

Erchy's face grew red, he gaped, Kate's eyes danced. 'Ay, my bonny man, there's no' much that goes past me – as you yourself have said often enough. I'm much the same as you in that respect – surely we've known one another long enough for you to realize that. But dinna fash yourself, Erchy, what I have to tell my Nancy will be common knowledge this time tomorrow. All you'll need is a wee bit patience and a good big pair o' willing lugs, and, as everybody knows, neither your nose nor your lugs have ever let you down yet, and for that, may the good Lord be thank-et.'

So saying, she took Wullie's arm and, chuckling, the pair of them went off to regale Nancy with the latest exciting news concerning the Clan McKinnon, leaving Erchy to make his dejected way back to Portcull and the empty harbour.

*   *   *

174

Croft Beag was Paddy's first port of call and Dodie gave a sigh of relief at being home. He had almost forgotten Wullie in the trauma of being stuck beside big, overpowering Mamma Jodl, who had made her disapproval of him quite plain by her scowls and her hanky held frequently to her nose. In his innocence Dodie had imagined that it was Curly's smells she objected to and as he saw his little croft coming into view he decided that Wullie was definitely the lesser of two evils. He climbed down gladly from the cart, away from Mamma, away from the rough Irishman with his leering smiles and sly eyes, and led away his precious lamb who had left his mark all over the cart, on the seat, on the floor, even on Mamma's shoes – though she had been so taken up with keeping her distance from the old eccentric she hadn't yet noticed the state of her footwear.

As Dodie reached his gate Paddy half rose up in his seat to flap his arms like wings and make hideous cackling noises, both of which actions were meant to represent Dodie's infamous cockerels.

Safely inside his gate, Dodie waited till the cart was moving away, then, with a great show of bravado, he yelled Paddy's name and when the Irishman twisted round to look, he held his fingers to his nose and waved them about, before fleeing as fast as his great, clumsy feet would allow up the path to his house, Curly gambolling and skipping behind him.

It was Mamma's turn next and she never imagined she could be so glad to see An Cala sitting so quiet and peaceful in its field overlooking the sea. Paddy brought the cart to a halt, Shamrock snickered and when Mamma got down he looked as if he was smiling as he felt the weight on his shafts lightening.

'I'll bid you good day, then, Missus.' Paddy nodded pleasantly. 'Unless of course you would care to invite me in for a cup.'

Mamma had to force herself to appear grateful for the lift but she couldn't bring herself to extend her gratitude any further than a rather gruff 'danke', after which she made to take herself off.

'Wait, Missus!' Paddy's command was imperative; unwillingly

she turned round to meet his hostile eyes. 'Tis manners in these parts to be pleasant to your neighbours, ay, neighbours! We're as good as your like any day and if it hadny been for us saving your bacon you would still be wandering about like a tink on these damt moors!' He made a great attempt to control his temper and went on in quieter tones, 'It's no' much to ask, a cup o' tea in return for a favour granted. I'm your friend, Missus, and I'd never see you stuck. Rachel likes us tinks, she wouldny turn any one o' us away from her door, so what do you say, mavourneen? Just a minute to slake my thirst and then I'll be off.'

With poor grace Mamma acceded to his request, and while she was making the tea Paddy roamed restlessly around the kitchen, finally taking himself off to the parlour the minute her back was turned. It was in this room that he found what he was looking for and his eyes fairly gleamed at the sight. Rachel had three violins to her name, but it was her cherished Cremonese that she had brought with her to Rhanna. It reposed inside a very old but extremely beautiful leather case, given to her years ago by a man who had restored her violin to its former glory and who had been horrified to see such a precious instrument housed inside a cheap and ordinary case. It was at the beginning of Rachel's career and she hadn't been able to afford anything better. She had been overwhelmed by the gift and had treasured it ever since. Paddy ran his rough hands over the soft leather grain. He couldn't open it, and he hadn't the time to try and discover the whereabouts of the key, but it didn't matter, the time wasn't yet ripe – and old Mo's violin wasn't going anywhere – yet . . .

An odd little smile quirked the corners of Paddy's cruel mouth. 'I'll be back for ye,' he muttered, patting the case with calculated tenderness. 'By rights ye belong to me: the old man wasny in his right mind when he gave ye away to that conniving little gypsy, but we'll soon fix that. Ay, indeed we will.'

Mamma appeared in the doorway, suspicion on her face, but Paddy was immediately all smiles and charm and grateful for the tea which he drank down in one gulp before taking himself off with all haste.

As soon as he was out of sight Mamma sank down into a chair, kicked off her shoes and gave vent to an enormous yawn. Never, never, in the whole of her life, had she walked so far or been so humiliated; never had she met such strange people, eaten such peasant food, ridden home in such primitive style.

She ached, she burned, she stank – almost as badly as that dreadful old man who had accompanied her in the cart. She needed to wash herself, to change her clothes, to eliminate all signs of the most terrible hours she had ever spent – but first she had to have rest. It had all been too much for her, especially in the delicate state of health she was in.

With a weary sigh she rose out of her chair and dragged herself upstairs to creep between the sheets and give herself up to bliss, too exhausted to care that Jon wasn't there to worry and fuss over her and listen with all of his ears to her tales of woe and deprivation.

Rachel and Jon had had a very enjoyable time at Croft na Ard; Anton had been delighted to see his old friend again. The three of them had gone off to work in the fields till Babbie came home at dinnertime when they had laughed and talked and reminisced over a good Scottish meal of mince and tatties followed by apple pie and cream.

Jon broached the subject of the lack of a bathroom at An Cala, following it up rather tentatively with a request for his mother to use the facilities at Croft na Ard. Babbie and Anton had willingly agreed to the proposal though Babbie had laughingly added, 'Don't forget, I'm out all day and Anton is usually in the fields: sometimes the kitchen fire isn't lit till evening to heat the water, especially in the summer when quite often we just boil kettles on the stove and bathe in the zinc tub here in the kitchen.'

'Ah no,' smiled Jon, 'Mamma will never use the tub, that is the main reason we make our request to you to use your bathroom. My mother . . .' he searched for the right words, 'she is a woman of generous build. She would, perhaps, have difficulty climbing in and out of something she calls a big basin.'

Rachel grinned at this and she and Jon went home in the best of moods only to be greeted by an empty house and the sight of Mamma's equally empty shopping bag lying on a chair.

'She didn't get her apfelstrudel,' Rachel observed with a few quick gestures. 'In fact, she didn't get anything, her bag is completely empty – except' – she stared – 'for a few little hard balls of sheep's sharn.'

'Where *has* she been and what has she been up to?' Jon said with a frown. 'She isn't here, yet she must be, unless her bags and her coat and hat came home under their own steam.'

A quick search upstairs provided the answers. Jon came downstairs smiling. 'She is fast asleep like a baby. I think today my mother has had some adventures,' he sighed, 'and no doubt we'll hear all about it till we are deaf with her tales of woe.'

Rachel went to put on her apron. 'I'll make her an apple tart,' she decided in an odd burst of affection for her mother-in-law. 'It won't be the same as apfelstrudel but it's the next best thing. Babbie's apple pie has put me in the mood for baking, but don't expect too much, it's a long time since I guddled with pastry and I might have forgotten the art.'

She spent a busy afternoon baking tarts and scones and cooking a delicious evening meal. Her apple tarts were perfection, light and tangy with just a hint of nutmeg and cinnamon to add to the flavour, but when Mamma came stomping downstairs early in the evening she was in no mood for anything except to talk about her day's misfortunes.

Jon listened, he sympathized, he soothed, but when Rachel served Mamma with a tempting savoury tea and it was rejected after only a few mouthfuls, he frowned. When she pushed away the apple tart without tasting it at all he burst out, 'Mamma, Rachel has spent many hours making this meal for you, she made the apple tart specially, she . . .'

'It is not the apfelstrudel,' Mamma spoke heavily. 'The pastry, it looks heavy and I will not ruin my stomach with the stodge.'

She pushed back her chair, she got up and without another word she went to the stand in the hall to take down her coat and hat and don them before going back to the kitchen to announce,

'I go to your friend's house for the bath, I smell myself badly, the hot soak I need to have.'

Jon's face reddened. 'Mamma,' he said sternly, 'you can't go to Croft na Ard at this hour, Babbie and Anton will be at their evening meal, they work hard all day, they . . .'

But she was off, the door closing behind her firmly and loudly. 'I'm damned if I'll see her up the road!' Jon cried, for once in his life really angry at his mother's inconsideration.

Rachel set about clearing the table. Let the old witch stay away all night if she wanted! There was nothing at An Cala to occupy her anyway, she would only talk and talk, and rant and rave, and all about herself as usual. Rachel felt sorry for Anton and Babbie but glad that she and Jon would have the house to themselves, free to pursue their own pastimes and pleasures.

Mamma was only gone a short time. The house of Croft na Ard had been empty and deserted, there was no one in: she wouldn't get her bath after all, she would have to wash here in the kitchen, but not in the tub, never in the tub, she was a lady, she would not be humiliated, she would sponge herself down, she would be clean somehow!

Rachel disappeared into the parlour, glad to get away from Mamma and her ceaseless chatter. Even though it was just Jon and his mother left in the kitchen it was soon a hive of activity, with son running to do mother's bidding, stoking the fire, filling kettles, setting them to boil and laying out towels and soap and face flannels.

'And now, go,' Mamma ordered when everything was to her satisfaction and the curtains and blinds had been tightly drawn, the doors firmly locked.

Jon escaped gladly. In the softly lit parlour Rachel was burning incense, the room reeked with the sweet, evocative odour of jasmine, and she was playing oriental music on her little battery operated tape recorder. When he came through the door she went straight into his arms and they both swayed round the room in a dreamy silence. That afternoon Babbie had given Rachel red roses from her garden and she had woven them into her hair; the perfume of them filled Jon's nostrils. She was wearing a flimsy blouse with nothing underneath, her breasts were warm and soft against his chest. He forgot his mother, desire flooded his loins, he pressed himself hard against her and she responded by winding her arms round his neck and drawing his head down till his lips met with hers.

'Rachel,' he whispered against her hair, 'you are a temptress. I want you very badly, tonight you are lovelier than ever.'

Her kisses melted on his mouth. With a groan he buried his face in the creamy skin of her neck and took the ripe fullness of her breasts in his hands. She swayed and moved against him, his breath came quicker, they stopped dancing and gave themselves up to one another. His hand slid down to her thighs, he heard the soft intake of her breath, their limbs quickened and merged, their kisses became deeper, more demanding, more bruising than the one before, and then he opened her blouse and his lips found the hard, burning tips of her nipples.

Lost in passion, helpless with desire, they sank down on to the rug in front of the fire, forgetting everything and everybody in their heart-racing excitement. Her long, lithe legs captured his hips. He pushed up her skirt, undid his trouser zip . . . and at that precise moment Mamma appeared in the doorway, her head swaddled in towels, her body wrapped in a voluminous purple silk dressing gown with dragons luxuriantly embroidered on the back.

She stood there dumbfounded for a few brief moments, but soon found her tongue. 'Jon!' she cried, her voice hard with shock, deliberately using the admonishing tone she had used to him when, as a small boy, she had caught him out in some naughty act. 'I bathe, I turn my back only a short time but enough for my son to change himself into an animal of the field. Since your boytime I teach you the manners, the breeding, the respect, all these you have lost since your meeting up with this – this untamed, disrespectful child! I will not have it, Jon! She has turned you into a heathen!'

While she was ranting, Jon and Rachel were fixing their clothing, scrambling to their feet. Jon was breathing heavily in a mixture of frustration, receding passion and rage.

'Mamma!' he said furiously. 'Rachel and I are not committing a sin: we are married – remember? And it is our house; we love one another, I have been away from her for a long time and we haven't had much chance to be alone since I came home. We – I – thought you would take a long time to wash. You told me at least an hour . . .'

'So, I was too quick for you, eh, Jon?' Mamma said heavily. 'How could you do these things while I am in the next room! Was last night not enough for you? You have the noisy bed, all night long I hear the bedsprings creaking. I lie awake listening – creak! creak! creak! – and always there are the sighs and the moans and all the other sounds it is not nice for a woman of my age to hear!'

Rachel was livid. Her eyes were black, burning coals in the pallor of her face. Her hands curling into fists, she stared at the older woman and she wondered, had all that loud and raucous snoring of last night been a front? Had the old bitch deliberately pretended to be asleep when all the while she had been listening through the wall as hard as she could . . . ? Another thought struck Rachel: had this dreadful woman intentionally rushed through her toilet in order to creep and snoop through the house hoping to spring humiliation on Jon and herself?

Rachel's nostrils dilated, she could control herself no longer, her fingers were a blur of movement as she told Mamma just what she thought of her.

But it was all lost on Mamma Jodl: she hardly understood one single symbol of her daughter-in-law's sign language and merely snorted when at last Rachel's nimble fingers grew still.

'Pah!' Mamma snorted. 'All this flapping about with the hands, it is very undignified and also extremely tiring to watch. Why didn't you marry a girl who could speak with her mouth, Jon? Life would have been much simpler for us all.'

At that Rachel couldn't contain herself, how dare the old battle-axe speak about her as if she wasn't there? She looked as if she could easily kill her mother-in-law there and then. Every muscle in her body became tightly coiled, her black eyes were wild and dangerous, she looked like a leopard ready to spring

181

and Jon, knowing that his wife was perfectly capable of striking out when thus enraged, made haste to intervene. But she shook him off, nothing or nobody was going to stop her now. The large, fat, ignorant old bugger she had inherited when she married Jon might not understand the deaf and dumb language but there was one sign that was universally recognized and, by God, she was going to let her have it! Rushing up to the other woman, she stuck her two fingers so forcibly into her face that Mamma had to move back a pace in order to avoid them being rammed up her nose.

The old lady could pretend obtuseness when it suited her but on this occasion, with the V-sign almost touching her eyeballs, she could do nothing but recognize it for what it was. Her mouth dropped open in utter dismay while Rachel, breathless and beside herself with fury, just kept on poking her two fingers in the air while she glared threateningly into the older woman's eyes.

Jon's rancour against his mother, for causing yet another scene, was in no way diminishing, but when he looked from Rachel's ferocious young face to Mamma's flabbergasted expression he suddenly saw the funny side of the situation and fell back in his seat in a fit of laughing, quite unable to stem the flow of mirth once it had started. It was more a nervous reaction than anything else. Jon wanted only harmony in his life, and he especially wanted to enjoy this precious holiday on Rhanna with his wife, but his mother's disruptive presence was making the possibilty of any sort of pleasure more remote by the minute, and his laughter was tinged with an odd sort of hysterical desperation.

For Rachel, the sound of her husband's merriment was the last straw. She had to get away, get out from under the feet of both mother and son, anywhere, everywhere, just as long as she could flee this house that had, in the space of just a night and a day, become a hell instead of the haven she had always considered it to be.

With an odd little half-sob she ran to the hall and wrenched her coat from the stand. Jon was at her back, pleading with her to either stay or let him go with her but again she shook him off and ran from the house, struggling into her coat as she went.

She had no clear notion of where she was going, her feet carried her along swiftly, pounding the short turf of the clifftop, slithering and sliding on the loose, sandy soil of one of the many sheep tracks that led down to the shore.

A fresh, cool breeze blew up from the sea, the clouds were scudding across the sky so that the moon sailed in and out of purple-grey cumulus and fitfully cast its silver-white light over the great grey-bellied reaches of the Sound of Rhanna.

Bitterness boiled in Rachel's breast as she hurried along. She hated Mamma, she hated Jon: he had laughed when he should have been supportive and helpful, he had never stood up to that monstrous old bitch he called mother. All along she had smothered rather than mothered him and he had gone along with it till now it had come to this, an open rivalry between the two women in his life for his love and attention. Well, he could have Mamma if that was what he wanted, she'd had enough, she wouldn't stay in that house another day. Tonight she would pack her bags, tomorrow she would go and stay with Ruth till the steamer came on Friday. There was nothing to keep her here now, nothing . . .

The wind tugged her hair, pulled at her coat; the sigh of wide and lonely places surged in her ears; the beat and roar of the ocean filled her senses.

Dazedly she paused in her flight and gazed around her. She was on windswept Burg Bay, to her left the cliffs rose up, black and sheer against the glowering night sky. The towering fangs of the reefs, those grey, forbidding old men of the sea, hunched themselves into eerie shapes and seemed to gaze moodily down at the water restlessly swirling round their feet. Moonshadows wavered on the sand, flitting in and out of the rocks according to the whim of the wind-tossed clouds until the moon was obliterated completely by banks of blackness and it was dark, dark, lonely, desolate, but complete and magnificent in its wild, hushed, secretive whisperings with only a seabird's lone cry to intrude into the solitude.

But not so dark – up there – on the cliffs – a light shone like a beacon through the velvet night gloom, beckoning, signalling, guiding . . .

Then she knew why she mustn't leave Rhanna: someone up there needed her, for his sake she had to stay. She sensed loneliness, sadness, fear, all mingling with strength and power and love of life. She had to go to him: he was calling, calling. In her heart she could hear his voice; in her soul she could hear his music.

Again her feet took wing . . . and this time they weren't running away.

Chapter Fifteen

Rachel entered Tigh na Cladach via the back porch and without hesitation went straight to the softly lit sitting room. There she found Otto sprawled in a chair by the fire, deathly pale, his pain-filled eyes black and dazed so that at first he wasn't aware that she had entered the room.

'Otto!' Her heart cried his name. A few quick strides took her to his side and as she stooped to gaze into his face she knew why she had experienced these moments of pain and poignancy whenever they had been quiet and alone together. He was a very sick man: this big, wonderful Austrian, with his marvellous physique, his vigour, his delight of life, was dying.

All along she had sensed it – the shadow of death had been there in his eyes even while he had talked and laughed and played his spellbinding music. She had known, but even so, now that the moment of truth was here, the knowledge hit her like a sledgehammer.

'Rachel.' His mouth struggled to form her name. He seemed to come back from a very long way and his hand came up to enclose hers. 'Pills – in the bedroom – get them – quickly please.'

She didn't remember running upstairs but quite suddenly it seemed she was standing in the bedroom with its rose-sprigged walls and camped ceilings, its rose-coloured bed light shining down on the big, soft feather bed.

Frantically she gazed around, blinded at first by anxiety and fear, then her eye fell on the bedside cabinet – nothing there except a volume of Burns' poems, another of Robert Louis Stevenson's *Kidnapped*. But wrenching open the little drawer she saw them, a motley collection of brown pill bottles, full, half-full and some empty.

Her hands shook slightly as she picked them up and looked at the labels. He had asked for pills but which ones? Wildly she wondered if she should take them all down to him but then she remembered his pain and seizing the one containing morphine she raced down to the kitchen where she filled a glass with water and went back into the sitting room.

Taking the bottle from her trembling grasp he gulped down two of the pills and sat back to look at her. 'In a little while I will be better,' he told her breathlessly. She sat there with him, quiet and still by the fire, her mind strangely calm, her hands, those slender, delicate, soothing hands, wherein lay a power that could not be denied, placed cool and tender upon his clammy brow.

Gradually he relaxed, pain departed, he took several deep breaths and taking her face in his hands he turned it towards him till he could look deep and straight into her eyes.

'You know, don't you, *liebling*?'

She nodded; he gave a funny little half-smile. 'From the beginning I felt you were different from anyone I had ever known. You have the sixth sense, the eyes that see deep and clear beyond the soul. I have been ill for a long time, Rachel. I have the treatment, the spells in hospital till I am sick and tired of it all and want only to die in peace – but first – I must come home to my grandmother's island, the beloved lands whose memories take her sweetly and serenely through all the years of her exile.'

He told her then what he had told Kate that morning – of his connections with the Clan McKinnon, of Magnus his maternal grandfather, his plans for a clan gathering – and of things he hadn't told Kate – his determination to visit the island where it had all began for him and where, in a spiritual way, it would end for him.

'I will go back to Vienna to pass my final days. But here,' he placed a clenched hand over his heart, 'this part of me will remain behind on Rhanna. In my boytime I hear the ocean, I walk the hills, I smell the perfume of the moors, all through my grandmother's voice, I wasn't to know that coming here would capture my heart for all time and never let go of it, no matter how far I might travel when the time comes for me to go away.'

She made no gesture, her heart was too full for her even to attempt to let him know how she felt. A time like this needed words and those she could never utter. She filled the minutes with practical actions, piling the fire high with peats, placing his slippers on the fender to warm, going through to the kitchen to pour milk for Vienna, rolling newspapers into twists for the morning fire, finally making cocoa, which he and she drank in an oddly tranquil silence.

At one point she knelt by him and placed his slippers on his feet. His hand came out to touch the top of her dark head. '*Liebling*,' he said huskily, 'something brought you here tonight – when I needed you, you came. Today I learn that your husband has come home to you – but – would it be selfish of me to ask . . . would you stay with me for a little while?'

For answer she curled herself at his feet and clasped her hands round her knees. The eyes that gazed into the fire were big and dark with the pain that burned in her heart. Her beloved stranger had touched her life only briefly but she knew that the strange sweet power he had over her spirit transcended the bonds of flesh, the passage of time. He would remain with her forever, long after he was dead and gone and only the voice of his living soul spoke to her in the eternal winds blowing over the land.

For Otto Klebb was life, a life that would flourish beyond the grave. His magic, his music, his memory, would remain behind for always and at the thought of that a wonderful sense of peace flooded her being. And the peace remained with her for the rest of that evening spent with him. They felt no need to communicate, each was content in the knowing that the other was there, a harmony of everything that was the essence of understanding and love in the human consciousness.

The hands of the clock on the mantelpiece were at two a.m. when she finally rose to take her leave. She wanted to help him upstairs to bed but some of the old vigour was there in his voice when he held her close in his arms and said into her hair, 'My

187

liebling, there are some things I must do on my own, going to bed is one of them, dying is still a good way off for me and to have you there in the intimacy of the bedroom might prove to be a temptation I could not resist.' He held her away from him to look into her eyes. 'We could not live with ourselves if we betrayed what we feel for one another with the weakness of the flesh. I make a vow to you, when my dying time is here, when I pass over to the valleys of the unknown, I will carry with me cherished memories of a young girl who is more to me than flesh. You are of my soul, Rachel *liebling*, and, no matter how hard it is for me to touch you without possessing you, I will not tarnish what we have found together on this earth by giving in to the needs of my body.'

Her eyes were dark and shiny with unshed tears, her heart knew the beauty and pureness of his words. Helplessly she nodded and kissed him gently on his brow.

He smiled. 'We have many things to do, you and I. I have some months left to me and I want to fill them with the knowledge of your world. You will teach me your sign language so that I can understand all the things you want to say to me, I see many expressions in your eyes but not enough to let me know what is in your heart. And now . . .' his mouth nuzzled hers, 'you must return to your husband, I will not be the cause of enmity between you – so go quickly, before all my good resolutions crumble into the ashes of meaningless talk.'

Unwillingly she let go of his hands. Every fibre in her, every cell in her body, begged her to stay and surrender her love to him. She knew her weaknesses only too well, one encouraging gesture from him would be her undoing, and so she went away quickly as he had bid, into the loneliness of wind-washed night where the sad murmurs of empty places found an echo in a heart that was full to bursting with emotion.

She was cold by the time she reached An Cala. Jon had left a lamp burning in the hall, the soft halo of light only served to emphasize the surrounding darkness and she made her way upstairs swiftly and silently.

The coolness of the sheets embraced the coldness of her flesh but there was no comfort to be had from Jon. This time it was he who kept his back turned on her. His quiet breathing told her nothing: he could have been asleep, or half-asleep, or wide awake, listening for her coming home, whichever way, she knew he would make no move towards her that night and the silence of the room enshrouded her, with not even a grunt or a snore from Mamma's room to break the stillness.

For a long time she lay thinking about Otto, her feverish thoughts taking her round and round in endless circles. Then she remembered his strength, his stoic acceptance of what was to be, the beautiful words he had used to describe his feelings for her, now and hereafter. The tension left her limbs, leaving her weak; peace once again flooded her being, making her strong. She sighed and pressed herself into Jon's warmth. He half turned and put his arms around her and in the comforting reassurance of that familiar embrace her fears melted like snowflakes and she was soon asleep.

The news concerning Otto's connection with the McKinnons flashed round the island. In a very short time every corner buzzed with the juiciest piece of gossip to have hit Rhanna for ages. In cottage, croft, barn, biggin, shop, shieling, anywhere people could meet, tongues wagged, heads nodded and a most enjoyable time was had by all.

'Hmph! The McKinnons again!' Old Sorcha expostulated when the news seeped through to her head via her deaf aid. 'Why is it they get all the attention? And that Kate! There will be no living wi' her. She'll steep herself in airs and graces and go about behaving as if she was the only body wi' a clan to her name.' In her excitement she turned up her hearing aid so that everybody in the vicinity was just about deafened by the high-pitched wailing noise it emitted. Face red with ire, Sorcha continued, 'Do you mind that time, last year, when that nice wee English wifie looked to Kate for information about her McKinnon connections? And Kate, the sly besom, telling her all those lies about being a Mull McKinnon when all the time she belongs to that bunch o' cut-throats over on Uist?

'She's just no' worthy o' all the attention paid to her when here is me, old enough and able enough to mind o' things that happened in the last century! It's no' fair! It's just no' fair!'

'Here, I'll thank you to keep a hold on your tongue,' Todd the Shod interposed with an aggrieved air. 'My mother was a Uist McKinnon and a finer branch o' the line I have yet to meet. They never cut anybody's throats, maybe just punched each other's noses now and again at a ceilidh, but nothing worse than that. Here,' his ruddy face brightened, 'I've just reminded myself, seeing as how my mother was a McKinnon it means I'll be legally entitled to go to this grand Clan Gathering that Mr Otto is planning on. I must get Mollie to mend that wee hole in the back o' my kilt for it will be a Highland dress affair, and even though mine's a McDonald tartan I canny let the side down wi' holey pleats.'

Todd wasn't the only one on the island to rake up a convenient McKinnon connection that would enable attendance at Otto's Ceilidh, as it was quickly becoming known. Everyone, it seemed, had a McKinnon relative buried in the family closet, and even though bringing them out for an airing might risk the uncovering of some unsavoury skeletons, it was a risk that was considered worthwhile in the event.

'Otto doesny know what he's letting himself in for,' Fergus predicted dourly. 'Every bugger wi' a bit McKinnon tartan to his name will lay claim to clan rights – the hall hasny yet been built to accommodate them all.'

'What about you?' Kirsteen said mischievously. 'Have you got any McKinnons lurking in your cupboards?'

He glowered at her and she burst out laughing. 'Och, c'mon, Fergie, just think, if you could pull a long-lost Uncle McKinnon out o' your hat you might just get to attend Otto's Ceilidh and would be free to drink schnapps till it was coming out your ears!'

Fergus still had a sinking feeling every time he thought about 'the night of the schnapps'. His pride had been badly bruised at

190

the very idea of being 'drunk and incapable', as Behag would have put it, and the realization that he had been put to bed by Lachlan, Mark James, and their womenfolk, was enough to bring him out in a cold sweat whenever he pictured it in his mind. He was therefore not at all amused by Kirsteen's teasing remarks and inwardly vowed to get his own back on Otto 'one o' these days' by making him drink whisky till it was coming out *his* ears.

When all the fuss and talk reached the hairy lugs of old Magnus of Croy he was inclined to the belief that it was all 'just a lot o' exaggeration', but when Kate and Tam came to see him with the news that he was 'the grandfather o' a very fine foreign gentleman', and hastily filled him in with the facts, he turned very pale and collapsed into the nearest chair.

'Be getting me a dram from the sideboard' he instructed with great dignity. With alacrity Tam went to carry out his instructions, pouring a generous amount of whisky for everyone 'by way o' a wee celebration'.

Kate hugged herself at the look on the old man's face when little by little the news sunk in and he sat back to say huskily, 'I never kent that my Sheena went away from Rhanna carrying my bairn – and now this – our grandson, after all these years, I canny rightly take it all in and it will be a wee whilie before I can really believe it's true.'

'You'll believe it when you see him,' Kate assured him happily. 'He is a big, fine, bonny chiel wi' a good McKinnon face on him and a talent for music that was surely passed on to him by his very own grandfather. Ach, just you wait, Magnus, when you meet him you'll know he's your flesh and blood, for the bond has aye been there between you. He was very close to his Grannie Sheena, ever since he could understand what she was talking about she told him about you and about this island. Such bonny stories, I had a wee greet to myself they were so sad, and you and he will just talk and talk till you are blue in the face and fair gaspin' for breath the pair o' you.'

*   *   *

And she was right. The day that Mark drove Otto to Croy Beag in Thunder was one that would forever live in the minds of both grandfather and grandson.

It was a warm, balmy day, the sea was blue beyond the cliffs, the little bays sparkled with sun diamonds. Tiny inshore islets were alive with basking seals; a school of dolphins arched through the water, their glistening bodies riding the waves with grace and delight; gannets plummeted and soared; rows of cormorants stood on the reefs, drying their wings in the crystal cool breezes blowing over the ocean.

Nearer to hand, cows grazed the machair; chickens clucked and poked; lapwings rose up from the heather uttering their unmistakable musical alarm calls; burns tinkled down from the hills; a tabby kitten pranced and danced after the heath moths that flitted about from one tiny wildflower to the next – and from a thatched white cottage whose windows and doors were painted a cheerful bright red, peat smoke rose up into the sky and strains of fiddle music floated out to join the rest of the music of a perfect summer's day.

The two men stood listening, Mark in appreciation, Otto in wonder, his strong, handsome face rather pale in a mixture of anticipation and apprehension.

'My friend,' he said after a while, 'would you come in with me? The occasion, it is of great moment, I am not sure I can handle it on my own.'

But Mark shook his dark head and placed an encouraging hand on the other's shoulder. 'No, Otto, I'll bide out here for a while. You've waited a long time for this moment and it's only right that it should belong to you and old Magnus. I guarantee you'll only be in the house a few minutes and you'll think you've aye belonged – and think o' this – your grandmother used to come here – her feet have trod the path you see before you. Go along it and look at it all as if you're seeing it through her eyes, and when you see the old man for the first time, remember how he and your grandmother loved one another, how they were parted with love binding them over the miles and the years. If you think you feel strange, just remember how it must be for him, believing that he had no family left in the world till you came to the island. Everybody loves Magnus, you will too, and he'll welcome you with open arms.'

He was right: no sooner had Otto stepped over the threshold than Magnus was up on his feet, his wonderful blue eyes misty with emotion as he beheld his grandson for the first time – a tall, handsome man, darkly bearded, broad shouldered, standing in a ray of sunlight spilling in through the door.

'Son,' he murmured and going stiffly forward he clasped the big man to his bosom with such a strength of love that Otto found himself returning the gesture, his heart full to bursting in the knowledge that, at last, he had come into the heart and the home of 'Grannie Sheena's man'.

'Son,' Magnus said again, standing back to gaze at the powerful face, the magnetic eyes of his grandson, his beguiling, one-toothed smile coming readily to his nut-brown face. 'Come you in and sit you down. First we will have a strupak and then we will talk – ay – by God and we will.'

Otto remembered Mark and looked beyond the small-paned window, but Mark had taken himself off on a walk over the moors and was already just a speck in the heat-hazed distance.

An hour passed on timeless wings. The old man's house was a wonderland of knowledge and learning. Dusty shelves were filled to overflowing with books; reams of poetry, music, songs, all written and composed by Magnus himself, spilled from every conceivable space. A tiny enclosure, which Magnus proudly referred to as his 'music room', housed an ancient piano, an accordion, two fiddles, a set of kettle drums and another of bagpipes. 'Though I havny the breath to play them much these days,' he explained regretfully, 'only sometimes, on a summer's night when the moor has that strange sort o' bewitchment about it, I canny resist taking a wee walk over to Baldy's Burn where I can sit and play my pipes in peace.'

Otto was enchanted by everything he saw, touched and heard, and the hour was too short for the pair to say all that they wanted to say to one another.

Mark returned from his walk and gratefully gulped down two

193

cups of tea, and then it was time to go with many promises from Otto to come back at every available opportunity.

Otto was tired by the time he and Mark reached the five-barred gate, and when he climbed into Thunder he sat back in the ancient leather seat and closed his eyes.

Mark glanced at him. Was it his imagination, or had the big Austrian grown a bit thinner since coming to Rhanna? He certainly seemed fit enough and his zest for life was gaining strength the more he familiarized himself with the people of the island, but there was something about his face, some slight change, that Mark found rather disquieting.

But he made no comment till they were at the gate of the shorehouse when he turned to Otto and said lightly, 'I'm about to let poor old Thunder have her summer siesta. I'm a bicycle man during the longer days,' he smiled, 'much to the disapproval of old Behag who thinks it's undignified for a minister to go fleeing about the place on a bike. The point I'm trying to make is this, it does my old motor no good at all to be laid up for too long and you would be doing me a favour if you would take her off my hands and keep her on the road for me. She's had a complete overhaul by one o' the more mechanically minded village lads and shouldn't let you down too badly. It would mean you could go and visit Magnus whenever you have a mind so all in all, everybody would be happy.'

Otto looked gratefully at Mark. He didn't fancy Erchy's infamous bus and had been wondering how he would make the difficult journey to Croy Beag without transport. He knew that this 'man o' God' had deliberately made the acceptance of Thunder easy for him and he said quietly, 'I would be honoured to have the use of your car and I'll take good care of her, I promise you that.'

Mark grinned. 'She has a mind o' her own – she'll take care o' you in her own particular way, it might no' always be what you have in mind for she can be gey unpredictable but at least you'll have some fun – and frustrations – getting to know her.'

And so it was settled. Otto, who had hitherto kept rather a low profile, never venturing very far from Burg Bay, soon became ubiquitous. Wherever he went he was invited to partake of strupaks and his company was eagerly sought at ceilidhs and other such social gatherings. He soon felt himself to be an accepted member of the island community and became a familiar sight driving along the roads in Thunder.

One or two of the islanders thought that they had seen him somewhere before but couldn't be sure where and when, if indeed they had seen him at all, but Barra McLean, who all along had puzzled over Otto's identity, went home one day to look through the collection of records that she had brought with her from Glasgow. She hadn't played them for a long time, simply because there was no electricity supply in her house to work her record player, which meant that it had lain at the back of a cupboard gathering dust. She had soon found what she was looking for and she sat back on her heels, staring at the face of 'the foreign stranger' on one of the record sleeves – younger looking to be sure, but the black hair and beard, the riveting eyes, were unmistakable just the same.

'Karl Gustav Langer,' she whispered, 'at last, I know who you are.'

She felt awed, honoured to think that such a great man had come to Rhanna to live among its people – and more – that the very same man was a McKinnon with Hebridean blood running proud and strong in his veins. She realized that, for all the obvious reasons, he wanted to remain anonymous, and she vowed to herself there and then that, as far as she was concerned, his secret was safe for as long as he wanted it to be.

So Otto went on his way undiscovered, delighting in his freedom, meeting people who had only been names to him before. One of these was Shona McLachlan, only daughter of McKenzie o' the Glen, who helped her husband run his veterinary practice at Mo Dhachaidh, the old house which had once belonged to Biddy McMillan, a fondly remembered character who had nursed the island population for most of her life.

The surgery was quiet when Otto went there with Vienna, who

195

had worried him with some rather strange behaviour of late. At the sound of the bell, Shona came out into the hall, tall, slender, attractive, her mane of auburn hair tied back with a black velvet ribbon, her amazingly blue eyes shining with interest in her fine-featured face. She knew Otto at once, having seen him many times passing Mo Dhachaidh in Thunder, but this was the first face to face meeting and, holding out her hand, she introduced herself.

He couldn't keep the admiration out of his eyes, this was unmistakably Fergus McKenzie's daughter – that proud tilt of her head, the same fearless eyes, the way she had of carrying herself, the same quizzical half-smile at the corners of her mouth, the dimpled cleft in the middle of her firm little chin.

As they stood there, a mini tornado in the shape of five-year-old Ellie Dawn McLachlan, burst out of one door in the hall and in through another, a few seconds later popping her head out to say 'hallo' to Otto before disappearing once more.

Shona smiled. 'My daughter, the eldest, the other is only two but already she bosses her brother about something terrible.'

Otto nodded. 'Children, they are a joy. Myself . . .' he held up the basket he was carrying, 'I only have a cat, she adopted me when I first arrived and now she will not leave my side. But she is unwell, her behaviour is very peculiar, she mopes in the house, she hides in cupboards, she scratches up the cushion in her bed, she makes hideous wailing noises, she eats like a horse and now she will not eat at all. I thought perhaps your husband could have the examination of her.'

Shona lifted the cat out of the basket. Gently she pressed the soft belly and laughed. 'You can save yourself the bother and the expense of seeing Niall: your cat is having kittens, that's all. Her time is very near and that is why she is looking for a quiet place to give birth.'

Otto stared. 'But she never leaves the house, she is a home cat, she only goes out when it is strictly necessary!'

Shona's eyes twinkled. 'Indeed, that is why she is pregnant, it must have been a necessity for her to sneak out on the tiles for a clandestine meeting with her suitor – probably Murdy

196

McKinnon's big tom, he's very charming and persuasive and has fathered umpteen generations of cats.'

Otto threw back his head and gave vent to his deep, booming laugh. Niall came out of his surgery at the sounds of merriment and the three of them stood chatting till Otto decided it was time to go home on a matter of great urgency, namely the birth of Vienna's kittens.

'You must come to the McKinnon Clan Gathering,' was his parting shot. 'Everyone else seems to be pulling McKinnons willy nilly out of their hats so you must do the same. It doesn't matter if they have been dead and buried for hundreds of years, your claim will still be valid. I have decided to hold my gathering at the end of July, so that gives you ample time to produce something reasonably suitable. Bring your parents too – I know Fergus will want to pay me back for all that schnapps I made him drink and Lachlan must be there to keep order.'

When the door had closed on him, Shona and Niall looked at one another. 'I can see now why the island is fascinated by him,' was Niall's verdict. 'The magnetism of the man is unmistakable and he is also very persuasive.' He took her arm and kissed the tip of her nose. 'Let us repair to the kitchen for a good hot cuppy and over it we can rake up our dead relatives – figuratively speaking, of course. We'll see what we can come up with in the shape o' some poor old ghost who is just hanging around waiting for us to discover his McKinnon connections!'

Bit by bit, Otto became well known to everyone and it wasn't long before he was being hailed as *Mac nan Èilean*, which in Gaelic means Son of the Island and was one of the greatest accolades he could ever receive since it was normally only born and bred islanders who were bestowed with Gaelic titles of such a fond nature.

At every opportunity he visited his grandfather till it seemed the two had known one another all of their lives. Together they composed songs and sat in the music room playing the treasured collection of musical instruments – Otto the ancient piano, Magnus the fiddle, and sometimes the bagpipes out there in the open moors, much to Otto's enchantment.

He also took his grandfather to Tigh na Cladach where a ceilidh had been arranged. It proved to be a memorable musical evening. Rachel, Jon and Lorn played together on their fiddles, and were soon joined by old Magnus on his, his silvery white head a startling contrast to the three dark young heads close by.

Mark James sang 'Song of Rhanna' in his rich baritone voice. The words, composed by him, had been set to a poignantly beautiful tune of Rachel's making. Three years ago it had been something of a hit in the music world and every time an island wireless was turned on the strains of the song had soared forth till very soon it was on everybody's lips.

And now Mark James stood in Otto's sitting room, looking not in the least 'minister-ish' in an open-necked blue shirt and cord slacks, his ruggedly handsome face serious and just a little sad as the words soared forth:

> Take me back where I belong,
> Where the skylark sings his song,
> And the peace of island life is all around.
> Where the people raise a hand,
> And there's a welcome in the land,
> And honest, friendly faces can be found . . .
> Take me home, oh, take me home,
> For I no longer want to roam,
> My heart is yearning for the hills, the glens,
> For the sea's tumultuous roar,
> For the spume upon the shore,
> For the mist that veils the corries on the bens . . .

'*Wunderbar!*' Otto applauded in delight and went immediately to the piano to pick up the tune. The others took up their fiddles, everyone began to sing, and very soon 'Song of Rhanna' became a symphony of words and music that just went on and on because no one wanted the uplifting experience ever to end.

198

But then came a pause in proceedings when the merrymakers sat back to rest and partake of a well-earned drink.

From a corner of the room Jon watched Rachel and Otto. There was something between the two that he couldn't quite fathom, it was as if they shared some secret that no one else knew of. She was very attentive to him, he equally of her, yet not once did they touch or even communicate very often, but each glance, every quiet smile, held more meaning than any physical contact ever could.

Suspicion and jealousy smote Jon to the quick. He had been married to Rachel for almost seven years yet he was still besotted by her. He was only too aware of the power she wielded over men, wherever she went they surrounded her in admiring droves and little wonder, hers was a dark and fiery beauty with her tumbling mass of jet black hair, her flashing dark eyes, her superb body and her long, shapely legs. All that, together with her intensely passionate nature, was a combination of physical and mental attraction that few men could resist, and Jon often felt that he was perhaps too tame and quiet for a young girl of such vitality. He was in his forties, old enough to be her father, but Rachel had never minded that – in fact – now that he came to think of it, she always got on well with older men and Herr Otto Klebb must be nearer fifty than forty.

Jon thought back to that night she had run from the house after the row with his mother. She hadn't returned till the early hours of morning and next day when he had challenged her she had admitted quite frankly that she had gone to visit Otto. After that he had noticed a distinct change in her: she was withdrawn and distant, she went off on long, lone walks, she didn't play her violin as often as she used to and when he spoke to her about it she just looked at him with smouldering fathomless eyes and turned away from him without explanation of any sort.

Not even Mamma's continued presence, her interference in the running of the home, and her loud and frequent complaints seemed to affect Rachel any more, and Jon's thoughts would turn to the vague hints and innuendoes concerning his wife and Otto, that he had only half listened to on his return to Rhanna.

199

Not that Rachel was any less loving towards him, in fact their love-making was more sensuous, more wonderful than it had ever been, but always there was Otto. She went to visit him as frequently as she dared and quite often accompanied him to Croy Beag to visit his grandfather.

She had been instrumental in organizing this ceilidh, gathering together the best musical talent in the village to entertain both Otto and Magnus. She had been adamant about not inviting Mamma. 'She will just want to talk about herself in that loud voice of hers,' she had indicated quite plainly to Jon, 'and that is the last thing I want at this ceilidh. She hasn't met Otto yet and will only monopolize him all night, and I'm also afraid that she might recognize him as Karl Langer and let the whole world know.'

To say that Mamma wasn't pleased at this decision would be putting it too mildly. She had told Rachel she was mean, petty, selfish; she thought only of herself, her needs, her desires; she cared nothing for a sick old woman who was a virtual outsider in this small-minded community with its gossip, its sly sneers, its unfriendliness.

Rachel merely listened to all this without so much as a bat of an eye before calmly turning on her heel and walking out of the room, leaving Jon to console his mother as best he could. He finally hit on the only solution he could think of, that of suggesting she could go over to Anton and Babbie's for the evening, and rushed to Croft na Ard next morning to guiltily tell them the news.

They had received his rather garbled explanation with admirable poise and so Mamma had been delivered to their doorstep late that afternoon, complete with a pack of cards, which she loved to play and could never get Rachel interested in, a quantity of cold ham for her tea because she was afraid of the 'stodgy' Scottish food, and her soap bag and talcum powder, since she might as well avail herself of 'the soak' while the opportunity presented itself.

In truth, Jon was glad that his mother wasn't at the ceilidh – he knew she would have talked too long and too loudly about herself, as Rachel had said. As it was, it had been an exceptional evening and he had enjoyed it, but now, seeing his wife and Otto so attuned to one another in every way, he was wishing that he hadn't come either and he turned away from the sight of them, his sensitive face pensive, his brown eyes bewildered and hurt.

He wasn't the only one to see that there was something going on between Otto and Rachel, Ruth too watched and wondered, and as the evening wore on all her former suspicions returned with renewed force. She hadn't seen nearly so much of her old friend as she had hoped, when Rachel came to Fàilte it was almost as if she did so more from a sense of duty than from a real desire to visit, but her pleasure in seeing the children was as genuine as ever. She brought them small gifts, she played with them and entertained them in her own inimitable way, but somehow she didn't have nearly so much to say to Ruth as she used to and after a while she would make some excuse and rush away as if someone or something far more exciting awaited her.

'She's frightened you might start asking awkward questions,' Lorn said when Ruth broached the subject. 'She knows you only too well and doesn't want to be forced into a corner.'

'And just what do you mean by that, Lorn McKenzie?' Ruth flashed at him, tossing her fair hair back from her angry little face. 'What awkward questions would I ask? And why would I force her into a corner?'

'Ruthie,' Lorn said with a sigh. 'You know full well what I mean. Rachel and you are like sisters, you can almost read one another's minds. She knows that you were suspicious about her and Otto, she's aware that there has been talk and she just doesn't want to hear you lowering yourself to the ranks of the island gossips, that's all.'

'Oh, that's all, is it?' Ruth returned tearfully. 'Well, she doesny know me as well as she thinks she does, I would never stoop as low as Behag or Elspeth, or any o' the other scandalmongers o' this place! I'll admit I thought she was growing a bit too fond of Otto but Jon's home now and all that's over and done with!'

But now Ruth wasn't so sure – she saw what Jon saw, she

thought what Jon thought – she glanced at him and noticed the flush of humiliation staining his thin face and her heart went out to him. She and he had been through all this once before; Lorn had come back to her, more loving, more devoted than he had ever been, but would Rachel ever be truly Jon's? Could that exciting, beautiful, restless creature ever truly be any man's one and only love?

A sudden burst of gypsy music filled the room, Rachel had seized her violin and she was playing in a fever of wild abandon, her black hair falling over her face, her dark eyes shining in passionate acknowledgment of music, and love and life.

Her roving, mischievous glance fell on Ruth. She smiled; Ruth didn't return the smile, instead she pretended not to see it and turned away from it as if it was a wicked thing unworthy of response.

Rachel didn't notice, her smiles didn't reach her heart, she only played her violin to cover up for Otto who had gone upstairs to take the pills that would ease the spasms of pain that had suddenly seized him.

The minutes passed. All the attention was focused on her, her flying fingers, the evocative, carefree tunes spilling effortlessly out. When Otto came back, her bursting lungs let go of the air she had held in while she waited for him. He threw her a glance of reassurance together with a slight nod, signifying there was nothing to be afraid of.

She smiled at him, she wanted to take him in her arms and soothe away his hurt and his fears. Two people in the room saw the meaningful glances and they each felt sick at heart and terribly alone in their doubts and worries about the future.

Chapter Sixteen

It was official! Captain Mac was moving in with Elspeth! Bob the Shepherd, who owned a fine new van that he had bought from a win on the football pools, was there at the gate of Elspeth's cottage, helping Captain Mac move in his few bits and pieces of possessions.

The old shepherd was wearing a grim expression on his weatherbeaten countenance because never, never, had he imagined that any man, far less one of Mac's intelligence, could sign away his freedom in such a rash manner and to that sour-faced cailleach into the bargain.

Bob had never allowed himself to 'fall into a woman's clutches', as he put it. When his win on the pools had become common knowledge, half the spinsters on the island had tried to ingratiate themselves into his favours but he was having none of that and had soon sent them packing with a few choice words.

The prospect of marriage had never entered his head until the advent of 'Aunt Grace' Donaldson on to the island, but she had gone and wed herself to Old Joe whose death last autumn had left the way clear for Bob. But out of respect for Joe they had decided to wait 'a whilie' and now the old shepherd was impatiently waiting for her to say the word. He had never met a woman like Grace: she was an excellent cook, she kept her home spick and span, yet she liked to see a man smoking his pipe and enjoying a dram. Her sense of humour was frank and down to earth, she never put on airs and graces for anybody, and more importantly, she was a warm-hearted, kindly little soul with a way about her of making a man feel he was the most wonderful being that the world had ever produced, yet she never cloyed or clung or did any of the things that other women of Bob's experience were inclined to and he could hardly wait to leave his lonely biggin on the slopes of Ben Machrie and move with her to the fine house he had bought for her some time ago.

Ay, Grace was a woman any man would want in his home, but that Elspeth was a different kettle of fish altogether with her vinegary nature, her razor-sharp tongue and an inclination to cleck and gossip about everybody's business except her own.

Bob was not the only one to hold these views. In general, the men of the island were flabbergasted to think that any man in his right mind could willingly lay himself bare to the dangers of such an arrangement – and 'wi' that greetin' faced cailleach too.'

'She'll chew him up and spit him out in wee pieces,' said Tam in disgust. 'Thon poor man o' hers led a dog's life and was aye glad to get back to sea just to get away from her endless nagging.'

'Ay, I mind o' the poor bugger drinkin' himself senseless just so's he could sleep away the hours on dry land,' nodded Jim Jim solicitously, even though he'd had plenty of altercations with the deceased Hector in his lifetime.

'It wasny all Elspeth's fault,' Robbie dared to say uncomfortably. 'Hector aye had a drouth on him for strong drink, long before he ever wed himself to the cailleach. I mind when he was just a lad, drinkin' himself sober at the ceilidhs, pickin' a fight wi' anybody he could and tryin' to get the lassies into a corner wi' just one thing on his mind.'

Tam grinned appreciatively. 'Oh ay, Hector was aye good at gettin' his hands up the lassies' skirts. How he ever came to pick Elspeth for his wife beats me for I doubt he would get his fingers bitten off him if he tried that on wi' her.'

'I heard tell she was hot stuff in her time,' Jim Jim murmured cryptically.

'Ach, you're blethering!' hooted the men. 'The only thing that was ever hot about Elspeth was her tongue!'

'Na, na,' Jim Jim insisted. 'One time, when she was just a bit girl, she near went mad wi' lust one night at a village dance. She had been having a wee fly tipple to herself and the whisky must have done things to her blood, for it was said she got this poor innocent lad into a hayshed and just about tore the breeks off him in her hurry to get at his equipment. In no time at all she had overpowered him and, by jingo!, she let him have it – the lot – everything was hangin' out! She was plumper then, wi' good rounded hips on her and breasts as fine and rosy as any man could wish for. She went at that poor lad till he was raw and done in and pleadin' for mercy but she wouldny let him go till all her fire was spent and she lay back, laughin' and gaspin' like a hoor wi' the croup.'

Jim Jim's eyes were gleaming; the men looked at him. Tam's big happy smile beamed out. 'You fly old bugger!' he said delightedly. 'The innocent young lad wi' the unwilling equipment! By God! Now I've heard everything! I thought I knew all there was to know on this island but it just goes to show, there's aye some juicy wee titbit lurking about in the haysheds!'

Jim Jim had turned bright scarlet, he tried hard to plead innocence but to no avail. His cronies forgot the fate of Captain Mac and turned instead to 'teasing the breeks' off poor old Jim Jim who squirmed as his weak bladder filled up, and prayed that none of this would reach the ears of his wife Isabel who fondly believed that she had hooked 'a virgin mannie' when she had taken Jim Jim to be her lawfully wedded husband.

The womenfolk were generally more tolerant than the men and told one another that the pair 'couldny do much harm at their age.'

'Good luck to the sowels – Captain Mac needs somebody to look after him and Elspeth is just a poor lonely cratur' who needs a good man about the place,' Kate intoned magnanimously, even though she was hugging herself at the idea of being able to 'torment the shat out the cailleach' now that she had 'a man biding wi' her in sin.'

Behag was not one of those to wish Elspeth luck. She was beside herself with self-righteous disapproval of such an immoral arrangement, while inwardly a glow of excitement smouldered:

she had waited a long time for this day and she went scuttling indoors to polish her spyglasses in readiness.

As for Captain Mac, he didn't give a fig for all the speculation about his decision to live with Elspeth. He was heartily sick of his unsettled way of life and was actually looking forward to 'putting his feets up in comfort' and to sitting down at a table where the food was that good you were 'feart to eat it in case it would disappear.'

His cousin, Gus, who was eighty and a worse cook than Mac himself, had not been an easy man to live with. At night his snores resounded through the house. He dropped food into his beard and ate the particles as and when he found them, hours or days later. He did terrible things with his nose: sometimes he pummelled it till it squeaked wetly, other times he picked it and wasn't too fussy where he wiped his fingers afterwards, but mostly he drew it over the already glazed surface of his sleeve, and with that same sleeve he often took it into his head to polish the beer glasses.

He wheezed, grunted and cackled when he was listening to a wireless set that was as ancient as himself. It was powered by an accumulator and it crackled and groaned in unison with the old man. To make matters worse, Gus was half deaf, and kept the volume of the wireless turned up at full blast so that it was difficult to make out anything for all the noise.

He broke wind at the table – from both ends of his anatomy, great gusting burps, loud generous belches, combining so boisterously with the other sounds that Mac was frequently moved to wonder how anybody could produce such rip-roaring eruptions and still remain intact.

Gus kept three ferrets in his wee hoosie at the bottom of his overgrown garden. All his life he had kept ferrets to catch the rabbits which formed a greater part of his diet. But now he wasn't as active as he used to be in that respect and the little creatures had become restless due to lack of employment. In their desire for action they rattled the spars of their cages and altogether combined to make such a din that Mac was loath to visit the place after dark, with the result that half of the time he was constipated and the other half he was running to the wee hoosie, several times in a day, owing to the laxatives he was forced to take to keep his bowels from 'going out o' business altogether'.

On one memorable occasion one of the ferrets had escaped and had bitten Mac on his well-rounded bottom just as he had dropped his trousers on one of his 'cascara runs'. His yells had brought Gus running, a sight which in itself was well worth seeing as one leg was 'laid up wi' the rheumatics' and the other was 'seized up' owing to a war wound from his Merchant Navy days. The resulting stilted gait had once been described by an observer as 'a hirpling hen wi' the gout', which was an apt, if picturesque, summary of the old man's condition.

He had been totally unsympathetic about poor Mac's wounds, being more concerned about the safety of his ferret than anything else, and had yelled on his cousin to do something about catching 'the buggering thing'. But all Mac could do was hop about from one foot to the other in a mixture of pain from his bites and frustration in knowing that his calls of nature were receding further and further into the distance till soon they would be lost beyond recall.

Gus had caught his buggering ferret, but Mac's bite marks had festered and he had been forced to call out Megan and had had to suffer the untold humiliation of 'baring his bum to the leddy doctor'.

The same lady doctor had only just managed to keep a straight face in the course of her administrations to Mac's private parts, but the minute she stepped outside the house she had erupted into helpless laughter and had had to run to her car with her hanky stuffed tightly against her face just in case anybody should be looking from the window.

It had taken Mac a long time to forgive his cousin for that painful episode in his life. He hadn't been able to sit down comfortably for days and was so afraid of going to the wee hoosie he had again become badly constipated and this time he'd had to visit Megan in her surgery on an embarrassing quest for 'something to ease his blocked tubes', which was the only

207

way he could think of to describe his problem without too much damage to his pride. Megan, completely misunderstanding, had produced her stethoscope to solemnly listen to his chest, and he had left her surgery with a bottle of cough medicine, his 'tubes' becoming more blocked by the minute. Next day, in complete desperation he had gone back to her, and almost dying of shame he had blurted out the exact nature of his trouble, the red stain on his normally happy countenance concerning her so much she had taken his blood pressure and sounded his heart for good measure.

After that, Mac hadn't spoken to Gus for a week but that didn't worry the old man, he had a number of cronies the same age as himself who came to play cards till all hours and who drank rum the likes of which Mac would only have used to rinse out his chamber pot.

So all in all Mac was mighty glad to escape his cousin for a while, though the old man assured him his bed was 'aye ready', adding with a wicked chuckle, 'fleas and all'.

Gus had never married, and little wonder was Mac's opinion, no self-respecting woman would have put up with him for one minute – though, of course – and at this juncture in his musings Mac's jolly bulbous nose turned a shade paler – he must have been young at one time and possibly quite eligible, which just went to show how dangerous it was for anybody to marry anybody.

Mac's thoughts were rather garbled at this point and in his dismay he vowed afresh to keep Elspeth at a safe distance and never to let her think for one moment that theirs was anything more than a purely business arrangement.

Though Elspeth was absolutely overjoyed at having Mac in her home at last, not one muscle of her stern face gave away the fact. She was determined to show him that theirs was a purely platonic friendship – for the moment – and she allowed him to settle in at his leisure, giving him ample time to arrange his room the way he wanted, never saying a word when the smell of tobacco smoke filtered hazily downstairs and all through the house.

208

In fact, she stood at the sink and positively revelled in the manly odour. It had been many years since a pipe was smoked in her home and it was good, oh so good, to have a man about the place again and one that she was truly fond of into the bargain.

She spent the afternoon concocting a mouthwatering evening meal, a strange little drone issuing from her throat, which was the nearest she ever got to singing as she worked. Phebie had said she could have the day off, after they had come to an agreement that Elspeth should now only work part-time at Slochmhor, except when Mac went off on one of his frequent fishing trips or to his sister Nellie's house on the island of Hanaay.

Phebie was secretly delighted that at last she would have her house to herself more often. When the children had been at home and when she herself had been kept constantly busy helping Lachlan run his practice, Elspeth's help had been more than welcome, but though he was now retired and Fiona and Niall married with homes of their own, Elspeth still clung to the belief that she was indispensable and that no one knew how to look after Lachlan the way she did. There had been times when Phebie could have screamed with the frustration of being bossed about in her own kitchen but both she and Lachlan put up with it because Elspeth had been such a longstanding and faithful housekeeper and a staunch devotee of the entire McLachlan family.

To have turned her away in her lonely old age was simply unthinkable to the kindly McLachlans but now Mac had afforded them a way out and Phebie could have personally pinned a medal on his chest so relieved was she that he had provided a solution to her problems.

So quite a few lightened hearts went about their business that fateful day of Mac's move. He himself began to feel more at ease as the day wore on and nothing very terrible happened to make him feel threatened in any way. Indeed, it was a pleasure to be in Elspeth's home, which was clean without being clinical and tidy without being too orderly. Here there was no loud blaring

209

wireless to contend with, just the nice rhythmic tick of the 'waggit the wa'' clock, the singing of peats in the cosy hearth – and no Gus picking food from his beard or picking his nose behind a crumpled edition of the *Oban Times*, which would later be torn into untidy squares for use in the wee hoosie.

Elspeth's wee hoosie was a pleasure to visit, discreetly situated as it was behind a flourishing floribunda rose where bees buzzed and the perfume of the flowers invaded the air. The wee hoosie itself was a small, private world with a good big snib on the door. Real toilet paper hung on a properly placed holder, a lavender-smelling air freshener dangled from the low roof and the floor was cosily covered in flower-sprigged carpeting. On a tiny shelf sat a basin and a jugful of water with a bar of white toilet soap nearby; behind the lavatory pan stood a bucket of water to flush toilet waste down into a pipe and from there to a crude septic tank that Hector had built in his more sober and visionary days. It was a unique arrangement, much envied by those neighbours who only had dry lavatories, which had to be laboriously emptied at least three times a week.

Mac was much taken by it and spent some time examining its structure before his eye took to roving once more. It was surprisingly bright in the small enclosure – white painted walls reflected light from a tiny muslin covered window. A picture of a kneeling, virginal-looking woman dressed in white, with tightly clasped hands held to her lips, hung in a strategic position. Mac gulped when he saw it. A small stab of anxiety pierced his contentment: he knew that Elspeth was a fairly religious woman but wasn't this taking matters just a bit too far?

Then he chuckled, maybe she was like him, praying for a good deliverance as she sat in the wee hoosie, staring at the picture. Perhaps she found inspiration and hope in those praying hands – for all he knew, maybe she emulated the action and sang a hymn or two as well – anything was possible in a wee hoosie of any sort and the old sea dog thoroughly enjoyed his first visit to this tiny sanctum. He even remembered to wash his hands and place the towel carefully back on its hook, and when he emptied the pail down the pan he went dutifully to fill it again from the old well near the house.

At teatime Elspeth served up a delicious and filling meal, she was attentive to his needs without fussing and when it was over he sat back replete, telling her that it was the best food he had tasted for a long time and that she was 'a grand cook'.

'Ach well, tis a long time since I had a man in the house to cook for,' she said primly, her eyes turned down so that he wouldn't see how much his compliments pleased her. 'I'm used to doing for Lachlan and Phebie but somehow it is just that wee bittie better when I'm working at my own stove.'

He rose to his feet, offering to help with the dishes but she pushed him back, saying that he wasn't to do woman's work, and directed him instead to sit down and smoke his pipe as she 'fair enjoyed the reek o' it.'

Mac's cup was full to overflowing when evening came round and it was just him and Elspeth, seated at opposite sides of the fire, she quietly darning, he smoking his pipe, his stockinged feet firmly planted on the hearth, his tot of rum at his side, his large hairy-backed hands holding firm on the poker as he waited for it to grow red hot in the glowing heart of the fire.

'It's nice this, Elspeth,' he said contentedly, his big, happy nose glowing redder by the minute from the fire's heat.

'Ay, it is that, Isaac,' she returned. 'It makes a change to have a bit o' company in the evenings.'

Picking up his rum he held it against the lamplight so that he could enjoy what he called the 'ruby lights dancing in the glass'. He always did this before downing the liquid, it was a prelude to anticipated enjoyment, a moment to reflect the quiet, good things of life and the simple pleasures yet to come.

The poker was almost ready. Mac made to withdraw it from the embers but Elspeth's hand came out to enclose his. 'Let me do that for you, Isaac,' she said and without hesitation she plunged the red-hot tip of the poker into the glass of rum. As the sizzle and scent of burnt rum filled the air, Mac's nostrils twitched, for no smell on earth was sweeter to him than that, it brought back memories of seafaring days when hot rum had chased the cold from his bones and heated the blood in his veins.

'Ay, tis a grand smell,' Elspeth said, much to Mac's surprise. 'It minds me o' my father, sitting warm by the fire after a day half frozen tending his sheep on the hill. He wasny what you would call a drinking man but he liked his tot rum and my mother never minded, for she knew well enough how hard he worked his bit croft. There he would sit, his feet on the hearth, she rubbing the chill from his hands and when the time was ripe, taking the poker from the fire to thrust it into the glass. I used to sit back and watch and never to this night have I seen and smelt the likes. Tonight you minded me o' those times, they were hard but happy and I often think how it used to be when Mother and Father were alive.'

Her eyes had grown moist. It was a side of Elspeth that Mac had never dreamed could exist. He moved uncomfortably in his chair and placed one big purpled hand over hers, he made a few soothing noises and told her that when he stayed with his sister Nellie on Hanaay they often sat at the fire talking over the old days when their parents had been alive.

'Ay, lass,' he said softly, 'they were the best times o' our lives, when we were young and all the world was busy and full and our mother and father aye to hand to listen to our ails and worries.'

Elspeth sniffed, impatiently she drew a hand over her eyes. 'Ach, I'm just a silly old woman,' she said gruffly, 'but if you don't mind, Isaac, I'd like a spot o' your rum – just to keep you company, of course,' she added hastily and with a touch of her old asperity.

Mac stared, he chuckled, he poured her a small quantity of spirits and for the rest of the evening the two of them sat, companionably sipping burnt rum and reminiscing about their individual upbringings. The hours slipped easily by and he didn't even mind when she demanded one of his socks so that she could mend the hole in it while her darning box was out.

There was something very comforting about a woman with

busy hands. Mac hadn't enjoyed himself so much for a long time. He discovered that Elspeth wasn't nearly as strait-laced as she would have everyone believe: she laughed at some of Mac's cleaner jokes and made one or two quite rude ones of her own, she was also a fairly good mimic and at one point had him holding on to his stomach as she imitated Behag's mournful tones and made an astonishingly accurate portrayal of Holy Smoke's actions in his butcher's shop, and another of Canty Tam's leering grin and predictions of gloom and doom.

But as bedtime drew nearer Elspeth reverted to her old self. Her tones became brisk as she informed Mac that there were certain rules in her home that must be adhered to, no smoking in bed was one, breakfast at eight sharp was another, 'and of course,' she went on firmly, 'we like to steep ourselves in the tub twice weekly, Monday nights and again on Saturday to make ourselves decent for the Sabbath.'

'We?' Mac hazarded faintly, and when she said it was only a figure of speech she sometimes used he thought to himself she was just emulating a certain queen of Victorian times who had first coined the expression.

'I'll no' expect you to accompany me to the kirk, Isaac,' she continued. 'Only if you have a mind to do so and only if you want to be seen wi' me; I'll no' force you to do anything you don't want, so you need have no fears on that score.'

Mac was mighty glad of that: he was still reeling from the shock of having to 'steep' twice weekly, for, even though he was very fussy about his appearance and kept his white beard and hair squeaky clean, he was otherwise wont to have a quick sponge-down in front of the fire when it suited him, and not before, since it was his belief that too much water was a bad thing for the skin. But on the whole he thought that her requests were reasonable enough and told her so, adding that he hoped she didn't mind but he would be going off fishing with the lads early on Monday morning.

She didn't mind, in fact she was positively anxious for him to pursue his usual wanderings, adding, 'They will be needing me at Slochmhor. Phebie tries but will never admit she's no use at

213

all when it comes to running a home and, of course, Lachlan must have proper food and has aye relied on me for that.'

After that the pair retired to bed on the best of terms, each going their sedate and separate ways. But the second Elspeth's door closed on her she stood with her back to it, pressing her clasped hands to her mouth, a spot of crimson burning high on each gaunt cheekbone. He would be off on Monday! She could hardly wait for it to come! At last! At last! She would have the moment she had been waiting for all these weeks and a strange little strangulated gurgle of excitement broke from her throat as she thought about Monday with shining eyes.

Late on Monday morning Behag looked from her window and saw a row of flimsy garments hanging on Elspeth's washing line, completely unlike the usual assortment of sensible vests, flannel nighties, and long-legged knickers. There had been a time when Behag was shocked to see pink silk bloomers on the line but this – this was beyond belief and rushing for her spyglasses she focused them on Elspeth's drying green. What she saw nearly gave her apoplexy for there, flapping gaily about for all the world to see, was a row of satin lingerie and nightwear, the like of which Behag had only ever seen in a brochure full of sex aids and sensual garments that had been sent to her from some firm with a London address.

Behag never knew how such a publication had found its way into her home. She had been shocked to the core, she had thrown it in the bucket, she had vowed never to set eyes on it again – but it had haunted her. In her head she kept seeing things she had never dreamed existed; she had fought a terrible battle with her conscience and after much anguish and soul-searching she had guiltily retrieved the glossy leaflet from her bin and had avidly devoured every page. Praying that nothing and no one would disturb her, she had studied each illustration from every angle. With popping eyes she had stared at weird contrivances designed to be attached to the human body to induce 'the ultimate in sexual pleasure'.

She had been appalled, amazed, intrigued, for in her innocence

214

she had imagined that human beings only needed their own natural accoutrements to get through life and even then, the good Lord had only meant them to be used for the means of procreation. At this point she had blushed profusely as even to dwell on such matters was to her mind the ultimate sign of degradation.

She then turned her attention to the garment section, which bore the heading, 'Things to Please the Man in Your Life'. Luscious silk pants and peep-hole bras; furry knickers – here Behag gulped and wondered if they tickled – see-through black nighties; things that were described as G-strings which seemed to cover nothing at all and must have been extremely uncomfortable to wear; sheer black stockings; frilly garters . . .

Eagerly she flipped over the pages until she got the biggest shock of all: a whole section devoted to 'our exciting selection of the latest in rubber wear' – figure-hugging trouser suits; black masks with evil-looking eye slits; others with what looked like mini-elephant trunks where the nose should be. Behag paused – it couldn't be . . . it was! Her eyes nearly fell out her head. Why would they want to put a thing like that on a mask when men had been created with perfectly efficient ones in their trousers . . . ?

She couldn't go on, violently she hurled the offending literature into the fire then scuttled as fast as her legs would carry her to the sideboard wherein was kept the 'medicinal whisky'. On this occasion Behag felt fully justified in helping herself to a good tipple and she sat back, her glass held tight in her shaky hand, her palsied head nodding to and fro as she watched the flames licking the elephant trunks and the peep-hole bras. Never, she vowed, would she look at such degenerate trash again – and now here was Elspeth, brazenly displaying the fact that she was a fallen woman who had succumbed to wicked temptation and vice. True, the things on her line were more glamorous than shocking but even so, Elspeth and Captain Mac must be having a fine time to themselves, the evidence was there for everyone to see, flagrantly displayed without subtlety or shame . . . the . . . the hussy!

And wait! Wasn't that Elspeth herself coming out to survey

her washing with a decided air of satisfaction? She had turned, something in her hand glinted, she was holding it to her eyes and – Behag's heart jumped, her face grew hot – the saucy besom! *She was standing there with a pair of spyglasses, watching to see if Behag was watching her!*

Behag quickly turned her own spyglasses away from Elspeth's domain and pretended to pan them over the rugged slopes of Sgurr nan Ruadh, trying hard as she did so to compose her bloodhound features into lines of complete and perfect innocence.

Elspeth lowered what she called her 'peepscope' and laughed till the tears ran down her face. No one who knew her would have believed she could have been capable of such abandoned mirth but then, never before in her life had she done anything so daring, and she scuttled into the house to hurl herself into a chair where she hugged herself in a gluttony of self-satisfied glee and wondered who would be the next to notice the contents of her washing line.

Chapter Seventeen

As expected, Behag was not the only one to notice the contents of Elspeth's washing line: everyone who had to pass her house to get to the village couldn't help but see the display of silks and satins dancing gaily in the breezes. It was a provocative sight and in the main the reactions ranged from downright shock to disbelief, and – in some cases – amusement.

If it had been Rachel's washing it would possibly have merited a few dry comments but would have been allowed to pass since she was 'a young woman o' the world wi' a lot o' fancy ideas inside her head'. The same might have applied to many of the younger island girls who shopped a lot by mail order catalogue, and even if they couldn't be described as women of the world they were certainly prone to much temptation as they perused glossy pages containing the latest in feminine fashions.

The older women also made use of mail order catalogues but their interests lay mainly in good sensible garments, both for their menfolk and themselves, and if they considered under-garments at all it was with practicalities in mind and they were apt to settle for things that would help them combat the rigours of long, cold winter days and nights.

It was therefore not surprising that they could hardly believe the evidence of their own eyes when they surveyed the array of frilly knickers, seductive nighties and lacy petticoats pegged in such a way on the line as to show the plunging necklines, the frothy edgings . . . and . . . when rays of sunshine slanted from behind, the transparent quality of the material.

It wasn't long before a small group of housewives were huddled together in the village street, talking about Elspeth in hushed tones – except for beings like Old Sorcha whose deafness led her to the assumption that, in common with herself, everyone had to be shouted at; and folk like Kate McKinnon who very seldom whispered about anything and who certainly had no intention of discussing Slochmhor's housekeeper in a subtle manner.

'The cailleach has been acting gey strange this whilie back,' she stated with conviction. 'In my opinion she is going off her head altogether and Mac had better watch that she doesny murder him in his bed one o' these fine nights.'

'Ach, come on now, Kate,' said Isabel nervously. 'There is no need to go that far, she is just having a wee bit fling to herself before it's too late. She will settle down when she comes to her senses and if I know Elspeth that will be sooner rather than later.'

Kate exploded: 'A fling! Surely you are no' trying to tell us she's sowing her wild oats at her age! She scattered those long ago if she scattered them at all . . . though, mind you' – she eyed Isabel contemplatively as Tam's tale about Jim Jim's youthful experiences with Elspeth in the hayshed leapt suddenly into her lively mind – 'from what I've been hearing about her she's no' aye been as prudish as she makes out. Seemingly she robbed at least one mannie o' his virginity way back in the year dot and for all we know, there could have been others.'

Isabel looked at her askance and the others clamoured to know more, but Kate, feeling rather ashamed at divulging what had been a confidence, declined to enlarge on the subject, much to the chagrin of her cronies.

'Ach, it is just a lot o' fuss about nothing,' Aggie McKinnon suggested in her fat, gentle voice. 'Elspeth has as much right as anyone to wear nice things if she wants to and surely it is nobody's business but her own if she hangs them out to dry in her own green, I would do the same if they were mine and be proud o' it.'

Secretly, Aggie longed to be able to wear the kind of things that were the talk of the moment, but with her physical proportions it was out of the question, though that didn't stop her from dreaming or from poring over the enticing displays of feminine garments in her own mail order catalogue.

Kate glanced sympathetically at Aggie's generous rolls of flesh. 'Och well, you are a young woman and would have every right to wear such things if you wanted,' she said kindly and the others nodded for, despite their talk about Elspeth, it would be apt to say that more than just one of them had, at some time in their lives, hankered to be glamorous and to look as seductive as the film stars they gazed at on the silver screen on their shopping trips to the mainland.

At this point they were joined by one or two of the menfolk who had been 'fair tickled' at the sight of Elspeth's smalls, even though they wondered at Captain Mac's rashness in allowing himself to be taken in by 'a few wisps o' lace' that wouldn't decently have covered a 'clockin' hen's arse'.

None of them could picture Elspeth in frills and froth, and Robbie, grinning from ear to ear, echoed Aggie's words when he told the women, 'It is just a flash in the pan and will blow over in no time at all. It is none o' our business what other folks do wi' theirs and it might be better if we don't say a word to either Captain Mac or Elspeth.'

'Ay,' agreed Tam, whose embarrassment for the old seafarer was as acute as if it had been Kate displaying 'her goods' on the washline, 'he wouldny like it if he thought we had been washin' his dirty linen in public . . .'

He paused, surprised at himself for the paradoxical turn of phrase. Robbie grinned dryly, the women giggled, making Tam feel that he had said something really quite amusing.

At this juncture Sorcha looked over Kate's head and in her excitement at what she saw turned her deaf aid down and exclaimed in her loudest tones, 'Well, some folk have no shame and that's a fact! Fancy, the cheek o' it!'

As one, every head swivelled round and there was 'the hussy' herself, calmly making for Merry Mary's shop, swinging her shopping bag in an oddly carefree manner, her head held proud and high, not one single muscle betraying anything but the utmost confidence as she paused for a moment to haughtily survey the tight little gathering in the street before she marched firmly into Merry Mary's.

'I'll say this for her,' said Tam, 'she aye did handle herself well and you can bet your boots she'll no' stand anything from you lot if you as much as breathe one word about her frilly knickers.'

'The thought never entered my mind, Tam McKinnon!' Kate said indignantly, hoisting her own shopping bag into a prominent position. 'Her knickers, and what she does wi' them, is no concern o' mine and I'll thank you no' to keep me back a minute longer. I have my messages to get and Mary said she would keep me a fresh loaf and a bag o' rolls which I said I would collect before ten o' the clock – so, if you'll be excusin' me . . .'

Along the pavement she marched with alacrity, followed by her cronies anxious not to miss any of the fun that would surely develop in Merry Mary's premises. Kate might not come right out with anything that could be construed as straightforward cheek but, mischievous devil that she was, she would hint and tease and torment Elspeth unmercifully, and it was always interesting to see how a situation like that would develop.

Only Aggie hung back. She was a kindly, soft-hearted soul and she had no great desire to hear the formidable Kate tearing poor old Elspeth to pieces, she would visit the Post Office first and by the time she got back to Merry Mary's it might be quieter and she could shop at her leisure while she waited for the bus.

Mamma had had enough of the house, so, squaring her shoulders, she set off briskly in the direction of Portcull. It was a beautiful day: Mara Òran Bay sparkled in the sun, the translucent green water was calm and peaceful though a lively breeze rippled the blue surface of the Sound so that it sparkled and shone in a myriad of breathtaking colours.

The lapwing chicks had grown into downy speckled balls with long legs that carried them swiftly through the grass, but the parent birds were never far away and the minute they sent out their alarm calls down the chicks cooried till danger was past. Skylarks sang in the blue vault of the sky, a glorious tumble of sound that seemed never-ending, for as soon as one bird swooped to the ground another would rise up, warbling out a joyous melody that peaked to a crescendo high above the earth. The scents of summer perfumed the air – Anton was cutting his hayfields – the rich, sweet smell drenched Mamma's senses as she walked along, wearing only a print dress and a cotton cardigan.

Something about the wide, clean beauty of the Hebridean landscape touched Mamma's awareness. She paused to gaze over the heat-hazed moors rolling away to the velvet green slopes of Ben Machrie; she looked with appreciation at the great cliffs of Burg in the distance, misty and blue, plunging down to meet the deeper blue of the ocean. The journey over those same cliffs in Erchy's bus had paled a little in her memory; she hadn't been back to the village since that day but had decided that morning it was now or never to take the bull by the horns and face once again those dreadful island women.

Mamma was badly in need of some stimulating company. Jon was very quiet these days and was withdrawn and pensive; Rachel was also preoccupied with her thoughts and took herself off on long walks so that she was hardly ever in the house, and when she was she spent her time moping in her room and seldom played her violin, much to Jon's bafflement. Relations between the two were somewhat strained, but for once Mamma didn't dare say anything in case she got her head chewed off. She hadn't yet forgiven Rachel for her rudeness – the girl was positively bad mannered, she had scant respect for her elders and seemed unable to tell the difference between right and wrong – but of course, what else could one expect, springing as she had from a background in which no one had much grasp of life's little niceties.

The dazzling white houses of Portcull were drawing closer; Mamma's steps slowed, she stopped swinging her string shopping bag and clutched at it instead. Passing Ranald's craft shop she received pleasant nods from one or two people she didn't know and had no wish to know. The harbour was quiet with only some fishermen spreading their nets and a row of pipe-smoking old

221

men sitting on the wall. From them she received curious glances together with a few friendly grins. The amount of teeth those smiles revealed depended on the age of the worthies: toothless gaps were much in evidence and some had no teeth at all. Mamma thought it disgraceful that anybody should appear in public without teeth – especially in this day and age when a good set of dentures were easily come by. She didn't stop to consider that 'a good set of dentures' were rather difficult to procure on an island where 'the dentist mannie' only visited twice a year. This meant that for the rest of the time the islanders had to visit a mainland dentist, or, in the case of the old and infirm, keep their ill-fitting 'teeths' steeping in a cup, except for the purpose of masticating food, or for Sabbath vigils in kirk when they were given an airing for cosmetic purposes.

'Sour-faced cailleach,' muttered Hector the Boat as Mamma went on her unsmiling way, heading first for the butcher's shop because she had heard that he kept very good home-grown meat.

Holy Smoke's eyes gleamed when he peered between a row of black puddings hanging in his window and saw her approaching. Quite unconsciously he rubbed his hands together: he hadn't yet encountered Jon's mother and saw only a 'towrist', a foreigner at that, no doubt with plenty of money to spend and only a hazy idea of the value of British currency. No one else was in the shop, they were too busy gossiping about some silly petticoats old Elspeth had hung on her wash-line, and for once the butcher was pleased to have empty premises, since the presence of Kate or Barra would only undermine his influence over this promisingly ignorant customer.

But Mamma had had ample time to do her homework and she made mincemeat of Holy Smoke. With magnificent aplomb she sailed majestically into the shop, grimacing as flakes of sawdust worked their way into her open-toed sandals to irritate her feet. Wasting no time she demanded to be served with frankfurter sausages, when these weren't forthcoming she flared her nostrils impatiently and turned her attention to the neat lines of black and white puddings dangling from hooks behind the counter.

Holy Smoke's confidence returned and he spent several minutes praising the merits of his home-made mealy puddings, but when he stopped to get his breath it was to the realisation that he might as well not have spoken at all, because his customer had completely lost interest in any of his puddings, be they black or white.

In the end she settled for a large, juicy-looking haggis, three lamb chops, a pound of stew, two kidneys, a small string of plump beef sausages and a quantity of steak mince 'for the cat'.

Mamma didn't have a cat, in fact she wasn't keen on them at all but she wasn't going to tell that to Holy Smoke. When he had deftly wrapped her meat into a bulky package and was toting up the price, Mamma stopped him when he mentioned how much it would be for the mince.

'In my country, cat meat is cheap,' she said haughtily. 'The same applies here, does it not? I give you sixpence, no more, no less.'

Holy Smoke's face turned purple, Kate would have revelled in his discomfiture and would have patted Mamma on the back for turning the tables on him.

'Sixpence!' he cried. 'My dear lady, I'll have you know, I gave you the best mince in the shop! I'm no' a rich man by any means and if . . .'

'I am not your dear lady,' Mamma said firmly, 'and I take myself out of your shop with nothing if you persist in cheating me just because you see before you a woman who is not of this place. Cheap cat meat – or nothing.'

It took the butcher all his time not to argue back but he had his reputation to think of and, muttering darkly under his straggly limp moustache, he marked up sixpence against the mince even though it went against his grain.

Mamma, however, had not finished with him. When it came to counting the money into his hand she made him so thoroughly confused with her loud, verbal conversions of German and British currencies, he ended up cheating himself of ten shillings and was never so glad to see the back of a customer in all his life.

She left him standing at the counter, shaking his head, his brow furrowed in puzzlement as he went through his list all over again, tapping his head with his pencil, counting with his fingers, growing more and more confused as he mumbled on about German marks and schillings.

Mamma was feeling light-headed with triumph as she left the butcher's shop. No one was going to get the better of her on this island, she had put the boot on the other foot, she had shown that dreadful little meat man who was the boss . . . She straightened her back and puffed out her vast bosoms. She, Frau Helga Jodl, was ready now for anything . . .

Agnes McKinnon was coming along the street, all sixteen stone of her, marching stolidly towards the Post Office, which was situated on Mamma's route. Mamma hadn't forgotten her confrontation with Aggie in Merry Mary's, she had no wish for another, and she shrank back a little as the young woman came thundering along. There was certainly no avoiding this magnificent McKinnon and Mamma girded her loins as she prepared herself for battle.

'It is yourself Mistress Jodl,' greeted Aggie, her round pink face the very essence of good nature, no sign of ill-will in her attitude or in her plumply cosy, lilting voice.

Mamma was completely taken aback and more than a little relieved to be hailed in such a fashion, though she wasn't too sure about the 'mistress' part of it. She had still to learn that in Scotland it was a form of address that frequently took the place of 'Mrs' and was considered a sign of respect in the homes of the gentry where it would have been impolite to refer to the lady of the house as anything else but 'mistress'.

Mamma, however, knew nothing of this but in view of Aggie's friendliness she was prepared to let it pass this once.

'I have been looking out for you,' Aggie went on, 'and I'm right glad we have met, for I have been wanting to say sorry to you for shouting at you in Merry Mary's shop.'

'Say sorry – to me?' Mamma repeated the words in disbelief, no one had apologized to her for anything since her arrival on Rhanna.

'Ay, you see, I was in a hurry, but that was no excuse to talk to you the way I did and you a stranger on the island,' Aggie stated, beaming at the older woman in the most cordial fashion.

Mamma was completely flummoxed. She drew a deep breath. 'Myself, I was rude,' she found herself saying, 'I go first when first is not my place.'

'Och well,' Aggie continued to weave her spell, 'we all make mistakes, and wi' you being new here it must all seem a bittie strange.'

Mamma shook her head sadly. 'It is the same wherever I go: I am rude, I push in my way, I speak too much the mind. People, they tell me I am domineering and unkind.'

It was like uncorking a bottle that had been jammed tightly for a long time but once unstuck it all seemed to pour out. The flow of self-loathing continued, she appeared only too anxious to lay the blame for everything at her own door. Aggie nodded and clucked sympathetically and wondered if she should get envelopes as well as stamps when eventually she got to the Post Office.

Mamma paused for breath, her face crumpled. 'No one likes me, Jon is the only one who has any time for me. My husband, he was the little man, he give in to me whatever I say – it was not good – I never did anything he wanted and now I find it very hard to listen to anything anybody has to say.'

Aggie's soft heart melted, she laid a plump hand on the other's arm. 'Och, there now,' she soothed. 'You mustny worry, it is never too late to mend your ways.'

But Mamma would not be consoled, dismally she shook her head. 'I am not wanted here, Rachel dislikes me more than anyone, I have given her good reason to behave to me as she does. I think, perhaps, I will go back to Hamburg.'

'Oh no, you mustny do that.' Aggie was beginning to feel she had bitten off more than she could handle. 'Give yourself a chance, I'm sure you are a very nice lady underneath your – er – skin.'

Mamma drew a shuddering breath. 'It is no use, no one wants to know me. Jon has Rachel, I am shut out. The feeling in here' – she placed her hands over her massive chest – 'it is of loneliness. They have their music and the secret glances and the funny swaying they call dancing; they have no time for me and will not even play with me the penuckle. I learn it from the Americans after the war but Rachel has no liking for it.'

'*Penuckle!*' Aggie's face lit up, she fairly shouted out the word. 'Oh, I just love penuckle – poker too! Colin my husband is in the Merchant Navy and learned a lot o' card games when he was in America.' She gazed at Mamma with dancing eyes. 'You must come to our house for a wee night wi' the cards, some o' the neighbours come in too and we have a dram while we're playing. No' for money, you understand, well, maybe just a bob or two for the sake o' a bittie excitement. I'll get Rab McKinnon to come over for you tonight in his tractor, you'll fair enjoy yourself.'

During this discourse Mamma's handsome face had been alight with interest but it fell at Aggie's last words, she was remembering that the young woman lived halfway along the cliff road to Nigg. The journey there had been bad enough in Erchy's bus and she had vowed never to attempt it again in any sort of vehicle, far less one of those noisy monsters she had seen lumbering about the island.

'A tractor?' she repeated faintly, the appeal of a cosy evening with the cards diminishing suddenly.

'Och, you need have no fear of that,' Aggie assured her cheerfully. 'It is a very comfortable tractor and Rab is a good careful driver who never touches a drop till he is home safe and dry. The journey won't take long and the summer nights are good and light, and just think, you'll get to play penuckle till it's coming out your ears.'

Mamma was weakening, and in a sudden burst of decision she relented and said she would be happy to come.

Aggie nodded. 'That's settled then. If you care to wait till I come out the Post Office, I'll see you along the road, for I have still to get some things in Merry Mary's before the bus comes.'

'Ah, yes, the bus,' said Mamma, sympathy in her tones for anyone who had to travel that dangerous road in a vehicle that was, to her, equally dangerous.

'Och, I'm used to it.' Aggie laughed and made tracks for the Post Office, in that establishment avoiding a few curious questions as to her conversation with Mamma and making good her escape as soon as her purchases were made.

The two women walked companionably along, heads close together as they chatted.

'They have become bosom pals all of a sudden – in every way that I can see,' said Fingal McLeod, who, in common with a lot of the island men, liked to see a 'well-filled' woman.

'Ay,' agreed Ranald, his gleaming eyes roving appreciatively over Aggie's rear end as she passed by. 'Our Aggie is lookin' well these days – she is cheekier than ever.' He snorted with laughter at his own joke and went on, 'Colin Mor is taking a big risk leaving her as often as he does, there's many a man on Rhanna would jump at the chance of a night o' fun in her bed.'

'Who is the other one?' enquired Rab McKinnon, trying to keep his tone as disinterested as possible. He was sixty, a widower with a strong, weatherbeaten face that seldom gave anything away. His blue eyes looked out calmly on the world but there was a hint of steel in them and though he was mainly a silent man he was a tough advocate if he thought anyone was getting an undeservedly raw deal.

'Jon Jodl's mother,' supplied Murdy readily. 'She's a real tartar from all I hear and played havoc in Merry Mary's shop when she had only newly set foot on the island.'

Rab nodded. 'I heard o' that. They say Kate McKinnon sent her on a wild-goose chase to the other end o' the island where she lost herself on the moor and ended up supping broth at the tinks' camp over by Dunuaigh.' He frowned. 'It wasny nice o' Kate to do that to a stranger, she'll be thinkin' we're all tarred wi' the same brush.'

'Ach, she deserved it,' said Fingal heartlessly. 'She near

227

frightened the shat out o' poor old Dodie when she rode home wi' him in the tink's cart. He said he would rather meet a spook than cross paths wi' her again and hardly goes outside his croft these days in case he might meet her again.'

'Here, talkin' o' Dodie, is Wullie McKinnon doing anything about the cockerels?' asked Ranald. 'I hear tell he canny sleep at night for the noise and is willing to pay someone to do something about it.'

Ranald's eyes were shining, if anything he was even more of a money grubber than Holy Smoke and was always first on the scene when opportunity presented itself.

Rab left the men to their talk and went off to the harbour to wait for the bus, little dreaming that he had been earmarked to chauffeur 'the tartar' to Aggie's croft that very evening, whether he liked it or not.

Merry Mary, remembering her last encounter with Mamma, looked rather worried when that same lady came stomping into the shop with Aggie at her elbow. The little Englishwoman had spent most of her life on Rhanna and was so attuned to island ways, both in speech and manner, that only the very discerning observer could tell she wasn't a born and bred Hebridean.

She thought the same as any islander, her reactions to certain situations were the same, she felt and behaved like an island woman and even looked and sounded like one with her open, honest face, her whimsical speech and her big, cheerful smile that was never far from her mouth.

But she didn't smile when she saw Mamma entering her premises. The shop, which only minutes before had been full of blethering woman, had emptied itself as one by one the customers dispersed about their business, so Merry Mary had no one to back her up should the big bossy German woman start any of her nonsense.

But she needn't have worried, something had happened to Mamma in the last half-hour, she had opened up, she had blossomed, she actually stuck out her hand to seize a hold of Mary's and pump it up and down till the little lady felt sure her arm was about to drop off at any minute with muscle fatigue.

Aggie made her purchases and the three women stood chatting. Mary began to feel so relaxed she was soon leaning her arms on the counter in a characteristic gesture, beaming and nodding so much her limp ginger hair fell over her eyes, giving her the appearance of a rather scruffy tabby who had just spent a harrowing night on the tiles.

She even dared to ask Mamma about her adventures in Erchy's bus, even though Aggie was making warning signs that told her to hold her tongue.

But the change in Mamma, whilst anything but complete, was making rapid progress. She gave such a vivid and funny account of the episode, her broken English only adding spice to the telling, that she soon had the other two laughing and wiping their eyes and, thus encouraged, Mamma then plunged into a vivid description of the scene with Holy Smoke in the butcher's shop.

'You never!' Aggie cried admiringly. 'Oh, wait till I tell Kate, she's aye taking the rise out o' him herself but never has she managed to get one over him as good as that.' She glanced at her watch and gave a little yelp. 'Where has the time gone? The bus will be here soon so I'll just go and wait wi' Rab at the harbour and tell him about tonight.'

Mamma got up from the sack of potatoes on which she had been sitting. 'And I too must go, the dinner will be late in making but the cat, she will enjoy her meat all the more for waiting.'

The sly humour of the remark wasn't lost on Mary or Aggie, they stared at her appreciatively and as she departed the latter called, 'We will be seeing you tonight then, Mistress Jodl.'

'Please to call me Helga,' Mamma requested with dignity and walked away, a spring in her step and a new look of happiness on her hitherto dour and unsmiling countenance.

The change in Mamma became apparent the minute she stepped over the threshold of An Cala. She was humming a catchy little German tune under her breath as she unpacked her shopping bag and placed the things in the meat safe in the cool pantry by the back door. Without a single grumble she went out to the wee hoosie which had been the bane of her life since her arrival on Rhanna. For the first few days she hadn't used it at all for 'certain important functions' with the result that she had 'shat bricks for a week', according to Rachel, and had eventually been forced to take the syrup of figs offered to her by her daughter-in-law who simply couldn't keep the smiles from her face during the administration of the laxative.

After that she used the wee hoosie under great sufferance, but use it she did, complaining all the while about the flies, the midgies, the earwigs, 'the cows who look in the window and lick the panes', the spiders, the cobwebs, in fact everything and anything she could think of to make life uncomfortable for those who had to live with her.

Now, however, she said not a word regarding 'the inconvenience', as she had labelled the outside lavatory, instead, over the midday meal that Rachel had prepared, she regaled the young folk with her morning's adventures, her eyes glinting when she told them about her encounter with Holy Smoke, her face lighting when she recalled her meeting with Aggie.

'Tonight I go to play penuckle in her house, I meet the neighbours, I have the dram and the buttered bannocks that Aggie makes to soak up the whisky. I will not play for real money, only a bob or two to make the game exciting.'

She was really only repeating the things that Aggie had said and she didn't understand half of it but it sounded so funny to hear her talking about 'drams' and 'bobs' in her broken English that both her listeners thoroughly enjoyed her chatter.

So taken was she with the unexpected turn of events she ate every scrap of her meal, even though it was an Italian dish which normally she purported to despise. She even thanked her daughter-in-law for making it before scraping back her chair to tackle the dishes with haste in order that she could go upstairs to look through her wardrobe for something to wear that night.

*   *   *

When Rab duly arrived that evening in his tractor her enthusiasm paled a little, but he wasn't a man to stand any nonsense from anybody and succinctly told her to 'hop in' since the engine was apt to cut out if it idled too long.

Mamma, looking very spruce in her summer finery, climbed into the machine with some difficulty, but a helping pull from one of Rab's brawny arms soon saw her settled beside him and away they went, bumping and lurching on the road to Portcull, she wordless for once, he naturally so since he was a man of few words who 'couldny abide senseless chit-chat.'

Rachel and Jon stood at the door of An Cala watching them go. Such a strong sense of relief invaded them both that they held one another's hands till the tractor was out of sight, before wandering away down to the beach to walk by the sea, revelling in the freedom, delighting in the fact that, at long last, Mamma had found somewhere to go, something to do that she would enjoy, leaving them to pursue the simple joys that had always meant so much to them in leisure hours that were precious and necessary to them in the busy course of their lives.

Part Three

LATE SUMMER 1967

Chapter Eighteen

As the summer progressed the thing uppermost in most people's minds was the imminence of the McKinnon Clan Gathering. A great feeling of anticipation was in the air as people began to make their preparations. The question of what to wear was no problem for the menfolk: Sunday best suits were always to hand, hanging in the wardrobe, carefully preserved in mothballs, ready just to be taken out, brushed down and perhaps given an airing on the wash line if the weather was dry. But for this occasion something rather more special was called for and all over the island, kilts of every conceivable tartan were brought out of wraps to be carefully inspected for wear and tear before being cleaned, mended, and generally made spick and span for the big day.

It wasn't so simple for the womenfolk, however. A bit of appropriate tartan was certainly called for, be it a ribbon, a sash or a brooch, but trimmings like these had to be fixed on to something decent – it wouldn't do to don any old blouse or dress that had been worn dozens of times before – and soon the age-old cry went up, 'I haveny anything to wear! I'm sick o' looking at this old thing! I'll have to get something new!'

The bairns too had to be a credit to their parents at 'Otto's Ceilidh' and so trips to Glasgow or Oban were much to the fore and parcels from mail order catalogues began arriving every other day.

Erchy had seldom been so busy, he grumbled long and hard at all the extra work and for a time was forced to cut his bus schedule to just twice a week, which caused his regular passengers to grumble long and hard also.

Old Magnus of Croy, normally calm and collected, became quite upset when he discovered that the moths had made merry with his kilt, which had been carefully wrapped in tissue and placed in a bride's kist together with camphor-saturated wads and at least a dozen mothballs. But the old man had had little reason to wear Highland dress for at least ten years and somehow the moths and the grubs had invaded the kist. When he at last beheld the damage he shook his head sorrowfully and declared that he 'couldny go to his grandson's gathering looking like a second-hand tink!'

News of his plight soon reached Otto's ears and over to Croy he drove post-haste in Thunder to put his arm round his grandfather's shoulders and say softly, 'I am the only male McKinnon on this island with nothing appropriate to wear at my own clan gathering – and so – I make the trip to Glasgow to buy my first Highland dress. But I have no experience of such things, the help and advice I badly need, so how would it be if grandson and grandfather made the journey together? We will stay in the best hotel, we will paint the town red or purple or whatever colour you like, and while we are there you too can take the opportunity to buy the new kilt.'

'Ach, it will just be a waste at my age,' said Magnus gruffly, but his blue eyes were brilliant with excitement. He hadn't been off the island for many years and had never expected to see bright city lights again. Secretly he was delighted and thought it would 'make a wee change', out loud he announced with great restraint, 'You're right, son, they'll see you comin' a mile away and try to take advantage o' you. It might be wise for me to be there, just to make sure you get the right tartan and all the other bits and pieces to go wi' it. But there is no need to bide in one o' they posh hotels, they're a bunch o' robbers who are aye lookin' for you to cross they're palms wi' sillar for doing jobs they're paid to do. I have an old friend in Glasgow, he'll put us up no bother, his wife's a great cook and doesny talk too much, they'll no' be lookin' for a penny piece between them, just a good bit dram and a blether in return for bed and board.'

It was settled. Some days later Otto and his grandfather left the

236

island, the old man resplendent in his best Sunday suit, trembling a little with excitement but conducting himself with great dignity and bearing.

Otto had only been on Rhanna a few months but already he considered it home and felt strange to be leaving, if only for a short spell. He stood at the rails, a handsome figure in tweed jacket and light trousers, black hair and beard perfectly groomed, his magnetic dark eyes alight as he surveyed the hills and the glens he had come to love dearly.

But he had lost weight in the last month, his face was thinner, his clothes loose where once they had fitted, perhaps a little too neatly, but as yet only Rachel knew how ill he was, no one else seemed to notice the change in him. On the face of it he had kept up a good show of vitality and strength, and had become such a well-kent figure at functions of any sort that the islanders had come to expect *Mac nan Èilean* to be there amongst them.

Only recently there had been a summer fête in the grounds of Burnbreddie in aid of the church fabric fund. Scott Balfour, the laird, had asked Otto to open it and this he had done willingly, even going to the lengths of requesting the use of Burnbreddie's piano so that he and The Portcull Fiddlers could give a concert on the platform that had been erected inside the marquee.

The people of Rhanna had come to love and respect him and many a hand was raised in farewell as he and Magnus sailed away from the island on the steamer.

High on the cliffs above Mara Òran Bay, Rachel also watched the boat heading out towards the Sound, and a pain like a knife twisted in her heart. She didn't know how much longer she could hold Otto's tragic secret to herself. She had lost count of the times she had been on the point of sharing the burden with Jon but each time she had held herself back and taken herself off on one of her solitary walks, so many emotions boiling in her breast she thought she would explode with the hurt of them.

She wished things were as they had been at the start of spring when all the world seemed light and bright and she had looked forward so eagerly to a long, carefree summer on Rhanna. She had been relaxed and happy then, there had been no worries, just herself and the days: the dawns and the gloamings, filled with peace and gladness. She alone had known the seas and the skies, clean and clear, wide and bright, created for her pleasure as she wandered free and at will over empty places that demanded nothing but instilled quiet joy and deep appreciation for everything that was good in life.

Jon's coming had brought a mixture of feelings: she wanted so much to enjoy the island with him but Mamma's presence had overshadowed their happiness till now there was a barrier between them that somehow couldn't be surmounted. Yet she was wise enough to know that it wasn't all Mamma's fault. The knowledge of Otto's illness had been a traumatic blow for her, the world seemed to have ended that night he had taken her into his confidence. He had become very special to her, there existed between them an attraction that was more than just physical, a unique perception of one another's feelings that went far beyond anything that she had ever experienced before. She was aware of Jon's jealousy and she understood it even while it was beyond her to stay away from Otto. He needed her so badly in his lonely fight against an illness that was sapping his strength more and more as the days went by – and she needed him, she couldn't deny it, he was like a magnet, drawing her to him, making everything and everyone else seem mundane and dull in comparison.

As she stood there she remembered the shared joys they had experienced that summer: there had been some wonderful times in old Magnus's cottage with the three of them enjoying their own impromptu little concerts; once they had walked over to the tinks' camp at Dunuaigh where they were invited to sing round the camp fire in the gloaming – to drink smoke-flavoured tea and eat farls of oatcake straight off the girdle, piping hot and dripping with butter.

But best of all was the day she had spent at Burg Bay with both Jon and Otto. She had taken each of them by the hand and they had run barefoot into the sea where they had paddled in the shallows, splashing one another, laughing and playing like children, never wanting any of it to end. Later, with their shoes strung round their necks, they had walked along the beach before collapsing in the sand to rest. Jon had lain on his back, watching the fluffy clouds floating by; she and Otto had glanced at one another, their eyes meeting and holding, dark with the knowledge that moments like these were very precious to them and would get fewer and fewer as time went by. He had quickly learned the sign language so that now they could commune easily with one another and convey the things that were in their hearts.

They didn't know that Jon saw the way they looked at each other or that the jealousy in his heart was growing blacker and stronger with every passing day.

The boat had all but disappeared on the horizon, she sighed and she was glad, glad that she too was leaving the island for a time: too much had happened in just a few short months, she had to stand back from it, get it all into perspective. It wasn't just Otto and Jon, it was herself, she needed time to think, to look into her heart and her mind. She had to belong to herself again, for something so earthshattering was happening to her she couldn't really believe it herself yet. She had lain at night thinking about it, wondering if it could really be true: it seemed so impossible yet there was every reason for her to hope and pray and dream. But then came sleep and the dawn and the start of another day with people and emotions claiming too much of her attention.

For some time now, Jon had been growing anxious about the amount of time she was spending out of the public eye: at this stage in her career she needed to stay in the limelight, he told her, and it would be a good idea for her to take advantage of her time in Scotland. He had lined up a concert in the Usher Hall in Edinburgh, recordings at the BBC studios in Glasgow, and, if she agreed, he could arrange for her to appear in other cities throughout the country and still be back on Rhanna at the end of a fortnight.

At first she had fiercely resisted the suggestions. Jon had kindly but firmly tried to persuade her into accepting but she hadn't listened, she hadn't wanted to listen, instead she had

239

stayed away from the house as much as possible and had refused to even look at her violin. But as time wore on she knew she was wrong and he was right and for the past week she had been practising morning, noon, and night and was now ready to leave.

She would be back in time for Otto's Ceilidh – nothing or no one was going to make her miss that – and with a resolute toss of her head she went indoors and began to look out the things she would need for her trip.

Mamma wouldn't be accompanying them, she seemed more than willing to stay at An Cala on her own: she had made friends on the island, she had had some wonderful times at Aggie's house and Rab McKinnon was going to show her the island – not in his tractor, she only suffered that if it was completely necessary – no, definitely not the tractor. Rab was going to borrow his uncle's car, true it had lain rusting at the back of the byre for 'a good wee whilie', Rab had explained tongue in cheek, but with a bit of luck, some second-hand tyres, a squirt or two of oil, a bit of elbow grease, it would be as good as new in no time.

Mamma didn't question any of that, perhaps she didn't want to, Rab's word was good enough for her: he was to be trusted, he always meant what he said, he was dependable, strong, and reliable – and even if the car wasn't, it was a much safer bet than the tractor, and it was bound to look better than any tractor any day.

Wullie McKinnon awoke from a deep sleep, the morning was bright and early – too bright and early, the hands of the clock were at four a.m. Outside the window the pearly sky was rosily flushed; the hill peaks wore lacy caps of mist; on the green lower slopes the sheep and cows still lay in sleepy repose; not a wisp of smoke came from the scattering of little white cottages; shades covered the windows like secretive eyelids; not a soul was about, it was that special time of day when the land breathed quietly and gently and gave off an air of belonging only to nature.

At least it would have been quiet and gentle if it hadn't been for Dodie's cockerels, trumpeting away as loud as they could, so effectively drowning out a melodic dawn chorus that even the very birds gave up the effort and huddled themselves sulkily into their feathers.

Wullie sat up in bed and nearly wept. He had bags under his eyes from lack of sleep, his face was haggard and drawn. 'That's it!' he exploded, his nose frothing with rage. 'I'm going to do something about these bloody cockerels – this very day!'

Mairi stirred and grunted and opened one sleepy eye. Since childhood she had been deaf in one ear and though it was certainly a great inconvenience there were times when it was a blessing in disguise and especially so since Dodie and his cockerels had come to live in the adjoining croft. All she had to do was bury her good ear into the pillow and she became oblivious to all unwanted noise, she was therefore not as sympathetic as she might have been to her husband's woes, except in the daytime when the cockerels' continual vying for supremacy got on her own nerves and she might gladly have brained Dodie if she had been that sort of person.

But she was a gentle, tolerant soul in the extreme and had always concerned herself with the old eccentric's welfare. The summer days had passed, Wullie had fretted and fumed but had never carried out his grim threats against the nuisances; this morning, however, there was something in his tone that warned her he meant business and she too sat up, her hair standing in spikes, her newly wakened eyes slowly emerging from sleep and dreams till gradually the rather vacant brown depths betrayed a vapid sort of anxiety.

'Ach, Wullie,' she clucked, in a voice to suit the occasion, 'you'll no' go and do anything foolish, I hope. These birds mean a lot to auld Dodie and you know what he's like if he gets upset.'

But her husband was beyond all reasoning. 'Upset! After I've killed his chickens I'll thraw his bloody neck while I'm about it! I've tholed him and his pests till I canny take any more and you can talk yourself blue in the face about him and his worries for all the good it will do any o' you.'

For answer Mairi threw back the covers and hopped out of

bed. 'Och, calm yourself,' she said soothingly. 'I'll make us both a nice cuppy and we can drink it in bed while we talk this over like two sensible people.'

Mairi's answer to all seemingly insuperable problems was 'a nice cuppy', but it didn't work on this particular morning. As soon as the world was up and doing Wullie was up and doing also, seeking out Robbie Beag who, as one-time gamekeeper of Burnbreddie, must surely know all there was to know about fowl of any sort.

Robbie took off his cap and scratched his head whilst listening to Wullie's outpourings of troubles. He knew for a fact that Ranald and some of the other men had put forward one or two useless suggestions for dealing with the cockerels and Robbie was slightly annoyed that Wullie hadn't come to him sooner since he was obviously the man for the job. But Barra had warned him to bide his time and as he had never been one to push himself forward, he had waited patiently for his font of knowledge to be tapped.

And now here was Wullie, almost foaming at the mouth as he described his feelings, ending in a breathless rush, 'I'll make it worth your while, Robbie, it won't be much but enough to buy you a good dram or two.'

Robbie affected to think the matter over carefully. He hummed and he hawed and generally delayed his answer, then, when Wullie was almost at bursting point, he said with a nonchalant air, 'I'll no' deny you have a problem there, Wullie, and though I say it myself I'm the man you're lookin' for. But there are one or two wee risks attached and I'll be lookin' for more than just a couple o' drams – a bottle o' best malt would go down much better and would make it worth my while.'

Wullie pondered for only a moment before nodding so eagerly the latest drip flew off the end of his nose. 'Right, a bottle it is, where, when, and how?'

'Well, when I worked to Burnbreddie and we wanted to catch the young pheasants we used to put a wee drop o' whisky in a peck or two o' meal; before we knew it they were as meek as lambs and just askin' for us to pick them up and do what we liked wi' them.'

To Wullie this was a terrible waste of good whisky but he was ready to try anything and nodded his agreement.

'We canny do it during the day when Dodie is about,' Robbie went on, his genial face growing pink at the thought of the adventure ahead, 'and it's no use at night when the birds have gone to roost and wouldny come down even to eat their grannie.'

Wullie couldn't see the relevance of that but made no comment as the plan unfolded.

'Morning is the best time,' Robbie decided. 'Before anybody is up and about, including the chickens, we have to be there to make sure the cockerels get to the meal first, and as it's light so early we'd best just spend the night in the hen hoosie, it's a good big shed and we'll be comfortable enough wi' just a couple o' blankets and a tot or two out o' my bottle.'

'But I had thought to give you that when it was all over,' objected Wullie.

'Na, na, taste and try before you buy, my father aye told us that and I have never forgotten the sense o' his words.'

Wullie agreed grudgingly, final arrangements were made and both men went home to tell their respective wives of their plans. Mairi thought of 'poor auld Dodie' and called on the Lord 'to spare him'; Barra told Robbie he was going soft in the head in his dotage but went to the linen kist to look out some blankets and then to the dresser to seek out a pair of his thickest winter socks.

Early next morning the sun rose on a sleeping land. All was as it had been at the same time on the previous day, with one difference – there was no raucous crowing from Croft Beag to break the golden silence. Only the sounds of the summer countryside could be heard: the burns tumbled down from the hills; corncrakes rustled the grasses; a curlew bubbled out its liquid song on the shore; the sea lapped the silvered sands; peesies ran with their chicks; gulls rode the silken air currents;

small birds spilled out their tiny hearts in triumphant praise of the new day. It was perfection, it was bliss.

If Wullie had been safely tucked up in his snug bed he might have been more able to appreciate all of these things, as it was both he and Robbie had spent an extremely uncomfortable and smelly night. The odour of hen's droppings was anything but conducive to sweet dreams and the wooden floor seemed to produce ever more splinters as the night wore on. Despite the blankets, it was cold, draughty and hard, and at two of the clock Robbie had suggested that a swig from the whisky bottle might serve to make the situation more bearable, though 'only a wee one', since he had to be awake to make sure the cockerels availed themselves of the doctored meal.

On first entering the shed, Wullie had been keen to simply grab the cocks and throttle them there and then but, as Robbie had pointed out, there was the pecking order to consider. The biggest and most royal of the birds was right at the top, as befitted a king of his size and status, the other five were on different rungs of the ladder, so to speak, and to try and catch them all at the one time would have created a hell's own din and would undoubtedly have brought Dodie running helter-skelter to see what all the fuss was about.

'You would just waken the whole neighbourhood,' Robbie insisted. 'Far better to do it my way, I know what I'm talkin' about. If you're so smart why did you no' just do the job yourself and save me havin' to bide in this shitty shed when I could be home in my own bed wi' my feets on Barra's nice warm bum.'

Wullie was mad at himself for upsetting Robbie's placid temperament. He gave in, and producing the bottle of best malt he passed it to Robbie for the first swig and waited politely for his turn.

That had been more than three hours ago. Now the first faint fingers of sunlight probed gently but insistently through the cobwebby window pane. They found the spiders and sent them running into their corners, they caressed a heap of crumpled blankets on the floor and slowly crept up to touch two faces, one round, smiling and absolutely dead to the world, the other thinner, younger but equally serene, as its owner wallowed in the best sleep he had enjoyed for weeks.

The relentless light explored further; it found an empty whisky bottle clasped lovingly to Robbie's quietly heaving bosom, the glass winking and gleaming with every tranquil breath he took.

Otherwise the shed was empty of life: the cockerels and their harems had risen at first light, delighted to find breakfast served so early in the day. The tempting bowls of meal didn't last long, the potion was gobbled up in no time at all and out into the morning tripped the hens.

Now they were staggering about in the yard in varying stages of inebriation: some so drunk they had fallen on to their backs and there they lay, bellies to the wind, their funny big chicken feet stiffly saluting the heavens; others were just wandering about aimlessly, tripping themselves up, so that every so often one would take a nose dive into a grassy mound where it remained, impaled on its own beak.

As for the cockerels, they were a sorry sight: no more did their bright red combs waggle proudly, instead they flopped miserably, along with everything else that they normally carried upright. True, King Cock did make an attempt to find his voice, he arched his throat, stuck his beak in the air and opened his lungs, but only a strangulated hiccupping sound emerged. Thus discouraged, he settled himself moodily into his feathers, lifted one leg and promptly fell over.

Luckily for Wullie and Robbie there weren't many people abroad at that time of the day, only Canty Tam stood at the gate, staring with all his lop-sided might at the hilarious scene, his vacant eyes wide and wondering but unable to relay any message to his brain that made sense.

He leered, of course – Canty Tam always leered, no matter the occasion – then with a sense of importance almost choking him he ran to knock up Dodie. While he waited for signs of life he stood back from the door, looked up at the window and yelled on the old man to hurry up as all his hens were dead or dying.

His loud, excitable voice filtered into the hen hoosie. Robbie was the first to stir, grudgingly he emerged from what had been

245

a very satisfying dream in which he had been chasing Aggie McKinnon through the heather, brandishing a hat made out of King Cock's tail feathers. Aggie had been stark naked, her girth had slowed her down, and it had been an easy enough matter for Robbie to catch her and present her with the hat. Smiling at him coyly, she had placed the hat on her head and had stood there, looking at him invitingly, wearing nothing but the hat and her birthday suit. Robbie had been on the point of collecting his reward when he was rudely roused, and he had to sit very still for a moment while he gathered his senses together.

Wullie's sleep had been deep and dreamless, all he wanted was to remain in that state forever but some bugger was kicking up a terrible racket outside his window . . . those bloody cockerels were still at it . . . He awoke with a start, his heart thumping, surprised to find that he wasn't in his own bed with Mairi warm and sleepy beside him.

In some alarm he gazed dazedly around him. Awareness hit him like a blow, he looked at Robbie, Robbie looked at him, as one they scrambled to their feet and went racing outside, just in time to see Dodie and Canty Tam bearing down on them, their clumsy feet carrying them swiftly to the scene of drunken debauchery.

'My hens! My bonny bairnies!' The tears immediately coursed down Dodie's wizened cheeks as he beheld the scene before him. 'What have you done wi' them, Wullie McKinnon?' he cried, dropping on to his knees to take King Cock to his breast and rock him back and forward as if he was a baby.

'Ach, come on now, man.' Robbie tried to sound reassuring even though he was as surprised as Dodie by the sight of the inebriated poultry. 'We haveny done them any harm, they're no' dead – just – er – a wee bittie drunk.'

'Drunk!' Dodie's nose frothed as profusely as Wullie's who, standing in the full glare of morning light was a sorry sight to behold with his hair standing on end and 'the snotters blinding him', according to the nature of his affliction.

'Drunk!' Dodie repeated. 'How can my bonny hens be drunk,

they have never touched a drop o' the de'il's brew in the whole o' their lives?'

Robbie tried to pour oil on troubled waters, but it was no use, Dodie was so enraged he threatened to call in the police and both Wullie and Robbie gulped.

In the old days the law had been 'Big Gregor' who had spent his visits ceilidhing at relatives' houses and generally catching up on island news; now there was Clodhopper, named so because of his enormous size fourteen shoes and his peculiar habit of standing first on one foot and then on the other.

But there was more to Clodhopper than just big feet. His visits always held an element of surprise because there was never any warning as to when he might appear, he positively revelled in his position of power and thoroughly enjoyed snooping about at all hours of the day and night.

He took a special delight in hiding behind rocks and bushes and pouncing on people if he suspected them of wrongdoing. But his *pièce de résistance* was to lurk on the shore near the hotel, waiting for closing time and the revellers to emerge and drive off in their various modes of transport. Once he had booked Donald Ban for speeding through Portcull in his tractor, though Donald swore blind he had been going so slow he would have been faster getting out and walking.

Rhanna had been shocked to the core, for Donald hadn't even been drunk at the time, and folk told one another that things were getting so bad with Clodhopper he would be accusing them next of speeding on their bicycles.

Fortunately he only ever showed up about twice a year. Nevertheless, Dodie's threats were rather worrying for Robbie and Wullie, each of whom had given Clodhopper reason for suspicion on more than one occasion: Robbie for poaching, Wullie for driving his father's builder's van without a licence.

'Och, Dodie, you'll no' do that,' said Wullie, who was looking quite pale. 'You and me have been friends for a long time, you wouldny go and betray a man who has never grudged you a helping hand in the whole o' his life.'

'You're no' my friend anymore,' Dodie said with a watery

sniff. 'All you ever do is shout and swear at me and I'm that feart o' you I wish I was back in my own house up on the hill. I could do what I liked there and no one was any the wiser.'

'Ach, the Hellish Hags o' the Hill would have got you in the end,' Canty Tam said with conviction. 'I've seen them up there, black spooks wi' bat's wings and awful evil faces on them. They have hideous voices too, screechin' and cacklin' and flappin' about, just waitin' to pounce on anyone who goes near their lair. My mither warned me never to go on that hill on my own for fear one would catch me and carry me away forever.'

His predictions of doom and gloom had an immediate effect on Dodie, he forgot all about the police and burst into tears instead, which gave the two mischief-makers the chance they needed. Each putting an arm around Dodie's shuddering shoulders they led him away into the house to ply him with tea and sympathy, leaving Canty Tam to rush away and tell his tale, suitably embroidered, to anyone who would listen.

In days to come neither Robbie nor Wullie would be allowed to forget the episode of the drunken chickens, though for the moment that was the least of their worries. More immediate were their efforts to console Dodie and try to dissuade him from drastic action, which was rather difficult under the circumstances. The hens went off laying for a week and the cockerels didn't crow for at least two days, though on the afternoon of the third the familiar cacophony once more blasted forth.

Wullie's troubles had begun all over again, but help came to him from a most unexpected quarter.

One morning, on answering an abrupt knock at his door, he stared with surprise at a young man standing on the threshold. He was tall and lanky, his smooth skin sported a stubbly growth that was at least a week old, dangling from one ear was an ornament that resembled a curtain ring, and his greasy fair hair was tied back and held in place with an elastic band.

He introduced himself as Andy from Ayrshire, told Wullie he knew all about his problems with the cockerels and that he could have them crated and ready to leave on the afternoon boat.

'I'll tell the old man that my pal's a cockerel fancier,' he explained, rubbing his nose with a nicotine-stained finger. 'I'll gie him the patter, butter up his birds, offer him a price, and before you can say cock-a-doodle-doo, they'll be mine. Of course,' he went on glibly, 'it will cost ye. I'll have to pay the old geezer and I'll need something for my trouble. Thirty pounds and the job's done, half for me, the rest for him.'

Wullie nearly had a fit. Thirty pounds! It was too much! First a bottle of best malt for that useless gowk Robbie, now this queer-looking young fart with his hawk-like face and his earring.

Wullie withdrew into the house for a quick confab with Mairi who had been watching proceedings from the window.

'He'll be one o' they flower people they have over on the mainland,' she hazarded. 'They go about looking like that.'

'Either that or a hippie,' said Wullie, who wasn't too sure of what was in vogue at the moment and didn't much care. He was only too eager to see the back of the cockerels, but the thought of parting with all that money made him hesitate.

'Ach, it's worth it.' Mairi made up his mind for him. 'I have a wee bit money put by and everyone wants their hair done for Otto's Ceilidh so I'll soon make up the loss. You're my man after all and I canny have you going off your head for the sake o' a few pounds.'

To her surprise, Wullie kissed her soundly on the nose before rushing outside to tell Andy from Ayrshire he had a deal and the sooner the job was done the better.

True to his word, that very afternoon, the young man presented himself at Wullie's door complete with the birds that were confined in two ancient peat creels. 'I let the old man keep one,' Andy explained, 'he insisted on that.'

'One is better than six, Wullie,' said Mairi soothingly. 'And you'll hardly ever know it's there since they only crow if there are others to compete with.'

Wullie saw the reasoning in that. He handed over the thirty pounds, the young man thanked him politely, shouldered the creels and went on his way. Wullie watched till he was out of sight before letting out a great whoop of joy, then, before Mairi knew what was happening, he had swung her into his arms to carry her up to the bedroom for 'a bit o' a cuddle by way o' celebration'.

Ranald looked fondly at the five pound note nestling in the palm of his hand. 'Everything went according to plan then,' he stated glibly. 'I told you it would work, son.' He grinned, gazing fondly into Andy from Ayrshire's grubby face, delighted to think that he was the instigator of such a successful ruse. 'Fifteen pounds wasny much to ask for peace o' mind. And Dodie would be pleased to get a fiver for his cockerels, especially if he thought they were going somewhere they would be admired and cared for.'

'Oh ay, by the time I had filled his lugs wi' praise he would have given me the bloody birds for nothing and I would have got away wi' it.'

And that was exactly what had happened. No one ever knew what really transpired between Dodie and Andy from Ayrshire, but, on the strength of a promise from the young stranger, Dodie had gladly parted with his cockerels, receiving not a penny piece in return.

Andy had piled on the compliments. 'These birds are a credit to you. They'll have to prove their worth, of course, that's why I canny give you more than my word at the moment, but I know my pal will be that pleased wi' them he'll want more o' the same, so you keep the big one to carry on the line and I'll be back next year wi' cash in my hand.'

Dodie, beaming from ear to ear, felt that it had been an honour to do business with Andy from Ayrshire – and King Cock was staying, he would do his work well, he was forever treading the hens and was father to more clutches of chickens than Dodie could count.

Andy from Ayrshire hoisted his rucksack on to his shoulders and stuck out his hand. 'Thanks for the bed, Ranald, I've fair enjoyed my few days on Rhanna. I'll look you up next time I'm on the island' – he winked – 'by that time Dodie's cockerel will have got to work and Wullie will be only too pleased to stump up peace money.'

Ranald, feeling right pleased with himself, pumped the young man's hand and told him there was always a bed waiting for him. 'Though mind,' he added pleasantly, 'prices are aye going up and it might cost you a wee bit more to bide in my house next time.'

Andy merely grinned and walked away down to the harbour to check that the cockerels were all right before sitting himself down on a bollard to count his money. Twenty-five pounds, not bad for a day's work, the arrangement had been fifteen pounds to be split three ways – that poor bugger, Wullie, would be too embarrassed ever to admit to anyone that he had parted with thirty pounds to get rid of the cockerels, and the poor old boy with the funny smell had promised never to tell a soul of the deal he'd struck with a summer visitor.

Slapping his knee, he gave a chuckle of pure triumph. Ranald thought he was crafty, he didn't know the half of it – Andy from Ayrshire nearly choked with mirth as he wondered what the opportunist would have said if he had discovered that his holiday lodger was something of an expert on poultry and that he really did have a pal who was a cockerel fancier, and one, furthermore, who would pay a handsome price for Dodie's five prize birds.

Chapter Nineteen

One of the first things Rachel did when she arrived back on Rhanna was to go and see Lachlan. He was working in his garden, tending his herbaceous bed, which somehow managed to survive and thrive despite the fierce winter winds that could sweep through the glen with vicious intensity. It was now a riot of colour and at first Rachel didn't see him, so high grew the hollyhocks, so exuberantly bloomed the lupins, the delphiniums and the marguerite daisies.

But he saw her and he emerged from behind a clump of love-in-the-mist, to wipe the sweat from his brow with an earth-begrimed hand. He greeted her warmly, his brown eyes crinkling. 'Rachel, you're back – I heard you on the wireless only yesterday and thought you would be away for a good whilie yet.'

She hesitated, unsure of how to go about explaining her reasons for being there, wishing with all her heart that she could communicate in the normal way. It wasn't everyone who understood her sign language, though Lachlan had always taken a special interest in her and was able to some extent to know what she conveyed with her gestures.

He saw her face and took the matter out of her hands. 'Come on, let's go in. Phebie aye has a cuppy about now and I'm that· thirsty I could drink a potful all to myself. I was always more used to tending humans than gardens, but I'm learning, and in many ways plants are like people, a bit o' loving care and patience works miracles.'

When Phebie saw the visitor coming indoors with her husband she went to get an extra cup, but after she had drunk hers she didn't stay long in the room. Years of being a doctor's wife had taught her diplomacy, she saw that Rachel had something of great importance on her mind and Phebie, who was first and foremost a woman of great insight as well as instinct, had a very good idea what that something was, and with a murmured excuse she made her exit, leaving Lachlan to look questioningly at Rachel who, in a high state of tension, was sitting on the edge of the chintz-covered couch.

With a few swift movements she indicated exactly why she had come. Lachlan didn't need to understand the sign language to know what she meant. He sat back and studied her, remembering the day he had delivered her and Annie's shock when she had discovered that her beautiful baby had been born dumb. No one could have known that that same child would grow up to be so talented and successful, least of all Annie, who had never held out much hope of her daughter making anything special of her life.

But in recent years, the one thing that Rachel had wanted more than anything was a baby of her own. The passing of time had pushed that desire more and more into the realms of impossibility, now here she was, telling him very plainly that she thought she was pregnant and wanting him to verify it for her.

Going over to her he sat down and took her hand in his reassuring clasp.

'Rachel,' he began gently, 'much as I would love to, you know fine well that I'm not in the position to examine you and tell you what you want to know. Megan is the one you want, I canny just go behind her back and start diagnosing her patients. When I first retired, one or two of my old patients came to me wi' their ails but I was having none o' that and I'm sure a sensible lass like you can understand why.'

Rachel looked at him, she smiled and nodded, she seized a pad and pen from a nearby table and began to write furiously.

When he saw what she had written his smile was one of acquiescence. 'Facts and figures, eh? Dates and times. Right,' he looked her straight in the eye, 'everything points to you being about four months pregnant though I'm not going to be trapped into saying that you *are* pregnant . . .'

He got no further; she threw herself at him and hugged him so hard he emerged laughing and breathless and in time to see her disappearing out of the door. In minutes she was a blur on the glen road as she pedalled with energy to the Manse, where everything was quiet as morning surgery had finished fifteen minutes ago.

But Megan saw her just the same and told her what she already knew. In a hectic state of delight she took Megan's hand and shook it but that wasn't expressive enough for her passionate nature, a surprised Megan found herself being danced round the room then outside to her car where Rachel stood, pointing back towards Glen Fallan.

'Right.' Megan laughed, caught up in the girl's euphoria. 'You want me to take you to see Lachlan, I know fine you have a soft spot for him and I was going to see him this morning anyway before starting on my rounds. Just let me get my bag and I'll be right with you.'

Thus Lachlan found himself seated once more with Rachel in the parlour while Megan talked with Phebie in the kitchen.

Rachel had a lot of questions to ask and in her impatience her hands flew so fast he found it impossible to understand anything, so, with a great gusting sigh, she had to start all over again till he got the gist of her questioning, mainly why such a thing had happened after all this time.

'Och, it's not so long, lass, plenty of women have been wed longer than you before they conceived. You lead a very busy life, when you came to Rhanna you left pressures and commitments behind you for the first time in years, you shook off the fetters and relaxed, it's as simple as that. Go home now and tell Jon, he'll be over the moon, you've shared your joy wi' me, now it's his turn.'

But she shook her head and put her fingers to her lips, trying desperately to tell him, no, she needed time to adjust to this momentous happening, she wasn't yet ready for Jon to know. She saw Lachlan's face, surprised, puzzled. She smiled at him reassuringly and was on her way out when Megan stopped her in the hall to ask if she would like a run home, but she declined: it was a beautiful day, she would have to collect her bike from The Manse, she wanted just to walk and think and try to assimilate the wonderful thing that had happened to her.

None of it was quite real yet; she had to get used to the idea of a baby in her life before telling the world of her secret. She would wait till after Otto's Ceilidh, by then she wouldn't be able to keep her condition from anyone, far less Jon. Already she was growing bigger, her clothes were becoming tighter – and that sensation of butterflies in her stomach was strengthening and quickening – only it wasn't butterflies, it was a baby, and as if to prove it was real and living it suddenly moved strongly within her, making her stop and hold her hand to her mouth in a gesture of childish delight.

On the morning of the McKinnon Clan Gathering, Rhanna woke to overcast skies and drizzling rain that blotted out the hills and the sea in dismal blankets.

'Och, would you look at it!' Kate pushed aside her curtains to glare with animosity at the dripping scene outside. 'After such good weather too, the bugger has been saving itself for this particular day. Otto will be fair scunnered and after him going to so much bother too.'

'It will clear by midday,' Tam forecast knowledgeably. 'Sometimes the best days of all start off pissing and grey.'

And he was right, by early afternoon the clouds had melted away, allowing the sun to shine hotly on the refreshed countryside. Banks of mist unfurled from the hills to rise upwards and wreathe the purple peaks in gossamer scarves. Gradually the haar rolled back from the sea to cling mistily to the horizon so that it merged with little blue islands and gave everything an ethereal, magical quality.

Otto had arranged for a party of caterers to come over from the mainland and by two o'clock a huge marquee had been erected on the stretch of machair that skirted Portcull. Fragrant steam rose from urns of tea and soup. Plates piled with salads, sausage rolls, pies, and sandwiches, cold meat and rolls, filled one table; another groaned under an assortment of cakes and biscuits, jellies and trifles. Several enormous whole cooked salmon, with all the trimmings, were temptingly displayed and when Jim Jim saw them he wondered if they were meant to be eaten or were just there to be admired.

In a smaller marquee stood barrels of beer and a table whose surface was hidden under an array of spirits the like of which Tam said he had only ever seen in fantasies.

Prominently displayed were a dozen bottles of schnapps. When Fergus eventually set eyes on them he grinned wryly and told Otto it was whisky for him or nothing as never again would he risk a repeat of 'the night of the schnapps'.

'My friend,' Otto laughed, 'that was in another age. Since then I have acquired a taste for the *Uisge Beatha*; it is very refreshing – like the tea you are all so fond of.'

'We'll see if you can sup it like tea,' Fergus returned dryly, determined to get his own back on the big Austrian. 'There's a long night ahead o' us, no doubt we'll each have more than just a few drams – and may the best man still be able to say 'it's a braw bricht moonlicht nicht, the nicht' when the clock has struck midnight.'

Shona took his arm and drew him away. 'Och, Father,' she scolded, 'as if Otto could say that, even when he's sober – besides, it isn't fair to make him feel he has to keep up with you in that way, you know you've aye been able to hold your whisky; he's a novice compared to you.'

But Fergus was unrepentant. 'He has to learn sometime; he's built like an ox and ought to be able to keep up.'

Shona looked back at Otto and frowned. 'He *was* built like an ox, I'd say he's got thinner – even since I last saw him with his cat, he looks – frail somehow.'

'Frail! Otto! Havers!' scoffed Fergus. Nevertheless he too looked back at Otto and wondered if there was something in what Shona had said. She had always been perceptive, she seemed to sense things before anyone else, but the next minute he pushed his doubts away when he saw the man in question throwing back his head and laughing at something Jim Jim had said, and to Fergus he looked the picture of good health and high spirits.

The islanders didn't descend on the scene in droves, it was against their natural dignity to do so, but come they did, from all over the island: full-blown McKinnons, vaguely related McKinnons, uncles and aunts, cousins and friends of cousins, nephews, nieces, anyone who had any clan connections, no matter how vague, together with those who had no connections at all but just gatecrashed the scene to mingle with the crowd, including a few of the tinks who weren't going to miss the fun for anything.

'Hmph, would you look at them, they'll go anywhere if it means getting free food and drink,' Behag intoned heavily, fussily and pointedly adjusting the McKinnon tartan ribbon she wore on her frock. She had bought the ribbon just recently from a door hawker who had hastily parted with it for twopence after she had asked him if he held a vendor's licence and had hinted that she would report him to the authorities if he didn't. Behag was a great one for flaunting government bodies to anyone she suspected of unlawful dealings, it had always worked wonders for her: half the ironmongery in her kitchen had been acquired cheaply from travelling salesmen who had no wish to tangle with the authorities Behag spoke about so glibly, even though she couldn't have told one from another.

'I don't see anything wrong wi' the tinks,' Kate said, following Behag's gaze before bringing her own back to stare meaningfully at the ribbon pinned to the old woman's scrawny bosom. 'At least they didny buy their tartans at the door and pretend to be something they aren't.'

Behag's lips tightened but she said nothing more on the subject, certainly not to the formidable Kate, but when she saw Rachel welcoming the tinks she couldn't resist saying to Sorcha in meaningful tones, 'Have you noticed how she canny keep away from them? For all we know she might easily be one o' them seeing as how her mother couldny keep away from them either when she was young.'

Sorcha had been in such a hurry to get out of the house she had forgotten to insert her hearing aid and, moulding one ancient lug into a mottled brown trumpet, she shouted, 'Eh? What was that? Rachel a tink? You'd better no' let Kate hear you saying that.'

Kate turned round; the look she threw Behag was venomous in the extreme. Behag scuttled away with agility, her eye falling on Elspeth who was strolling haughtily towards the marquee on the arm of Captain Mac. Behag's eyes immediately sparkled with interest for despite her mournful demeanour she had had a wonderful time that summer: there were so many interesting things going on in the island, but best of all had been the affair between Elspeth and Captain Mac. Behag had noted that the display of luscious lingerie always appeared on the line after Captain Mac had taken himself off on one of his sojourns and the ex-postmistress's imagination had worked overtime. Everyone else had grown rather tired of the subject, the novelty of teasing Elspeth had begun to wear off, but for Behag it would never fade and in her mind she had called Elspeth everything from a hussy to a Jezebel.

Unlike Kate she had a healthy respect for Elspeth's able dialogue and had never dared to say anything that would incur a tongue-lashing, but her innuendoes, her tight-lipped, disapproving silences, had said it all and a little bit more besides.

To her complete and utter surprise Elspeth greeted her warmly and invited her to accompany both her and Mac into the beer tent as it was such a thirsty day.

'The beer tent!' Behag was shocked. So she had been right about Elspeth all along! All that so-called aversion to strong drink was just another front and those rumours about her being a secret tippler must be true. For all anyone knew she and Mac might be indulging in drink orgies and God alone knew what other debauchery.

'Ay, the beer tent.' Elspeth's own lips were very subtly beginning to tighten. 'There's more than hard liquor in there: I've been told there are soft drinks as well, though I might just have a small sherry to wet my thrapple.'

Behag hesitated; a small sherry was respectable, even ministers didn't turn up their noses at sherry, though of course Mark James couldn't even take that, not with his problem – but that was another story and one on which Behag held very firm views.

'Well, just a wee one to keep you company, Elspeth,' she conceded, and wondered why the other woman's eyes gleamed with something that might be called amusement.

By this time the scene was a mosaic of colour and life as half the island congregated on the green in front of the village of Portcull. Magnus of Croy arrived in style, driven by Todd the Shod who had at last learned to drive after years of claiming he would never sit behind a wheel of any sort after a lifetime of dealing with horses. He had spent a whole day cleaning and polishing his beautiful Rolls Royce and now it winked and gleamed and caused many a head to turn and smile at the sight of Magnus, sitting in the back, nodding and waving in a very regal manner.

As soon as the car stopped, Otto was there to help his grandfather alight and lead him away to the refreshment tent as he had expressed a desire to 'wet his whistle'.

'Neither o' them are wearing the kilt,' Kate observed in some disappointment. 'I had thought, wi' this being Otto's official introduction to the Clan McKinnon, he would have appeared in full Highland dress.'

'Ay, everyone else has made the effort,' said Isabel. 'I thought he went to Glasgow to buy an outfit for himself and Magnus – surely he's no' going to let a chance like this slip by him.'

'Ach, give the man time,' said Todd the Shod. 'He'll maybe surprise us all before the day is over.'

'Are you knowing something we don't?' Mollie questioned suspiciously but her husband merely threw her a knowing wink and went to join his cronies who were already making merry in the beer tent.

Halfway through the afternoon Dodie appeared on the scene, shining and scrubbed, thanks to Mairi's administrations on his person. At the time he hadn't been too appreciative of being dumped in the tub in order to receive a thorough overhaul by Wullie, who, armed with a large loofah and an even larger sponge, had scoured every inch of Dodie's skin till he said he hadn't any left and cried out for mercy. But afterwards, when Mairi had smothered him in body lotion and talcum powder and had cut and shaped his baby-fine hair, he had gazed at himself in the mirror for fully five minutes with a smirk of pure vanity widening his mouth.

She had also sponged and pressed his best suit and on the lapel she had fixed a large rosette of McKinnon tartan ribbon because she told him his mother had been of that clan and he had every right to wear the colours. In truth she didn't really know what his mother had been, but Dodie had taken her at her word, and was so pleased with himself he forgot to be awkward and shy in the midst of the large gathering and went immediately to seek out Otto who was sitting outside the marquee talking to Rachel.

Without any of his usual hesitation, Dodie presented Otto with one of his hand-painted stones, stuttering a little in his efforts to utter some appropriate English salutation that would be understood by 'the furrin gentleman'.

Dodie had been one of the first born and bred islanders that Otto had met on his arrival on Rhanna, and ever since the unique ride in Megan's car, shared by Dodie and his twin lambs, Otto had taken an interest in the old man and had endeared himself still further by always asking after Curly's welfare. In Dodie's estimation, Otto was a man of greatness and goodness, and in Otto's eyes, Dodie was a gentle, special creature whose simple beliefs and often staggering insights placed him in a category that was all his own.

Otto's greeting was therefore genuinely warm and he received his gift with pleasure, turning it over in his hand, something queer and sad touching his heart when he saw painted notes of music drifting into a blue and heavenly sky and the motto *Mac nan Èilean* painstakingly scrawled round the edges.

'How appropriate,' he murmured softly. 'How very appropriate, almost as if . . .'

He looked into Dodie's dreamy grey-green eyes. 'You're a genius, Dodie, in your own way, you're a genius, and this calls for a celebration.'

Throwing his arm around the old man's stooped shoulders he led him away to the beer tent and thereafter to the food table where he personally saw to it that Dodie's plate was well filled with the choicest and tastiest of fare.

It was a wonderful day for everyone: the sun continued to shine warmly, Otto had paid Erchy to run a special shuttle service and many of the old ones, who hadn't been outside their own little corners for years, were able to meet up with one another and catch up on all the little snippets of news.

Otto hadn't forgotten the children, in fact he was like the pied piper that day with the youngsters following him around and hanging on his every word. He had arranged games and amusements to keep them happy and half the time he joined in their fun, making them shriek with laughter at some of his antics.

'Ach, would you look at him,' said Tina, gazing fondly at the big man. 'He's so good wi' the bairns, it's just a pity he never— ' She came to an abrupt stop, reddened and turned away, leaving some of the womenfolk to wonder to each other what it was she had been about to reveal.

When it came time for the children to go home, Otto personally presented each of them with a wooden plaque bearing the McKinnon coat of arms and the inscription: *McKinnon Clan Gathering, Island of Rhanna, 1967*, and even though one lad told his friends, 'The last McKinnon in our family was buried fifty years ago,' he went rushing off, carrying his trophy with pride, impatient to show it to his mother who had conjured a very dusty McKinnon out of an equally dusty diary she had just recently found in an old trunk in the loft.

The food and drink had rapidly disappeared during the course of the afternoon, and by five o'clock everyone was beginning to disperse back to their homes to get themselves ready for the concert that was being held that night in the Portcull village hall.

Magnus and Otto repaired to Tigh na Cladach to rest and partake of a meal cooked by Tina.

Otto was very glad to go up to his bedroom and close his eyes; Magnus contented himself with the comfortable armchair in the sitting room; Tina busied herself laying out the clothes both men would wear that night. She beamed with pride as she gazed at the colourful array. 'You'll make a right bonny pair,' she said softly and went to get a clothes brush just in case she had missed anything when she had taken the garments out of their wrappings to air them.

Behag emerged from the beer tent, supported by Elspeth and Captain Mac. Her eyes were glazed, her spindly legs unsteady and she was thankful to have Captain Mac's strong hand under her elbow. Elspeth had mixed her a Mickey Finn and Behag, her palate receptive after three glasses of sherry, had drunk it down without so much as a grimace.

'You'll no' let anybody see me,' she pleaded with Elspeth. 'I canny think what's happened to me, I was fine for a whilie then something just seemed to hit me. My head feels gey queer and my legs are like jelly, but I'll be fine once I'm home wi' a good strong cuppy inside me.'

'I'll no' let anybody see you,' promised Elspeth and promptly steered the inebriated old woman into a hotbed of gossiping crones who stared at Behag with disbelieving eyes.

'She's drunk, the old hypocrite!'

'Ay, and after all her talk about the weaknesses o' the flesh!'

'Years o' it, aye looking down her nose at anybody who takes an innocent wee dram! She's a disgrace to the island.'

So the comments followed in the wake of Behag's erratic course. Because Elspeth made sure they bumped into everyone in their path, her mouth quivering all the while as never had she enjoyed herself more. She had waited for a moment like this for years and now that she had Behag quite literally in the palm of her hand she was going to make the most of every second.

Holy Smoke was bearing down on them. At sight of Behag he stopped dead in his tracks, eyed her with self-righteous disapproval and exclaimed, 'Miss Beag! Is it really you? I never thought to see such a thing in all my born days! May the good Lord have mercy on your soul.'

His droning, mournful tones penetrated the fog that was choking Behag's senses, and even in her stupefied state she tried to make the effort of escaping the one person she never had any desire to meet, be she drunk or sober. Wriggling out of Mac's supportive grasp she took two steps forward, her knees buckled, and she would have fallen had not Holy Smoke himself darted forward to catch her.

'No,' she moaned, 'Leave me be, Sandy McKnight, I want to go home, I can manage fine if I just take it slowly. It's the heat, too much . . . I canny stand noise and heat . . .'

'Ach, the sowel,' Elspeth intoned, sadly shaking her head. 'She'll no' face the fact that she's had one too many – it would be too much to expect her to admit to being human like the rest o' us.' She turned an innocent face on Holy Smoke. 'Isaac and myself have things to do, Sandy, would you make sure she gets home safe and sound? I know I can trust you no' to breathe a word o' this to another living soul, for Behag has aye been a body who prided herself on abstinence.'

Holy Smoke, brimming over with Christian duty, nodded his agreement and firmly led the protesting Behag away. Elspeth clapped her hand to her mouth, it was the final triumphant feather in her cap and she almost smothered in her efforts to keep back her laughter.

'We'll no' see her at the concert the night,' said Mac with a grin as he gazed after the unlikely pair. 'Mind you, I feel a wee bittie sorry for her, it's no' like Behag to let herself go like that, and it just shows how unused to alcohol she is when three wee sherries knocked her for six.'

'That's what she gets for meddling, Isaac.' Elspeth's chin tilted and she sniffed. 'She has spent the summer watching us through her peepscope and I for one am no' sorry to see her getting her comeuppance.'

She took his arm. 'We have better things to do wi' our time than stand here discussing Behag. I have my frock to press for tonight, I have a meal to serve, and you know how long it takes you to get yourself into your kilt and gear.'

He allowed himself to be led away, quite happy to be seen with her arm linked through his, for truth to tell he had spent a very contented summer with Elspeth: she was surprisingly good company, she kept a tight ship, her cooking was excellent, above all she hadn't nagged him once, and anything was better than smelly old Gus with his wind and his wireless, and his disgusting cronies with *their* wind and their other bad habits, not to mention their fondness for that awful brew that tasted like cat's piss and which they had the gall to call rum.

The village was quiet again, except for the notes of 'Onward Christian Soldiers' drifting faintly on the breezes. Behag was keeping her end up, it was the only thing her fuddled mind could think of that might convince the world she most certainly wasn't drunk but just as happy as anyone else that day and was singing to the Lord to prove it.

Chapter Twenty

Jon had never seen his mother so excited about anything as she was about Otto's concert. At last, she had declared, she was going to see some culture on an island where social activities confined themselves to ceilidhs, where everyone seemed to speak in that strange Gaelic language and entertained themselves with singing and music that had no place in modern-day life.

Patiently Jon had tried to explain that the music and language of the highlands and islands was a matter of tradition and that the culture of these lands was uniquely different and special, but she hadn't listened and in the end Jon gave up, hoping that, in time, she would come to realize it was a privilege to live among a people who were as natural as the hills and as unfettered as the very air they breathed.

Mamma hadn't attended the afternoon festivities, pleading a headache but in reality getting herself thoroughly glamorized for the evening concert.

She had gone to Mairi's the day before to have her hair and nails done, expecting to find a proper hairdressing premises, but instead she found a notice pinned to the crofthouse door which read: MAIRI'S SALOON, PROFESSIONAL HAIRSTYLING AND BEAUTY TREATMENTS – INCLUDING FACE MASKS, PEDICURES, OLD AGE PENSIONERS, (AND NAILS) HALF PRICE, EVERY WEDNESDAY.

There followed a list of prices and opening times with an extra proclamation added at the bottom: *Never on the Sabbath – under any circumstances – except for funerals and christenings if completely necessary.*

When a puzzled Wullie had asked why she had made a concession for these two events she had said in her kindly way, 'Ach well, some o' they young mothers would forget their heads if they wereny screwed on and might be wantin' a hairdo at the last minute, and if someone goes and dies on you at the weekend, Sunday would be the only day they might have time to spare.'

'But, if they're dead, they would have no time for anything and couldny very well get up out their coffins to get their hair done.'

Mairi shook her head at her husband's lack of understanding. 'Och, Wullie,' she chided gently, 'I mean the relatives, of course: a dead body wouldny be caring if they went to their grave lookin' like a scarecrow, would they now?'

When Mamma, whose grasp of written English was as halting as her speech in that language, had finally absorbed the contents of the notice, she gave a snort of derision and, without so much as a warning knock, pushed open the crofthouse door and marched in . . . only to see a baldly naked Wullie in the lobby as he emerged from the kitchen tub to make his way up to the bedroom to dress.

He let out a nasal shriek of surprise; Mamma also let out a shriek, only hers was a mixture of shock as well as surprise, to see a man as thin as Wullie so well equipped in the luggage department.

With bulging eyes she stared – and stared – while Wullie strove to shield his private parts with the inadequate coverage of his hands before darting like a bullet upstairs.

Mairi appeared in the hall to welcome Mamma with a fondly shy smile then led her into the room that had been converted some years ago for the purpose of beautifying the island's population.

Frau Helga Jodl was less than pleased by what she saw: a tiny, cramped space containing a few kitchen chairs; a pulley strung from the ceiling hung with an array of towels; two hairdryers that looked as if they might have been rescued from the Ark; one badly marked mirror; a small table that groaned under a pile of magazines, together with copies of the *Oban Times* dating back twenty years; and a trolley spilling over with rollers, curlers, tongs, hairgrips and nail polish.

In the midst of this motley assortment was the washbasin, standing over by the window, the only modern piece of equipment in the room. Powder blue, pristine clean, presided over by two gleaming chrome taps with a little plaque above them which read: *This saloon was officially opened in 1964 by Scott Balfour, the Laird of Burnbreddie.* Opposite the hairdryers was a handwritten notice which joyfully instructed: *Rest, linger, enjoy being pampered. Free tea to all friends and visitors, home-baked scones twopence each, except when the coal lorry is late.*

Mamma did not appreciate the promise of free tea. Tea! Pah! She had drunk tea till it was coming out her ears! No one here seemed to have heard of coffee – as for resting and lingering, she wouldn't stay one moment longer than necessary in this disgraceful travesty of a hairdressing salon.

Turning to the beaming Mairi, who was watching her with expectant interest, she said with cutting sarcasm, 'My eyes, they are deceiving me; I look but I do not believe. I think it is the comedy! Money you cannot expect from people coming here! You should pay them for having the courage to set a foot inside your house!'

Mairi looked as if she had been struck, her guileless brown eyes filled with tears and she turned away on the pretence of folding a clean pair of towels that were already neatly folded and laid ready beside the washbasin.

But that had only been the beginning of Mamma's reign of domination over the little sanctum that was Mairi's pride and joy. She had gone on to ever greater heights of wounding criticism, she had been bossy, imperious, loud and demanding, completely unnerving poor Mairi, draining away her confidence so badly that very soon she had none left. She had become flustered and unsure; gradually but surely her reflexes grew slower, like a clock slowly unwinding till it was only just ticking and no more.

In the end she had dithered about so much she had spilled hairgrips all over the floor and when she bent to pick them up she had bumped her head on the washbasin which made her brain whirl and slowed her down more than ever. A mass of fingers and thumbs, her eyes watering, her head spinning, she

267

had had quite enough of Frau Helga Jodl and told her so in no mean terms.

For placid, kindly Mairi to get angry was, in itself, an almost unheard-of happening; for her to lose her head altogether went against everything that made up her simple, tolerant nature – and the result was disquieting.

With terrible, frightening calm, she bent down, glared into Mamma's startled face and gritted, 'Just you be listening to me, you ugly, bossy, big bitch! I'll tell you what I'm going to do to you so that you will never again speak to me as if I was a bit cow dung brought in from the midden. First I'm going to tear every last hair from your fat, swollen head, then I'm going to hold it under the taps and laugh while I watch you drowning!

'After that I'm going to sit back wi' a good strong cuppy and wait very calmly for Clodhopper to come and take me away. I don't care if I rot in jail for the rest o' my life, it will have been worth it just for the pleasure o' getting to kill you wi' my own bare hands!'

So saying, she set about tearing the curlers from Mamma's head. Mamma shrieked in pain but the relentless attack went on – and on – and on – and the odd thing was, although Mamma was built like a battleship, she was no match for slim little Mairi whose fury lent her the strength of a bull.

Tears of rage running down her face, her arms working like pistons, she went on wrenching, tugging, pulling, till the curlers lay in hairy heaps all over the floor, as quite a considerable amount of Mamma's hairs had come out with them.

If fate hadn't intervened, in the shape of Kate McKinnon herself, Mairi might well have carried out her threats, for she had worked herself up into such a state she was quite simply beyond all control and was just itching to get Mamma's wildly disarranged head into the washbasin.

Kate, who had the next appointment, came in breezily, but stopped dead in her tracks to take in the scene of carnage with bulging eyes, before rushing forward to wrest her daughter-in-law away and fold her into her strong, capable

268

arms, where, her anger suddenly spent, Mairi lay, sobbing helplessly.

Mamma, her hair a knotted tangle, stared at the pair of them with horrified eyes. She had already met her match in the able Kate, now it seemed the daughter-in-law was tarred with the same bristly brush and Mamma was genuinely scared, upset, and only too eager to try and make amends.

'I go, I make the cuppy,' she blabbered, and rose to her feet, causing a stray curler to roll from her shoulder and bounce on to the floor. 'Tea, it is the Scottish cure for everything . . . even attempted murder,' she added with what might be described as a touch of humour.

But Kate pushed her back into her seat with a heavy hand. 'I'll make it,' she said disdainfully, 'you wouldny know how to make a decent cuppy – and I'll tell you this, Frau Helga Jodl, I've known Mairi all o' my life and never, never have I seen the poor lass in such a state. You have a knack of instilling rage in the mildest o' souls, but, as you've seen for yourself, even a body as gentle as our Mairi has its breaking point, and if she ever has reason to kill you again – I'll no' stop her – I'll help her.'

So saying she flounced away to get the tea, returning to the sight of Mamma meekly sitting beside Mairi, talking to her in soothing tones and actually patting her shoulders, albeit awkwardly.

The three of them sat sipping their tea in silence until, revived by the brew, they very gradually began to talk. Half an hour later a feeling of camaraderie existed between them, with Kate at her best describing some amusing incident concerning Holy Smoke before going on to congratulate Mamma for having outwitted him over the question of money.

Mairi listened, clucking and clicking in her usual mild way, Mamma laughed as she hadn't done since her meeting with Merry Mary and Aggie, and for the second time in her life knew the uplifting experience of participating in island gossip instead of being on the outside, just listening.

Eventually, her good humour restored, all idea of revenge forgotten, Mairi rose and proceeded to tackle Mamma's hair, earning an extra pound at the end of the day from one grateful and thoroughly chastened customer.

Todd had insisted on collecting Otto and his grandfather from the shorehouse, even though they said they could easily walk the short distance to the hall.

'Na, na,' beamed Todd, 'everything must be done in style tonight, it is a very special occasion and I didny spend all day polishing my motor just to pick Magnus up from Croy – though of course I was honoured to do that,' he added hastily.

He was looking very swish that night: Mollie had mended the moth holes in his kilt and had bought him a sparkling white evening shirt for the occasion. He had managed to remain reasonably sober despite the temptations of the beer tent that afternoon, and now he stood by his Rolls Royce, resplendent in his finery, opening the doors with a flourish when Otto and Magnus came down the path, Tina having gone home to get herself ready after she had seen to the menfolk.

At sight of the two men, Todd beamed and rubbed his hands together. 'My, my,' he greeted them, 'you are a sight for sore eyes and no mistake, and a credit to clansmen everywhere, no matter their tartan.'

As soon as he brought his motor to a halt outside the hall he extricated his bagpipes from the back seat and went rushing away, in his hurry forgetting his manners so that his two very important passengers had to make their own way out of the Rolls and forward into glory.

Todd, breathless after his rush, hoisted his pipes to his chest, raised the chanter to his lips and waited for the appropriate moment, glad of a respite that he might fill his lungs with air before filling his bagpipes with the air from his lungs.

On the other side of the door, Torquil Andrew McGregor, gold medallist at Highland Games, big-muscled, ruggedly handsome in the McGregor tartan, having tuned his pipes in readiness, now waited impatiently to get started.

Magnus and Otto approached, Todd and Torquil looked at one another, nodded and struck up at the same moment. At first the drones were all that could be heard, then the opening tune came, skirling and spilling forth, and to the stirring blast of 'Highland Laddie', Magnus and Otto were piped into the hall in style.

As one, the packed hall turned to stare, murmur and admire, for Otto had spared nothing when he had gone to Glasgow to purchase his very first Highland dress. He had the build, the bearing and the dignity for such garb, and, more importantly, he had the right to wear it. His McKinnon tartan kilt was of the very best quality, his white evening shirt sparkled against his black Argyll jacket with its triangular silver buttons, the amber Cairngorm stone in his sgian-dhu shone and winked in its silver setting, his silver kilt and tie pins bore the McKinnon crest and altogether he was a splendidly proud figure.

Beside him, Magnus of Croy, his devoted grandfather, was also an eye-catching sight. Otto had treated him to an entire new rigout, his blue eyes were snapping with excitement in his lively brown face, his head was held high, his back ramrod straight and, for a man of his years, he was altogether a credit to himself and his clan.

A burst of applause broke out. Otto acknowledged it with shining eyes, his heart brimming over with emotion in this, the proudest moment of his life.

The islanders had made a fine job of the hall: balloons and streamers hung from the rafters and walls, and strung across the ceiling was a huge tartan banner bearing the message: '*Ceud Mile a'Fàilte, Mac nan Èilean*', meaning, 'A Hundred Thousand Welcomes, Son of The Island'.

Scott Balfour, the laird, came over to personally shake Otto by the hand and fifteen minutes later, when all the noise and fuss had settled down, Scott climbed up on the platform to officially welcome this notable McKinnon to the island, going on to say a few appropriate words before beckoning Otto to come up and join him.

He stood beside the laird and looked down with affection at the faces he had come to know so well these last few months. They had made him feel welcome and wanted, they had befriended him and had very quickly made him feel as if he had belonged here on Rhanna all of his life, and something sore and sad tightened his throat in the knowing that the years were rapidly coming to an end for him and that too soon he must relinquish this land and these people that he loved so well.

The ache inside him misted his eyes and hushed his voice when he thanked the laird and looked straight at the gathering to say simply, 'All of my life I have waited for this moment, all of my boytime in Austria, I listen to my grandmother's voice telling to me the tales of her Hebridean childhood and of all the places she loved and never forgot to her dying day. Through her words I have seen the skies and the seas, I have walked on the moors and beside the ocean, I have heard the birds and listened to the beat of the waves breaking on the shore, the scents of the wildflowers were the perfumes I smelt in my dreams, and I hugged it all to myself and could never get enough of her memories.

'But the best was yet to come – the chance to see and hear all of these things for myself – and in my wildest dreams I could never have imagined the reality to be so breathtaking. I came here as a stranger, but when the time comes for me to go I know I will leave with the knowledge that I didn't just find friends on my island of dreams, I found my family as well and discovered for myself the true meaning and the joy of having kin I could call my own.'

He gazed at his grandfather down there at the edge of the crowd. He extended his hand. Magnus went up to him, grandfather and grandson looked at one another for a long time before they shook hands and embraced, Magnus a bit red in the face, Otto delighted and obviously enjoying every second.

'Ach my, are they no' lovely just?' Kate furtively searched for her hanky and blew her nose hard. 'Tis proud I am to be kin to such a bonny man as Otto, he has such a fine way o' putting himself over and of course, I was the first person on the island to hear about his grandmother and to find out who he was.'

But Kate did not know everything about Otto, as the next few minutes proved. While he was up on the platform Mamma had been watching him with a puzzled frown on her features, it was the first chance she had had to see Otto face to face and she stared at him intently. Her frown cleared and she cried out in a voice that everyone could hear, 'Karl Gustav Langer! The famous pianist! Oh, I have heard your music many times, I attend a concert of yours when you come to Germany, and also in Vienna when I stay with Jon in Austria.'

It was the moment Rachel had dreaded, all along she had known it would happen sometime and in some way, but not like this, in front of everybody, all eyes staring, all heads turning. Frantically she signalled for Jon to do something to shut his mother's mouth but he showed no inclination to do anything that might help a situation which was now beyond saving anyway.

Barra, who had kept Otto's secret well, glared at Mamma and rudely told her to hold her tongue, while Magnus, who had found out his grandson's true identity while they were in Glasgow, was furious with the big loud woman whom he had first encountered at Croy Beag not so very long ago. His recollections of her were anything but fond and he came sprachling down from the platform to take her arm and give her a piece of his mind.

Everyone was looking at everyone else. Word was passed from McKinnon to McKinnon that Herr Otto Klebb wasn't just a long-lost clansman, he was also one of the most renowned pianists in Europe. Many of them had listened to him on the radio, and though none of them had ever seen him, his name was familiar and one to be held in respect. Now there was an explanation for those glorious waves of melody pouring from the shorehouse, and the reason for the beautiful piano being shipped over specially was all at once clear.

Tam and his cronies eyed one another as they remembered that day of sweating and groaning in their efforts to get the Bechstein in through the doors of Tigh na Cladach. Yesterday had seen a repeat of that performance, only this time it was from Tigh na Cladach to the hall as Otto had insisted on having his own piano at the concert. And no one could blame him there, since the

273

hall's ancient old 'wheezebox' had seen better days and those very decidedly in the dim and distant past.

The men also remembered the 'affair o' the Oxo cubes' and the impromptu ceilidh that had followed, with the spirits flowing like water and Otto there at his piano, laughing, joining in the fun, allowing his mask of dourness to slip and letting the warm, generous man to shine through.

'And to think,' Tam whispered breathily in Kate's ear, 'he is one o' us, a McKinnon, the very finest you could get. My, I'm that proud I could burst.'

'Ay, well don't do it here,' returned Kate dryly. 'You would flood the place wi' all that beer you've been drinking and you wi' your reputation to uphold as a first-rate McKinnon.'

Lachlan climbed on to the platform and said a few words in Otto's ear, the next minute he held up his hand and demanded everyone's attention.

The islanders had always listened to him and they listened now. He asked them not to let Otto's identity be known outside of Rhanna. The man was here to have a rest, he told them, the last thing he wanted was for the media to find out where he was, if they did it would be exit Otto, and who among them wanted that on their conscience?

No one, it seemed, was keen for that to happen. A ripple of consternation ran round the room at the very idea, heads nodded, rapid exchanges took place.

Herr Tam, electing himself as spokesman, held up his hand and shouted, 'You can rely on us, we'll no' be telling a soul – and if we hear o' anybody breathing a word you can bet your boots it will be their last.'

Lachlan grinned. 'I hope there will never be any need to go that far. I trust you all, as for Otto, he wants you all to treat him as you've always done, without undue deference or difference – and while he is with us he is Otto, just that, Karl Langer belongs to the world – Otto belongs to us, and while he doesn't want any favours from us, I for one am honoured to have him here on Rhanna and will personally make certain that his stay here will be one that he will remember for the rest o' his days.'

A cheer went up, someone shouted '*Mac nan Èilean*', and before long the affectionate nickname was ringing from the rafters. Otto acknowledged the show of strength with a triumphant fist raised in the air. Lachlan lifted up his own hand and called for 'the show to go on', which had the effect of bringing the gathering down to earth and getting on with the business in hand.

From that night on, the islanders closed ranks. They could be a tight-lipped lot when they liked and vowed to one another that nosy visitors would get nothing out of them, if anyone ever asked about the foreign gentleman they would receive nothing except polite but evasive answers in Gaelic, which was usually a very effective way of dealing with questions that no one wanted to answer.

But for now, it was 'on with the show', which was more in the nature of a dance-cum-ceilidh-cum-concert. The chairs had been cleared to one side of the hall and during the first part of the evening The Portcull Fiddlers, in the shape of Rachel, Lorn and Jon, took the platform to provide music that soon had everyone itching to take to the floor. Torquil and Todd played rousing tunes on the pipes; Magnus gave a stirring solo on his kettle drums and later took up his accordion to provide a medley of feet-tapping airs.

Wild skirls and hoochs rent the air, becoming more pronounced as the evening wore on, with the merrymakers taking full advantage of the bar that had been set up in a curtained-off section of the room.

Fergus and Otto drank glass for glass of whisky till before very long the rest of the menfolk realized that they were witnessing a contest of stamina in the drinking field and, in their enthusiastic way, boosted proceedings by holding their own little 'may the best man win' sessions.

Mamma watched all of this with mounting concern. 'This you call culture?' she complained to Rab who, in his quiet way, was thoroughly enjoying himself. 'Myself, I call it barbaric: the dancing, it is wild, the music is designed to fill the head with primitive behaviour and bring out a madness that is frightening.

But, of course' – she sniffed disdainfully – 'they have never known anything else, they are not people of the world.'

Rab's eyes were calm enough when he looked at her but there was a warning glint in them that promised greater things to come. 'And just what is your concept of worldly people, Mistress Jodl? Your own daughter-in-law is a world famous violinist yet she knows how to let her hair down when the opportunity presents itself.'

'Rachel! We cannot count Rachel, she was born and brought up in this place, the madness was in her right from the start and will always be there, no matter how far in the world she travels.'

'Of course we can count Rachel, and Ruth McKenzie too, she has made her mark in the literary world. Both lassies are a credit to the island, and look at these other youngsters, many o' them attend college in Glasgow, they are educated and they are clever and, of course – they have the good manners on them that makes certain they never deliberately demean other folk.'

Mamma chose to ignore that point. 'Pah! Glasgow! What is Glasgow? It is not the world. If they came to Germany they would know the meaning of culture. In Hamburg— '

'Hamburg?' Rab interrupted, pronouncing it in such a way as to make it sound like 'Humbug'. 'And where in the world is that, I'd like to know?'

'If you do not know where Hamburg is then you too are lacking in the worldliness.'

Rab shook his head, his eyes were now icy cold. In his soft, slow voice he drawled, 'We have a saying here on Rhanna: "You haveny lived till you've been to Glasgow and you haveny been born till you visit the Hebrides." Cities like Hamburg are ten a penny; give me Glasgow or Edinburgh any time, because you see, Mistress Jodl, the people in them are human beings who are known and respected the world over.'

At that Mamma proceeded to have a fit of the 'solkiness' and Rab immediately deserted her to dance with Eilidh Monro who had had her sights set on him for some considerable time and who hated Mamma's guts for having arrived so unexpectedly in the mating ring.

Mamma looked after him with worried eyes; she had made a great effort with her appearance for this man though she wouldn't admit, even to herself, how much she had come to like and admire him. As soon as the music stopped she sought him out, elbowing Eilidh out of the way in her eagerness to make amends with him.

'The apology I make,' she announced to him with an effort. 'You are right, the evening is here to enjoy, but the hall is too hot and I ask of you to get for me the small glass of schnapps.'

Rab's eyes gently gleamed, he went off and returned with the desired drink, which Mamma downed in one gulp before requesting another. When it too had been consumed without a grimace she allowed Rab to lead her on to the floor and show her how to perform a reel, watched by a glowering Eilidh and several other womenfolk whose tongues were soon red hot with enjoyable speculation.

Mamma was not a figure to be missed in any crowd. Mairi had slightly overdone the blue rinse but even so, Jon's mother was an impressive sight in more ways than one and when Rab had danced her to a gasping halt, quite a few of the menfolk jostled for her attention. But she had eyes only for Rab and he, whilst making sure that she didn't monopolize him too much, paid her sufficient attention to make Eilidh retire to the edge of the ring for the rest of the night and join with her cronies in that most satisfying of all female pastimes, that of criticising other females in their choice of dress, hairstyle and footwear.

By nine-thirty everyone had danced themselves to exhaustion and were only too glad to avail themselves of tea and sandwiches before arranging the chairs in rows for the next part of the evening, beginning with the Portvoynachan Ladies Gaelic Choir singing a selection of traditional Gaelic airs, followed by the school choir's eager rendering of popular Scottish and English songs that soon had everyone tapping their feet.

The light shone on the shining cherubic faces; parents hardly recognised their offspring – the immaculate little dresses, the neatly pressed trousers, the clean, glowing skin, the innocent smiles. Neil Black stepped forward to sing a solo in his soaring, sweet, soprano voice, and his parents almost burst with pride and forgot the grimy, untidy ragamuffin Neil in the utter joy of the moment.

Neil received his applause with suitable aplomb and stepped sedately back to his place as little Lorna McKenzie came forward to recite a poem she had composed herself. Ruth and Lorn listened to their daughter with bated breath; Fergus watched his dark-haired granddaughter and squeezed Kirsteen's hand. Lorna concluded her poem, her big, solemn eyes swept the upturned faces, with great restraint she refrained from waving to those members of her family dotted about the audience and she too went back to her place to thunderous applause.

In a spurt of jealousy Margaret Black tugged Lorna's hair and in one minute flat the angels turned into devils. A good going scuffle ensued, parents stormed the platform to rescue, slap, or reprimand their offspring, according to the measure of their misdeeds, while the Portvoynachan Ladies Gaelic Choir rescued the day by singing Brahms' 'Lullaby', which, if inappropriate, successfully filled the gap till order was restored.

It was Jon's turn next. He was a brilliant musician and could have made a notable career for himself, but when he met and fell in love with Rachel, he had buried his own ambitions in order to allow her to pursue hers, for in her he had recognized a talent far greater than his own. But he had never allowed himself to neglect his music and soon Sarasate's 'Gypsy Airs' flowed from his violin, haunting and evocative, filling every corner with trembling ecstatic notes that rose and fell, soothed and excited.

Rachel watched his long, sensitive fingers running over the strings. His thin, gentle face was somehow lost and sad in its repose, making her throat tighten with pain. She knew that she had to make him happy again and she vowed to tell him about the baby that very night. It would bring them together again as nothing else would and when Lorn took the platform

278

to play a gay selection of strathspeys and reels, her spirits lifted with the music and she knew that everything was going to come right between herself and Jon.

With hardly a break the entertainment went on. When Rachel took up her own violin to play Massenet's meditation from *Thais*, an enthralled silence embraced the audience. Mamma looked at her daughter-in-law's lovely rapt face and for the first time she knew the power and the glory of Rachel's talent. She had never been to any of her recitals and something akin to shame touched her, a feeling that grew when, with Otto at the piano and Rachel on the violin, the audience were treated to a soul-stirring performance of the beautiful Poème by Chausson.

Then came the moment that everyone had been waiting for. The platform cleared, Otto seated himself in front of Becky, adjusted his kilt so that he wouldn't sit on the pleats, shrugged his cuffs away from his hands and began, starting with a selection of Chopin's piano solos, including the enchanting Nocturne in E flat, which Otto finished with a great flourish before going on to the exalted and stirring Polonaise No 6 in A flat.

'This is what I wait to hear,' breathed Mamma, going into such vocal raptures that Barra hissed at her to be quiet and let everyone else enjoy the playing. And enjoy it they did, many of them had never paid much attention to such music before, but then, none of them had had the opportunity to hear a live performance from the hands of such an accomplished maestro, and the excitement of it carried them away on wings of fantasy as crescendos of wonderful sound poured and crashed, thundered and reverberated, till the very rafters seemed to tremble and the foundations shake.

Otto gave of his best, his hands flying, his face bathed in sweat. He was in another world, and when he at last jumped to his feet to spread his arms wide and bow to the audience he was Karl Gustav Langer, revered throughout Europe, wildly hailed by other nations over the sea, expecting worship and receiving it, for as one the hall had risen to its feet to cheer and whistle and applaud in wave upon wave of unstinted appreciation.

Tam nudged Fergus and told him, 'The man can hold his

whisky as well as he can the Schnapps. Just look at him, McKenzie, you would think he had drunk nothing stronger than tea, you'll no' get your own back on a man wi' his build and stamina.'

'Ay, well there's aye a next time,' returned Fergus who was himself feeling the effects of his indulgences but would never admit to it. 'It could easily hit him suddenly, I've seen stronger men than him felled at the end o' an evening's drinking just when everybody was thinking they'd drunk themselves sober.'

The performance had exhausted Otto but his adrenaline was flowing, somehow keeping him on top of fatigue and pain so that he was able still to smile and be thrilled when the laird presented him with a framed illuminated scroll, beautifully inscribed in copperplate and bearing the words, '*Otto McKinnon Klebb of Croy, Friend and Kinsman, McKinnon Clan Gathering. Island of Rhanna, 1967*', and at the bottom the by now familiar '*Mac nan Èilean*'.

Officially, the most wonderful concert the island had ever known had come to an end but no one was letting go that easily, the musicians didn't need much persuading to take to the limelight once more and this time everyone joined in. 'Song of Rhanna' had never been sung with such enthusiasm, then 'Amazing Grace' with Torquil and Todd on the pipes and Torquill as the solo piper at the end. Song after song, melody after melody, hit the roof.

Otto sat down once more at the piano, the flowing, infectious music of Johann Strauss II came tumbling out: waltzes, marches, polkas.

Rachel, as carried away as everyone else, turned to look at Otto and realized suddenly that he was at the end of his strength, only his indomitable will was keeping him going and she was thankful when he came at last to a halt and all that remained was for 'Auld Lang Syne' to be sung before everyone went home.

But it wasn't the end: someone, it might have been Fergus, began singing 'Vienna, City of my Dreams'. It was seized upon, taken up, those that didn't know the words hummed the tune till before long a swelling vibrancy of melody rose up to make for an enchanting finale to the evening.

Otto stood by his piano, shaking his head, so moved by the tribute that tears filled his dark eyes as the evocative words filled every space inside his head.

> Farewell Vienna mine,
> I'm in the spell of your charms divine,
> Dressed like a queen with lights so gay,
> You are the love of my heart today . . .

Otto swayed, his legs crumpled beneath him, blindly he felt for the piano stool and sank on to it, his face deathly white.

Tam and some of the other men grinned and told Fergus, 'You were right, McKenzie, the *Uisge Beatha* has played its trump card, Otto has had it by the look o' him and might need some help to get home.' There was a move forward but Rachel, who was still up on the platform with Magnus and Otto, got there first.

Rushing to Otto's side she saw that he was in great pain and immediately she looked around for Jon to help. But he had disappeared into the crowd and was nowhere to be seen and it was as well that Mark and Megan had noticed Otto's distress and were first up on the platform, to be seized upon by Rachel who frantically tried to convey to them that she needed help to get Otto outside.

Without hesitation they each put a shoulder under his armpits and got him as quickly as they could out of a side door and down to Todd's car, followed closely by Rachel and Magnus.

Somehow they bundled the big man into the back seat and got in after him. Todd had left his keys in the ignition, Mark started up the engine just as Todd reached the scene to peer in the window with enquiring eyes.

'We're taking him home,' Mark quickly explained. 'All he needs is a gallon of strong tea to sober him up. McKenzie o' the Glen has won this round by the look o' things.'

Todd beamed in complete understanding and stood back to watch his gleaming Rolls disappearing off into the night, only too happy to help *Mac nan Èilean* in this, his hour of need.

As soon as Otto was safely settled on the sitting-room sofa, Rachel took Megan's hand and led her up to the bedroom. She couldn't keep this terrible thing to herself any longer, her heart was leaping in her breast with the dreadful strain of the last few minutes, and she didn't pause once when they reached the bedroom but went straight to the little bedside cabinet to pull open the drawer and reveal its contents.

Megan stared, one by one she picked up the brown bottles to look at the labels, and her hazel eyes were serious and sad when she said with a strange little catch in her throat, 'Rachel, how long has he been taking these? There are dozens of them, he certainly must have brought a good supply with him but most of them are now empty. Can you tell me, please, just how ill is he?'

'He is dying.' Rachel's lips formed the words, gently Megan took her arm and made her sit on the bed.

'You've known this for a long time, haven't you, Rachel?'

The girl nodded, the miserable dull ache in her heart forcing her head down to her breast so that the other woman wouldn't see her eyes. But she couldn't stop the tears from springing; she had locked away her pain for too long, and once the flow started it wouldn't be stemmed, and with a cry of sympathy, Megan folded her arms round the slender body and held on tightly till the trembling gradually ceased.

Only then did Rachel raise her swollen face. She had never felt more frustrated by her lack of speech, she wanted to pour it all out, so much to say and no voice to say it with, her head pounded with unspoken emotions, her silent screams of heartache reverberated inside her skull, her swimming eyes were blinded by weepings and wantings, and all she could do, all she could ever do, was wave her hands about in wordless speech that might or might not, be understood.

She clenched her hands into fists, her turbulent black eyes looked at Megan, once more her lips formed words. 'Help Otto.'

Megan squeezed the girl's hand. 'Of course I'll help him, he's going to need a lot of medication, I'll send for some stuff right away but for now I must get over to the Manse to see what I have there.'

At the door she turned. 'Magnus should be told,' she said softly. 'He has a right to know: Otto is his grandson. Can I ask Mark to tell him?'

Rachel hesitated, wondering if she had the right to take on that kind of responsibility. Otto should be consulted first – she thought of her beloved stranger – he was strong, stubborn, wilful – the last thing he would want was for people to make a fuss and tell him what he should and shouldn't do.

But he was so alone, so vulnerable; he needed love and comfort at a time like this and Magnus of Croy was the last man on earth to make an issue of anything – even death.

She nodded, Megan inclined her head in acknowledgement and went quickly downstairs to seek out Mark. She was remembering that night of the ceilidh in the shorehouse – Otto's eyes, something about them that she couldn't quite fathom. She of all people should have known, Mark had said it was the drink but she had felt there was more to it than that and tonight she had found out what it was. Drugs! The black pupils had been glazed with them and all the time only Rachel had known the lonely secret of a dying man . . . and had carried the burden of that knowledge as only a young woman of her discipline and devotion could.

Magnus sat alone in the armchair by the fire. Otto was in bed, helped there by Mark and Megan after she had given him something to ease his pain. They had gone home, leaving Rachel up there with him. She would stay till he fell asleep and maybe longer, Rachel was a good person to have at a sick bed, something about those hands of hers: she had the touch, the power to help the ill, soothe the dying.

But Otto wasn't dying yet; someone, Magnus couldn't remember who, had said he still had some time left, weeks, months, it was difficult to know for certain in cases like these.

Magnus gazed into the fire. A few months. That powerful, vibrant man, that musical genius, a few months. Magnus felt as if his heart had turned to stone within him, he felt nothing, only the homely things, like Vienna warm and purring on his knee, the heat of the fire burning his legs, the safe, tranquil cosiness of the chintzy room, the clock, tick-tocking the minutes away.

Minutes, hours, days . . . months. The last few months; summer; sweetness; sun; wind; rain; a big, black-bearded bear of a man coming to him out of the blue to relay the news that he came as one who had sprung from Rhanna soil, grandson of Sheena and Magnus of Croy . . .

Sheena . . . A mist blurred the old man's vision. Sheena of the summer shielings, Sheena whose feet had trod light and sure over the heather braes, whose laughter had rung in the corries, soared among the bens. He could still hear the echoes of it, for him it would always live in his heart . . . and her lips, soft and sweet as a wild rose, tasting of nectar and dewdrops, driving him crazy, so crazy with his love for her . . .

And then she had gone, and there had been nothing, no one, only the emptiness of spaces. Gone were the shielings from the hills, wild grew the heather, cold blew the wind, untouched sprung the sweet briar on the hedge; no one to share the quiet joys of lonely places; lonely; lonely; only the memories, the sad echoes of love, reaching far over the sea, seeking but never finding, mortal joys, gone forever . . .

Until Otto, a man who came as a stranger but who had soon become a beloved friend, a man who had known and loved Sheena, who had heard the ring of her voice, who had listened and had listened well. Through her font of memories he had known the call of the islands, he had breasted the ocean . . . that same ocean that had taken her away all those years ago . . .

Otto, his and Sheena's grandson.

The old man's hands tightened in his lap . . . his snowy head sunk to his breast, the cat purred, the clock ticked . . . a few months . . . The stone in his breast melted . . . he put his head into his hands – and he wept.

Chapter Twenty-one

'It isn't mine!'

The statement was brutally terse and Rachel stared at her husband in horror, hardly able to believe the evidence of her own ears. She had buoyed herself up for this moment, she had felt the time was now ripe to share her wonderful news with her husband, an excitement had mounted in her as she had visualized his face, anticipated his reactions – in her blackest of nightmares she could never have imagined that he would turn on her like this, say the things he was saying.

Everything in her, all the love, the joy, the life, drained out of her body, dispersing like dust in the wind, leaving her feeling fatigued and miserable beyond measure. This should have been the happiest moment of their lives, they had waited so long to have a child and over the years they had discussed with one another how it would be when the longed-for day actually came.

He couldn't mean what he had just said. Frantically she spoke to him with her hands but he wouldn't look at her and a sob of sheer frustration bubbled in her throat.

'It isn't mine!' he repeated forcibly. 'And you're not going to deceive me again, Rachel, we both know who the father is! I've watched you with Otto, you can hardly keep your eyes off him – just like you couldn't keep your eyes off Lorn McKenzie not so many years ago. I tried very hard to forgive you that time, I knew I was no match for that particular young McKenzie. I told myself that it wouldn't happen again and fooled myself into believing it. But I was never a match for those other men in your life. I'm too tame, too serious, too easily taken in!'

She had never heard him speak like this before, his voice throbbing with emotion, filled with such terrible deep conviction that when he at last turned to face her, it seemed as if a wild beast looked out of his eyes, those eyes that had always before regarded her with gentleness and love.

Jon! Her fingers were a blur, forming words, trying to make him see how wrong he was, but it was no use.

'It's the last straw, Rachel,' he told her angrily, and something cold and hard replaced the feverish expression in his eyes. 'After all this time you tell me you are expecting a baby and try to make me believe it is mine. You're so obsessed with Otto you can't even bear to have other people see his faults or his human weaknesses. I was watching you last night trying to cover up the fact that he was so drunk he couldn't even make it outside on his own. You went home with him, didn't you? And you came creeping back here at some godforsaken hour of the morning. Was he as good in bed drunk as he is when he's sober? Why don't you tell me about it, I might be able to pick up a few hints. As for trying to pass this child off as mine, you can forget it, I'm leaving Rhanna, I've had enough, tell your wonderful Austrian lover that you're expecting his child, or are you afraid that he'll want nothing more to do with you when he's faced with that kind of a burden?'

She felt as if icy fingers were clutching her heart, Jon, her wonderful, kindly Jon, speaking to her as if he hated the very sight of her, looking at her as if she was some sort of fearsome stranger instead of the wife he had always cherished with such selfless love.

He would have to know about Otto, she should have told him long ago but it wasn't too late, it wasn't . . . But even now something held her back, anger flooded her being, she told herself she shouldn't have to use Otto's illness as a lever to make things right between herself and her husband. Her head went back, her chin tilted, wilful pride, black resolution filled her breast. Let Jon think what he would, she wasn't going to beg or bargain for any favours. He could leave Rhanna if he wanted, he could go to hell for all she cared, but one thing was certain, wherever he went she wasn't going with him, she was staying here on Rhanna till her baby was born – and no one – nothing – was going to change her mind on that score.

There was nothing more to be said, Jon had said it all in just a few short minutes, and turning on her heel she ran out of the house, down to Mara Òran Bay where the sea sighed over the pebbles and the wind rustled the seed pods on the whins. She could hardly see where she was going for tears, her head ached with weariness after a night spent at Otto's sickbed, her heart was heavy and sore in her breast. Everything that she had ever hoped and dreamed of was crumbling about her ears, and she was too unhappy in mind, body and spirit to see how unfair she was being to her husband in not letting him know the reasons for her unswerving allegiance to Otto, not only last night, but all the other nights and days she had spent away from the one man who had devoted himself to her, every minute of every day of all of their years together.

Jon watched her go, she who had been his whole life, who had made his world a wonderland of music and light, laughter and love, excitement and adventure. Ever since the day he had met her on the road with Ruth, Lorn and Lewis, he had been fascinated and bewitched by her. He had come as a tourist that warm spring of 1950, complete with rucksack and maps, looking for Croft na Ard, the home of his former commander, and once the children had gotten over their initial shyness, they had been only too willing to help, especially Lewis, who, with his brown limbs, black hair, and mischievous smile, was the epitome of health and youthful beauty.

He had been the leader, there was never any doubt about that, an aura of great authority emanated from every gesture, every laughing glance – and he had only been nine years old, approximately the same age as the others who had all been born in the same month of the same year.

Of them all, Lewis had seemed the strongest, the most robust . . . the most passionate. He had been Rachel's first great love. They had been wild together – untamed – each of them a free spirit that had laughed at life and had taken everything it had to offer. And then Lewis had died, his magnetism, his greedy delight of life, all gone in just one swift burst of tragic illness. In the end he had died on the beach after falling off his horse, his dying eyes had seen the skies and the seas that he had so loved, before they had closed forever on the wonder and the beauty of his world.

But by then Rachel belonged to Jon . . . or had she? Had that golden-skinned gypsy ever really belonged to anyone? No, he decided as he stood there at the window, the visions of the past floating through his mind, Rachel was an entity unto herself and always would be. Sometimes he was lulled into believing that she was really his and then something, or someone, would enter their lives to shatter his illusions and make him aware of how fragile his hold was on her.

Lorn had been the next of her tempestuous affairs. It had been a brief infatuation, lasting only a summer, but inflamed desires and intoxicating passions had consumed them both till the fires had been quenched and they had returned to the reality of how much hurt and harm they had caused. Ruth and Lorn had nearly split up because of it but Jon had forgiven and had tried to forget, though he couldn't help feeling threatened by the presence of the many men who surrounded her in the course of her existence.

Now there was Otto, out of nowhere it seemed, a man of great charm and mystique, one with similar talents and interests as her own, one furthermore who had the same alluring qualities as herself: power, personality, a passion and a thirst for life that made everyone else look impassive in comparison. She was obviously bedazzled by him, she had spent every minute she could with him. Without consideration of what her actions were doing to her husband she had openly, and for all the world to see, paid court to a man who had pretended friendship with her husband when all the while . . .

Jon raised a trembling hand to his eyes, he removed his glasses to clean them but still a mist blurred his vision. His tormented emotions tugged him this way and that, insecurity tightened his nerves. He shivered and wondered if he could ever really leave the girl who had infused his timid world with inspiration ever since that fateful day, long ago, when a curly-haired child had captured his heart forever with the radiance of her pearly smile . . .

He came out of his reverie with a start – that child had grown into a woman – one who had just told him she was expecting a baby . . . a baby. How he had longed for such news, how often they had both imagined what it would be like when the gift of a child came to them at last. But it wasn't his. She had robbed him of everything that had been good and sweet in his life and he could hardly bear the hurt of her final betrayal.

He turned away from the window. Let her go to *him*, let her stay here on Rhanna and have another man's child. She could go to hell for all he cared . . .

The years of his devotion were done with – it was finished.

Only a few people knew of Rachel's pregnancy; she was easily able to hide it since she was still at the stage when nothing much showed, except when she ran her hands over her belly and felt its taut roundness. She had always walked tall, her figure was superb, a flowing blouse was all she needed to deny her condition to the world and deny it she did. Jon's rejection of his own child had done that to her. If he had accepted it as joyfully as she had imagined, everyone would have known by now; as it was she felt no exuberance and had decided to allow the passage of time to tell its own tale.

Ruth only found out by accident from Phebie when they met one day in the village. 'You and Rachel will have more in common than ever now,' Phebie had said in a burst of cheery impulse. 'It will be nothing but baby talk and, of course, wi' you being an experienced mother, you'll be able to give her a few handy tips nearer the time.'

She saw the look on Ruth's face and her own fell. 'You didn't know about it? Och, Ruth, I'm sorry, I should have held my tongue. Lachy did warn me to keep quiet and let Rachel blow her own trumpets but I thought – wi' you being her friend . . .'

Ruth had gone home to pour her indignation out on Lorn, so

incensed by the fact that she had learned the news from someone other than Rachel she was beside herself with temper and in a mood to battle with anyone who got in her way.

As it was she wasted no time next day in making tracks for An Cala. If Lorn had been there to make her sit down and talk things over in a logical manner she might never have made the move she would later live to regret, but Lorn was working with his father in Laigmhor's fields, the children were with Shona at Mo Dhachaidh, and Ruth, with more time on her hands than usual, was in a mood to spend it dangerously, particularly since she had seen very little of her friend these last few weeks.

And no wonder, she fumed to herself as she started up the little car Lorn had bought her to celebrate the publication of her first novel, she's been too busy elsewhere to spare much time for the likes of me!

An Cala was empty but for Rachel, Mamma was out, so too was Jon, the way was clear for Ruth to say what every unreasoning emotion forced her to say the minute she stepped over the threshold.

Rachel looked up with a start at the suddenness of the unexpected intrusion. She was about to offer the usual hospitable cup of tea but got no chance to do so as Ruth, her fair face flushed with purpose, her violet eyes big with bottled-up indignation, went into the attack right away.

'I finally heard about the baby' – she said it like an accusation – 'from someone who thought I must already know and was quite shocked to learn that I didn't. In the normal way o' things I would be the first to congratulate you, Rachel, but this isn't the normal way o' things and I think I know the reasons for your secrecy. I've seen how you've behaved wi' Otto, how you run to him at every turn, leaving Jon to his own devices like you've left everyone else this summer. You've never even spared the time for your own mother. You never come to see us anymore, it's always Otto, isn't it? Right from the start it was Otto!'

For answer Rachel merely stared in total amazement, so taken aback she could do nothing to defend herself and Ruth, taking the reaction as an admission of guilt, slowly nodded her head.

'How could you, Rachel?' she cried aghast. 'How could you do this to Jon?'

'How could you with Lewis?' Rachel countered, her fingers spelling out the words, her eyes like black coals in the deathly pallor of her face.

'That was different!' Ruth flashed back. 'Lewis was dying!'

'So is Otto.' Rachel swiftly relayed the message before her hands went still, fluttering to her lap like spent butterflies. She was appalled at herself for giving away such a confidence, furious at Ruth for having dug below the surface of her defences with just a few cryptic words.

Stepping back a pace she sunk into a chair and covered her face with her hands, too overwrought to weep, too sick at heart to even be angry.

There was a stunned silence in the room. Ruth stood there, hating herself, deflated and uneasy, horrified and afraid.

'Oh, Rachel,' she whispered at last, 'I know it's too feeble to say sorry but I am, truly I am, I . . . I don't now what came over me. I know I'm guilty of being too quick to pass judgement, Shona pointed that out to me and though I was mad at her I saw later that she was right – also – I think I was jealous of the time you spent with Otto – I thought . . .'

She stammered to a halt, unable to go on, Rachel looked up, and her eyes were black, and hard, and cold, 'You can think what you like about me, Ruth,' wearily her hands moved, 'but never, never, must you tell anyone about Otto – not even Lorn. Otto plans to go back to Vienna to die but while he is here all he wants is peace – and peace is what he will have or you'll have me to reckon with.'

Desperately Ruth tried to make amends but it was no use, Rachel had withdrawn into herself, her whole demeanour was of one who had retreated into some inner world where no one could follow. She looked very alone sitting there and somehow so vulnerable Ruth wanted to rush forward and comfort her. But she didn't, she was too afraid of rejection, too horrified at her own folly to even begin to forgive herself, let alone expect Rachel's forgiveness.

Turning on her heel, she walked out of An Cala, her foot dragging so badly she tripped and had to hold on to the gate to steady herself.

She glanced back at the house. It looked empty somehow, as if no one lived there, neglected and sad and abandoned. It was only fancy, of course, but in her heightened state of awareness Ruth imagined that the spirit of life had left it, leaving it comfortless and bare where before, the very aura of Rachel's presence had enfolded it in a vibrant shroud of light.

'Oh, Lorn!' she cried when he got home that day and found her sitting by the empty grate in the parlour. 'Rachel and myself have had a terrible row! I think she might never speak to me again.'

Lorn was weary after a day spent in the fields and was in no mood to listen to details of an argument that had taken place between two battling women. Ruthie had been temperamental that summer. She was always restless and keyed up when Rachel was on the island, as if she expected exciting happenings to occur every minute of the day, but this time she had been more than usually tense and he sighed and wondered if the water was hot for a wash and if his tea would be late with her in her present mood.

'Where are the bairns?' he queried, ignoring her look of tragedy. 'I thought you were picking them up from Mo Dhachaidh.'

'Shona said they could stay and have tea wi' her . . .' She eyed him in some annoyance. 'Did you hear what I said, Lorn? Rachel and me . . .'

He ran a hand through his black curls and sighed. 'All right, what was the row about – this time?'

She wasn't slow to pick up his rather sarcastic tone and her golden head tilted stubbornly. 'I'm sorry, I canny tell you, it's something between her and me. One day you'll know, one day everyone will know but for now I canny say.'

'Women!' he cried in exasperation. 'What you really mean, Ruthie, what you aye mean when you're like this, is you could say but you won't.'

'No, Lorn, this isn't like that, it's – well – it's a matter o' life

292

and death – and could easily be my death if Rachel ever found out I had breathed a word to anyone.'

Lorn bent to pull on his slippers, having left his mud-caked boots in the porch. His stomach was rumbling, his hands were callused from hoeing turnips all day, he wanted only to sit down and allow every tired limb to relax, but there was no chance of that or anything else till Ruth had had her say.

Reaching out, he lifted her hair and let the silken strands slide through his fingers. 'Ruthie, if it will make you feel better you can tell me what ails you, I'll be very quiet and attentive and won't interrupt once and nothing can be as terrible as you make out.'

She shook off his hand and sat forward in her seat, her pupils huge and black with the enormity of the dark deeds she had done that day and which nothing she said or did could ever take back. 'I'm sorry, I canny tell you, Lorn: Rachel made me promise not to breathe a word, no' even to you – and you especially should know how frighteningly intense Rachel can be when she has a mind.'

Resentment was in the glance she threw at him. She knew she was being unfair but she couldn't help it, she was hating herself, hating everything she had done, and she was unable to stop herself transferring some of that feeling to her husband who had done nothing but just be there in the firing line.

His eyes were on her, suspicion darkening them till they were just as black as her own. 'This wouldny have anything to do wi' Rachel's baby, would it? Ruthie, I'm asking you a question and you're avoiding my eyes which means you're feeling guilty about something. You were in a funny mood when I left this morning, as if you had a burden on your mind and couldny rest till you had unloaded it on to someone.'

'Ach! You McKenzies! You're all the same! Too full o' fancies for your own good and I haveny the time to listen to your blethers. There's coal in the bucket, you can make yourself useful for a change and light the fire. If it wasny for me this place would go to rack and ruin and you would do nothing but stand back and watch it falling about your lugs!'

She sounded exactly like Morag Ruadh, her red-haired religious fanatic of a mother, who had ruled her with a rod of iron, and who had finally taken to her deathbed in mortal fear of what the Lord would do to her for having indulged in 'the sins of the flesh' when she had conceived her daughter in a fit of drunken lust, and ever after had never been sure who had fathered her child.

Ruth got up, she flounced away through to the kitchen, murmuring something about making the tea, adding under her breath that she was just a 'skivvy' who had no life of her own and it was a wonder she ever managed to find the time to write books.

Morag too had believed herself to be indispensable and Lorn stared after his wife with apprehension clouding his face. But he knew he was being silly, Ruthie could never turn out like her mother, she was too soft and sweet, and romantic – except during times like these when he could gladly have taken her across his knee and given her a good skelping.

'Home!' Mamma's face fell, she was thoroughly enjoying herself on Rhanna and had visualized a few more weeks on the island.

'Yes, Mamma, home.' Jon spoke firmly, the mood that had beset him since the row with Rachel had grown blacker and deeper with the passing days, leaving no room for him to easily deal with unnecessary trivia or to placate his mother in his usual patient manner. 'Though when I say home I really mean London. I have much business to catch up on, I have also applied for a teaching position at the Royal Academy of Music and want to be on hand for any likely interviews. You could always stay here with Rachel, of course, she won't be coming with us, she feels the need to remain on Rhanna for the foreseeable future, hence my reasons for wanting to take up teaching again.'

Mamma looked warily at her son. He hadn't told her about the baby, she only knew that all was not well between him and Rachel. The atmosphere had been very tense in the house and she had made herself as scarce as possible since all her old enjoyment of picking fault with her daughter-in-law had deserted her of late.

Nevertheless she had no wish to remain at An Cala without Jon. His news of seeking a teaching post in the musical world had taken away some of the sting of having to leave Rhanna and waving a nonchalant hand in the air she said graciously, 'With you to London I will come; Rachel has no need of me here but you, Jon, you must have someone to look after you. Rachel is not the type of woman to feel the obligation to carry out wifely duties, so I, your mother, will be happy to take them upon myself as I do not wish to go back to Hamburg, knowing you have need of me.'

Her slightly martyred air didn't fool Jon for one moment. He had seen a big change in his mother that summer: no more did she fret and whine and complain, she spent more time out of the house than in, she was cheerful, buoyant and happy, in fact her entire attitude and outlook on life had undergone a complete metamorphosis and sometimes Jon had to look at her twice to convince himself that this really was the same woman who had spent her entire life bossing people about and making things difficult for those who were nearest her.

She not only behaved and sounded different, her appearance had altered too. Her eyes held a new sparkle, her face glowed, her downcast mouth smiled more often, she laughed readily and he had discovered in her a sense of humour that had hitherto only manifested itself in a somewhat satirical way. She had always been a handsome woman in a rather hard and mannish fashion, now she was softer, more feminine, more attractive altogether; she spent a good deal of her time in front of the mirror and she made regular trips to 'Mairi's hairdressing saloon'. She had even gone to the lengths of ordering some fashionable clothes from Aggie's mail order catalogue, though oddly, and here even Rachel had to smile, along with all the finery had come a stout pair of wellington boots and a voluminous oilskin jacket, both of which items she had hastily explained away as being the only kind of apparel to wear in a place where it rained most of the time and 'even when it stops it forgets to be dry'.

That, of course, was only bluff. In due course the real reasons for the boots and the jacket became known, via that most reliable of communications, Highland Telegraph: quite simply, word of mouth – many mouths, all flapping away, exaggerating, elaborating, enjoying hugely anything and everything that held the merest whisper of interest.

No one escaped, particularly visitors, who were always a great source of curiosity, and Mamma, with her reputation for doing and saying outrageous things, demanded an even greater scrutiny than most. And Eilidh Monroe, incensed beyond measure at Frau Helga Jodl's monopolisation of Rab McKinnon, made very sure that the tongues were kept piping hot with conjecture.

But it was that ubiquitous personage Erchy, in the course of his innocent travels, who saw, with his very own eyes, the incongruous spectacle of Mamma, 'wrapped to the lugs in waterproofs', over there at Croft nan Uamh (Croft of the Caves), helping Rab bring the cows in for milking, or rather, ostensibly helping him, since, like all good cows everywhere, they didn't need much coaxing to plod through the gates into the byre to wait patiently for their udders to be emptied.

'Hmph, as if she could ever be any good on a croft!' was Eilidh's verdict when the news filtered through to her ears. 'Just wait till she has to help wi' a difficult calving or has to put the fork to a steaming dung midden in the rain. She'll no' look so smart then wi' her new welly boots covered in glaur and pig shit.'

It was amazing enough for Frau Helga Jodl to have actually participated in menial croft work, but it was a miracle that she had actually done so on land situated high on the machair above a group of awesome caves known as Uamh na Mara, (Caves of the Sea). At high tide the ocean spumed and roared into the fearsome caverns and local legend had it that once, long ago, during an almighty storm, the ground above the caves had trembled so much with the boom and might of the waves that the very crockery inside the croft had rattled about as if in the grip of an earthquake.

Despite all, Croft nan Uamh had managed to remain intact

on the same spot for the last hundred years and more, and was so sturdily built it looked as if it could easily still be standing with the passing of another century.

But that wasn't all that Mamma had endured and enjoyed that fateful summer, there had been sightings of her all over the island – rattling along in Rab's uncle's old motor car, parked on the cliffs, the moors, the machair – anywhere and everywhere off the beaten track, though never far enough off it not to be espied by somebody.

That was the thing that really had the steam coming out of Eilidh's ears and she fumed and fretted and wished for the day when it would be exit Frau Helga Jodl from the island.

Now that day was almost here and no one was more surprised than Jon when, on the eve of their departure, his mother confided some of her most personal feelings to him. 'I speak to you first of Rab McKinnon,' she began, an uncharacteristic hesitancy in her voice and a blush on her cheeks. 'All of my life I look for a man like him, he does not let me have too much of my own way, the authority I like, the strong silence I respect, he tells me to be quiet when I have the verbal diarrhoea, if I show the solkiness he tells me he has no use of women with the moods and so I do not have the solkiness anymore.'

Verbal diarrhoea! Mamma's vocabulary was certainly expanding and Jon looked at her with a new light of affection shining in his eyes.

'I have many good friends here on Rhanna,' she continued, the revelations pouring out of her. 'I was lonely when I live in Hamburg, here I am never alone unless I seek the solitude. Aggie has been kind to me, she befriends me when I think I have no friends, after that I find friendship with many people. At first I think they come from the moon, they have the strange language I do not understand, but then I see I also have the strange language and cross the bridges I must. Happy Mary always has the smile for me, Mairi is always ready to help and with her and Kate McKinnon I drink the tea and even grow to like it. Herr Holy Smoke never tries to cheat me anymore and always he gives me the cheap meat for my cat, on the road Erchy waves to me from his post van or his dreadful bus and I even forgive him for the knots I tie in my stomach when he took me to find the city of Croy that was not there. Yes, Jon, the people here I like very much.'

'But, Mamma,' Jon said with a smile, 'you don't have a cat, you don't even like cats! How can Holy Smoke . . .'

He saw the sparkle of humour in her eyes, he suddenly liked his mother very much and throwing his arm around her shoulder he gave her one of the most affectionate hugs he had ever given her.

Before she left, Mamma paid her daughter-in-law a surprising, if offhand, compliment.

'I have always liked one thing about you, Rachel,' she said nonchalantly, making Rachel think: at least one thing is better than none. 'You have the honesty, always you show to me the truth, you never hide your feelings from me like an actress. We have not always seen one another's eyes but in many ways, I like you.'

Rachel stared; she thought: if I was able to speak I would be so dumbfounded I wouldn't be able to speak. She smiled and Mamma, imagining the smile was for her, beamed back and with abrupt suddenness she took the girl to her mighty bosom, almost crushing the life out of her.

'You must not allow Jon to be too long on his own.' Embarrassed by her own display of affection, Mamma quickly reverted to her old self. 'It is not good for a husband and wife to be apart like this.' She frowned. 'For some time now I have not been able to speak to Jon, he has the anger in his chest that I do not understand but I will not interfere, you are his wife, you and he must arrange your lives between yourselves and sew up your disagreements.'

This was almost too much for Rachel, she had grown accustomed to dealing with a bellicose, interfering mother-in-law, and this vastly changed woman, who was regarding her with an expression that bordered on benevolence, was an entirely new departure and would take some getting used to – if Mamma continued along her present path – which Rachel very much doubted.

Even so, it made a pleasant change from the domineering matriarch, and Rachel, her senses lulled into peaceable lines, wondered if she and Jon were doing the right thing keeping quiet about the baby. They had discussed the matter, clinically and coldly, and had decided that it would be better if Mamma didn't know, considering the present set of circumstances.

'It will only make things more unpleasant,' Jon had said, not looking at his wife. 'She will start asking awkward questions and there's enough bad feeling in the air without her adding her voluble contribution. She'll find out soon enough when the baby comes and will have to learn the truth, till then it will be better for us all to keep everything on an even keel – the boat will inevitably rock and which of us goes down first remains to be seen.'

An even keel! Rachel's face reddened as she thought about that conversation, there had been something very final about it. She couldn't believe, even now, that it had ever taken place, but she wouldn't let him see, she wouldn't let anyone see, how much it had hurt her, and unconsciously her head went up in a gesture of proud defiance of everything that ached and burned in her heart.

For a moment she felt sorry for Jon's mother. Poor Mamma! She who had so longed for a grandchild, who had fumed and fretted and fussed when none were forthcoming over the years. All for nothing, the weeping and the wailing were done with— Rachel started. Was this the last time she would ever see Jon's mother? Was this the end of all the hints, the innuendoes, the arguments?

Rachel shuddered, she felt oddly sad at the thought, yet not so long ago she would have given a great deal of what she owned to see the back of this loud, demanding monument of a woman.

But Mamma had one or two trump cards up her sleeve and over the next few minutes she played them so cunningly that a flabbergasted Rachel was left wondering if her mother-in-law knew more than she was making out.

299

Looking beyond the window to the glistening ribbon of the sea she delivered her bombshell. 'I am glad I came here, Rachel, now I know why you and Jon like this island so much, the friendliness, it is all around, the freedom is like a good wine, it makes you want more of it. With Rab I have been to many places – much to my surprise, the car, it was not reliable, always it breaks down, everywhere, anywhere – and no one to come and help us to get started. The experiences, they were not good.'

Her tone belied her words, Rachel looked at her, her handsome face was glowing, her eyes were sparkling, she looked positively radiant.

Rachel drew in her breath, Mamma and Rab, it was impossible, it couldn't be – yet – those stories that had been flying around, Rachel had thought it was just gossip, built on flimsy ground, but occasionally these fables were woven from the fabric of fact.

Mamma's next words confirmed that there was more than a hint of truth in the tales. 'The ocean I will cross again,' she said almost dreamily. A promise or a threat? Rachel thought grimly. 'I come back to Rhanna when the snow is on the hills – at Christmas time. Rab will need someone to cook him a good dinner and Eilidh Monroe knows only the rabbit stew and the stodge. I make the German meal, the hams and the cooked meats, the spicy sausage, the apfelstrudel, the chocolate gateau, the baked apple stuffed with cinnamon and raisins . . .'

She went into raptures over the virtues of the food she would make, the festivities she would arrange, while Rachel thought: Christmas! When a child is born! Her child. Hers and Jon's, Mamma's grandchild – and she would be here after all, though by that time whether she acknowledged it as hers would be another story.

'Perhaps Karl Gustav Langer will still be here.' Mamma was enthusing, bringing Rachel back to earth with racing heart. 'He could give a concert, a Christmas concert. Oh, *wunderbar*! Never did I think I would meet such a great musician when I came to Rhanna.'

Then Mamma did a strange thing, for the first time ever she

was making a sign in the dumb language. She could have said aloud what she had to say, but in her uplifted mood she was letting Rachel know that she could converse with her perfectly well when she had a mind to do so.

Rachel stared fascinated as the be-ringed, somewhat stubby fingers, moved clumsily. The message read: 'I will take good care of Jon till you come back to him. He will put up with me because he is my son, but always it will be you on his mind. We cannot get rid of you so easily – we have to learn to put up with you – the Jodls are a very brave family.'

Despite herself Rachel smiled, Mamma was herself again, and oddly, Rachel was glad: the other Mamma was a stranger, she could cope better with the old one – for as long as she had to.

Part Four

AUTUMN/WINTER
1967/68

Chapter Twenty-two

It had been a golden summer, one that was unwilling to relinquish its hold on the land. The dawns, the days, the suns, the moons, rose and set as vigorously as ever but each of them wove their changes into the seasonal arrangement of things so that gradually there was a sharpness on the breath of morning. The berries ripened on the rowans; the grass on the hill became shaggy and coarse; the bracken was gold in the sun while the pearly mists of autumn lingered in the corries and banners of peat smoke hung suspended in the mellow air.

On the Muir of Rhanna the purple of the heather covered the land in a springy, thick mattress, interspersed by mounds of peat that had dried to brick-like hardness in the summer winds and would soon be ready to fuel winter fires throughout the island.

Gradually the visitors were leaving and in their camp over by Dunuaigh the travellers were thinking about leaving also, though for them it was an unhurried process. The autumn tourists had still to be met coming off the boat and persuaded to buy bunches of 'lucky heather' and never mind that there were acres of the stuff growing wild all over the place, the travellers picked it while it was still in bud and able to be passed off as the white heather so coveted by superstitious romantics of any age.

As the days shortened and the pace of life slowed for both man and beast, so too did a quieter tempo beat for Otto and Rachel, ruled not by the seasons but by the changing ebb and flow taking place within their own separate spheres.

Rachel knew the quickening of eager new life inside her own body, while for Otto the stream of his life was draining slowly but surely away. The time was coming for him to go back to Austria and it seemed to Rachel that everything that had been precious and good in her world was drifting off like smoke in the wind. He was dying, yet he was her strength; every day she saw some slight change on his wonderful face, but even as he grew thinner and weaker his spirit seemed to grow and expand till it filled her whole world with its light.

Hurt and alone after Jon's departure, she had turned more and more to Otto, and the solace they found in one another's company was a shining thing. He had been delighted when he found out she was expecting a baby.

'I told you it would happen for you, *liebling*,' he had said, taking her hand to hold it to his mouth and kiss it. 'But why has Jon deserted you at a time like this? He should be the happiest man in the world just now and certainly one of the luckiest.'

She had told him that her husband was busy, that he had gone to London to seek a teaching post and that she had opted to remain on the island for as long as she could and even try to have her baby here if it was at all possible. But she didn't fool Otto in the least. After that he was more attentive to her than ever and inevitably the tongues started wagging, especially with her in her 'condition' and no Jon there to keep an eye on her.

But the crones and the coteries didn't bargain on Tina, no one could have imagined that such a placid creature as she could be so tough and aggressive but, fiercely loyal to both Rachel and Otto, she protected them with such a might of verbal power she only had to be seen approaching a gossiping group to send them scuttling guiltily about their business.

Tina knew about Otto, she had been with him at Tigh na Cladach from the start and he had come to cherish her tranquil presence in his home. His trust in her was infinite and one day he had made her sit down on the couch beside him, had taken her hand in his and in a quiet, gentle voice had told her he hadn't very long to live.

She had reacted in a typically Tina-like way, first of all burying her face in her hands to have a 'good greet' before straightening up to scrub her face with his proffered hanky while at the same time endeavouring to capture loops of flyaway hair and confine them into kirby grips.

'Ach, Mr Otto,' she sighed, shaking her head, her brown eyes glazed with sadness, 'I knew fine something was ailing you. I've watched you growing thinner and more wabbit with each passing day but – I never thought – I canny believe . . .'

She was off again, her plump shoulders trembling with heartrending grief that alarmed Otto so much he enfolded her into his arms and crooned words of solace into her ears.

'Och, I'm such a fool,' she chided herself, emitting several watery sniffs before blowing her nose hard and handing the soaking hanky back to him. They looked at one another and laughed. She snatched the hanky back with an apology and a promise of rinsing it under the tap later, before collecting the hairgrips that had descended on to the couch and viciously jabbing them back into her hair. 'I'm the one who should be comforting you, Mr Otto, and I will, you can bet your boots on that. I did the same when I lost my Matthew, I just cried and cried for days then one morning I woke, collected myself up, and just got on wi' my life. Ach, but it's terrible just, a bonny big chiel like yourself, all that music and talent going to waste, but the angels will welcome you to heaven, I'm damty sure o' that, and you'll still get to play your music, and though they might no' have a piano they'll let you play their harps and anything else connected wi' life beyond the grave.'

Her simple philosophy cheered them both immensely, and after that day Tina 'collected herself up' and got on with life, devoting herself so wholeheartedly to 'Mr Otto' she was more often at Tigh na Cladach than in her own home, cleaning, cooking, tending fires, doing it all in her own unruffled fashion. But that was how Otto liked it: in Tina he found a sweet and undemanding companion, a comforting presence who could be as silent or as entertaining as the occasion warranted.

Tina knew that something momentous had happened between Rachel and Jon but she never pressed the matter. It would all sort itself out in its own time, she told herself, meantime she saw to it that both Rachel and Otto received as much care and attention

307

as she was capable of giving. She encouraged them to spend as much time together as possible because in her uncomplicated way she recognized their need for one another in their separate experiences of lonely waiting, one about to part with life, the other preparing to give it.

October came with a mellow sweetness that filled the air with the tangy scents of ripe apples and bramble berries, heavy and black on the bough . . . and Otto could wait no longer, if he didn't go back to Austria now he never would and he began to prepare for that departure with a torpid unwillingness, every fibre in him fighting against the decision he had made while he was comparatively strong and very much a stranger on Rhanna.

But he was a stranger no more, he had become part of the very fabric of the island. He knew and loved every contour of the hills; each bend in the road was as familiar to him as the palm of his own hand; he had walked the shores of Burg and had listened to the might of the waves; from his window he had watched the summer sun bursting above the hills; from his bed he had witnessed the blazing hues of sundown setting fire to the ocean before the moon's cold luminosity quenched the flames and replaced them with silvery spangles of light that spilled into the sea and flooded the world with mercurial beams.

He had seen it all and he had treasured everything and had felt regenerated with the beauty of an island that was, and always would be, his spiritual home.

'You don't have to go, son,' Magnus had said, his voice gruff with emotion. 'Bide here wi' me, it might no' be very fancy or sophisticated but it's homely and warm and it has everything in it to keep a body occupied. You'll never grow weary wi' books and music to hand and a fine view o' the sea when you want only to sit back and do nothing for a whilie.

'And just think o' this, son.' Magnus looked away so that his grandson wouldn't see the mist that shrouded his blue eyes. 'This is your home, if Sheena and me had wed, your mother would have been born here and you too when it came your turn, for that's the way we do things in the Hebrides: families stick together, they look after one another, and they do it in humble surroundings like these. It might only be a bit thatch and four thick walls but I've managed to thole it for ninety-seven years so it canny be that bad – and besides, you'll have me to keep you company till the end o' your days. I would see to it that you were well looked after, you wouldny want for anything, by God, you wouldny.'

'Magnus,' Otto took his grandfather's frail body into his arms and kissed the top of the snow white head, 'I could never lay such a burden at your door, but it would be heaven, to be here with you, to talk ourselves back over the lost years, to have my last rest in a place that I feel I've known all of my life – and with you here at my side, my flesh, my blood – and in the end, my last memory of what it was I glimpsed so briefly but held with such joy.'

'Then stay, Otto, stay,' urged Magnus. 'It would be an honour to have you here, folk that you love can never be a burden and I've had such a short time wi' you after a lifetime o' empty hopes and dreams. The twists o' life are cruel, to take you away after just finding you . . . and if you leave Rhanna now I'll never see you again – and I might as well be dead too.'

The memory of that conversation with his grandfather both tantalized and tormented Otto. Even while he knew that he could never seriously consider the offer, it would be too much to ask of anyone, never mind someone of his grandfather's great age; even so, Otto imagined what it would be like to spend his last days in the undemanding peace of Machair Cottage.

In the end it was Tina who made up his mind for him. 'You've already said your farewells to Vienna,' she told him with quaint simplicity, 'so what way would you be wanting to repeat yourself when all your friends are here on Rhanna? It might be a lot fancier to bide in a place full o' luxuries but it would be an awful lot lonelier – and just think, you wouldny have me to look after you. I'll come over to Machair Cottage, Magnus has plenty o' room and I'll bide there for as long as I'm needed. Eve is able and willing to look after herself and Donald, so just you gather up your bits and bobs and your cat and we'll get Bob the Shepherd to take them over to Croy in his van.'

'Tina, what would I ever have done without you?' he said huskily, hugging her with such affection she giggled girlishly and rescued a few errant hairgrips from the hairy tweed of his jacket collar.

When Rachel heard the news she went rushing over to Tigh na Cladach to throw herself at Otto and Tina and kiss them both in a passion of delight. She had been growing more and more depressed lately: Jon had left her, Ruth had rejected her, the thought of losing Otto as well had been almost too much for her to bear and she had halfheartedly toyed with the notion of going away from Rhanna to nurse her lonely grief in some place that held no evocative memories.

Now her beloved stranger was staying after all and she was so filled with relief that, after the first euphoric reaction, she ran home to sit down and simply burst into a flood of tears that unleashed every unhappy emotion from her heart and made her feel so much better she was able to burn her incense, switch on her music, and dance round the room in a swirl of gladness.

But just when it seemed that an element of joy had entered her world, fate took another cruel hand in things and dealt her a further blow. Ever since Jon had left Rhanna she hadn't had the heart to even look at her violin, but now, in a mood to pour out her feelings in music, she went to get her violin only to discover it wasn't there. She searched the cottage high and low but it was a fruitless effort, the case containing her beautiful Cremonese had simply vanished, only the key remained, affixed to the gold chain round her neck where she always carried it for safety.

It wasn't long before the news of Rachel's loss swept through the island.

'I'll kill the bugger who did this to the lass!' vowed Kate grimly. 'She's had more than enough to put up wi' this whilie back without this happening as well!'

'Ay, she's treasured that violin ever since old Mo gave it to

310

her,' nodded Tam. 'But it canny just have got up and walked away by itself.'

'Ach no, some thief has stolen it,' decided Annie with conviction. 'Och, it's a shame for my bonny Rachel, she's been looking peekit this whilie back but she'll no' even tell her own mother why Jon left her the way he did.'

Kate glowered at her youngest daughter. 'She'll no' tell you for the simple reason that you've never listened to anything she has to say. You haveny even bothered very much to learn her sign language and never even gave a wee celebration ceilidh when you heard she was expecting your first grandchild.'

Annie's nostrils flared. 'My house isny grand enough for the likes o' Rachel! She looks down her nose at everything when she deigns to visit once in a blue moon and I'll no' stand for that from my very own flesh and blood!'

'The flesh and blood you never wanted to acknowledge,' Kate flashed back. 'And she doesny look down her nose at your house – though I wouldny blame her if she did – the state you keep it in. Na, na, Annie, my girl, why can you no' face the truth, you could never accept that you gave birth to a lass that didny have all her faculties – except of course when she became famous and you just wallowed in the fame and the money . . .'

Annie's hackles rose at this. 'I never heard the likes! Me take money from Rachel! I never even let her buy me a house when she wanted to, just so's the likes o' you wouldny have anything to talk about!'

'Oh no, but you canny deny that she sends you money which you are busily stashing away in the bank. I'm no' daft, Annie— '

'Och, be quiet you two,' interrupted Nancy, Kate's sweet-natured eldest daughter. 'We're no' here to argue about money, I thought we were trying to help Rachel discover who took her fiddle. Father's right, it didny just walk away by itself, so where on earth is it? If it doesny turn up, Clodhopper will have to be called in, and a fine to do that will be, he'll start raking up all kinds o' dirt and you haveny renewed the insurance on your lorry, Father.'

Tam blinked and went into a panic at the very idea of Clodhopper roaming round the island looking for trouble, and he immediately set out to visit his granddaughter to try and persuade her 'no' to call in the law till he had a chance to insure his lorry'.

But for the moment, Rachel had no intention of alerting the police, as she was hoping to resolve the matter in her own way. She had remembered Mamma telling her about Paddy's suspicious behaviour the day he had wangled his way into the house on the pretext of wanting a cup of tea.

'It was not the tea he was looking for,' Mamma had said decisively, 'he was – how do you say it? – a snooper. And yes, he was snooping through the house the minute I turn myself. The unpleasant person he was, the others – they were kind to me – but him – he was rude.'

Tam wasn't the only one to be worried by the threat of a visit from Clodhopper, the travellers themselves, almost but not quite ready for the road, heard the news with dismay, and, wishing to keep several little misdemeanours under wraps, had every reason to avoid the law. It was therefore with great energy that they set themselves the task of searching for the missing instrument.

'Bejabers and bejasus!' Aaron said to Rachel. 'I never minded you havin' me brother's fiddle. I would just have sold it for a few bob and spent the money on booze. It was meant for you, me fine lass, and by the blessed St Patrick, you can indeed be certain we'll do everything we can to find it for you.'

And he was as true as his word, every traveller worth his salt helped in the search, Little Lady Leprechaun proving to be a great asset since she managed to get into the smallest spaces. The Abbey ruins, derelict cottages, barns, haysheds, peatsheds, even the very caves on the shore were given a thorough going-over, but to no avail. In the midst of all this Paddy surprised everyone by putting on a great show of willingness as he scrambled into the most unsavoury places, though he didn't fool Aaron in the least

Paddy had always grumbled about old Mo's foolishness in

giving his violin away to a girl who wasn't even remotely connected to the family, and by that he meant the group of itinerants who habitually travelled the roads together. But Aaron had never liked or trusted the rough-speaking Irishman and felt uneasy every time something unpleasant like this happened. Aaron was almost certain that Paddy was the culprit in this latest incident but he could prove nothing and could only hope for the safe return of Rachel's violin before the law had to be consulted.

Shona sat bolt upright in bed, wide awake and sparkling-eyed, even though she had just emerged from the land of dreams.

'Of course,' she breathed, 'the cave! Over there by Dunuaigh! That's where it will be, I can feel it in my bones.'

Niall's ruffled head erupted from the blankets. 'Eh?' he demanded in startled tones. 'Bones! You're dreaming, *mo ghaoil*, go back to sleep, it's too early to be awake, you'll rouse the bairns and I don't want Joe crawling all over me at this time o' the morning.'

'No, Niall, listen,' she spoke imperatively into his ear, 'I've had a marvellous idea, call it an inspired guess if you like. Och! Don't go back to sleep, I want you to hear me out, if you don't I'll tickle and torment you till you beg for mercy – and that's a promise.'

'Oh, all right,' he grumbled, hoisting himself half up on his pillows. 'Fire away, but not too loudly, I canny bear too much noise first thing and I certainly don't want to hear about bones, I see enough o' that sort of thing in my job.'

'Daftie, it isn't about bones, it's about Rachel's fiddle. I've been wondering where on this island anybody could safely hide a valuable instrument. All the obvious places have been searched but what about somewhere near the travellers' camp itself? If Paddy is the culprit as everyone seems to think, he would hide it near to hand so that he could easily collect it just before he leaves. And, listen Niall, what about our cave? The one over by Dunuaigh. It would be a perfect place, it's so well hidden yet easily accessible once you know it's there.'

Niall barely allowed her to finish. With a martyred groan he slid back down into the blankets and snuggled into her soft thighs. 'You're havering, Mrs McLachlan, all this talk about bones and caves has gone to your head, but since we're awake we might as well make good use of the time, so just you coorie in close to me and I'll show you one bone that will never need a splint.'

'Niall McLachlan! You dirty bugger!' she cried, letting out a snort of laughter. 'But you're no' getting away that easily. Come on, up! We'll get the bairns ready and go over to Dunuaigh.'

'What? Now?'

'Ay, now. I'll not rest till I've seen and searched our cave for myself.'

'And no one else will be allowed to rest either,' he grumbled but he had caught some of her mood and got out of bed willingly enough to throw on his clothes.

It was strange to go back to the cave at Dunuaigh after all these years, though it was so overgrown with thorns and ferns it took them some time to find the entrance. The October moor was a sea of amber and gold mingling with the purple of the heather and the bright red splashes of rowan berries.

A hazy sun had broken through the early mists, warming the hollows, bringing out the tang of the brambles that grew in abundance along the rocky face of Dunuaigh, the Hill of the Tomb. It was these same thorny bushes that made the finding of the cave so difficult, but they were guided by the birch tree that they had planted on this spot when they were just children. Somehow the sapling had survived the wild winds that swept over the moors, and even though it was cruelly twisted and warped it had kept its tenacious hold on life, and it was the little golden leaves on the bleached branches that caught Shona's eye and guided her footsteps forward.

As Niall pulled back the bracken and the brambles, the children stared fascinated, thinking this was some new kind of game, thoroughly appreciating parents who did some pretty daft things sometimes and were often like children themselves with their fun and their laughter and their willingness to join in childish games.

'Look, Niall,' Shona said wistfully. 'It's just as we left it all these years ago, the cruisie and the candles, even the sheepskin rug on the ledge. Oh, I want to cry, it brings back so many memories.'

Taking her hand, he squeezed it and kissed the tears from her eyes, much to the amusement of little Ellie Dawn who clapped her hand over her mouth and went into a fit of the giggles.

It didn't take them long to search the small enclosure. In minutes they found the violin, carelessly hidden in a fissure behind the stone 'fireplace' where, as children, they had made smoky tea while pretending to be man and wife living together in their own small world.

'I always said it!' Niall exploded, gazing in disbelief at the leather violin case. 'You're a witch, Shona *mo ghaoil*, how did you do it? Was it a dream, or a vision, or what?'

'Just an educated guess,' she said rather smugly. 'Some o' us were born wi' brains in case you didn't know, but of course, you were aye the glaikit one o' the family, so we have to make allowances.'

He chased her outside into the sunlight, brandishing the leather case, the children dancing and laughing behind them and asking if they could come back here tomorrow to play more games.

It was sleepy and quiet at the travellers' camp with everyone sitting round a smoky fire, drinking tea while they discussed their departure date. They hailed the visitors with surprised pleasure and proffered the teapot, but when they saw what Niall carried everything else was forgotten as they crowded round, all talking at once. Shona looked over Stink's head. Paddy was scowling and making ready to skulk away, all too plainly betraying his guilt but given no chance to go anywhere since he was soon apprehended and brought back to explain himself.

Niall and Shona left them to it and went back to where they had parked their car, getting in to drive post-haste to An Cala where they deposited the violin, along with an explanatory note, as Rachel was nowhere to be seen.

'A good morning's work, Mrs McLachlan,' Niall said approvingly on the road home. 'And now, please can we sit down to a proper breakfast? All together like a normal family, with no more of your weird premonitions to disturb the peace?'

'Only if you say you recognize the fact that you married a genius and remain very humble and polite for the rest o' the day.'

'I give in: I married a genius, I will kiss your hand humbly, I will be unnaturally polite for at least a week, I will not demand anything of you that will upset your brilliant thoughts – but would you mind if I have two eggs, six rashers o' bacon, one of Holy Smoke's black puds all to myself, not forgetting a mountain of toast and a gallon of tea to wash it all down, all for the purpose of keeping up my strength in order to do all the things that you ask o' me.'

She burst out laughing, the children clapped their hands and giggled, the McLachlans went home in fine fettle, well pleased with themselves and hoping that Rachel would be pleased with them also.

Rachel read the note, she opened the violin case and stared at the instrument reposing in its blue velvet nest. It wasn't hers, it was Jon's! Paddy had stolen the wrong one – then a terrible thought struck her, what if he hadn't, what if he had taken the two of them and had hidden this one in a place where it was sure to be found in order to put everyone off the scent of the real thing?

Devastated, she sank into a chair, wondering wildly what to do. Her beautiful Cremonese, still missing, perhaps never to be found. Paddy could easily deny all knowledge of it and come back to the island to collect it at a later date when the heat had died down.

She felt sick, frightened and very alone; everything and everyone seemed to be conspiring against her and depression settled over her like a black cloud. She had never visualised any of this when she had come so blithely to Rhanna and it

316

had only been thoughts of her unborn child that had kept her from sinking to the bottom of the deep, dark, despairing well of her innermost being.

Erchy was coming through the gate, whistling cheerily, avidly examining the letter he held so that he could tell Rachel who it was from. He knew nearly everyone's handwriting by this time and was apt to be deeply disappointed and mad at himself if by chance he got it wrong. But this morning he was full of confidence in his abilities and could hardly wait to open Rachel's door and shout, 'A letter for you, lass! From Jon by the look o' things, it's the way he strokes his t's, they just about fly off the top and that indicates a very ambitious person – I was readin' about it in a book,' he finished lamely when he saw that Rachel wasn't in a mood to appreciate his knowledge.

She took the letter, her hand shaking slightly. 'He'll be coming back soon, lass, never you fear,' said Erchy kindly before taking himself off with all haste. Sometimes those black eyes of Rachel's could look right through you and besides – he didn't fancy that tea she made, all funny and spicy and not at all like the good homely brews he enjoyed in other houses in the course of his rounds.

Rachel didn't know what to expect when she opened the letter but her heart had leapt with hope when she had heard Erchy shouting Jon's name.

The piece of paper she withdrew from the envelope could hardly be called a letter, it was more in the nature of a note, a curt, cold little message that simply said:

Dear Rachel

Just to say I took your violin by mistake, your case is much like mine and I was in a hurry when I left. Since you haven't been in touch about it I assumed you haven't been getting in any practice, unless of course, you have used mine. I got the post at the Royal Academy and have been playing the other violin we left here at the flat. Next week, however, I am giving a recital and wondered if you would mind very much if I used the Cremonese. The case

317

is locked, you have the key, you don't owe me any favours but I want to make a good impression next week and know you will understand this.

If you need anything, let me know and I will arrange to have it sent. Mamma is well and enjoying London. I hope you are all right and managing to pass your time on Rhanna.

Yours, Jon.

Rachel screwed the paper into a tight ball and threw it into the fire. A flush of anger burned high on her pale cheeks and her eyes were too bright.

Oh yes, she was managing to pass her time on Rhanna, and her treasured violin was safe. That was all that mattered – with the exception of her unborn child – and Otto, of course.

Jon was the stranger now, and the way she was feeling he could remain so forever – him and his precious Mamma!

Chapter Twenty-three

Rhanna was quiet again: the tourists and the travellers had departed, the latter preceded by Paddy who had left with his tail well tucked between his legs, having been all but banished from the group till he could prove that he had mended his unsavoury ways.

Silence settled over the land, that special sort of tranquillity that always brought with it a sense of repose from the bustle and life of summer. The gossamer days were done with, the short perfumed nights were only a memory, the slumbering earth yielded less of its bounties and in so doing afforded rest to those who worked its soil.

But even so there was still work to be done to ensure a warm winter. The peats had yet to be gathered and both Ranald and Tam had a profitable time hiring out themselves and their respective lorries to those beings who were able to afford such a luxury – if such a term could be applied to ancient machines with a distinct penchant for sinking into bogs and potholes, which meant long, grumbling delays while they were pulled out again by tractors or, if these weren't available, by the sheer might of human muscle.

The remainder of the population trundled to the moors by other available means but, whatever the mode of transport, it wasn't long before peat stacks had sprung up in back yards everywhere. And then came that most distinctive of island scents, that of peat smoke, puffing lazily into the chilly air of morning, invading the senses with agreeable enjoyment, bringing also a quiet pleasure in the picturesque harmony of hill and moor, ocean and shore, the little villages with their white sugar-loaf houses, the islanders going peaceably about their daily lives.

Everything moved at a slower beat, even the very clocks on the wall seemed to tick at a more leisurely pace and it was good to sit back and survey the harvests of a summer well spent and to look forward to the comforts they would bring in the long, winter days ahead.

For Otto, it would be his last summer. He had spent it well and had done all the things he had wanted to do in those final months of his life, even so, he couldn't help wishing he had known this enchanting island sooner and he took to sitting at his window, gazing, just gazing, at the silent hills; the sylvan fields; the beaches; the sea; the people passing by with cheerful smiles and waves, for they had heard that he was staying on in the island and expressed their approval in many different ways.

Kate often popped into the shorehouse for a crack and a cuppy, bringing with her the home-made bannocks and tattie scones for which she was famed. Tam also came, for a game of cards, a dram and a blether, and on one such visit, with the time fast approaching for his departure from Tigh na Cladach, Otto said rather wistfully to Tam, 'I'm going to miss you, Herr Tam. Soon I go to stay with my grandfather, I won't be coming back to Portcull.'

'Och, but surely Mr James will let you have that old motor o' his a whilie longer. I will aye be pleased to see you and you know fine what Kate's like, she would be black affronted if she thought that the best bloody McKinnon yet wasny for stopping by for a strupak.'

'Herr Tam.' Gently Otto laid his hand on Tam's shoulder. 'It is not to be, my days, they are counted, that is why I go to live with Magnus, we wish to be together for all the minutes that are left. It is my dearest wish to be with him. Tina is right, I have said my farewells to Vienna, all my friends and family are here on Rhanna. It is right that I should live for a while in the home of my grandfather; it is right that we share with one another the talk of the old days when he and my grandmother Sheena walked together through the summer shielings of their youth. I

320

will be surrounded by love and in that way I will not be alone when I die.'

For quite a few minutes Tam didn't comprehend the meaning of Otto's words, then his homely face crumpled and so overwhelmed by emotion was he that all he could say was, 'Oh ay, we'll visit you, Mr Otto, you can be damty sure o' that,' before he stumbled to the door, the drams, the cards, forgotten in the trauma of the moment.

Before Otto left Tigh na Cladach he walked with Rachel on the shores of Burg, his eyes devouring the ocean, the cliffs, the great sweeping curve of the silvery bay, everything that he had loved and treasured so well.

His arm was around Rachel's shoulder, her head was on his chest, she knew the warmth of his body, she could hear the beat and surge of his big, warm heart, beat, beating, strong, mesmerising, compelling, filling her own heart with a pain so great she felt the tears welling in her eyes and was glad that he couldn't see them because she wanted these last precious minutes on Burg Bay to be happy ones for him.

But as always he knew what she was feeling and raising her face to his he kissed her tears away and said huskily, '*Liebling*, these moments here with you mean so much to me. Whenever I think of this place I will remember how it was with you, sharing so much of my thoughts, my emotions . . .'

He paused to study her upturned face, struck anew by her dark, vibrant beauty, by the compassion and life blazing out of eyes so black and deep he felt as if he was being pulled into the very depths of her soul, and he knew an enchantment and a love for her that he had never known with any other.

It had always been there, from the start, but he knew he had no right to her, and he had pushed the knowledge of it away from him because to have succumbed to that kind of ecstasy would have been the beginning and the end of the very special relationship that had sprung up between them. They were the richer for having denied themselves the earthly joys of the flesh; their hearts and minds had remained pure and guilt-free; she

321

would go with him to the very end of his earthly existence and she would remember him with gratitude when all that was left of him were memories.

'Rachel,' he pushed wings of dark hair away from her cheeks and kissed her very gently on the mouth, 'you are a unique and wonderful young woman. Your loyalty to me has been a joy, it was happiness enough to come to this island and to have found everything I hoped to find, but you made it so much more for me, you enriched my days with your devotion, but now you must think of yourself and your own life – your life with Jon and the little one soon to be born. You aren't happy, I see it in your eyes; you and he should be together at this time. If you argued because of me then I am sad, but I also understand why Jon would be jealous of us. You gave me much of your time, now you must make it up to him, he is your husband, you need him as much as he needs you. I hope you told him why you were kind to me, if not you must do so right away and I want you to promise me that you will write to him and tell him how much you love him and miss him.'

Rachel took a deep breath. She knew the sincerity and the wisdom of his words, at first she had been very hurt by Jon's desertion of her, hurt had turned to anger, then bitterness, back and forth her emotions had swung, like a relentless pendulum, never giving up, never slowing down, but now she was angry again and though she recognized that much of Jon's behaviour owed itself to misunderstandings, she wasn't going to give in so easily, her wilful, stubborn heart wouldn't allow it.

She didn't need him! She was perfectly capable of making a life for herself and her child without him! Let him sulk and mope and stay in London forever, if that was what he wanted, but she wouldn't go to him, she would stay here on Rhanna and have her baby and if any of those gossiping crones wanted to make something of that – let them. She had always been able to stand up for herself, from early childhood she'd had to and now that she was grown she was more able than ever . . . just like Grannie Kate.

She smiled at this. Otto took her look as an acceptance of his words, he hugged her to him and urged her footsteps on and she allowed herself to go, not looking forward, not looking back, just letting herself drift with the order and inevitability of events.

Captain Mac was as furious as he could ever be, his eyes blazed, his snowy white whiskers bristled, his jolly, bulbous red beacon of a nose grew redder still as he faced Elspeth in the cosy warmth of her orderly kitchen.

Mac had had a very pleasant time of it since coming to live with Elspeth. Whenever he had felt like it he had gone off on his various pursuits and never a word of protest had she uttered; he had expected a lot of teasing from the local menfolk regarding his changed lifestyle but oddly enough Tam and the others had exercised a great deal of restraint in the matter, so much so that Mac had often wondered if he was missing out on something he ought to know.

On this particular morning the bombshell had dropped: he had been away on one of his fishing trips but because of a storm warning the trawlers had put into port earlier than expected. Tam and Robbie had been there at the harbour, the latter winking at him in a most meaningful manner while Tam smirked and said, 'Tis yourself, Mac, back from sea for more nights o' passion, a mite too soon for Elspeth because I passed her washing line just two minutes ago and all her frilly bits are still hanging out to dry . . .'

He got no further, Mac's welcoming smile faded, he demanded to know what Tam was on about but that worthy, realizing he had said too much, stuttered out some excuse and with Robbie on his heels he deserted the scene with alacrity.

A short walk from the harbour soon put Mac in the picture and he stared with incredulous eyes at the display of silks and satins gaily flapping about in the wind.

'Katie's birthday things,' he muttered in disbelief, shock blanching the colour out of his face as the full import of Tam's careless words slowly began to dawn on him.

Now he expressed his feelings to Elspeth with none of his usual economy of words. He told her she was a fallen woman with nothing more on her mind than sex and sin. He had trusted her, he had relied on her, he had truly believed that she had invited him to stay at her house with nothing but good intentions on her mind when all the while she had just been using him to exact revenge on other gossiping crones of her like. She had made him the laughing stock of the place but it was for the last time. He would never set foot inside her door again, even supposing he had to go and live in a cave for the rest of his days.

'And here was me, all this time, thinking I had never been happier since my Mary went and died on me! I should have known it couldny last. You were aye a silly woman, Elspeth, wi' naught in your head but cunning and bitterness and tis no wonder poor old Hector went the way he did, you likely drove him to drink – maybe to his death for all we know. Well, I'm no' for having the same thing happenin' to me so you can just bide here, alone and bitter to the end o' your days, for I want nothing more to do wi' you.'

With that he barged out of the house, never stopping to collect even his pyjamas, back to the bed that 'aye waited for him at Cousin Gus's – fleas and all'.

The door banged shut, Elspeth sank into a chair, her eyes wide and staring, her gaunt body trembling with reaction. She had lost Mac, through her own childish stupidity she had lost the one man who had ever brought any meaning into her lonely life. Her shoulders shook, the slow tears trickled unheeded down the deep seams of her face, the grey ashes of her life piled up in front of her mind – and made a far greater mound than the little heap of peat ash that had spilled out of the fire on to the gleaming hearth.

Ruth's heart was beating rapidly in her breast as she steered her car in the direction of An Cala. Ever since the row with Rachel she had had a miserable time of it, she had moped, she had mooned about, her conscience pricking her so badly it had been almost a physical pain. She had needled at the children, she had sulked with Lorn – in the end he could stand it no longer and had finally given her an ultimatum.

'Go to Rachel and apologize; if no' I'll take the bairns to Laigmhor and bide there with them till you come to your senses. I mean it, Ruthie, if I stay here wi' you a minute longer I might just be forced to take you over my knee and give you a good skelping.'

His anger had shocked her out of her self-pity. She didn't dare be angry back because a determined Lorn was a Lorn to be reckoned with, and after an agonizing night of indecision she had finally made up her mind and had run out to her car before her courage failed her.

Saying sorry didn't come easy to Ruth. When she was younger she had always apologized, mostly for innocent actions that her mother had chosen to interpret as sins, but in the end she had rebelled at having to be sorry for everything, even she sometimes felt, for her very existence, with the result that now she could hardly bring herself to utter that familiar expression of humility, even when she knew she was at fault.

This, however, was different. She had greatly wronged her dearest friend with her blind accusations and knew that nothing could ever be right between them again till she had made amends. But such actions took courage and Ruth's traumatic upbringing had very effectively quelled many of her natural strengths, allowing some of her weaknesses to push through in the process. Marriage to Lorn had certainly given her a lot of confidence, even so, the very idea of having to face the vibrantly powerful Rachel was almost too much for her and she gulped with nerves when the peacefully smoking chimneys of An Cala hove into view.

She needn't have worried, Rachel was delighted to see her and made no attempt to disguise her feelings. Ruth was so overwhelmed with relief she burst into tears, so thoroughly ashamed of herself for the way she had treated everyone these last few weeks that it was all Rachel could do to make her stop crying and accept a brew of her 'strange-smelling tea'.

Ruth dried her tears, she laughed instead, and clasping her hands round the cup she gulped down the liquid, never minding

325

the taste, something in her romantic soul making her see it as an offering of peace from a girl who could have thrown her apologies back in her face but who was far too big-hearted to be so petty.

Ruth couldn't wait to catch up on all the lost weeks of separation. She remained at An Cala for hours, and they talked and talked, Rachel's hands flashing, Ruth's face a study of animation. No holds barred, they brought everything out into the open and drew closer than they had ever been been since the golden days of innocent childhood. Rachel confided her innermost thoughts to her friend and Ruth wriggled uncomfortably when it became clear that Jon had left Rhanna, thinking the exact same things about his wife as Ruth had done.

Determined to make up for her hasty judgements, she offered to drive Rachel to Croy Beag whenever she could, and Rachel, who had been in a quandary wondering how she could get to see Otto, jumped at the chance with such eagerness Ruth threw back her fair head and laughed, her violet eyes shining in a face all at once happy and carefree.

With a very determined expression on her face, Nellie, having just arrived from Hanaay on the steamer, made her way to Cousin Gus's house looking for Captain Mac.

Ever since her brother had lost his wife, Nellie had maintained a fairly firm hold on his affairs but she hadn't seen him for some considerable time and might have left it like that for another few weeks had not a rather disquieting rumour reached her ears. She was therefore in quite a state of self-righteous indignation when she presented herself at Gus's door and was no sooner over the threshold when she demanded to see Mac at once.

'He doesny live here anymore, Nellie,' Gus explained rather fearfully, endeavouring to rub away a dinnertime soup stain on the greasy lapel of his ancient tweed jacket whilst he spoke.

Gus had a great respect for Nellie who never minced words, as far as he was concerned, and always gave him a biting piece of her mind whenever their paths crossed.

Nellie wasn't exactly a formidable figure: she was plump of

face and rotund of figure, her salt-and-pepper hair was rolled into a tight sausage round her head, her untidy skirts revealed dimpled knees on otherwise shapeless legs, her splayed feet, which Mac said reminded him of a pregnant duck, were stuck into stout brogues, and altogether she was a quaint figure to behold. But a perpetual frown on her round, jutting-jawed face belied her kindly nature and Gus never dared take any cousinly liberties when in her company.

At his words her nostrils flared. 'I'm no' surprised,' she snorted, glancing round her in disgust. 'The place is a piggery, no' fit for a dog, never mind a decent man like Isaac!'

Gus bristled a bit and jutted out his own jaw in some defiance of her criticism, but she was calling her brother by his 'Sunday' name, which meant she was really on her high horse, so Gus knew to go warily. 'Maybe no', but Mac *did* bide here for a good whilie, so it canny have been *that* bad. And as a matter o' fact, he turned up here the other day lookin' for a roof but went away again, just before you arrived . . .'

Gus stroked his beard as he recalled his cousin's parting words, 'It's no' possible to live here wi' you again,' had been Mac's biting assessment of his short-lived stay. 'No' after Elspeth and her clean and decent ways. You're just no' fit to bide under the same roof as another human being. You pick your nose; you rift and fart like a horse wi' the colic; you do awful things wi' your beard behind your newspaper and yon stuff you call rum would make a pig sick for a week. I've shat bricks for two days because o' these damt ferrets o' yours! I canny thole it any longer and if Elspeth will have me back then, by God, I'll never leave her again for she's a woman in a million and that's a fact!'

'And that's gratitude for you!' Gus had retaliated hotly but to Mac's receding back – he had left the house and was already hot-footing it down the brae to the village.

'And just where has Isaac gone?' Nellie demanded, in a tone that suggested she knew the answer but wanted to hear it spelled out.

Gus looked surprised. 'To that cailleach, Elspeth Morrison.

He's been livin' wi' her all summer, I thought you would have heard.'

'No! I didny hear! At least, no' from him!' snapped Nellie, her face turning a bright crimson. 'The bodach never breathed a word to me about it – and wi' that dried-up besom too.' She stomped to the door.

'Will you no' stay and sup a cuppy wi' me?' Gus offered in an attempt to ingratiate himself with her.

'Gus McIntosh! The last time I supped tea in this house *was* the last time! The cup was thick wi' tanning inside and black wi' dirt on the outside! The rim was chipped and cracked and was so full o' germs I had food poisoning for a week and skitters for a month, so just you keep your damt tea and put it where it will do the least harm – and if you don't know where that is ask the doctor and see if she'll risk showing you!'

Gus was hurt, mortified, and furious. Raising two fingers, he viciously prodded the air with them and shouted to the closed door, 'And that's to you, you po-faced hag! At least the doctor could find my backside – yours healed up years ago and two fingers in the air is about all you'll ever get from a man for he wouldny know where else to put them!'

At that precise moment, Mac stood facing Elspeth in her cosy kitchen, shamefaced and apologetic, his big red fingers worrying the pom-pom of his knitted woollen cap which he had removed in a most mannerly fashion on entering the house.

'Ach, lass,' he said kindly, noting the hurt and embarrassment on her gaunt face and the puffy eyes which denoted plainly enough a woman who had cried a lot in recent days. 'I'm sorry for all the things I said to you. I wasny thinkin' straight at the time and cared more for my own feelings than yours. Who gives a sow's erse if all the world talks about us? When I had time to think about it I pictured all the shocked faces and had the best bloody laugh I've had in years. I bet Behag nearly peed her flannel breeks at the sight o' all the satin knickers on your wash line. She will maybe have a permanent ring round those beady wee eyes o' hers from all her peekin' through her spyglasses, just like one o' they spotty dogs you see wi' floppy lugs and hair specs.'

Elspeth's lips twitched, a strangulated sound escaped her tightly held throat. She sniggered, she snorted, she threw back her head and broke into skirls and cacophonies of pure unadulterated laughter. Mac joined in, the two of them held on to the back of the couch and simply screeched with unrestrained merriment.

Mac wiped his streaming eyes with his woolly cap, his brimming brown eyes regarded her fondly. 'Ach, tis good to see you happy, lass, and I'm going to tell you something to make you even happier, how about you and me going to Oban on a shopping spree? We'll get Katie some new things for her birthday and at the same time I'll buy you the finest set o' underwear that any woman ever had. Anything you like, see-through, pee-through, the treat's on me, for your Christmas when it comes, the best bloody Christmas for us both in years.'

Elspeth's eyes were wet again, but this time she wept the tears of disbelieving happiness, her thin shoulders shook, her head trembled on her scrawny shoulders, with a wail of impatience she scrabbled in her apron pocket for her hanky, but before she could withdraw it Mac folded her into his hairy strong arms and gently wiped away her weepings with the corner of her apron . . .

And at that inopportune moment the door opened to admit Nellie who stared at the tender scene before her with tightly folded lips.

'I knew it! I knew it!' she snorted with thinly disguised disapproval. 'I heard that the pair o' you were up to no good but I didny realize that things had gone this far.'

'Nell.' Mac let go of Elspeth and steered his sister into the parlour. 'You have no right to speak like that in front o' Elspeth,' he continued as soon as he had closed the door. 'She is a respectful and decent woman and deserves some o' your respect in turn.'

'Oh ay, it's clear to see she has you well and truly fooled but it beats me how a sensible man like you can have allowed himself to be taken in by the likes o' that sour prune out there.'

'But, Nell,' protested Mac, 'I enjoy biding here wi' her, she's no' the targe everyone thinks, she and me get on fine, she's a kindly body and has never nagged me once.'

'No' yet, but wait you, she will. She'll dig her clooks in deeper and never let go – and of course – anything is better than livin' wi' that dirty old bodach of a cousin wi' his cracked cups and his soup stains. You had best come back to Hanaay wi' me, you know you aye have a clean bed and a full belly at my house.'

Mac's jolly countenance took on an unusually stubborn expression. 'It's no' the same, Nell, you've looked after me well, I'll grant you that, but you're my sister; Elspeth – well – she's . . .'

He faltered and came to an abrupt halt, leaving the way clear for Nellie to take up the cudgels. 'Ay, you've said enough, Isaac, we all know what Elspeth is and I'll no bide another minute under the roof of a pair o' – o' shameless sinners who are old enough to know better!'

With that she marched ben the kitchen where Elspeth was making tea, her shaky hands belying her calm demeanour. She had heard most of what had transpired in the parlour, simply because she had kept her ear glued to the door for most of the conversation, the result being that her first instinct was to make some cutting remarks to Nellie. But with an effort she stayed her tongue – she wasn't going to spoil things now – not when she had Mac just where she wanted him.

So she was polite to the visitor, she was the epitome of good manners and consideration. Graciously she invited Nellie to stay, with admirable efficiency she set about preparing a meal which later proved to be so palatable that even Nellie was moved to giving it some grudging praise.

'Of course, the pork could have been doing wi' a bit more crackling,' she added, 'and the carageen pudding needed a wee bit nutmeg to give it flavour but otherwise it wasny bad – no' too bad at all.'

Over her head Mac winked at Elspeth and it took him all his time to keep a sober face when she promptly and boldly winked back.

*　　*　　*

That night Mac sat happily back in his favourite chair, wiggling his stockinged feet on the hearth while he waited for the poker to grow sufficiently hot that he might plunge it into the tot of rum at his side. He thought about his life here with Elspeth and how easy she had been to live with, and even though she made him bathe twice a week and change his drawers every other day it had been a small price to pay for everything she had given him in return.

Picking up his glass, he watched the reflected light of the fire dancing like ruby-tinted nymphs in the liquid, and then he peeped at Elspeth over the rim. She had declined to join him in a drink, even though it had become an enjoyable habit of theirs to sit by the fire of an evening, savouring their drinks, the smell of burnt rum pleasurably invading their nostrils. He suspected that she was doing all in her power to impress Nellie with her restraint and he smiled to himself at the sight of the two women, sitting side by side on the couch sedately sipping cocoa.

With slow deliberation Mac pushed tobacco into the bowl of his pipe with a horny, tar-stained thumb, lit it and sat back, puffing the smoke into the air, watching it drifting and curling up to the ceiling.

'Oh, by the way,' removing the pipe from his mouth he spoke very casually, 'I meant to tell you, Nell, but wi' all the talk and pleasure o' seeing you again it just slipped my mind. Elspeth and me are to be wed in the spring, just a quiet affair wi' maybe one or two o' the family present. Oban, ay, it will likely be Oban, a registry office, seeing as how both Elspeth and me have been married before.'

Both women choked into their cocoa, coughing and spluttering so badly that Mac had to rush over and thump each one on the back in turn. Elspeth glanced up with streaming eyes, her expression was a study of bemusement and disbelief – and it was more than just the cocoa that had induced her wet eyes – for the second time that day she wept the tears of pure happiness – and this time she made no attempt to wipe them away.

Chapter Twenty-four

Otto was never short of visitors, every day there was always someone popping in for a 'crack and a cuppy' and very often an impromptu ceilidh would get going, with fiddles and 'squeezeboxes' providing the music; poetry from the island bards; Magnus or old Andrew drawing on their store of magical tales, traditional myths and folklore which had improved with age and which had never been written down but had been passed on orally from one generation to the next.

As more and more modern influences intruded into island life the days of the Seanachaidh were fast disappearing, therefore it was a precious thing indeed to listen to these old men with their seamed, wise faces and their air of authority. The hushed respectful voices of them stirred the imagination and mesmerized the mind till it really seemed that the witches and hobgoblins of yore came leaping, prancing, and skirling into the present day, thrilling and terrifying the listeners till, with expert ease, the senses were soothed by gentler stories of water kelpies that haunted the lochs and snow bochdans that roamed the hills in search of the spirits of children who had departed earthly life but still liked to come back now and then to play in the ice caves high on the corries.

Children who were very much alive and kicking loved these old men and their shivery tales and Otto encouraged them to come and visit and join in the ceilidhs, though they didn't need much encouragement, having grown to love the big Austrian as much as the grown-ups did.

Machair Cottage had a perfect atmosphere for such simple pastimes, its thatched roof and deep windows, its warm hearth and its booklined walls, even the very cobwebs in the corners, all combined to give the impression of a past era that had somehow survived into modern times.

And with Tina in charge there was no danger of the spiders or their webs being disturbed, since she was kept too busy cooking and cleaning for 'her menfolk' to bother her head with such harmless creatures as spiders who, in her opinion, had been put on the earth for a good reason and earned their place by catching flies and midgies and other pests.

'Though, mind,' she said once, 'if one o' they big hairy tarantulas came creeping in I would be the first to drop my duster and go screaming outside with everyone else!'

Her refreshing presence in Machair Cottage was a continual source of comfort and joy for both Otto and Magnus. Without her they could never have managed to cope, even though Otto's bed was in a recess in the kitchen so that he could be right there in the heart of things instead of being tucked away in a part of the house where he could see or hear very little.

Megan and Babbie were regular visitors, the one administering the drugs and the painkillers that kept Otto going, the other attending to his personal comforts, which also kept him going but which involved procedures that had embarrassed him so much in the beginning Babbie had been moved to cry out in exasperation, 'Och, for heaven's sake, you're no' the first man in the world I've had to bathe and you'll certainly no' be the last! I've seen hairy bums, pink bums, fat and thin bums, and bums with rashes and pimples that were often bigger than the bums they were on! So just you lie back and let me wash *your* bum and if you're very good I might even use hot water to do it with!'

At that Magnus had collapsed in his chair to chortle and wheeze in a gluttony of mirth that was so infectious both Babbie and Otto joined in, the former ending up so winded it was all she could do to wash her patient, who by that time was so exhausted himself he succumbed meekly to her tender mercies.

From that day forth he was never too ashamed to 'bare his bum' to her and indeed even began to look forward to her visits for, with her wonderful green eyes, red hair, and wide smile, she seemed to bring sunshine into the room and was never too rushed to spare the time for a cup of tea and a good chin-wag.

Ruth, as good as her word, brought Rachel to visit as often as she could and in so doing, the young writer with the poet's heart and romantic soul, found a treasure trove in Magnus's house that totally enthralled her from the moment she stepped over the threshold. The place was a paradise for musicians, artists and writers. Books on every subject under the sun were there for the taking; Magnus's own personal jotters, filled from cover to cover with the writings of a lifetime, were a particular joy for Ruth and she never wearied during her visits, rather she looked forward to them with a zest that almost matched that of Rachel and could never get over fast enough to Magnus and his 'magical house'.

From his bed Otto could see the ocean from one window and the moors from the other, and he loved just to lie there, watching the calm or the rage of the sea, the cloud patterns moving over the shaggy wilderness of the great amber plains, in his mind smelling the perfumes of summer and the lark song high in the heavens.

Tina sometimes sang to him in her sweet, clear voice, slightly off-key, but something so poignant in the tremble and tone of it, he would find a lump in his throat, and taking her hand he would squeeze it and urge her to carry on singing, making her cry inside of herself for her 'dear Mr Otto' who watched her with dark eyes that were weary yet hungry for everything that was still good and precious in his life.

But the hands and the eyes that soothed him most were those of the girl who had come to him out of nowhere it seemed and who still came to him out of a deep wild sea of forbidden dreams. She haunted his sleep, she disturbed his awakenings, but only when she wasn't there. The reality of Rachel was like balm on a deep, raw wound. She sat by his bed, so soothing in her silence, the voice that could never speak finding expression in her eyes and in her hands, healing hands that caressed his brow with a tenderness that brought him comfort beyond compare and a conviction that the heartbeat of his life would never fade or falter as long as she was there by his side.

Whenever she came he often felt so good he would get up and get dressed and together they would slowly walk over the machair to the cliffs, each of them heavy and waiting, both of them content to sit there on the edge of the world and watch the ocean tossing in its restless bed far below.

One day he took her hand and held it tightly. 'How long now, *liebling*?'

'Three weeks – round about Christmas.'

He frowned. 'Jon must come soon,' he said sternly. 'He should be here now, sharing this time with you, giving you his support.'

The wind was springing up from the sea, cold and penetrating; she huddled herself further into her jacket and made no reply. Her anger, her bitterness was spent; she wanted Jon to come, she longed to see him again. Perhaps he would relent at the last minute, she thought forlornly, and knew a pang of fear at the thought of having her baby without him there at her side.

Megan, on one of her routine visits to An Cala, was stressing to Rachel the importance of having her baby in a mainland hospital. Rachel had been burning incense, the house reeked of it and Megan thought the tea reeked of it too as she sat sipping the brew that Rachel had courteously made for her.

Despite a flash of annoyance in the girl's dark eyes, she managed to remain polite when Megan, continuing the conversation that the arrival of the tea had made her break off, said that she would make all the necessary arrangements with the hospital and it might be wise to go a week or so earlier just in case the weather turned nasty.

But Rachel was having none of that: she wanted her baby to be born on Rhanna, she had set her mind on it and nothing was going to make her change it, and she conveyed this to the doctor by means of pen and paper and any other means that would stipulate she meant what she said.

335

Reluctantly Megan agreed, but only on condition that the girl came to live at the Manse till after the birth. Again she came up against fierce opposition. Rachel's chin jutted, her mouth set itself into determined lines and, grabbing pen and paper once more, she insisted that she wanted to stay on at An Cala till it was all over.

'But you don't even have a phone,' Megan pointed out. 'You are all alone in the house and might easily go into labour in the middle of the night with no one to turn to for help. Also' – at this point she groped for the right words to say – 'as this is your first child it's only fair to give it a good start. You are young and strong and healthy but supposing something went wrong? Some babies suffer from birth defects that could easily have been prevented if the mothers had been in hospital at the time.'

Rachel knew what Megan was trying to say and she flushed with anger but couldn't express how she felt to someone with only scant understanding of her sign language. But Ruth was an expert on the subject, she had learned to read that particular language almost from the moment Jon had taught it to Rachel and, arriving in time to hear Megan's arguments, she immediately took up the cudgels on her friend's behalf.

'Ach, Doctor Megan,' she chided softly, 'neither Rachel nor myself got our wee bit flaws at birth, they were caused by our mothers' having had German measles when they were carrying us. They canny be passed on because they aren't what you would call congenital. Lachlan explained everything to me before I had my two and no doubt he did the same to Rachel.'

Megan flushed. 'I see you're well up on the subject, Ruth, and of course I know that what happened to you and Rachel can't be passed on, the fact remains, however, that she is all alone in this house, unless . . .' – she turned to Rachel – 'your mother or grandmother could come and stay here with you.'

Rachel looked horrified at the very idea of her untidy mother making An Cala into a replica of her own disgracefully muddled house, and though Grannie Kate was a cheerful and welcome presence in most circumstances, it was too much to visualize her loud and boisterous intrusion at the birth of any child, even that of her very own great grandchild.

'I'll come.' Ruth made the decision quickly and was well rewarded by the expression of relieved gratitude on her friend's face. 'I would love to do it, I'll ask Shona or Kirsteen to take the children' – she giggled – 'They can halve them between them if two is too much for one, if you see what I mean, and Lorn can stay at Laigmhor. I'll go home right now and ask him.'

Lorn wasn't exactly over the moon about the arrangements. He hummed and hawed and permitted himself one or two grumbles but gave in eventually as he knew Ruth wouldn't be happy until she did this for Rachel to further atone for her earlier misjudgements.

'If only Jon would come back,' she said unhappily. 'It's terrible to see Rachel alone at a time like this. I know fine she waits for Erchy to bring some word from Jon but he never writes and soon it may be too late for both o' them to ever make up.'

Tina was thinking the exact same thing and on one of Ruth's visits to Machair Cottage she took her aside and asked her outright if she had any idea what had happened between Jon and Rachel to have caused such a rift in their marriage,

Shamefaced, Ruth told her that Jon believed the baby to be Otto's – as she had done – he hadn't known then about Otto's illness and by all accounts he didn't know now. If he had, things might have been different but the damage had been done, and with Rachel stubbornly refusing to write and tell her husband the truth, the future looked bleak for them.

In response, Tina clicked her tongue loudly and gave vent to such an uncharacteristic tirade of rebuke, Ruth felt her ears growing hot and her face turning crimson.

'How could you, Ruth? You've aye been a mite too ready to believe the worst o' people!' Tina scolded, in her agitation prodding loose hairgrips into her skull with such viciousness she hurt her own scalp and let out a yelp of pain.

Ruth felt very glad it wasn't *her* scalp that was on the receiving end of such treatment and she was only too willing to supply the older woman with Jon's address when she demanded it.

'Right,' Tina glared at the scrap of paper in her hand, 'just you leave this to me, my girl. But for now, away you go ben the kitchen, you'll be safe there, for the way I'm feeling right now my hands are itching to skelp somebody's erse and if you bide in here a minute longer it might easily be yours!'

That night, when the house slept and she could at last be alone, Tina took a pen, a notepad and an oil lamp to the kitchen table and sat herself quietly down, her gaze roving every so often to the quiet bed in the corner where Otto breathed deeply in his drugged sleep.

Ach, my poor, dear man, she thought, you are a gentleman just and I'd kill for you, that I would. If any other bugger tries to tarnish your good name they'll have me to deal with – and may the Lord forgive me for such harsh thoughts – but I canny seem to help myself these days. I'm seeing a side o' myself I don't like very much but I'd do anything for you, Mr Otto, and right now I'm going to clear your name o' blame – if it's the last thing I do.

But it wasn't so easy to find the words she wanted to write and she sat there at the kitchen table, lost in thought, her hands folded tranquilly in her lap, her languorous brown eyes surveying the night shadows on the walls without really seeing them. The halo of light from the lamp blurred all the surrounding edges so that she felt as if she was in a small sphere of peace that was all her own. Just her and Mr Otto, alone together in the room but separate, he from her by sleep and dreams, she from him by wakeful ponderings that wouldn't let her rest till she had done what she had to do.

She shrugged herself out of her reveries and smiled. Mr James was always telling her she thrived on romance and nonsense and he was right enough in that respect – and at her age too! But och, she never did anyone any harm by just dreaming and she would never get this damty letter written if she didn't focus her mind on it.

Nevertheless she deliberated for another ten minutes before she seized her pen with a decisive gesture and began to write purposefully.

Christmas was just three days away and it was Rachel's birthday. Ruth, determined to make it as happy an event as possible in the circumstances, had baked a little cake covered with pink icing, which she had decorated with a little chocolate violin and one single red candle, which was all Merry Mary had in the shop at the time as she had been cleaned out of such frivolities because of the festive season.

But Rachel had been delighted anyway. Kate and Annie and a few others had come, bearing little gifts. Lorna had made a squinty Chinese lantern in school and had proudly presented it to her adopted aunt while little Douglas handed over a crumpled bag containing chocolate drops which he had promptly devoured when no one was looking.

At dinnertime everyone departed, including Ruth who wanted to get some supplies at the shops before taking the children back home, Douglas to Laigmhor, Lorna to Shona at Mo Dhachaidh.

The house was quiet again. Rachel stood at the window, watching the steamer coming round Mara Òran Bay as she had watched it so often since Jon had made his hasty departure from Rhanna – but he had never returned – and she had given up wishing and praying for the boat to bring him home again.

She sank into a chair, glad to be alone for a little while. She was feeling lethargic and fretted that she hadn't been able to visit Otto for some days now, but her time was very near and Megan had made her promise not to leave the house unless it was strictly necessary. She was also suffering from nostalgia. Her birthday – and Jon hadn't sent so much as a card to mark the event when in days gone by he had showered her with gifts and had made it altogether a special occasion.

Jon. She spoke his name in her heart, please come back to me, I love you, I miss you . . .

She was totally unprepared for the searing pain in her lumbar region and she gasped, gripping the arms of her chair till the moment passed.

She closed her eyes. The waiting was done with, the day she had longed for had come at last – and Jon wasn't here to share it with her . . . She wept, for all the things in her life that had been precious and sweet, for Jon, for Otto . . .

Poignancy swelled in her breast, her heart pulsed in her ears, deafening her, pounding through all of her body till it seemed the whole world was just one big heartbeat with herself trapped in the echoing roar of it. She didn't hear the opening of the door but some separate sense made her open her eyes and turn her head to see Jon framed in the doorway, like some impossible vision without substance.

But it was Jon, all right, very much alive, bounding towards her to take her in his arms and crush her to him, warm, whole, real, kissing her tears away, murmuring words of love into her hair, her face, her neck. The light from the window poured over his face, it was thinner than she remembered, he looked as if he hadn't slept properly in months. Her heart turned over and she knew then how much she had wronged him by not taking him into her confidence, the one person in the world who deserved her honesty and had failed to get it.

Jon. Her lips formed his name, her fingers traced the contours of his face as if to reassure herself that he was really here, her mouth nuzzled his, she fought down another spasm of pain because she couldn't bear anything to interfere with those precious moments of reunion . . .

And then she looked over his head and saw Mamma Jodl coming into the room, burdened down with an enormous suitcase that Jon had dropped in the porch in his anxiety to get inside.

Rachel's heart fell. Mamma had kept her word, she had said she would be back for Christmas and she had certainly meant what she said.

Then Mamma did a surprising thing, she swept over to her daughter-in-law to take her to her bosom in a mighty hug. Her eyes were alight, her face was glowing, she looked

340

really pleased to see Jon's wife and wasn't slow to express herself.

'For Christmas I come, but more than that I am here for the birthtime of my grandchild. Jon tells me this only last week; the shock to my heart was not good. I scold Jon for not telling me sooner. My son! Leaving alone his wife to carry the burden of his child. No argument is worth such selfishness and this to him I tell.'

Rachel stared. Had Mamma been the instigator of Jon's change of heart? Had she taken leave of her senses altogether? Scolding Jon! Sticking up for her daughter-in-law! All at once Rachel realized that she was really quite pleased to see her mother-in-law and, with a small glow warming her heart, she returned the crushing embrace with a more restrained one of her own.

Mamma straightened, she gazed around her with pleasure. 'To my room I must go,' she announced. 'I have pictured the scenery in my mind, now I will look at the real thing from my window. Portcull will be there in the distance, soon I will see Happy Mary and Aggie and all my other cronies, I will listen to the gossip and the cleck, Mairi will give me tea, Kate will give me her worries. I have much to do while I am here – and Christmas to make for Rab McKinnon.'

She disappeared upstairs, they could hear her clumping about, familiarizing herself once more with the house. She hadn't forgotten anything or anyone it seemed, her mode of speech had been liberally sprinkled with quaint local expressions, she had spoken with great fondness of 'her cronies', she had remembered the landscape vividly and obviously couldn't wait to see it all again. Mamma had very definitely changed her first opinions about Rhanna and had vigorously returned to re-acquaint herself with everything.

Jon and Rachel gazed at one another, shy suddenly, too filled with the wonder of the occasion to trust themselves to express their feelings.

Wordlessly Jon withdrew a letter from his pocket and handed it to his wife.

It was from Tina, beautifully written in a style that was almost copperplate, but the lovely and unique thing about it was that Tina wrote with her pen in the same dialect as her tongue, which gave the impression that she had whispered the words as she was writing them.

Dear Jon,

You might be thinking this is none o' my business but when Ruth told me that you thought Mr Otto was the father o' your child then I just made it my business, since that thrawn wee wife o' yours would rather die than swallow her pride by writing to you herself.

First of all, the dear good man I have come to love like a brother has only a short time left to live. Rachel knew this almost from the start and kept the burden of it locked away tightly in her staunch little heart.

He didn't want folks knowing and maybe pitying him and she made sure it remained a personal matter till he himself knew he couldn't keep it a secret any longer.

Maybe they did start off loving one another as man to woman, but he is a gentleman just and would never take what isn't rightly his. After that, he and Rachel shared a rare kind of companionship, a sort of understanding o' souls, it was a beautiful thing to see, they were like a a pair o' children, innocent and relaxed together, and I sometimes had a wee greet to myself just watching them. I was there every day and special friends was all they ever were, dear, good friends who understood one another and found so much to share and laugh about.

He was so happy for her when he found out she was expecting a baby. Mr Otto could never have children of his own, that was one o' the reasons that he and his wife separated. He told me this in confidence and now I'm telling you in confidence, trusting you will hold your tongue in the matter.

I know fine you love Rachel as she does you. I hope this letter brings you both to your senses, if no' I'll

342

personally take the pair o' you and knock your silly heads together.

When my Matthew died I realized how privileged I was to have had a good man, the amount o' years we had together wasn't the important part, it was how we spent our time that counted, loving and caring for one another and trying to live wi' the faults we both had. Since his death I have never had a moment's regret, for we treated each other kindly, Matthew and me, and I will never look back in sorrow and anger for things left undone.

Your baby will soon be here, the one you have both been waiting for, so just you catch the next boat or the bairn will arrive before you.

I remain yours respectfully,
Tina

Rachel crushed the letter to her breast, her eyes were glazed with unshed tears. God bless you, Tina, my dear, dear friend, she thought. Reaching for Jon's hand she held on to it tightly. Her pains were coming faster, growing more intense, little beads of sweat glinted on her brow and Jon gazed at her anxiously. He had come armed with birthday gifts and had been looking forward to seeing her opening them but all that would have to wait.

Rachel had gone into labour in earnest and it was thanks to Tina that he had come when he did or his baby might well have arrived before him.

The trauma of not being able to express her pain vocally would live with Rachel forever. Racked with the torture of childbirth, she writhed and tossed in a silent agony of endurance, feeling at times that she was sinking into a deep red pit of oblivion which never totally engulfed her even though she prayed for the relief it would bring.

Out of one nightmarish trough after another she climbed, clinging to Jon's hand, vaguely hearing his voice as he spoke to her and encouraged her and suffered some of her ordeal with her.

She knew Mamma was there too, bathing her brow, speaking soothing condolences in broken accents that were oddly comforting because they were familiar sounds in a frighteningly unfamiliar situation.

And even in the midst of her suffering she wondered how she could ever have hated Mamma and wished her out of the same vicinity as herself, for the hands that touched her were gentle and the voice that spoke her name was sincere and caring.

She liked Mamma Jodl in those tormented moments and she knew that no matter how much her mother-in-law might anger her in the future, she would never dislike her with quite the same intensity as she had done in the past.

Minutes, hours, days – she had no idea of the passage of time, for her, each pain-filled second was endless, each hour eternity that had no dusk or day.

In fact, it was a short, if violent, labour. It ended in an explosion of sensations: pain, relief, exhaustion, an eruption of trembling emotions, a baby's cry, Babbie's wonderfully sane voice, bubbling, laughing.

'Happy birthday, Rachel, she's all yours.'

She put the baby into Rachel's waiting arms, a tiny daughter with a mop of black hair and a voice that almost deafened everyone in the room. To Rachel it was the most beautiful sound she had ever heard and both she and Jon gazed at the tiny screwed-up face with utter wonder on theirs.

Mamma was beside herself with delight. She had been a good help to Babbie and Megan, she had fetched and carried, she had administered to Rachel, she had tried to domineer Ruth in the kitchen, but had soon discovered that the fair-haired, slightly built girl was stronger than she looked and was having none of Mamma's bossiness. After that she had tucked in her horns and had set about helping Ruth in every way she could, including keeping the big kettle boiling on the stove all afternoon. Hot water was an essential, endless 'cuppies' even more so, but Mamma was growing used to the Scots' thirst for tea and had herself sat with her feet on the fender to drink two steaming cups, one after the other, during a lull in proceedings.

Despite her busy day she didn't look in the least fatigued; she held her new granddaughter, she beamed, she crooned. 'The next will be a son,' she said in her incorrigible way, and seeing a pair of headlamps coming down the road from Portvoynachan, she rushed to put on her hat and coat in order to go outside and stand waving her arms in the middle of the road.

It was Erchy, coming back from his Christmas deliveries, and he was easily persuaded to take Mamma to Rab's house when he heard the news about Rachel's baby.

'A wee lass, eh?' Erchy slapped his knee, as tickled pink as Mamma herself. 'Rab will want to wet its head so I'd best come in wi' you to make sure he does the job properly.'

'Wet its head?' queried Mamma in puzzled tones.

'Ay, it's a Scottish tradition,' Erchy explained happily. 'A way o' welcoming a new bairn into the world – it doesny have to be there, of course, we leave it to the minister to do the real thing at the christening, but as long as we wet our own thrapples wi' a good dram o' whisky the bairn will have all the good luck it ever needs to start it off in life.'

Erchy wasn't the only one to be 'wetting his thrapple'. Babbie, Megan, Ruth, Jon, all drank a toast to the new baby while Rachel drank a well-earned cuppy, a wonder in her that only that very morning she had wakened alone in her bed and had risen to face a birthday without Jon. Now she was a mother, Jon was a father, all in the space of a few short hours – and it was still her birthday, complete with the most precious gift she could ever have wished for.

At last she and Jon were alone in the room with their new daughter. He stood there at the bedside, gazing down on the small, red face, quiet now, one tiny fist jammed into the pink little blubber of a mouth, the other clenched beside one paper-thin ear as she slept the deep and dreamless sleep of the newborn infant.

'Let's call her Karla,' Jon said quietly, 'Karla McKinnon Jodl.'

Rachel looked at him quickly: surely he wasn't still thinking that this was the child of Karl Gustav Langer! But the quiet brown eyes that sought hers were innocent of guile as he went on, 'I want us both to always remember a great man. If you agree then she will have a name to be proud of, Karla for him, McKinnon for you, and Jodl for me, it seems as if it was meant for her.'

The name rang inside Rachel's head like a melody, Karla McKinnon Jodl. It was beautiful, it was perfect. With tears in her eyes she held her arms out to her husband and he went to the breast that had newly suckled his baby to kiss the creamy skin and nuzzle the warm flesh before curling up beside her, holding her close till she fell asleep in the safe stronghold of his loving arms.

Christmas came on the teeth of a sou'westerly gale that shrieked over the island, whipping the trees into frenzy, lashing the shores, rattling the chimney pots, wailing at windows and doors as if all the witches of hell had been let loose and were trying to gain their demented footholds. But the stout walls held firm; doors and windows remained grimly closed; hardly a soul ventured out of doors but were quite happy to remain by cosy hearths where Christmas lights twinkled and tables groaned under festive fare.

Mamma had never been happier. She organised, she arranged, she cooked, baked, sweated, and produced enormous amounts of food, not just for Rab but for everyone: great smoked hams, mouthwatering cheeses, batch upon batch of apfelstrudel, pastries stuffed with cream, buns bulging with raisins, puddings rich with spices, gateaux dark with chocolate, cakes thick with almonds.

Rachel was very glad to let her mother-in-law take charge, though all the time she fretted, not because Mamma had taken over her kitchen, but for her enforced confinement to the wind-battered house. She had quickly recovered from the birth of her baby and her desire to be up and about was imperative: every minute, every hour, brought Otto closer to death. She had heard that he was failing fast and his last words to her had been a request to see her baby.

So Rachel wouldn't allow herself to rest. Much to Megan's dismay she arose from her bed only hours after giving birth in it, and she refused to sit still for any length of time but insisted on wandering about the house 'like a demented spook', to quote Annie who had arrived expecting to find her daughter in bed but had instead found her up and fully dressed, going about as usual.

Megan thought the description was apt enough. She had come to know Rachel well in the last year; in the girl's turbulent dark eyes she recognized a yearning soul and knew that nothing would bring her appeasement till she could visit Otto for the last time and let him hold her baby in his arms.

The little thatched house that overlooked the sea was quiet and peaceful when Jon and Rachel at last took their baby to see Otto. Tina had decorated the kitchen, a tiny tree stood on a table near the window, a row of squinty paper stars were strung across the room, dozens of Christmas cards filled every available space. The homely smells of baking and cooking hung agreeably in the air, a large tray of spicy buns stood cooling on a shelf, presided over by Vienna who was addicted to cakes and pastries and would do anything to sink her fangs into them, while Tina in her turn would do anything to ensure that the 'big, sleek brute o' a cratur' never so much as tasted the reek o' a scone'.

But she didn't mean it, even though cats had never rated very highly with her, she put up with them and treated them well because the menfolk in her life appeared to dote on them. Mark James had three 'sly sleekit brutes' as she called them; they sized her up, tripped her up, stole food from the table, left bird and mouse corpses in the living room and 'frightened the shat out o' her' by leaping at her from dark corners when she was least expecting it.

But Vienna was special because she was Mr Otto's cat, and Tina was feeding her a piece of spicy bun when she heard the visitors and turned to welcome them. She had been crying, her eyes were red and dull with sadness. She smiled at the baby, indicated the chairs by Otto's bed, and took herself ben to the little parlour that led off from the kitchen.

Otto's condition had greatly worsened since Rachel's last visit, he was gaunt and pale, the shadow of death lay over him, and it was difficult to believe he was the same big giant of a man who had arrived on Rhanna not so many months ago.

Even so, his eyes were bright and eager for life; he was delighted to see the visitors and immediately stretched out a hand to pull away the shawl from the baby's face.

'This is Karla,' Jon spoke in a low voice, 'Karla McKinnon Jodl.'

'Karla.' Otto repeated the name in disbelief. He sank back into his pillows as Jon placed the baby in his arms. 'Karla.' He stared at the tiny, sleeping face. 'How perfect she is, such miraculous perfection, you must have more like her, I would have had dozens but it was not to be – my wife left me because of it.' He gripped Jon's arm. 'My friend, I thank you for bringing her here – and also for honouring my name in such a generous way. You are a good man and I'm happy to see you all together – my life is complete now and I will die in peace.'

Jon took the baby and stumbled out of the room, hardly able to see where he was going for the mists that blinded him.

'Rachel.' Otto reached out and took her hands, his were thin and frail, those once-strong, beautiful, pianist's hands with their long, slender fingers. 'Soon it will be goodbye, *liebling*.'

A sob tightened her throat, she who had once run to him on effortless feet couldn't bear the pain of being with him any longer.

She drew her hands away, briefly her fingers whispered over his face, lingered on his mouth, their eyes met and held . . . moments passed, laden with a million unspoken dreams and longings . . . then she stepped back from his bed and went quickly away.

*　　*　　*

Death came gently and kindly to Otto. He went with the night that rolled slowly back from the shadowed horizon and he never saw the promise of day silvering the purple-black clouds. Dawn came, rosy and sweet above the sea, chasing the quiet shadows from the hills, spreading light on the sleeping bens, stirring the herds and the flocks in the fields, glinting on the ice-cold burns tinkling over the stones.

The kitchen was quiet when Magnus arose, he knew before he looked at his grandson that he had lost him and he went outside, into the cold morning, feeling the peace of lonely places enfolding him, that special peace that he and Otto had often shared without either of them losing anything of its quality.

Tina looked from the window and saw the old man there, alone on the cliffs, his thatch of white hair blowing in the wind. Her heart went out to him; she followed him outside, but being Tina she stopped first to take his jacket down from its peg, her hand trembling, her tears spilling.

'Ach, Tina,' Magnus murmured huskily, allowing her to tuck the jacket round his shoulders, 'did I do right? Bringing a fine gentleman like him into my humble home?'

'Where else would he have died so peacefully?' Tina said gently. 'He was loved to the last, surrounded by family and friends. I know fine he enjoyed every minute for he told me so himself, also he was honoured to have shared the last part o' his life here wi' you, his very own grandfather. You yourself have lived here all o' your days and there is no gentleman in the land as fine or as wise as our very own Magnus o' Croy.'

It was January, the snow was on the hills, Rachel walked quickly along the road from An Cala. She, Jon, Mamma and the baby, were leaving the island next day but she couldn't go without saying her last farewells to Otto. Her footsteps slowed when she reached that lonely grave on the Hillock with the sea and the sky and the silent bens all around.

The inscription on the gravestone was deceptively simple, in days to come it would mystify the casual observer though the people of Rhanna would always know what it meant;

KARL GUSTAV LANGER,
WHO CAME TO THIS ISLAND
AS OTTO KLEBB,
AND DIED A McKINNON.
NEVER FORGOTTEN.
MAC NAN ÈILEAN.

He had been a very generous Son of the Island. He had gifted his beautiful Becky to the village church hall and had set up a trust fund for talented island youngsters. Tina had been left five thousand pounds, various McKinnons had also benefited, the coffers of the Church Fabric Fund had greatly swollen, baby Karla would one day be a rich young lady, and not even Vienna had been forgotten, but it was Magnus who had received the bulk of his grandson's fortune.

'Buy a new house,' he had been urged, but he had just shook his head at that and, smiling his beguiling one-toothed smile, he had said firmly, 'Na, na, this cottage has done me fine all o' my days and I'm no' going to move now, though the money will come in handy and will see me into my old age.' He had finished with a chuckle which might have fooled some but not those who knew how much he grieved for his grandson.

The world beyond Rhanna had learned of Otto's death and the reporters had come snooping, but the islanders had closed ranks. Magnus had told them as little as he could but even so there had been splashes in the newspapers about the famous musician spending his last days in the humble thatched cottage of his maternal grandfather.

But all that was past now, the kirkyard on the Hillock slumbered once more, the silence of it shrouded Rachel as she stood there alone, remembering.

But it was too quiet, too sad. In life Otto had known the freedom of wide, wild spaces, she raised her head and gazed towards the great bastion of Burg and she knew where she had to go to find him.

She walked away from the kirkyard, through the gate and down the Hillock. Kate was coming along, her face like thunder. 'That Tam!' she exploded. 'I told him I wanted a washing machine for Christmas, ready for the day when the electrics came to Rhanna. He said he had sent for my present; it came this morning. You'll never guess what the mean bugger gave me! A scrubbing board! The bodach, he'll never move wi' the times, and it wasny even here in time for Christmas!'

Rachel's lips twitched, Kate's own generous mouth widened and she gave a snort of laughter, then she sobered and laid her hand on the girl's arm. 'Life goes on, *mo chridhe*, life goes on,' she said gently and went on her way, pensive and quiet, throwing over her shoulder, 'You'll bring the bairn to see me before you go away, Rachel, I'll be looking out for you.'

Rachel nodded, she too went on her way, her steps taking her along one of the many sheep tracks that led to Burg Bay. There she stood, surrounded by the soar of the cliffs, the tumble of the ocean, and in her mind Otto came to her, striding along the sands, a smile lighting his face, crinkling his eyes. Glancing up she saw Tigh na Cladach and just for a moment she imagined that a spark of light illuminated the windows, reminding her of that day when waves of music had come pouring out, soaring, soaring, filling her world with power and gladness.

This was where Otto was, where he would always be; never again would she walk the shores of Burg without seeing him and hearing him and sensing that his soul touched hers as it had done when he had filled her life with his joy and vitality.

His spirit was here, whispering to her in the wind, caressing her heart with love and beauty. He would never die, never! She spread her arms and threw back her head, she wanted to shout his name but her lack of speech didn't matter anymore. His own words, spoken before he died, came to her as if on the breath of the breeze: 'I have never heard your voice but you have no need of it, I have always known what you were feeling and thinking, always it will be so.'

Always, always, now and forever!

Mac nan Èilean! The joyous benediction rang inside her

351

head, and as she stood there she seemed to hear the echo of it, springing out of the sea, tossing up from the waves, reverberating against the cliffs, over and over, like the notes of a great symphony pulsing and throbbing, drifting free and unfettered over the clean wide spaces of the shores of Rhanna.

where the dialogue and action of i. i. 66–86 (Oxford text) is summarized in one direction. Good texts do not call for prolonged action without dialogue except under unusual circumstances.

Some directions actually appear to describe action already witnessed:

There the fiue Moones appeare (i. xiii. 131)
He leapes, and brusing his bones, after he was from his traunce, speakes thus; (ii. i. 12)

The text of the *T.R.* is very "foul". "Permissive directions"[1] at i. xi. 110, ii. ii. 1, ii. iv. 1 confirm that we are dealing with foul papers. Repetition of words and phrases *ad nauseam* suggests that the writer (or writers) worked under pressure.

At least two styles are noticeable, the one pretentious, using many blustering words and larded with Latin tags. S. Rowley, whom various *T.R.* tricks recall, may have had a hand in the writing.[2] Munday (or Chettle, the co-author), whose Robin Hood plays also contain verbal peculiarities which can be parallelled in the *T.R.*, may be associated with the *T.R.* more confidently, if any significance may be attached to a freak spelling.[3] The form "Hughbert" (for "Hubert") occurs three times on one page of the *T.R.* (Part ii, sig. A₄), but on no other page; in *The Death of Robert, Earle of Huntington* (1601) it is common, the most revealing corruption being: "Its Lord *Hugh Burgh* alone, *Hughberr*, what newes?" (sig. H₃).

It has been argued that the printer, hoping for a double profit, was responsible for the two-part publication of the *T.R.* Chambers noted that the lines "To the Gentlemen Readers" prefixed to both parts do not claim to be prologues.[4] Wilson agreed that the division into two parts could have no dramatic reason:[5] and there are strong reasons against the production of the *T.R.* in two parts. It should be added that both the title-page and lines "To the Gentlemen Readers" of Part i promise the death of John, which takes

1. Cf. Greg, *The Editorial Problem in Shakespeare*, p. 36. The *T.R.* directions are "Enter *Peter* a Prophet, with people"; "Enter King *Iohn* with two or three and the Prophet"; "Enter K. *Iohn*, *Bastard*, *Pandulph*, and a many priests with them" respectively.

2. Pope asserted in 1723 that the *T.R.* was by "W. Shakespear *and* W. Rowley" (Pope's Shakespeare, iii, 115). Perhaps a tradition that Shakespeare and "Rowley" were connected with it reached Pope. For S. Rowley's early hackwork cf. Introduction, p. lv.

3. *The Death of Robert* is probably a bad quarto, in which case Munday himself would not be responsible for the *T.R.*

4. *The Elizabethan Stage*, iv, 23.   5. *King John*, p. xvii.

place in Part II. Such overlapping can be parallelled c. 1590 in two-part learned works with separate title-pages and signatures, but seems suspicious in plays.

Only one scene (I. xi) in the *T.R.* wholly lacks its opposite number in *John*. The *T.R.* (nearly 2,900 lines) is also slightly longer than *John* (nearly 2,600 lines). Part I of the *T.R.* is disproportionately long (1,750 lines approximately) in comparison with Part II (1,150 lines approximately), which, again, discountenances two-part production.—Part I seems to have been written on 45-line pages, and Part II on 55-line pages: the lines per scene, at least, fall in quite neatly with these figures. This need have no significance, but systematic divergence between the two parts [cf. (ii) above] deserves thought.

Whether or not only one man wrote the *T.R.* is hard to decide. The two styles may be due to the lapses of one author at times falling below his best. But the printer's copy may have been padded with interpolations to disguise the shortness of the two parts. The lines "To the Gentlemen Readers", almost certainly written for the press, resemble the style of much of the text. And if the theatrical foul papers were not expanded for the press the *T.R.* was somewhat longer than the other one-part plays owned by the same company at the same time.

Bearing all these textual pecularities in mind it is as well to ponder again Prof. Alexander's misgivings about the *T.R.*:

It is difficult to understand how this work, so well digested in the scenes as to permit Shakespeare to follow it nearly scene by scene, should yet show so little corresponding modesty or cunning in its writing as to appear like a tissue of borrowed and only half-assimilated phrases from *Henry VI, Richard III*, as well as *King John* itself. This reasoning would date all these pieces before 1591 . . .[1]

For the disparity between clever plotting and very uneven verse (or prose) was a standard feature of "bad" and "derivative" play-texts in the Elizabethan period.

1. *Shakespeare's Life and Art*, p. 85.